# BASES OF
# HEARING
# SCIENCE
## THIRD EDITION

# BASES OF
# HEARING
# SCIENCE

## THIRD EDITION

**JOHN D. DURRANT, PH.D., F.A.S.H.A.**
Professor of Otolaryngology and Communication
Director, U.P.M.C. Center for Audiology
University of Pittsburgh
Pittsburgh, Pennsylvania

**JEAN H. LOVRINIC, PH.D., F.A.S.H.A.**
Professor of Speech-Language-Hearing
Adjunct Professor of Otorhinolaryngology H. N. S.
Temple University
Philadelphia, Pennsylvania

WILLIAMS & WILKINS
BALTIMORE • PHILADELPHIA • HONG KONG
LONDON • MUNICH • SYDNEY • TOKYO
A WAVERLY COMPANY

*Editor:* John P. Butler
*Managing Editor:* Linda S. Napora
*Copy Editor:* Bruce Totaro
*Designer:* Ann Feild
*Illustration Planner:* Ray Lowman
*Production Coordinator:* Anne Stewart Seitz

Accurate indications, adverse reactions, and dosage schedules for drugs are provided in this book, but it is possible that they may change. The reader is urged to review the package information data of the manufacturers of the medications mentioned.

*Printed in the United States of America*

First Edition 1977
Second Edition 1984

**Library of Congress Cataloging-in-Publication Data may be obtained from the Publisher.**

**ISBN 0-683-02737-9**

95 96 97 98 99
1 2 3 4 5 6 7 8 9 10

*To the memory of*

## *Ray Carhart*

*—teacher, scientist, and a leader in the field of audiology*

# PREFACE

HERE WE GO again, another edition. With a basic textbook such as this, one struggles to find ways to reinvent a "new and improved" version. However, much new information has emerged over the decade since the publication of the Second Edition, and there is always room for improvement. Indeed, it was as difficult to decide what not to include in the Third Edition as what to include, given the objectives of an introductory-level text. The general guiding principle employed was to remain faithful, overall, to the original "mousetrap," assuming that there must be some reason for the sustained demand for this book. Furthermore, our approach was to present an authoritative treatment of diverse topics represented in these seven chapters without reverting to an edited, multiauthored text (that is, the familiar expert-per-chapter approach). To achieve this, we have made liberal use of experts in acoustics and hearing science who critically reviewed each chapter, with each proposing various additions or deletions, thereby effectively amplifying our expertise/authority in these areas. Consequently, much credit is due to our reviewers. These are truly good folks whose love for the field motivates them to perform this heroic task for little more than the glory. In this edition, we have imposed upon the good will of both old friends from the first two editions and other friends who were not previously involved. Thus,

we gratefully acknowledge the following individuals for their highly constructive comments and criticisms on the chapters indicated: For Chapters 1, 2, and 3—Dr. William Hartmann, Michigan State University and Dr. J. Robert Boston, University of Pittsburgh. For Chapters 5 and 6—Dr. Jonathan Siegel, Northwestern University. For Chapter 7—Dr. Lawrence Feth, Ohio State University. Of course, we remain very much in the debt of other contributors to the first two editions, as follows (in alphabetical order):

Dr. Charles Berlin (Preface, First Edition)

Dr. Barbara Bohne (Chapter 4, Second Edition)

Dr. Peter Dallos (Chapter 5, First Edition)

Dr. Solomon Erulkar (Chapter 6, First Edition)

Dr. Alfred Fink (Chapter 7, First Edition)

Dr. Richard Ham (full volume, First Edition)

Dr. Mary Harbold (Chapters 2 and 3, First Edition)

Dr. Merle Lawrence (Chapter 5, Second Edition)

Dr. M. Charles Liberman (Chapter 6, Second Edition)

Dr. Aage Moller (Chapters 1–3, Second Edition)

Dr. Wayne Olsen (Epilogue, Second Edition)

Dr. Carson Schneck (Chapter 4, First Edition)

Dr. James Saunders (Chapter 6, First Edition)

Dr. Tom Tillman (Introduction, Second Edition)

Mr. Neil Walter (Chapters 2, 3, and Appendix B, First Edition).

We wish also to thank Ms. Susan Shimko and Mr. Donald Kochi for their technical assistance (secretarial and graphic arts, respectively). The cover art was revised for this edition by Mr. Marc A. Durrant.

We sadly acknowledge the passing, since the publication of the Second Edition, of several world-class scientists who did so much to shape the development and progress of hearing research, including Drs. Halowell Davis, Glenn Wever, Juergen Tonndorf, Solomon Erulkar, and Heinrich Spoendlin. This book would be significantly thinner were it not for these great scientists. We hope that, in some small way, this book will help to preserve their memory and to keep them alive in our science.

We also wish to acknowledge our colleagues and students, too numerous to mention, who have expressed keen interest in this text and encouragement for our continued investment of effort in its production. Of course, books that do not sell do not remain on the market, so we certainly appreciate those teachers who have seen fit to use this text in their courses and/or to recommend it to their students.

Last, but certainly not least, we must acknowledge the continued support and indulgence of our respective significant others, Carol and Bill, for whom *déjà vu* has new meaning.

J.D.D. AND J.H.L.

# CONTENTS _____

## CHAPTER 3

## MEASUREMENT OF SOUND ................................................................ 63

## CHAPTER 4

## ANATOMY OF THE EAR ................................................................... 102

CHAPTER 5 ────────────────────────────────────────────

# PHYSIOLOGICAL ACOUSTICS OF THE AUDITORY PERIPHERY

CHAPTER 6 ────────────────────────────────────────────

# NEUROPHYSIOLOGY OF THE AUDITORY SYSTEM

## CHAPTER 1

# PHYSICAL CONCEPTS

The field of physics is fundamental to all sciences, so an understanding of certain basic physical concepts is a prerequisite to the mastery of the more advanced concepts embodied in acoustics, physiological acoustics, and psychoacoustics—the topics that will be covered in this book. From physics derive the principles and terminology by which it is possible to explain how sound is generated, how it behaves, and, in part, how it is detected and translated into meaningful information by the hearing system. Physical concepts underlie the measurement of acoustic intensity, sound pressure, and other quantities of interest in hearing science, so the standard units of measure used in the quantification of sound also find their bases in physics.

Quantitative measurements play a very important role in all of science, because careful and exacting observations are essential to the scientific method. Quantification involves assigning a number to a quantity that represents its magnitude in a generally accepted form. Consequently, the first order of business is to define various physical quantities and to explore some useful numbering and measuring systems, in general.

## 1. Numbers, Quantities, Measures, and Dimensions

This initial plunge into physical concepts, unfortunately, may be found by the reader to be a bit soporific. There is probably some way to make scientific notation exciting, but in the interest of brevity, we have opted for a "bite the bullet" approach. However, once a little time is spent with such topics, considerable benefit will be realized in dealing with more substantive matters. In practice, the quantification of sound and other physical quantities involves a wide range of numerical values, so it is worthwhile to adopt a number system at the outset that permits this wide range of values to be handled easily. *Scientific notation* fits this need. Not only does scientific notation provide a simple way to represent both large and small numbers with equal ease, it also provides a convenient basis for computations with such numbers, for conversions between metric measures, and for conversions of numbers to logarithms, as discussed in Chapter 3. Scientific notation involves translating any number into the product of a coefficient (namely, a number from 1.000 . . . to 9.999 . . .) multiplied by some power of 10. Of practical importance is the fact that subdivisions or multiples of standard metric units of measure (centimeters, kilograms, etc.) commonly encountered in science are powers of 10. Therefore, the use of scientific notation will pervade much of the discussion of physical principles contained in this and later chapters.

An essential step in developing an un-

**TABLE 1.1.**
**Powers of Ten and Corresponding Metric Prefixes**

| Derivation | | | Prefix |
|---|---|---|---|
| 100,000 × 10 | = 1,000,000 | = $10^6$ | mega = M |
| 10,000 × 10 | = 100,000 | = $10^5$ | |
| 1,000 × 10 | = 10,000 | = $10^4$ | |
| 100 × 10 | = 1,000 | = $10^3$ | kilo = k |
| 10 × 10 | = 100 | = $10^2$ | |
| 1 × 10 | = 10 | = $10^1$ | deca = da |
| 1 | | = $10^0$ | |
| 1 ÷ 10 | = 0.1 | = $10^{-1}$ | deci = d |
| 1 ÷ 100 | = 0.01 | = $10^{-2}$ | centi = c |
| 1 ÷ 1000 | = 0.001 | = $10^{-3}$ | milli = m |
| 1 ÷ 10,000 | = 0.0001 | = $10^{-4}$ | |
| 1 ÷ 100,000 | = 0.00001 | = $10^{-5}$ | |
| 1 ÷ 1,000,000 | = 0.000001 | = $10^{-6}$ | micro = $\mu$ |

derstanding of scientific notation is to become familiar with the exponentiation of the number or *base* 10, that is, 10 raised to various powers. Table 1.1 demonstrates how numbers such as $10^3$ are obtained by multiplication or division, as the case may be. This table also lists various standardly used prefixes of metric units and the numbers with which they are associated. For example, $10^3 = 10 \times 10 \times 10 = 1,000$ and corresponds to the prefix *kilo*; 1 kilometer (km) = 1,000 meters (m). In scientific notation the number 1,000 is written as $1 \times 10^3$, as shown in Table 1.2. The basic rule of conversion of a number into scientific notation is that to form the coefficient, the decimal point is moved until the remaining number is between 1.000 . . . and 9.999 . . .; the number of times the decimal was moved becomes the power of 10. If the number with which one begins is 10 or greater, the decimal point will be moved to the left, and the exponent will be positive. On the other hand, if the number is less than 1, the decimal must be moved to the right, and the exponent will be negative. For instance, 0.00001 in scientific notation is $1 \times 10^{-5}$. Following the rule above, the decimal was moved five places to the right, yielding an exponent of −5. Had the number been something such as 36,540,000, the (implicit) decimal point

would be moved seven places to the left, yielding an exponent of (+)7. Therefore, this number in scientific notation is 3.654 × $10^7$. It is worth emphasizing here that *a decimal point is always present in a number*, either explicitly (for example, 17.32) or implicitly (for example, 17 = 17.000 . . .). Furthermore, although numbers in scientific notation may be rounded off, just like any other numbers, the number of decimal places bears information, even if all the numbers to the right of the decimal point are zeroes. The number of decimal places indicates the precision with which the number has been determined.

It should be evident that a number of any size can be translated into scientific notation. Incidentally, the fact that 1 equals $1 \times 10^0$ (or simply $10^0$) is not pointless, because it is a frequently encountered outcome of computations in scientific notation. Numerous examples of numbers that have been translated from "long form" to scientific notation are presented in Table 1.2. It should be noted that the purpose of this table is not to provide a conversion table per se, but to provide a wide range of examples and to facilitate comprehension of how the conversion is accomplished.

Calculations involving multiplication and division with numbers written in scientific notation also follow fairly simple rules. To *multiply*, simply *add* (algebraically) the exponents of the base 10 and multiply the coefficients. To *divide*, *subtract* the exponents and divide the coefficients. If in the process the resulting coefficient moves out of the range of 1.0000 . . . to 9.9999 . . ., move the decimal to bring it back into this range, and adjust the power of 10 accordingly. The following are examples to illustrate such calculations.

**1. Find the product of 500 × 0.2:**

$$500 \times 0.2 = (5 \times 10^2) \times (2 \times 10^{-1})$$
$$= 5 \times 2 \times 10^{(2+(-1))}$$
$$= 10 \times 10^1$$
$$= 1 \times 10^2 \text{ (or } 10^2 \text{ or } 100)$$

TABLE 1.2.
**Examples of Numbers Written in Scientific Notation**

| Long Form | Scientific Notation | Long Form | Scientific Notation |
|---|---|---|---|
| 0.00001 | $1 \times 10^{-5}$ | 10 | $1 \times 10^{1}$ |
| 0.000011 | $1.1 \times 10^{-5}$ | 11 | $1.1 \times 10^{1}$ |
| 0.0000115 | $1.15 \times 10^{-5}$ | 11.5 | $1.15 \times 10^{1}$ |
| 0.0000154321 | $1.54321 \times 10^{-5}$ | 15.4321 | $1.54321 \times 10^{1}$ |
| 0.00002 | $2 \times 10^{-5}$ | 20 | $2 \times 10^{1}$ |
| 0.000025 | $2.5 \times 10^{-5}$ | 25 | $2.5 \times 10^{1}$ |
| 0.00003333 | $3.333 \times 10^{-5}$ | 33.33 | $3.333 \times 10^{1}$ |
| 0.000056789 | $5.6789 \times 10^{-5}$ | 56.789 | $5.6789 \times 10^{1}$ |
| 0.00009999999999 | $9.99999999 \times 10^{-5}$ | 99.9999999 | $9.99999999 \times 10^{1}$ |
| 0.0001 | $1 \times 10^{-4}$ | 100 | $1 \times 10^{2}$ |
| 0.00011 | $1.1 \times 10^{-4}$ | 110 | $1.1 \times 10^{2}$ |
| 0.000115 | $1.15 \times 10^{-4}$ | 115 | $1.15 \times 10^{2}$ |
| 0.000154321 | $1.54321 \times 10^{-4}$ | 154.321 | $1.54321 \times 10^{2}$ |
| 0.0002 | $2 \times 10^{-4}$ | 200 | $2 \times 10^{2}$ |
| 0.00025 | $2.5 \times 10^{-4}$ | 250 | $2.5 \times 10^{2}$ |
| 0.0003333 | $3.333 \times 10^{-4}$ | 333.3 | $3.333 \times 10^{2}$ |
| 0.00056789 | $5.6789 \times 10^{-4}$ | 567.89 | $5.6789 \times 10^{2}$ |
| 0.0009999999999 | $9.99999999 \times 10^{-4}$ | 999.999999 | $9.99999999 \times 10^{2}$ |
| 0.001 | $1 \times 10^{-3}$ | 1000 | $1 \times 10^{3}$ |
| 0.0011 | $1.1 \times 10^{-3}$ | 1100 | $1.1 \times 10^{3}$ |
| 0.00115 | $1.15 \times 10^{-3}$ | 1150 | $1.15 \times 10^{3}$ |
| 0.00154321 | $1.54321 \times 10^{-3}$ | 1543.21 | $1.54321 \times 10^{3}$ |
| 0.002 | $2 \times 10^{-3}$ | 2000 | $2 \times 10^{3}$ |
| 0.0025 | $2.5 \times 10^{-3}$ | 2500 | $2.5 \times 10^{3}$ |
| 0.003333 | $3.333 \times 10^{-3}$ | 3333 | $3.333 \times 10^{3}$ |
| 0.0056789 | $5.6789 \times 10^{-3}$ | 5678.9 | $5.6789 \times 10^{3}$ |
| 0.009999999999 | $9.99999999 \times 10^{-3}$ | 9999.99999 | $9.99999999 \times 10^{3}$ |
| 0.01 | $1 \times 10^{-2}$ | 10,000 | $1 \times 10^{4}$ |
| 0.011 | $1.1 \times 10^{-2}$ | 11,000 | $1.1 \times 10^{4}$ |
| 0.0115 | $1.15 \times 10^{-2}$ | 11,500 | $1.15 \times 10^{4}$ |
| 0.0154321 | $1.54321 \times 10^{-2}$ | 15,432.1 | $1.54321 \times 10^{4}$ |
| 0.02 | $2 \times 10^{-2}$ | 20,000 | $2 \times 10^{4}$ |
| 0.025 | $2.5 \times 10^{-2}$ | 25,000 | $2.5 \times 10^{4}$ |
| 0.03333 | $3.333 \times 10^{-2}$ | 33,330 | $3.333 \times 10^{4}$ |
| 0.056789 | $5.6789 \times 10^{-2}$ | 56,789 | $5.6789 \times 10^{4}$ |
| 0.09999999999 | $9.99999999 \times 10^{-2}$ | 99,999.9999 | $9.99999999 \times 10^{4}$ |
| 0.1 | $1 \times 10^{-1}$ | 100,000 | $1 \times 10^{5}$ |
| 0.11 | $1.1 \times 10^{-1}$ | 110,000 | $1.1 \times 10^{5}$ |
| 0.115 | $1.15 \times 10^{-1}$ | 115,000 | $1.15 \times 10^{5}$ |
| 0.154321 | $1.54321 \times 10^{-1}$ | 154,321 | $1.54321 \times 10^{5}$ |
| 0.2 | $2 \times 10^{-1}$ | 200,000 | $2 \times 10^{5}$ |
| 0.25 | $2.5 \times 10^{-1}$ | 250,000 | $2.5 \times 10^{5}$ |
| 0.3333 | $3.333 \times 10^{-1}$ | 333,300 | $3.333 \times 10^{5}$ |
| 0.56789 | $5.6789 \times 10^{-1}$ | 567,890 | $5.6789 \times 10^{5}$ |
| 0.9999999999 | $9.99999999 \times 10^{-1}$ | 999,999.999 | $9.99999999 \times 10^{5}$ |
| 1.0 | $1 \times 10^{0}$ | 1,000,000 | $1 \times 10^{6}$ |
| 1.1 | $1.1 \times 10^{0}$ | 1,100,000 | $1.1 \times 10^{6}$ |
| 1.15 | $1.15 \times 10^{0}$ | 1,150,000 | $1.15 \times 10^{6}$ |
| 1.54321 | $1.54321 \times 10^{0}$ | 1,543,210 | $1.54321 \times 10^{6}$ |
| 2 | $2 \times 10^{0}$ | 2,000,000 | $2 \times 10^{6}$ |
| 2.5 | $2.5 \times 10^{0}$ | 2,500,000 | $2.5 \times 10^{6}$ |
| 3.333 | $3.333 \times 10^{0}$ | 3,333,000 | $3.333 \times 10^{6}$ |
| 5.6789 | $5.6789 \times 10^{0}$ | 5,678,900 | $5.6789 \times 10^{6}$ |
| 9.999999999 | $9.99999999 \times 10^{0}$ | 9,999,999.99 | $9.99999999 \times 10^{6}$ |

**2. Find the product of 0.0022 × 0.006:**

$$0.0022 \times 0.006 = (2.2 \times 10^{-3})$$
$$\times (6 \times 10^{-3})$$
$$= 2.2 \times 6 \times 10^{(-3+(-3))}$$
$$= 13.2 \times 10^{-6}$$
$$= 1.32 \times 10^1 \times 10^{-6}$$
$$= 1.32 \times 10^{(1+(-6))}$$
$$= 1.32 \times 10^{-5}$$
$$\text{(or } 0.0000132)$$

**3. Find the quotient of 12.5/2500:**

$$\frac{12.5}{2500} = (1.25 \times 10^1)/(2.5 \times 10^3)$$
$$= (1.25/2.5) \times 10^{(1-3)}$$
$$= 0.5 \times 10^{-2}$$
$$= 5.0 \times 10^{-1} \times 10^{-2}$$
$$= 5.0 \times 10^{-3}$$

**4. Find the quotient of 0.4/0.00002:**

$$\frac{0.4}{0.00002} = 4 \times 10^{-1}/2 \times 10^{-5}$$
$$= 2 \times 10^{(-1-(-5))}$$
$$= 2 \times 10^{(-1+5)}$$
$$= 2 \times 10^4 \text{ (or 20,000)}$$

Now, everyone knows that any number divided by itself equals 1, but it is a useful exercise to demonstrate this via scientific notation:

**5. Show that 100/100 = 1:**

$$\frac{100}{100} = 10^2/10^2$$
$$= 10^{(2-2)}$$
$$= 10^0$$
$$= 1$$

It also is often necessary to find the reciprocal of a number; this computation is facilitated through the use of scientific notation, as demonstrated by the following example:

**6. Find the reciprocal of × when × = 600:**

$$\frac{1}{X} = \frac{1}{600}$$
$$\frac{1}{600} = (1 \times 10^0)/(6 \times 10^2)$$
$$= 1/6 \times 10^{(0-2)}$$
$$= 0.1666 \ldots \times 10^{-2}$$
$$= 1.67 \times 10^{-1} \times 10^{-2}$$
$$= 1.67 \times 10^{-3} \text{ (or 0.00167)}$$

It is noteworthy that example 6 involves one of those annoying numbers that results when the remainder keeps repeating itself ad infinitum; 1/6 actually equals 0.166666666 . . . . We, being on the lazy side, merely calculated the result to three places to the right of the decimal point of the coefficient and rounded off. In this example, the calculated result actually overestimates the exact result by 0.00167 − 0.001666666 . . . = 0.00000333 . . . ; this is the part that is rounded off. Again, the number of decimal places in the coefficient indicates the precision of the number. For some purposes, rounding off to two places or even one place may yield adequate precision; in other cases, three or even more places may be required for adequate precision.

The rules governing the computations in the examples above are known as the *laws of exponents* and are discussed in more detail in Appendix A. Of course, with inexpensive pocket calculators being so readily available these days, it is tempting to skip over all of this. However, even when using a calculator, some knowledge of scientific notation is essential, because most of these instruments cannot display numbers with more than six to eight digits directly. Thereafter, they too must revert to a form of scientific notation. For instance, given the figure 0.00000001234, the display might show "1.234 − 8," meaning $1.234 \times 10^{-8}$.

Quantification yields only one piece of

information about a physical quantity, namely, a numerical value that reflects its size or **magnitude**. This often is not sufficient. For instance, the speed of an automobile does not entirely describe its motion. The direction in which it is moving is likely to be equally important, as when reporting the movement of a stolen vehicle. Quantities that have both magnitude and direction are called **vectorial quantities** (or, simply, *vectors*), whereas quantities that are characterized only by magnitude are called **scalar quantities** (or, simply, *scalars*). Scalars of like dimensions, for example, two volumes of a liquid, can be added or subtracted directly, assuming the same units of measure. This is not the case when vectorial quantities are involved, for example, forces. With vectors, direction must be taken into account to fully specify the quantity. As illustrated in Figure 1.1, this may be more complicated than simply observing sign or polarity, wherein algebraic summation or subtraction would be sufficient. The difference in direction may vary in two (the case illustrated in Fig. 1.1a), three, or more dimensions; in such cases methods of vectorial analysis must be applied. Although most of the quantities described in this text are vectors, only the magnitude of the quantity will be considered in most cases. Such an approach simplifies computations. Nevertheless, it never should be forgotten that these quantities, in fact, have direction as well as magnitude.

Quantification in the physical sciences thus is the process of representing, indicating, or determining magnitude, size, etc., and expressing this amount by a numerical value. To do so and to facilitate the universal communication of a given quantity requires **units of measure**. Throughout this text, various units of measure will be defined and applied. However, of more fundamental importance are the **dimensions** of a physical quantity. The expression "of like dimensions" was used previously. The point of this phrase is that physical quantities cannot be com-

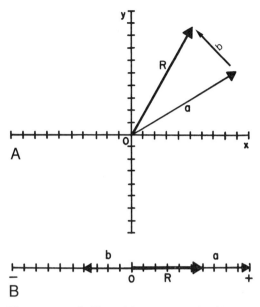

**Figure 1.1.** **A.** Vectorial summation, in this case in two dimensions. Vectors *a* and *b* are added, yielding the resultant, *R*. **B.** Special, one-dimensional, case in which algebraic summation alone would suffice, because direction is either positive or negative.

bined in just any manner; their dimensions must be considered. The problem is exemplified by the old adage that one cannot add apples and oranges. The dimensions of all physical quantities encountered in mechanics and acoustics are **length, time,** and **mass**. Length, time, and mass also are the names of three of the most basic physical quantities. Indeed, these quantities are so basic that their names and the names of their dimensions are identical. Because all other mechanical and acoustical quantities are derived from these three basic quantities, it is useful to analyze the dimensions of each physical quantity discussed. A shorthand system will be used to represent dimensions; length, time, and mass will be represented by the letters $L$, $T$, and $M$, respectively. These terms can be manipulated algebraically. For instance, if a particular derived quantity involves the dimension length multiplied by itself, the expression of the dimensions of this quantity would contain the term $L^2$, because $L \times L = L^2$.

If the quantity involved something per unit time squared, the term $T^{-2}$ would appear in the dimensions, because $1/T \times 1/T = 1/T^2 = T^{-2}$. So, the specific units of measure and their numbers are clearly important in specific situations. Yet, if the dimensions of a quantity are known and understood, the rest is simply a matter of arithmetic.

As hinted in the previous paragraph, it would be very difficult to communicate the magnitudes of physical quantities if everyone used a different system. It is thus necessary to adopt a *standard system of units of measure*. The **metric system** will be used throughout this book, because it is the system of measurement accepted by the scientific community at large. Various multiples and/or subdivisions of the basic metric units have attained conventional usage as well. The two major metric subsystems are the MKS and CGS:

| System | Length | Mass | Time |
|--------|--------|------|------|
| MKS | M(eter) | K(ilogram) | S(econd) |
| CGS | C(entimeter) | G(ram) | S(econd) |

There has been a general appeal for the uniform adoption of the MKS system. Yet, the CGS system has received widespread use in the past and probably will continue to do so in the future. Even if complete compliance with the MKS system were to be observed immediately, the unalterable fact is that scientific literature is replete with references to measurements in CGS units, not to mention the appearance of these measures in textbooks and on dials and meters of equipment in laboratories throughout the world. The most practical solution to the problem of selecting a system is to be knowledgeable of both. Actually, this is not an awesome task. After all, both the MKS and CGS are metric systems, so conversion from one to the other is merely a matter of multiplying or dividing by 10 raised to the appropriate power. Using scientific notation, this task is even simpler—adding or subtracting, respectively, exponents of the base 10 (as demonstrated below).

**TABLE 1.3.**
**Elements of Quantification**

| | |
|---|---|
| I. Types of quantities: | scalar and vector |
| II. Dimensions: | $M$, $L$, and $T$ |
| III. Physical quantities: | mass, length, force, etc. |
| IV. Systems of measure: | MKS, CGS, etc. |
| V. Numerical transformations: | Scientific notation, logarithms, etc. |

The concepts embodied in the previous discussion are summarized in Table 1.3. The three basic quantities, separately or in various combinations, define the dimensions of all quantities to be discussed. These quantities, in turn, are measured in units that have been established by convention. In more general terms, quantities are either vectors or scalars. Last, the magnitude of a particular quantity may be represented numerically in various ways, as exemplified by scientific notation. More elaborate numerical schemes are possible, such as the decibel system (discussed in Chapter 3), which is based on a logarithmic transformation. At this point, it is necessary to define explicitly the physical quantities of length, time, and mass and identify useful units of measure of these quantities.

## 2. Fundamental Physical Quantities

The physical quantity of **time** needs little explanation. The units of time used in everyday life are simply subdivisions of the solar day: 1 hour is 1/24 day; 1 minute is 1/60 hour; and 1 second is 1/60 minute. In the metric system, the unit of time is the *second*, although even smaller units of measure are often needed in scientific measurement:

msec (millisecond) $= 10^{-3}$ sec

$\mu$sec (microsecond)

$$= 10^{-6} \sec \text{ or } 10^{-3} \text{msec}$$

Time is a scalar quantity. The dimension

of time is represented by the letter $T$. Both the MKS and CGS units of measure of time are the second.

*Length* is also a familiar quantity, determined by comparing the unknown quantity to a standard of measure, such as the *meter*. Units both larger and smaller than the meter have assumed popular usage:

km (kilometer) $= 10^3$ m (meters)

cm (centimeter) $= 10^{-2}$ m

mm (millimeter) $= 10^{-3}$ m or $10^{-1}$ cm

$\mu$ or $\mu$m (micron or micrometer)

$= 10^{-6}$ m or $10^{-3}$ mm

The notion of *distance*, that is, the spatial separation between two points, is also familiar. Its dimension is one of *length*, denoted by $L$, and it is a scalar quantity. Perhaps less familiar is the term *displacement* ($x$). When an object moves from one point to another, for example 3 km north, it is said to have been displaced. Displacement, or change in position, has both magnitude and direction and is, therefore, a vectorial quantity. The dimension of displacement, like distance, is $L$, and its magnitude is measured in meters (MKS), centimeters (CGS), micrometers, etc.

The basic quantity of *mass* is less easily conceptualized, perhaps because of the common (but fallacious) assumption that mass and weight are synonymous. In actuality, mass is more fundamental than weight, because mass is a property of all matter. Whether the substance is gaseous, liquid, or solid, it has mass, regardless of amount. Even subatomic particles have mass. Additionally, any given substance will have the same mass regardless of its location in the universe. A substance may well be weightless, but it cannot be massless. Weight is a measure of the pull of gravity on a particular mass. Gravity does vary in the universe; an astronaut will weigh about one sixth as much on the moon as on earth. In orbit, of course, the

astronaut is weightless. Mass is a scalar quantity and has the dimension $M$. Using a device known as a *balance*, mass is measured by comparing the unknown quantity to a standard measure such as the gram (CGS) or kilogram (MKS):

kg (kilogram) $= 10^3$ g or

g (gram) $= 10^{-3}$ kg

For instance, 2,500 g $= 2.5 \times 10^3 \times 10^{-3}$ kg $= 2.5$ kg. The milligram is also a useful unit of measure:

mg (milligram) $= 10^{-3}$ g

The milligram is popular in such areas as the life sciences, in which relatively small quantities of substances are commonly used. For example, the stereotypical treatment for the common cold, "Take one aspirin and call me in the morning," is a prescription for the consumption of 250 to 500 mg of the active ingredient (that is, 1/4 to 1/2 g).

*Derived quantities* have varying degrees of complexity, beginning with those involving the dimension of length alone. *Area* is one such quantity and is measured in units of square meters ($m^2$) in the MKS system and square centimeters ($cm^2$) in the CGS system (because 1 $m^2 = (10^2$ cm$)^2 = 10^4$ cm$^2$). The dimensions of area are $L \times L = L^2$ (analogous to the area of a square). Using the same logic, the dimensions of volume are $L \times L \times L$ or $L^2 \times L = L^3$. The MKS unit of volume is the cubic meter ($m^3$), whereas in the CGS system it is cubic centimeter ($cm^3$). Frequently written as cc, the cubic centimeter is equivalent to the milliliter (ml).

The next level of complexity of derived quantities involves combining the dimensions of length and time. The simplest of these quantities is *velocity*. The movement of an object from one point to another consumes time. It is thus useful to determine the rate at which this distance is traversed in describing and quantifying this motion. The quantity known as *speed* immediately comes to mind; however, speed is a scalar. A speedometer, for example, merely indicates the time rate change in distance traveled by an automobile. Velocity, on the other hand, is defined as the time rate change in *displacement*. As such, velocity is a vectorial quantity. This is true because displacement, a vector, is divided by time, a scalar. *A vector divided by a scalar is a vector.* Consequently, the complete specification of velocity must include direction, not just magnitude. The dimensions of velocity and speed, nevertheless, are the same—$L/T$ or $LT^{-1}$—as are their units of measure. The MKS unit of measure of the magnitude of velocity (or speed) is the meter per second (m/sec), whereas the CGS unit is the centimeter per second (cm/sec) (1 m/sec $= 10^2$ cm/sec).

In its simplest form, velocity may be calculated using the equation:

$$\bar{v} = (x - x_0)/(t - t_0)$$

Specifically, this is the equation describing the magnitude of the *average velocity* (indicated by the dash over the $v$), where $x$ is displacement, and $t$ is time. When the initial displacement, $x_0$, and time at which the motion is initiated, $t_0$, are zero or can be treated as such, the form of the equation simplifies to:

$$\bar{v} = \Delta x/\Delta t \qquad (1.1)$$

where $\Delta x$ and $\Delta t$ are the *change* in $x$ and $t$, respectively. For example, if an automobile travels 200 km in 2 hours, the magnitude of the average velocity could be computed via Eq. 1.1 as follows:

$$\bar{v} = 200 \text{ km/2 hr} = 100 \text{ km/hr}$$

From common experience, it is easy to appreciate that it is possible to maintain, on average, a fairly constant speed for some distance while traveling in an automobile. However, this same experience demonstrates the difficulty of maintaining precisely the same speed all the time. Variations constantly occur as the terrain changes, traffic conditions change, the pressure applied by the foot to the accelerator changes, etc. These variations are generally observable as fluctuations in the position of the speedometer dial. It follows that a distinction must be made between *average* and *instantaneous* velocity. For $\Delta t$ approaching zero, Eq. 1.1 defines instantaneous velocity.

These fluctuations or instant-to-instant changes in velocity themselves constitute a physical quantity, **acceleration**, which is the time rate change of velocity.

$$\bar{a} = (v - v_0)/(t - t_0)$$

or, if $v_0$ and $t_0 = 0$,

$$\bar{a} = \Delta v/\Delta t \qquad (1.2)$$

Acceleration, too, can change from moment to moment, so *instantaneous* and *average acceleration* must be distinguished. In traveling by automobile, acceleration is experienced as the car speeds up or slows down. Although slowing down is also referred to as *deceleration*, this term simply denotes negative acceleration. On the other hand, an object that is in motion, that is, it has velocity, may not be accelerating. When velocity is constant, including the condition of velocity equal to zero (namely, an object at rest), then acceleration is zero.

By virtue of its roots, acceleration is a vectorial quantity. Considering Eq. 1.2, it can be deduced that the dimensions of acceleration are $LT^{-1}/T = LT^{-1} \times T^{-1} = LT^{-2}$ or $L/T^2$. The MKS metric unit of acceleration is the meter per second squared (m/sec$^2$), and the CGS unit of measure is the centimeter per second squared (cm/sec$^2$) (1 m/sec$^2$ $= 10^2$ cm/sec$^2$). As a physical unit, sec$^2$ (or the dimension $T^2$) defies expression in common-sense terms, but what it signifies—*the time rate change of a time-varying quantity*—is very important.

From the foregoing discussion, it can be seen that there are three aspects of the motion of an object that may be of interest: its displacement (change in position), velocity (rate of change in displacement), and acceleration (rate of change in velocity). Mathematically, the relationships between these quantities are most readily derived through the use of the calculus. For instance, velocity is defined as the first derivative of displacement and acceleration as the second derivative of displacement or the first derivative of velocity. These derivations are summarized in Appendix B. However, for purposes here, the simpler notions of average velocity and acceleration expressed in Eq. 1.1 and 1.2 will suffice. In general, these quantities are important for the development of yet more complex derived quantities, because there are physical quantities whose dimensions involve all three basic quantities. **Force** is the most fundamental of the derived quantities. An understanding of force, in turn, is requisite to an understanding of work, energy, and power. Furthermore, the common measures of sound magnitude—sound pressure and acoustic intensity—are intimately related to force. Because force and the physical principles surrounding it are so crucial, they deserve further discussion.

---

## 3. Force, According to Newton

In the simplest language possible, a *force* may be defined as a push or a pull. The nature of force and the basis for its measurement are embodied in three laws of Isaac Newton[1], as presented in Table 1.4. The first two of **Newton's laws** express, in essence, the idea that a force is required to change the motion of an object. This may represent a change from zero velocity, in which case the object initially is at rest (for instance, setting into motion an automobile that has been stopped at a

---

[1] With few exceptions, this text will focus on principles from classical physics, of which Newton's laws are exemplary. These principles have widespread applicability and validity; nevertheless, they do not adequately account for all physical phenomena. To explain events concerning the microscopic world of atomic particles, for example, it becomes necessary to invoke more modern principles, such as quantum mechanics. It is well beyond the scope of this book to delve into such matters, but the interested reader is encouraged to refer to a physics textbook to learn about quantum theory and other aspects of modern physics.

**TABLE 1.4.**
**Newton's Laws of Motion**[a]

1. An object at rest tends to remain at rest; an object in motion tends to maintain the magnitude and direction of its velocity (unless acted upon by an extraneous force)
2. The net force acting upon an object in motion is equal to the product of its mass and the acceleration imparted to it by the force (in the same direction as the force)
3. The forces of two bodies on each other are always equal and directly opposite

[a] Liberally interpreted.

traffic light), or it may be a change in the existing motion of an object (such as speeding up). In either case, it is clear that acceleration will take place, because acceleration is, by definition, the time rate change of velocity. The reason it takes a force to accelerate an object is because it has mass. Consequently, it also has **inertia**. Inertia is the property by which a body tends to resist any change in motion. That is, an object at rest tends to stay at rest, and an object in motion (that is, $v > 0$) tends to remain in motion. *Change in motion* includes variations in the direction, not just in the magnitude of velocity. Thus, for example, a car turning a corner at a perfectly constant speed, has acceleration. This is experienced by the riders in the car who, in response, have a tendency to lean during turns.

From the definition of inertia, it follows that a force is required to alter the motion of an object. Herein lies the means by which force can be given a more specific and physical definition than simply a "push" or a "pull." This definition is given by Newton's second law (Table 1.4), which reveals, simply, that force is determined by just two factors: acceleration and mass. Specifically, force is the product of mass and acceleration, or expressed in the form of an equation:

$$F = ma \qquad (1.3)$$

Equation 1.3 suggests that if two objects have different masses, a greater force will be required to equally accelerate the larger mass. Similarly, greater acceleration of the same mass requires increased force. Note that only two of the three variables in Eq. 1.3 are independent; given any two, the third variable can be derived mathematically. In other words, because $F = ma$, it is also true that $m = F/a$ and $a = F/m$, simply using algebraic manipulation of Eq. 1.3. Force is a vectorial quantity, because, again, the product of a scalar (in this case mass) and a vector (acceleration) is a vector.

Force has the dimensions $M \times L/T^2$ (or simply, $MLT^{-2}$). Consequently, in the MKS system the unit of measure of force is kg-m/sec$^2$—an awkward set of letters with which to contend! To avoid coping with such a complex unit of measure, and in honor of Newton, it has been given the name *newton*, abbreviated $N$. One newton thus is the force required to accelerate a body whose mass is 1 kg at a rate of 1 m/sec$^2$. In the CGS system the unit of measure of force is called the *dyne* ($d$). (This word is a Greek "import," by way of France, and comes from the word *dynamis*, meaning force.) One dyne = 1 g-cm/sec$^2$; it is left to the reader to verify that $1 N = 10^5 d$ or $1 d = 10^{-5} N$. (Hint: convert the basic units of measure constituting the newton to equivalent CGS terms.)

Equation 1.3 reveals yet another point of interest. If there is no change in motion (that is, $a = 0$), then force is zero ($F = m \times 0 = 0 N$). This physical state is called **equilibrium**. It does not mean necessarily that there is no force acting on the object in question; it means specifically that the net force acting on the object is zero, as illustrated in Figure 1.2a. Therefore, there can be no change in motion. A simple example of equilibrium is an object at rest on a table. Rest is merely a special state of motion, namely, zero motion. The table offers an equal and opposing force to the force of gravity that tends to pull the book down, or more explicitly toward the center of the earth. If the table is suddenly pulled out from under the book, the force of grav-

ity will accelerate it downward. When the book strikes the floor, it will again come to rest, that is, resting equilibrium once more will be established (although the book may be slightly ruffled from the abrupt stop). The downward force of gravity now will be balanced by the upward force afforded by the floor.

In contrast to the condition of resting equilibrium, if forces of unequal magnitude but opposite directions are acting on an object, the object will move in the direction of the greater force with an acceleration proportional to the net force acting on it (Fig. 1.2b). Forces acting in the same direction will add (Fig. 1.2c). However, if two or more forces are acting in different directions, there will be a resultant force whose magnitude is less than the sum of the magnitudes of the forces acting on the object. As shown in Figure 1.2d, the direc-

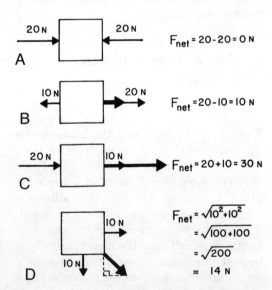

**Figure 1.2.**   Net (resultant) forces under various conditions. **a.** Equal forces acting in opposite directions. **b.** Unequal forces acting in opposite directions. **c.** Unequal forces acting in the same direction. **d.** Equal forces acting in directions perpendicular to one another. In **a–c** the resultant can be computed using algebraic summation; in **d** vectorial summation is required. The magnitudes of the component (*thin arrows*) and resultant forces (*bold arrows*) are indicated in newtons (N).

tion of the resultant force, and thus the resulting motion, will be a compromise among the component forces and the directions of motion that would have been induced otherwise by each component force acting alone. As learned earlier, the solution for the resultant requires vectorial analysis. In the case shown in Figure 1.2*d*, because the two forces act perpendicularly to one another, the solution is obtained by solving for the hypotenuse of a right triangle, with each leg being one component force (more on this particular solution later). Of course, the situation could be made even more complex, involving component forces of differing magnitudes and varying directions. A familiar practical example of how forces interact in the ways just described is that of a sailboat in motion. In essence, the push of the wind against the sail is opposed by the combined forces of the water acting against the keel and the rudder.

Another useful concept in the definition of force is *momentum*. Momentum is the product of mass and velocity ($mv$). Force, then, is the time rate change of momentum:

$$F = \Delta(mv)/\Delta t \qquad (1.4)$$

Thus, a force must be applied to a body to bring about a change in its momentum. A thrown ball has momentum that may be sufficient to carry it through a glass window, unless the glass is sufficiently strong to be impenetrable. Were the pane of glass laid horizontally and the ball set on it, the glass probably would not be broken. So, it is the combination of the ball's mass and its velocity that makes it so destructive (potentially) when thrown at the window. Equation 1.4 provides perhaps a more fundamental and universal definition of force than Eq. 1.3, because the mass of a body may not be constant. For instance, a moving dump truck full of gravel loses momentum as it spreads its load of gravel onto a roadway under construction. In many other situations, though, mass is constant, in which case

$$F = \Delta(mv)/\Delta t = m(\Delta v/\Delta t) = ma$$

as stated in Eq. 1.3. For purposes here, mass always will be assumed to be constant.

## 4. Force, According to Hooke

Thus far, only one possible consequence of applying a force to an object has been considered—acceleration of that object. Something else might occur to the object; it might be deformed. If the deformation in shape, size, or length of the object is within certain limits, known as the *limits of elasticity*, the object will return to its original shape when the applied force is removed. The property by which this is all possible is called *elasticity*. Just as mass is a fundamental property of matter, so is elasticity. All substances, no matter how incompressible they may seem (yes, even diamonds!), are elastic to some extent. Of particular interest here is a class of mechanical devices that can withstand extensive deformation and yet recover their original shapes, called *springs*.

Common experience with simple coiled springs demonstrates that when the ends are pushed together (or pulled apart), the spring pushes (or pulls) back. This is caused by the development of a force that opposes the displacement—the *restoring force*. Experience also demonstrates that some springs (or substances, in general) require greater force than others to be deformed to the same extent, either via extension or compression in the case of a simple coiled spring. It follows that they also differ in the amount of force required to deform them and, thus, the amount of restoring force developed for a given change in length, size, or shape. These springs or substances thus are said to differ in *stiffness*. The stiffer the spring or substance, the more force is required to extend or compress it. The relationship between restoring force, stiffness, and amount of deformation or displacement (such as change in length) is expressed by (Robert) **Hooke's law:**

$$F = -kx \qquad (1.5)$$

where $k$ is the spring constant, a measure of stiffness, and $x$, again, is displacement. Equation 1.5 holds only if the elastic limits of the spring are not exceeded. The minus sign in the equation simply indicates that the restoring force opposes the applied force. The dimensions of the spring constant can be determined by solving for $k$ in Eq. 1.5 (ignoring the minus sign) and substituting the already known dimensions, from Eq. 1.5:

$$k = F/x$$

Substituting known dimensions,

$$k = MLT^{-2}/L$$

Consequently, the spring constant is measured as the force per unit displacement. In the MKS system, the spring constant is specified in units of newtons per meter (N/m), and in the CGS system it is dynes per centimeter (d/cm).[2]

The development of a restoring force by an extended spring is demonstrated by the spring balance, as illustrated in Fig. 1.3. Gravity pulls down on the object being weighed, but it ultimately reaches a point at which the force of gravity, acting on its mass, is equally opposed by the restoring force developed in the spring. This is essentially the way in which common bathroom scales work.

A more general index of the elastic properties of a substance is the **modulus of elasticity**. The simplest example of a modulus of elasticity is *Young's modulus*;

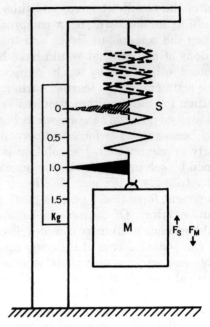

**Figure 1.3.** Determining the mass of an object using a spring balance. The downward pull ($F_M$) caused by the force of gravity acting on the mass ($M$) is balanced by the upward pull caused by the restoring force of the spring ($F_S$).

it is defined in terms of the ratio of the force per unit area, or *stress*, acting on an elastic body to the change in its length, or *strain*. Despite the change in terms, the relationship of stress to strain is still very much "Hookian." Therefore, Hooke's law may be stated in the form:

$$stress = \kappa \times strain$$

where $\kappa$ is Young's modulus. However, $\kappa$ does not have the same dimensions as the spring constant, $k$. In fact, $\kappa$ is a dimensionless ratio. But, that is another story. The concept of modulus of elasticity is what is important here. In discussing basic principles of acoustics (Chapter 2), it will be the modulus of elasticity, not the spring constant, that will be of primary interest. In general, the solution of a practical mechanical problem is likely to require a modulus of elasticity rather than a spring constant. Elastic moduli have been determined for various substances, in-

---

[2] The mathematically inclined reader may be compelled to write the dimensional equation of the spring constant as $MLT^{-2} \times L^{-1}$ or to simplify the dimensions to $MT^{-2}$. Neither version is used here in deference to the practical matter of the actual units of measure in conventional use. In the MKS system, this, again, is newtons per meter, not grams per seconds squared! Illogical? Perhaps, but the authors bear no responsibility here. This is a tell-it-like-it-is text. Perhaps some day, the scientific community will decide to give newtons per meter a name, maybe honoring Hooke as they have Newton; 1 N/m = 1 Hooke?

cluding fluids and gases. Air, for instance, can make a pretty good spring!

Moduli of elasticity will prevail later in the discussion of sound and acoustic principles (Chapter 2). For now, the more basic concepts of elasticity—stiffness, springs, and spring constants—will suffice. Still, stiffness is not always the quantity of most direct interest, even when discussing elasticity at the most basic level. Another way of quantifying elasticity is to measure **compliance**. Compliance is the reciprocal of stiffness. A more compliant spring is less stiff, and vice versa. The more compliant the spring, the less force required to displace it. Therefore, compliance indicates the amount of displacement per unit force, as reflected in its dimensions: $L/MLT^{-2}$. The MKS unit of compliance is meters per newton, whereas in the CGS system it is centimeters per dyne.

## 5. Friction

Now consider the situation illustrated in Figure 1.4. Force is acting to move an object along a surface. Motion will be opposed by **friction** between the surface of the object and the substratum. As long as velocity is maintained at a constant value (namely acceleration equals zero), a *steady state* exists in which the applied force is balanced by the frictional force. If the frictional opposition or "resistance" is overcome, the object is accelerated, and steady state no longer exists. Further-more, were friction not present, even the smallest continuous force applied to the object would cause it to accelerate indefinitely. Therefore, at constant velocity, an applied force, which otherwise might cause an object to be accelerated, is canceled by the opposing force of friction. In other words, the net force is zero. This situation reveals that the opposing force of friction is velocity dependent. To impart a higher velocity to the mass, the applied force must be increased. But the frictional force will increase too. It thus may be stated that friction seeks to limit velocity.

Unfortunately, in many practical physical problems, friction is not easily characterized, even in the case illustrated in Figure 1.4. In this example, friction seems simple enough—a tangential force developed between the surfaces in contact with one another. Yet, its quantity—the **coefficient of friction**—depends on both the nature of the surfaces and the force holding the surfaces together. In this case, that force is weight (that is, gravity acting on the mass of the object). The coefficient of friction also depends on whether the object is at rest or in motion. For purposes here, a simpler form of friction will be considered, namely that of fluid friction or *viscosity*. The resistance felt while stirring paint is caused by the viscosity of this fluid. Viscosity imparts *damping* to vibrational systems, as discussed later in this chapter. The shocks in the suspension systems of automobiles use viscous damping. In such systems,

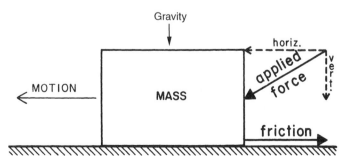

**Figure 1.4.** Movement of an object caused by the application of force applied at an oblique angle and opposed by friction. An additional force acting on the mass is gravity.

$$F = -rv \qquad (1.6)$$

where $r$ is the **mechanical resistance** in the system. The dimensions of $r$ may be found in the same way as they were for the spring constant (again, ignoring the sign), from Eq. 1.6:

$$r = F/v$$

Substituting known dimensions,

$$r = MLT^{-2}/(L/T)$$

(although, admittedly, the dimensional equation could be simplified further to yield $MT^{-1}$). Consequently, $r$ is measured in terms of force per unit velocity, that is N/m/sec (MKS) or d/cm/sec (CGS). Borrowing from electrical concepts, the unit of measure of mechanical resistance also is known as the (mechanical) *ohm*. One MKS ohm, for example, equals 1 N/m/sec.

## 6. Energy and Related Concepts

### A. WORK

In common parlance, the word *work* has many connotations, but perhaps it is most often associated with a more or less exhausting activity. Certainly, merely sliding a shaker of salt across the table to a dining companion would not evoke the comment, "Whew! That was a lot of work!" Indeed, the idea of work would probably not even come to mind, yet the physical reality is that work has been done in this seemingly effortless activity. In general, when a force acts through a certain distance, work is said to have been done. The equation for net work is given as:

$$\Delta W = F \Delta x \qquad (1.7)$$

Compared with its common usage, the word *work* thus has a more explicit meaning in physics. The salt shaker scenario is rather like the physical problem illustrated in Figure 1.4. A force is applied to an object (mass), and it is moved a certain distance. However, not all of the applied force in the problem illustrated in Figure 1.4 will accomplish work. Note that the direction of the applied force (recalling that force is a vector) is oblique to the direction of the resultant motion. The applied force, however, can be broken down into horizontal and vertical components. Because the substratum balances the vertical component, the object cannot move downward, so no work is done by this force component. By the same token, the force of gravity acting on the mass is not doing any work either. The horizontal component, on the other hand, moves the object; therefore, work is accomplished by the horizontal force component. Had the applied force been directed horizontally, more work would be done.

In general, according to Eq. 1.7, the more force applied to the object, the more work that is done. Similarly, the greater the distance over which the object is moved, in other words the greater the magnitude of $\Delta x$, the more work that is done. Again, the vertical component and gravitational components are ineffective in terms of work done. Indeed, because the distance the object can move in this direction is zero, no work can be done, regardless of the force applied (assuming the substratum to be impenetrable and the object incompressible).

### B. ENERGY: KINETIC VERSUS POTENTIAL

Work is a special form of the more general concept of *energy*. Indeed, the expression that "so-and-so amount of energy has been expended" really means that a certain amount of work was done. Energy also is a bit more complicated than work. Energy can assume one of two completely interchangeable, general forms: *potential* or *kinetic*. The classical physical *law of conservation of energy* dictates that energy can be transformed from one form to another, but it cannot be destroyed. In the scenario of a book resting on a table, the book has potential energy. When the table is suddenly jerked out from under it, the book plummets downward, because of the pull of gravity. The reason that the book on the table has potential energy is that work was done putting it there, namely, lifting it against gravity. By definition, work was accomplished in lifting the book onto the table—again, a force acted through a certain distance. The energy used must be available to do work once more. Consequently, energy is stored in the book resting on the table, namely in the form of *potential energy.*

There are other ways of storing potential energy, such as in a compressed or extended spring. More generally speaking, a deformed substance has potential energy by virtue of its elasticity, because work was done in deforming the substance. When the applied force is removed, the restoring force is available to do work. In fact, *elasticity* may be thought of as *the ability of a substance to store potential energy.*

In contrast to the energy situation associated with an object at rest, an object in motion has **kinetic energy**. Work is done in setting an object into motion, so the energy expended in the process must be conserved. *Inertia* may be thought of as *the ability of an object to store kinetic energy.* When the table was pulled out from under the book, potential energy was gradually converted to kinetic energy; that is, it gained kinetic energy as it fell toward the floor. The word *gradually* is used here to emphasize that the object does not begin to move instantaneously. The same inertia that makes it possible to ultimately convert all of the object's potential energy to kinetic energy opposes instantaneous changes in motion, including no motion, as discussed before. The conversion from potential to kinetic energy is a completely reversible process. For example, if a ball is thrown up into the air, work is done, because a force is required to counteract the force of gravity and to impart momentum to the ball. However, a point in time is reached at which the momentum is overcome by the force of gravity. The ball

then begins to travel earthward. During this trajectory, there is a continuous trade-off occurring from kinetic (when the ball is first thrown) to potential (at the peak of the trajectory) and back to kinetic energy (as the ball falls back to earth). At the instant it strikes the ground, this energy once again will be converted completely to potential energy, stored in the elasticity of the ball. This back-and-forth conversion will proceed as the ball bounces along the ground.

The ball might keep bouncing up and down forever were it not for one other factor (besides mass and elasticity): friction. Indeed, no practical physical problem can be analyzed completely without taking the influence of friction into account. Friction is also involved in the transformation of energy. In this case, the conversion is from one kind of energy, mechanical (for example, the kinetic energy of an object sliding across a surface), to another, heat. When this particular transformation occurs, energy is said to be **dissipated**. Whereas energy is stored by virtue of elasticity or mass, it is lost, for purposes of useful work, in friction. This transformation may be readily appreciated if one's hands are briskly rubbed together; the energy dissipated by friction between the hands is experienced as a warming sensation. *Friction* may be viewed as an index of a substance's *ability to dissipate energy in the form of heat.*

What of the bouncing ball? Well, even an object moving through air encounters some resistance because of friction. There are also frictional losses encountered each time the ball strikes the ground. In reality, springs and mechanical systems, in general, are characterized by a certain amount of internal friction. Thus, not only does the bouncing ball lose kinetic energy because of friction along its surface, but also because of dissipation via internal friction each time the ball compresses and expands as it bounces along.

The dimensions and units of measure of work and energy are identical: $MLT^{-2}L$

(consistent with Eq. 1.7). In the MKS system, the unit of measure is defined as a force of 1 N acting through a distance of 1 m and is called the *joule*. The CGS unit of measure, correspondingly, is defined as a force of 1 d acting through a distance of 1 cm and is called the *erg*. One erg is equal to $10^{-7}$ joule (or 1 joule $= 10^7$ erg).

## C. POWER

Although the concepts of work and energy are pervasive in physics, they do not in any way reflect the time within which the work is done or the rate at which the energy is expended. Equation 1.7 has no time term; that is, time appears in the dimensional equation of the joule (or erg) only by virtue of the underlying equation of force. The same energy may be involved whether an object is moved from one point to another in 1 sec or 1 year. Yet, intuition, if not experience, suggests that remarkably different amounts of effort are involved. Consequently, to reflect this temporal factor, another physical quantity is needed: *power*. Power ($P$) is the rate at which work is done:

$$P = \Delta W / \Delta t \qquad (1.8)$$

The dimensions of power are $MLT^{-2}L/T$. The unit of measure of power is the *watt* in both the MKS and CGS systems: 1 watt $= 1$ joule/sec $= 10^7$ erg/sec. The watt is perhaps more familiar from electricity, whereas the English unit of measure, horsepower, is more familiar in the context of mechanical power. Both, however, are measures of power.

Examining Eq. 1.8 more closely, together with Eq. 1.7, it can be seen that

$$P = \Delta W / \Delta t = F \Delta x / \Delta t = Fv \quad (1.9)$$

Therefore, power may be defined as the product of force and velocity. More power, therefore, is required to increase either force or velocity in a given situation. For example, the achievement of higher accelerations and velocities in automobiles requires engines of greater horsepower. The relationship expressed in Eq. 1.9 will be

elaborated later in this chapter in the context of vibratory motion. Before doing so, it is necessary to define vibratory motion and to detail some of its nuances, especially for certain special cases of interest here.

## 7. Simple Harmonic Motion

Thus far, the concepts of inertia, elasticity, friction, force, work, energy, and power have been developed in the context of fairly simple and straightforward forms of motion—linear motion—in which an object moves from one point to another in a straight line. Often the object is assumed to be in equilibrium. This section and those that follow deal with a form of motion that is of more direct interest in hearing science: *vibratory motion*. It was learned earlier that the application of a force to an object (or mechanical system, in general) may have one of several consequences, depending on the amount of mass, elasticity, and friction involved. Mass, by virtue of inertia, opposes change in motion or acceleration. The restoring force, because of elasticity, opposes the deformation of an object or, in a sense, displacement. Friction opposes motion or velocity. Each of these phenomena involves energy in a particular manner. Kinetic energy is stored in the motion of an object because of its mass. Potential energy can be stored in a compressed spring because of its elasticity. Friction dissipates energy in the form of heat. All of these basic principles also are applicable to vibratory motion, which, however, is motion that constantly changes over time. To be able to even discuss vibratory motion, as well as the effects of mass, elasticity, and friction on such motion, it is necessary to present some new concepts.

### A. SIMPLE SPRING-MASS SYSTEM

The simplest form of vibratory motion is *simple harmonic motion*. Similarly, the most fundamental vibratory machine

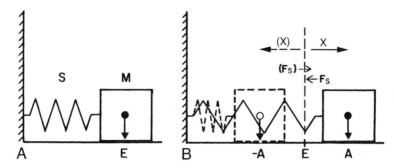

**Figure 1.5.** The simple harmonic oscillator. **a.** Resting equilibrium. **b.** Position of mass ($M$) at two instants in time, $A$ and $-A$, namely, at the extremes of displacement ($x$). $F_S$, Restoring force of the spring ($S$); $E$, equilibrium position.

is the *simple harmonic oscillator* or *simple spring-mass system*, as illustrated in Figure 1.5*a*. A spring is fixed to a rigid wall at one end and a mass at the other. For now, this system will be considered frictionless. It is true that this situation cannot exist in real life, but, for the sake of discussion, reality will be put on hold temporarily (although not for long). With the spring neither extended nor compressed, the mass is at resting equilibrium. If the mass is left undisturbed, nothing will happen.

What is needed now is an applied force to start this machine. This can be accomplished by pushing or pulling the mass to one side of the point marked $E$ (equilibrium position) and then releasing it (Fig. 1.5*b*). If brought to one point momentarily and then released abruptly, only the magnitude of this displacement will have any specific influence on what transpires thereafter; the farther the mass is displaced, the greater the subsequent motion. It should be noted that, for this machine to run properly, it is important not to exceed the elastic limits of the spring. (The importance of this rule will become apparent below, and the consequences of violating this rule will be discussed further in Chapter 3.) When force is applied to reposition the mass, say by pulling it to the right to point $A$, a restoring force is developed in the spring. The release of the mass now permits the energy stored in the

spring, namely potential energy, to do work. Consequently, the restoring force tends to pull the mass back toward the equilibrium position. However, the mass will not start back instantaneously by virtue of its inertia. Indeed, at the first instant the mass is released and the restoring force unleashed, the mass just sits there! In the next instant, though, it will begin to move as the potential energy stored in the spring begins to be transformed into kinetic energy and the mass picks up momentum. As time continues to pass, it actually will pick up so much momentum that it will travel past point $E$, rather than simply coming to rest there once more. At the instant it passes through $E$, all the potential energy originally stored in the spring has been converted into kinetic energy. Once past this point, the spring begins to be compressed; a restoring force is again developed; and kinetic energy is progressively converted back into potential energy. Consequently, the mass begins to slow down. Finally, at one instant the restoring force of the spring becomes sufficient to bring the mass to a halt at point $-A$. In the next instant, though, the whole process is repeated in reverse, as the mass begins to move in the opposite direction. And on and on this cyclic motion goes, back and forth, as the mass oscillates between $A$ and $-A$. In this make-believe frictionless system, this motion is not only monotonous, it is perpetual. Because of the law of conservation of energy, the work done in initially displacing the mass, and thus the potential energy stored in the extended and compressed spring, can be released only into the form of kinetic energy, stored in the moving mass.

The motion of the mass in the simple harmonic oscillator clearly is not constant, because the velocity varies continuously in both direction and magnitude. Thus, the mass is continually accelerating or decelerating, and even acceleration is never constant. There are other facets of this particular form of vibration that characterize it, but first, it is necessary to define several useful parameters by which this form of motion can be quantified.

## B. PARAMETERS OF OSCILLATION

### Amplitude

The distance between the equilibrium position $(E)$ and the peak excursion $(A)$ in Figure 1.5b is called **amplitude**. Because the excursion of the travel of the mass to the left of $E$ is as great as that to the right, that is $A - E = (-A) - E$, it is sufficient to specify amplitude, that is the magnitude of maximum displacement, from $E$ to $A$. In anticipation of later uses of amplitude measures, amplitude will be represented here by the abbreviation $A_{o-p}$ (known also as **peak amplitude**). (The symbolism here will become more apparent momentarily.) Furthermore, it also will be worthwhile to define peak-to-peak amplitude $(A_{p-p})$, that is, the distance from $A$ to $-A$. Therefore, $A_{p-p} = 2A_{o-p}$. Now, the magnitude of displacement can be measured at any instant in time, but all values will fall within the range delimited by the peak-to-peak amplitude (in other words, from $-A_{o-p}$ to $A_{o-p}$). Besides describing the magnitude of displacement, the concept of amplitude is also used to describe velocity, acceleration, force, power, and other physical quantities. The units of measure involved will be those appropriate for the specific physical quantity—velocity in

meters per second, etc. Also, there are more elaborate ways of measuring amplitude that will be described in Chapter 3.

### Period

A **period**, represented by the letter $T$, is the time required for the traverse of the mass from one point and back again to the same point while moving in the same direction. In the example illustrated in Figure 1.5b, this would be the time expended in the travel of the mass from $A$ to $E$, $E$ to $-A$, and back through $E$ to $A$ again. This describes one **cycle** of the motion. The period thus is the time required to complete one cycle. The period need not always be determined at the peaks of the excursion. The point of equilibrium, or any other point for that matter, also could serve as the reference point, as long as it is the same point from one cycle to the next. Period is generally measured in seconds (in reality, seconds per cycle), or subdivisions thereof (for instance, milliseconds per cycle).

### Frequency

**Frequency** $(f)$ refers to the number of cycles completed per unit time. Consequently, frequency is the reciprocal of period, and vice versa. That is,

$$f = 1/T \text{ and } T = 1/f$$

Frequency is measured in cycles per second. This unit of measure has been given the name Hertz (Hz) in honor of the physicist Heinrich Hertz. For example, if the period of a vibration is found to be 0.001 sec, its frequency is

$$f = 1/T = 1/10^{-3} = 10^3$$
$$= 1000 \text{ Hz or 1 kHz}$$

Similarly, if the frequency is known, the period can just as easily be obtained:

$$T = 1/f = 1/10^3 = 10^{-3} \text{ sec} = 1 \text{ msec}$$

Other examples of the interrelationship between frequency and period are pro-

**TABLE 1.5.**
**Frequency versus Period**

| Frequency (Hz) | Period | |
| | (sec) | (msec) |
| --- | --- | --- |
| 100 | 0.010000 | 10.000 |
| 250 | 0.004000 | 4.000 |
| 500 | 0.002000 | 2.000 |
| 1000 | 0.001000 | 1.000 |
| 2000 | 0.000500 | 0.500 |
| 4000 | 0.000250 | 0.250 |
| 8000 | 0.000125 | 0.125 |

vided in Table 1.5. These examples are within the frequency range of the vibrations that give rise to audible sounds for humans; in fact, they are standardly used in clinical hearing testing. It is important to note that, within certain limits, frequency (or period) is completely independent of amplitude. In the case of the simple harmonic oscillator, these limits are set by the elastic limits of the spring, namely, the range of amplitudes over which Hooke's law (Eq. 1.5) holds true.

## C. BLOW-BY-BLOW DESCRIPTION OF SIMPLE HARMONIC MOTION

Having established the various parameters by which vibratory motion can be characterized, it is now possible to proceed with a more detailed description of simple harmonic motion and the relations between these parameters. First, it is necessary to plot the time course of the displacement of the mass, that is, to graph the amplitude of displacement at each instant of time. Imagine a rather large spring-mass system of the form illustrated in Figure 1.5. Suppose it is possible to magically stop the mass at various points in time during a cycle. For practical purposes, only a limited number of measurements are made. The period is 1 sec (that is, $T = 1$ sec), and the amplitude is 1 m (that is, $A_{o-p} = 1$ m). The measurements are begun some time after the oscillation has started, so that they can be made whenever it is convenient. In this case, the tracking of

the displacement is initiated when the indicator on the mass (Fig. 1.5) just reaches $E$ on its excursion to $A$. The results of the hypothetical measurements are shown in Table 1.6. The exact values are not as important here as the pattern of change in displacement over time, as shown by the graph in Figure 1.6. It is notable that of the 0.25 second expended during the excursion from $E$ to $A$ (that is, $T/4$ or one-quarter cycle), only 0.08 second is required to reach half the amplitude, whereas the next half of the amplitude consumes 0.17 sec—more than twice as much time! This is because, again, the mass must slow down and ultimately stop to reverse its motion. Given the futility of measuring the displacement at each and every instant in time, it is fortunate that the time course of this motion is described by a well-known function from trigonometry, the **sine**. Simple harmonic motion is thus said to be **sinusoidal**. The graph of the sine function (Fig. 1.6) has a characteristic shape or **waveform** and is often described as a **sine wave**. From knowledge of the behavior of the sine function, it is possible, in effect, to fill in values at every instant in time, thereby forming a continuous line (Fig. 1.6).

**TABLE 1.6.**
**Time course of Simple Harmonic Oscillation**[a]

| Time (Elapsed, in sec) | Amplitude (Displacement in m) |
| --- | --- |
| 0.00 | 0.00 |
| 0.08 | 0.50 |
| 0.17 | 0.87 |
| 0.25 | 1.00 |
| 0.33 | 0.87 |
| 0.42 | 0.50 |
| 0.50 | 0.00 |
| 0.58 | −0.50 |
| 0.67 | −0.87 |
| 0.75 | −1.00 |
| 0.83 | −0.87 |
| 0.92 | −0.50 |
| 1.00 | 0.00 |

[a] $f = 1$ Hz, and $A_{o-p} = 1$ m.

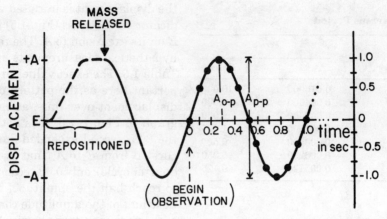

**Figure 1.6.**   Time course of the displacement of the mass in a simple harmonic oscillator in Figure 1.5. The oscillator is started (*dashed* portion) by repositioning the mass to a point (*A*) some distance from the point of equilibrium (*E*), in this hypothetical case 1 m away. Therefore, the amplitude ($A_{o\text{-}p}$) is 1 m, and the peak-to-peak amplitude ($A_{p\text{-}p}$) is 2 m. The instantaneous displacements, denoted by the *dots*, are given in Table 1.6. The frequency of vibration is 1 Hz.

## 8. Sinusoid—Its Generation and Related Concepts

The relation of the sine function to simple harmonic motion may not be immediately obvious, given that it is a trigonometric function whose dependent variable is an angle, not time. However, it can be shown that angle and time are interrelated in this case. Referring once more to Fig. 1.5*b*, imagine that the mass is vibrating back and forth. Its movement could be tracked visually by watching the dot on the side of the mass. The movement of the dot might be thought of as a point moving around a circle, as the mass travels from *E* to *A*, *A* back to *E*, and so forth, each time a cycle is completed. As illustrated in Figure 1.7, at each instant in time, a different angle $\theta$, also known as the **phase angle**, is subtended by the radius (*r*), connecting the center of the circle to the point, and the *E axis*. The instantaneous displacement is measured by dropping a vertical line (*a*) from the point to the *E axis*. Because *r* and *a* form a right triangle with the *E axis*, the sine of the angle $\theta$ can be obtained as follows:

$$\sin(\theta) = a/r$$

(that is, the sine of the angle of a right triangle equals the length of the opposite side divided by the hypotenuse). The rate at which angle $\theta$ changes, or the rate at which the radius rotates, is called the **angular velocity** or **angular frequency**, $\theta/t$, and

$$\theta/t = 2\pi f = \omega$$

Therefore,

$$\theta = 2\pi f t = \omega t$$

in radians. The constant, $\pi$, is approximately equal to 3.14; $2\pi$ radians equals 360°, which is one cycle. The position of the mass in the simple harmonic oscillator, at each instant in time, thus can be specified by a phase angle. When displacement is plotted as a function of the angle $\theta$, the sinusoid emerges, as shown in Figure 1.7.

An equation now can be written that succinctly describes simple harmonic motion:

$$x(t) = A_{o\text{-}p} \sin(\omega t + \phi) \qquad (1.10)$$

where $\phi$ is the starting phase that, for most purposes here, will be assumed to be 0°. This is a way of saying in the "symbolic shorthand" of mathematics that displacement, as a function of time ($x[t]$), is equal to the (peak) amplitude ($A_{o\text{-}p}$) multiplied

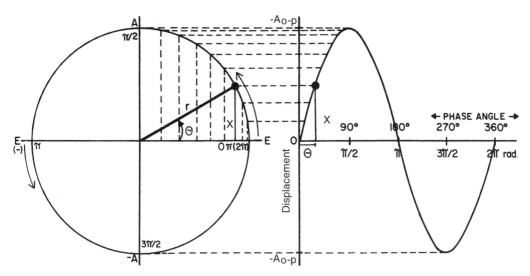

**Figure 1.7.** Generation of a sinusoid from the rotation of a vector ($r$). The diagram is keyed to the motion of the simple spring-mass system illustrated in Figure 1.5. $E$, Resting equilibrium point; $A$ and $-A$, Extremes of displacement. The direction of motion is indicated by *arrows*. The instantaneous displacement ($x$) attained at different points along the circumference of the *circle* are plotted as a function of the (phase) angle subtended by $r$ and the *horizontal axis*.

by the value of the sine at each instant of time ($t$). The value of the sine itself ranges from $-1$ to $1$; therefore, in simple harmonic motion amplitude varies between $-A$ and $A$ (or $\pm A_{o-p}$), as described earlier.

In the specific example given for simple harmonic motion, illustrated in Figures 1.5*b* and 1.6, the starting phase was 90°. **Phase** ($\theta$) is yet another parameter by which vibratory motion can be characterized, like amplitude, frequency, and period. In many instances it may be assumed, for simplicity, that the starting phase is 0°, and $\phi$ may be dropped from Eq. 1.10. Still, phase is of special interest when attempting to compare two or more vibratory components. As demonstrated in Figure 1.8, it is possible that the only distinction between two vibrations is the *phase difference*. Here, there is a phase difference of 90°. The function starting at peak amplitude is said to *lead* the function starting at zero amplitude. Conversely, the second function is said to *lag* the first.

The interrelationship between displacement, velocity, and acceleration also can be shown to be a matter of phase dif-

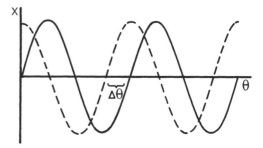

**Figure 1.8.** Phase difference, $\Delta\theta$, between two sinusoids. In the case shown, the sine function in *dashed lines* is leading that in *solid lines* by 90°.

ferences, as illustrated in Figure 1.9. This is because velocity is greatest when the mass in the simple harmonic oscillator passes through the resting equilibrium position (zero axis crossing in Fig. 1.9), whereas it is zero at the peaks of displacement. Therefore, *velocity leads displacement*. Similarly, acceleration is greatest when velocity is zero, because velocity changes most dramatically in the vicinity of the zero crossings of the velocity function. *Acceleration* thus *leads velocity* (and displacement). Conversely, it can be

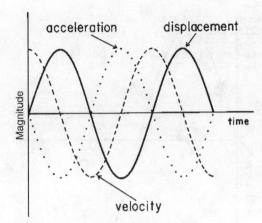

**Figure 1.9.** Relationship between displacement, velocity, and acceleration in simple harmonic motion.

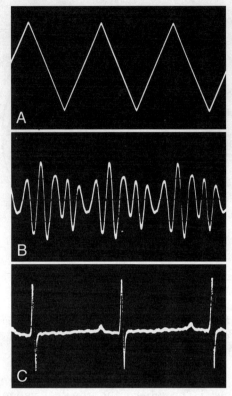

**Figure 1.10.** Oscillographic tracings of different periodic but nonsinusoidal waveforms. **a.** Triangular waveform generated electronically. **b.** Sustained phonation of the vowel [a]. **c.** Electrocardiogram of a guinea pig.

stated that displacement lags velocity and velocity lags acceleration. (These points will be elaborated further in the section on forced vibration below.)

Simple harmonic motion is merely one of a broad category of vibratory motions described as *periodic*. The sine function is a periodic function, because it repeats itself at regular intervals. If a function, $f(t)$, is periodic, it will have the same value at any time, $t$, as well as at time $t$ plus any integer multiple of the period $T$ (that is, at $t + nT$, where $n$ is an integer multiple). Figure 1.10 illustrates several other examples of periodic functions. Like the sinusoid, these functions have a fundamental frequency that is equal to the reciprocal of the period, that is, $T^{-1}$. However, the waveforms of the periodic functions in Figure 1.10 are clearly not sinusoidal. Therefore, although the sine is a periodic function, not all periodic functions are sinusoidal. On the other hand, the motion of the (ideal) simple harmonic oscillator is purely sinusoidal in nature. The factors determining this special kind of motion now will be described.

## 9. Free Vibration: Doing What Comes Naturally

The most intriguing aspect of simple harmonic motion is that, even though no specific frequency of vibration is imparted to the system during the initiation of the motion, the system vibrates at one specific frequency—its *natural frequency*. Recall that the simple harmonic oscillator is started by merely displacing the mass from its equilibrium position and releasing it. This abrupt initiation of the motion of the mass does not impart any one frequency of oscillation to it. Consequently, the system is free to vibrate as it chooses. The natural frequency is uniquely determined by the amounts of mass and stiffness in the system. This is so because the oscillatory motion occurs by virtue of the interaction of the motion of the mass and the restoring force of the spring, which is deformed whenever the mass is displaced. Once the oscillator is started, the only force, per se, acting within the system is the restoring force. Given the basic definition of force itself (Eq. 1.3) and that of the restoring force (Eq. 1.5), the following equation can be written:

$$ma = -kx$$

Therefore,

$$ma + kx = 0 \qquad (1.11)$$

Equation 1.11 simply shows that there is no additional force required to keep the ideal or frictionless simple spring-mass system in vibration. Even more important is the fact that one of the well-known solutions to Eq. 1.11 is the equation of the general sinusoid; that is, Eq. 1.10 may be written in the form

$$x(t) = A_{o\text{-}p}\sin[(k/m)^{1/2}\,t + \phi] \qquad (1.12)$$

Equations 1.10 and 1.12 differ only with regard to the term $k/m^{1/2}$. In other words, the square root of the ratio of stiffness to mass is equal to the angular frequency, $\omega$ (or $2\pi f$), so it is this ratio that specifically determines the natural frequency. The individual effects of mass and stiffness are as follows: *the natural frequency is proportional to the square root of stiffness ($f \propto s^{1/2}$) and is inversely proportional to the square root of mass ($f \propto 1/m^{1/2}$).* For example, if stiffness is increased four times, the natural frequency will double. Likewise, if mass is increased four times, the natural frequency is halved.

Thus far, the simple harmonic oscillator has been assumed to be frictionless; that is, the mechanical resistance in the system is zero. As discussed earlier, friction opposes motion because of the dissipation of energy in the form of heat, which cannot do useful work. There is also mechanical resistance in the simple harmonic oscillator. With resistance added to the system, the oscillation will not go on endlessly but ultimately will fade away. The oscillations are then said to be *damped*. In a highly damped system, the vibrations will fade or *decay* quickly. The

greater the amount of resistance in the system, the more the oscillations are damped and the faster the decay. As resistance is increased, a condition will be reached, known as ***critical damping***. At this point, the mass, after the initial displacement and release, will simply return to the equilibrium position. The system is then nonoscillatory.

An example of a damped oscillation is shown in Figure 1.11; the function graphed in this figure is specifically characteristic of viscous damped (free) vibration. Two points are noteworthy. First, only the amplitude of the vibration changes over time, not its frequency.[3] Second, lines can be drawn through the peaks and troughs of the oscillatory function that define the ***envelope*** of the waveform. The envelope itself may be represented by a mathematical equation (just as the sine function represents simple harmonic motion). The envelope function in this case is ***exponential*** and is an example of the phenomenon of ***exponential decay***.

## 10. Forced Vibration and Consequences of Trying to Push Vibratory Systems Around

Again, some degree of damping is inevitable in the real spring-mass system. But if just enough energy is supplied continuously to the simple spring-mass system to make up for the loss of energy (because of mechanical resistance), it is possible to maintain a constant amplitude of oscillation. This is an example of ***forced vibration***. Unlike free vibration, demonstrat-

---

[3] The frequency of the oscillation itself is somewhat affected by the introduction of damping into the system, relative to the natural frequency of the undamped system. In the simple spring-mass system, the shift in frequency is downward. However, the effect of increased damping on the frequency of vibration is relatively minor compared with the effects of increased stiffness or mass. Thus, for small amounts of damping, the frequency of oscillation is nearly equal to, but slightly less than, the natural frequency of the undamped system.

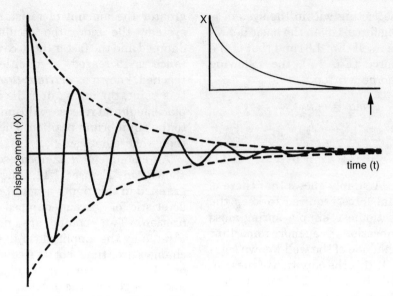

**Figure 1.11.** A damped sinusoidal oscillation. Graph of the decay function alone is shown in the *inset*.

ing the **natural response** of a vibratory system, the **forced response** of the system is dependent on the characteristics of the externally applied or "driving" force itself, although not exclusively. The forced response is dependent on the same physical properties that govern the natural frequency of free vibration. Yet, it is possible to drive the simple spring-mass system into oscillation at frequencies other than the natural frequency. However, as the frequency of the applied force increasingly deviates from the natural frequency, an increasing amount of opposition to the motion develops. This opposition is associated with the influence of the mass and stiffness in the system, that, of course, make free vibration possible. In other words, the system "reacts" to the driving force. The respective "reactions" associated with mass and stiffness act in direct phase opposition to one another, showing a 180° phase difference. Each is 90° out of phase with velocity, as shown in Figure 1.12. This is because the opposition afforded by the mass in the system is proportional to acceleration, whereas the restoring force is proportional to displacement. Therefore, it is because acceleration and

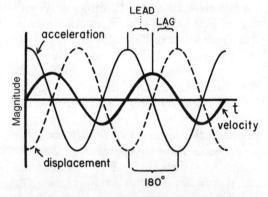

**Figure 1.12.** Relationship of acceleration and displacement to velocity in simple harmonic motion. Amplitudes were arbitrarily chosen for purposes of illustration.

displacement are "out of step" with the motion that mass and stiffness inherently offer a certain amount of opposition to the motion imparted by the driving force.

The particular form of opposition just described must be distinguished from that caused by mechanical resistance; consequently, it is not called resistance. Indeed, the two forms of opposition to motion are fundamentally different. In one case (resistance), energy is dissipated; in the other, energy is stored. For these reasons the particular form of opposition to motion afforded by mass or elasticity is called **reactance**. Mass reactance is sometimes called *positive reactance* because, again, in the simple spring-mass system the acceleration leads velocity. Mass reactance ($X_M$) is not only determined by mass but also by the frequency of the driving force, namely,

$$X_M = 2\pi f m = \omega m \qquad (1.13)$$

Similarly, because the restoring force of the spring lags velocity, elastic reactance is sometimes referred to as *negative reactance* ($X_S$). Elastic reactance ($X_S$) is also frequency dependent:

$$X_S = k/2\pi f = S/\omega \qquad (1.14)$$

Because the two reactive components are opposites, it can be deduced that the least net opposition to the driving force must occur at a frequency at which the mass and elastic reactances are equal, that is $X_M = X_S$. This frequency is known as the **resonant frequency**. The resonant frequency, $f_r$, can be computed using Eqs. 1.13 and 1.14 as follows:

$$2\pi f m = k/2\pi f$$
$$(2\pi f)^2 = k/m$$
$$2\pi f = (k/m)^{1/2}$$

$$f_r = f = (k/m)^{1/2}/2\pi \qquad (1.15)$$

Therefore, the resonant frequency is proportional to the square root of stiffness and inversely proportional to the square root of mass.

Figure 1.13 provides a summary in graphic form of the dependence of mass reactance and elastic reactance on frequency and the interaction between the two reactances for driving forces of different frequencies above and below the resonant frequency. The index of the response of the simple spring-mass system is *admittance* ($Y = Z^{-1}$) and will be discussed

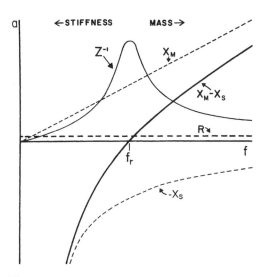

**Figure 1.13.** Magnitude of reactance and of resistance as a function of frequency in a simple spring-mass system under forced oscillation. The response is shown in terms of the inverse impedance, $Z^{-1}$ (also known as admittance); power transfer to the system is proportional to $Z^{-1}$. Maximal response occurs at the resonant frequency ($f_r$), where the effects of mass and stiffness cancel one another ($X_M - X_S = 0$), leaving only frictional resistance ($R$) caused by damping. Thus, at low frequencies the system is stiffness dominated, near $f_r$ resistance dominated, and at high frequencies mass dominated.

in more detail in Section 11 below. Because frequency is in the denominator of Eq. 1.14, elastic reactance increases as frequency decreases (that is, as the denominator gets smaller). Conversely, mass reactance decreases with decreasing frequency of the driving force (Eq. 1.13). Elastic reactance, therefore, provides the most opposition at relatively low frequencies. For this reason the response of the system *below the resonant frequency* is said to be *stiffness dominated*, whereas the system is said to be *mass dominated at frequencies above the resonant frequency*. This is in keeping with the effects of mass and stiffness in free vibration, in which the natural frequency is lowered by increased mass (corresponding to less opposition to forced vibration at relatively low frequencies) and is raised by increased stiffness (less opposition to high frequencies of vibration). Another way of looking at the behavior of the simple spring-mass system under forced vibration is that, to obtain the same amplitude of response at frequencies above and below the resonant frequency, more force is required.

At this juncture, it is useful to reiterate the distinction between reactance and (mechanical) resistance. Resistance ($R$) causes energy to be wasted for purposes of useful work (namely, dissipated in the form of heat), whereas energy is merely stored momentarily in the case of reactance ($X$), either in the form of potential energy of the deformed spring or in the kinetic energy of the moving mass. As damping in the system is increased, the contribution of reactance to the total opposition of the system is increasingly "diluted." This, in turn, reduces the frequency wise selectivity of the response of the system to the driving force, as illustrated in Figure 1.14. In the ideal or undamped simple harmonic oscillator, a very sharp peak would be expected in the system's response at the resonant frequency. If a continuous vibratory force of the same frequency as the resonant frequency were applied, the response amplitude at resonance would become infinite. However, with the addition of damping to the system, this peak is diminished. Motion is limited. The more damping, therefore, the "flatter" the **response characteristics** of the system. In more elaborate vibratory systems than the simple harmonic oscillator, there may be more than one resonant peak (that is, mechanical circuits involving multiple components of mass and stiffness). Still, the influence of damping is to smooth the **frequency response** of the system, that is, the response as a function of frequency. Although such smoothing may be desired, it is important to recognize that it is accomplished at the expense of efficiency, because more energy is being dissipated.

## 11. Impedance and Related Concepts

### A. COLLECTIVE OPPOSITION—IMPEDANCE

The driving of a simple spring-mass system, or indeed any vibratory system, is actually a matter of power transfer between the driver, or **source** (of the applied force) and the drivee, or **load** (the system to which force is applied). The transfer of power is optimal only under certain conditions. The most intuitively obvious condition is resonance, in which the only opposition to motion is that supplied by damping (that is, the net reactance is zero). However, resonance obviously is a special condition, and neither the resonant frequency, the mechanical resistance, nor the reactance individually is adequate to characterize the system. A quantity that does characterize the system well is **impedance** ($Z$). Ideally, the impedances of the source and load should be matched. Substantial mismatches of impedance will diminish the efficiency of power transfer

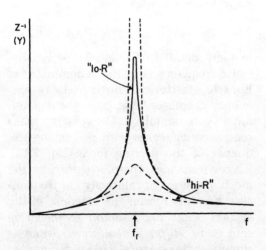

**Figure 1.14.** Effects of damping on the forced response of a simple spring-mass system. The inverse impedance, $Z^{-1}$ (or admittance, $Y$) is plotted as a function of frequency and is the index of the response. The *finely dashed curve* represents the response of the undamped (or ideal) system. The other curves show three different degrees of damping from low (*low-R*) to high (*hi-R*).

from one system to the other. The impedance concept is most readily grasped, again, from its analysis in the case of the (damped) simple spring-mass system. The impedance of this system is equal, mathematically speaking, to the complex sum of the resistance and reactances:

$$Z = R \pm jX \qquad (1.16)$$

where $j$ is an *imaginary number*. Imaginary does not mean "make believe." Rather, it is a special number—the square root of $-1$. Accordingly, $X$ and $R$ are referred to as the *imaginary* and *real* parts of the impedance, respectively.

Putting the number $-1$ into a pocket calculator and trying to compute the square root actually will result in an error! Can't be done! So, what is important about $j$ is not its numerical value but what it signifies, namely that values of $X$ and $R$ cannot be added arithmetically. The manner in which reactances and resistance combine to form impedance is shown in Figure 1.15. The individual components of reactance and resistance are vector-like quantities, known as **phasors**. Vectors, again, are quantities that have both magnitude and direction. *Phasors* are quantities that have *magnitude* and *phase*. The impact of $j$ now becomes apparent; reactances are plotted along an axis at right angles to the axis along which resistance is plotted. This, in turn, follows from the fact that in reactive components force and velocity are not in phase, as they are in resistances. Mass and elastic reactance lie along the same axis (the imaginary axis) but are of opposite phase or *polarity*. This is because acceleration and displacement are 180° out of phase, as illustrated previously in Figure 1.12. For purposes of illustration, $X_M$ is shown as being greater than $X_S$, a situation that occurs in a damped simple spring-mass system when the driving frequency is higher than the resonant frequency and, therefore, the response of the system is mass dominated (in other words, for frequencies falling to

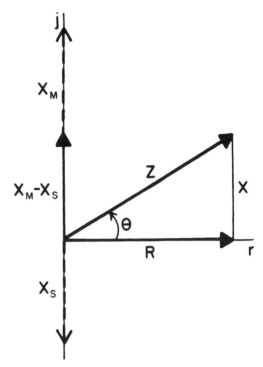

**Figure 1.15.** Phasor representation of impedance ($Z$) and its constituent components, resistance ($R$) and reactance ($X$), in a simple spring-mass system. This example is with the system forced to oscillate at a relatively high frequency, at which its response is mass dominated ($X_M > X_S$). At relatively low frequencies (stiffness-dominated response; $X_M < X_S$), $Z$ would fall below the $r$ axis. The phase of the impedance is denoted by $\theta$, the angle subtended by $Z$ and $R$.

the right of $f_r$ in Fig. 1.13). The reactances may be combined *algebraically* to find the total reactance ($X$). However, resistance ($R$) and reactance must be added vectorially. The resultant, the magnitude of the impedance ($Z$), can be calculated by a trick used earlier to find a resultant force in a similar situation (Fig. 1.2). The resultant is treated as the hypotenuse of a right triangle with $X$ and $R$ forming the other two sides. Consequently,

$$Z = [R^2 + (X_M - X_S)^2]^{1/2} \quad (1.17)$$

In words, impedance equals the square root of the sum of the resistance squared and reactance squared.

It follows from its derivation that $Z$ also is a phasor and thus has both magnitude and phase. Furthermore, it is frequency dependent. In fact, it is possible to define the resonant frequency (in the simple spring-mass system) in yet another way—the frequency at which $Z$ is minimal and equals $R$ alone. Impedance, like resistance and reactance, is measured in ohms. Incidentally, complex numbers, such as impedance, can be represented in several ways. Equations 1.16 and 1.17 express impedance in the *rectangular* form. Impedance also can be represented by its magnitude and phase; this is called *polar* form.[4]

In the simple spring-mass system, for simple harmonic motion, impedance also can be related to amplitudes of force and velocity:

$$F = Zv \qquad (1.18)$$

When the impedance is purely resistive (namely, net reactance is zero and motion is limited only by damping), Eq. 1.18 reduces to

$$F = Rv$$

which is essentially the same as Eq. 1.6. Also, if Eq. 1.18 is solved for $Z$, then it can be stated that

$$Z = F/v$$

Therefore, impedance can be defined as the (complex) ratio of force to velocity. This is a simple enough relationship; more force is needed to increase velocity against the opposition posed by a given impedance. If impedance is increased, a greater force is required just to maintain the same velocity of motion. Taking the derivation another step forward, power is seen to be the product of force and velocity and also

can be expressed in terms of impedance. Solving for $v$ in Eq. 1.18,

$$v = F/Z$$

Substituting this expression for $v$ in Eq. 1.9,

$$P = Fv = F(F/Z) = F^2/Z \qquad (1.19)$$

Recall Eq. 1.9: $P = Fv$. Similarly, it can be shown that

$$P = v^2Z \qquad (1.20)$$

(Note that between Eqs. 1.9 and 1.18 there are only two independent variables.) Power, the time rate of energy consumption, is clearly dependent on impedance.

## B. ADMITTANCE

As a final consideration in this discussion of impedance, it is worth commenting briefly on the use of the reciprocal of impedance $(Z^{-1})$ in Figures 1.13 and 1.14. The reciprocal of impedance is known specifically as **admittance** $(Y)$. Because $Y = Z^{-1} = 1/Z$, if $Z$ increases, $Y$ decreases, and vice versa. Admittance was used earlier (Fig. 1.14) as the index of the simple spring-mass system's response, because the power transferred to the system (from the source) is directly proportional to admittance, whereas it is inversely proportional to impedance (Eqs. 1.19 and 1.20). Admittance is defined as the complex sum of conductance $(G)$, the reciprocal of resistance, and susceptance $(B)$, the reciprocal of reactance:

$$Y = G \pm jB \qquad (1.21)$$

Whereas the units of measure of impedance are (mechanical) ohms, admittance is measured in units called *mhos*. (This apparently is because it was easier to just spell *ohm* backward than to come up with a truly unique name for the unit of measure of admittance.) In various applications, such as in the audiological test known as tympanometry (a measurement of the mobility of the eardrum and the bones of the middle ear), it may be more convenient to use admittance than imped-

---

[4] The magnitude and phase of the impedance are more obvious in the polar form: $Z = M < \theta$. *This actually is the solution for the magnitude of the impedance M that would be obtained in converting from the rectangular to the polar form. Similarly, the phase of the impedance can be shown to be* $\theta = tan^{-1}(X/R)$ *($tan^{-1}$ being the arctangent).*

ance. Incidentally, the word *immittance* has been coined as an all-inclusive term to identify measurements of either impedance or admittance for hearing research and clinical applications. However, immittance has no physical meaning in the quantitative sense. The units of measure used are simply those applicable to the actual measurement involved (ohms or mhos).

## C. SHOCKING EXAMPLES OF IMPEDANCE

The concepts of resonance and impedance may be illustrated by a familiar example: a car that begins to shimmy vigorously at a certain speed. The speed of the car is a function of the revolutions per minute (RPMs) of the engine (not to mention the gear ratio through the transmission and differential). Revolutions per minute and Hertz (Hz, cycles per second) are fundamentally the same units of measure, so the engine provides an oscillatory driving force or source. Other such sources may exist, for example, a wheel out of alignment that is causing a periodic wobble. An automobile has mass, of course, and is mounted on springs; therefore, it has all the makings of an oscillatory system. When the revolutions per minute of the engine approach the resonant frequency of the car, it begins to shimmy. At other speeds (or revolutions per minute), the impedance of this automotive vibratory system is sufficiently great that the shimmy is minimized. Actually, an automobile is designed to respond minimally to various forces that might cause it to vibrate excessively and give a rough and/or noisy ride, as when hitting a pothole in the road. The car has *shock absorbers*, which are dampers; they absorb the vibratory energy stored by the springs of the suspension system, thus damping the vibrations. Indeed, one way to test the shocks is to jump on and off the bumper quickly and see how long the body continues to bounce up and down. It is generally desirable that there be only one bounce; in other words,

this vibratory system, ideally, should be critically damped.

Another example of what can happen when vibration is insufficiently damped, an example of potentially catastrophic proportion, is found in the well-known military principle that troops should not be marched in cadence across a bridge. The troops marching in step a represent periodic source. Consequently, the accompanying vibration has a fundamental frequency. If this frequency equals the resonant frequency of the bridge, and if the amount of damping in the bridge's structure is inadequate, vibrations might be excited that could exceed the structural limits of the bridge. This example also aptly illustrates the notion that at the resonant frequency, power transfer from the source to the load is optimal.

These examples demonstrate that the concept of impedance does not apply uniquely to the simple spring-mass system. Therefore, the concepts discussed above can serve to provide at least an intuitive understanding of the workings of more elaborate systems and across types of systems—mechanical, acoustic, and electronic. The basic quantities involved are universal. The concept of impedance and the various other concepts developed earlier will now be extended and given more direct relevance to the subjects of primary interest here—sound and hearing.

## BIBLIOGRAPHY

Block, M. G., and Wiley, T. L. (1994). Overview and basic principles of acoustic immittance. In *Handbook of Clinical Audiology*, 4th ed, pp 271–282, edited by J. Katz. Williams & Wilkins, Baltimore.

Feynman, R. P., Leighton, R. B., and Sands, M. (1963). *The Feynman Lectures of Physics*, vol 1. Addison-Wesley Publishing Co., Reading, MA.

French, A. P. (1971). *Vibrations and Waves*. W. W. Norton & Co., New York.

Hall, D. E. (1980). *Musical Acoustics: An Introduction*. Wadsworth Publishing, Belmont.

Hewitt, P. (1974). *Conceptual Physics*. Little, Brown & Co., Boston.

Kinsler, L. E., and Frey, A. R. (1962). *Fundamentals of Acoustics*. John Wiley & Sons, New York.

Morse, P. M. (1976). *Vibration and Sound.* American Institute of Physics, New York.

Olson, H. F. (1958). *Dynamical Analogies.* D. Van Nostrand Co., Princeton.

Prout, J. H., and Bienvenue, G. R. (1990). *Acoustics for You.* Krieger Publishing, Malabar, FL.

Rossing, T. D. (1990). *The Science of Sound.* Addison-Wesley Publishing Co., Reading, MA.

Speaks, C. E. (1992). *Introduction to Sound: Acoustics for Hearing and Speech Sciences.* Singular Publishing Group, San Diego.

Tonndorf, J. (1980). Physics of sound. In *Otolaryngology: Vol. 1. Basic Sciences and Related Disciplines,* 2nd ed., pp 177–198, edited by M. M. Paparella and D. A. Shumrick. W. B. Saunders Co., Philadelphia.

Van Camp, K. J., and Creten, W. L. (1976). Principles of acoustic impedance and admittance. In *Acoustic Impedance and Admittance: The Measurement of Middle Ear Function,* pp 300–334, edited by A. S. Feldman and L. A. Wilbur. Williams & Wilkins, Baltimore.

## CHAPTER 2

# ACOUSTICS

Sound is one of the more familiar forms of energy. It is a physical phenomenon to which one is exposed incessantly. Even if extreme measures are taken to shut out sounds from the environment, most people cannot escape the noise of their own bodies. Despite the pervasiveness of sound in everyday life, it is a somewhat elusive phenomenon to understand in common-sense terms. Like electricity, sound is not easily visualized, either literally or conceptually, but the consequences of its presence are readily apparent. Given that sound is a physical entity, physical laws govern its behavior. The science of sound classically has stood apart as a major subdiscipline of physics, known as ***acoustics***. Acoustics is of special interest here, because sound is the physical stimulus that evokes the sensation of hearing. It is this inseparability of hearing and sound that dictates the need for a basic understanding of acoustics to attain a working knowledge of hearing and its measurement.

## 1. Sound—Its Nature, Dimensions, and Measures

The physical bases of vibratory motion were described in Chapter 1, and sound is, fundamentally, a form of vibration. To be more precise, vibratory mechanical motion is required to generate sound, yet sound is distinct from this mechanical vibration.

## A. THE DISTURBANCE CALLED SOUND

Consider the following experiment. An alarm clock is placed in a bell jar, which is connected to a vacuum pump. While the alarm rings, the air gradually is pumped out of the jar. As the air is evacuated, the magnitude of the sound diminishes, but when the air is leaked back into the jar, the ringing gradually returns to its original magnitude. This was, in essence, the experiment carried out by Robert Boyle in the latter part of the 17th century. Based on his observations, Boyle concluded that for sound to exist there must be a ***medium***. He reasoned that the alarm sounded softer when air was evacuated from the bell jar because he had reduced the medium.[1] As Boyle observed, sound is an energy form that exists within a medium and that moves through that medium as a wave.

***Sound waves*** do not occur sponta-

---

[1] There actually is a better explanation for the decrease in the sound heard, based on the assumption that Boyle did not obtain a perfect vacuum, in all likelihood. Consequently, a small amount of air was left in the bell jar. What really changed was the density of the medium. This, in turn, means that the impedance of the air was greatly reduced, whereas that of the glass was unchanged. Because optimal energy transfer occurs between media of like impedances, the air-to-glass boundary became increasingly more difficult for the sound to cross as air was pumped out. This increasing impedance mismatch caused a reduction in the magnitude of the sound heard. (The impedance of media for sound and its determinants are discussed in detail in Section 2 of this chapter.) Regardless, Boyle's conclusion was correct.

neously but must be started by a vibratory source, such as the alarm clock in Boyle's experiment. This vibration gives rise to movement of the particles of air surrounding the alarm. The air particles thus constitute the medium, and the sound may be thought of as a disturbance in the medium. This disturbance, in turn, causes movement of other adjacent parts of the medium. Thus, a sound wave represents an orderly change in parts of a medium over space and time caused by the vibratory motion of an object. Consequently, sound is described more thoroughly as a *propagated disturbance in the medium*. The sound source actually delivers energy to the medium, and a sound wave carries this energy away from the source.

The study of sound is thus a study of waves and their behavior. There are many kinds of waves—light waves, radio waves, and water waves, to name a few—and, of course, sound waves. Although these waves differ in important ways, they are also similar in some fundamental ways. For example, all waves move (propagate) and carry energy. Therefore, waves provide a means by which energy can be moved from one place to another.

The energy in the wave can be measured at various places or at different times during the wave's travel. From these measures, important physical phenomena and principles can be defined or appreciated. Furthermore, from these measures, waves can be described by parameters such as speed and shape. Some attributes of waves are determined by the medium in which they exist, and when a wave moves from one medium to another, these aspects of the waves change. Waves propagating in the same medium also may be changed when they encounter objects or obstacles. These phenomena and the detailed effects of the properties of the medium and other considerations are the substance of the sections to follow. First, some of the phenomena and effects mentioned above must be examined with greater scrutiny.

## B. THE SOUND MEDIUM

Boyle's experiment led him to conclude that for sound waves to occur, there must be a material medium. Although that is a correct conclusion for sound waves, light waves and radio waves (for example) can be generated and/or propagated in a vacuum, as illustrated by the fact that the alarm clock did not disappear as a vacuum was approximated, although it certainly became less audible. Substances in all three major classes—solids, liquids, and gases—are suitable media for sound. These substances obviously differ in their physical properties, so it might be expected that the transmission of sound waves in these media will be dictated by their physical properties.

The fundamental properties of the medium, however, that determine speed of sound and other physical characteristics are common to all media and substances and are, in the end, already familiar. Namely, the medium for sound must be compressible, that is, elastic, and it must have mass. Media differ from one another in terms of shape and size, so the relevant measure of mass here is not the total mass of the medium. Rather, the parameter of importance here is **density** ($\rho$). Strings and wires are described by their linear density (mass per one dimension, or $M/L$), large flat surfaces, such as membranes, drumheads, and plates, by their area density (mass per two dimensions, or $M/L^2$), and media such as gases, including air in tubes, columns, and rooms, by their volume density (mass per three dimensions, or $M/L^3$). Volume density of a substance thus is the mass per unit volume and has dimensions $M/L^3$ or $ML^{-3}$. Volume density is also applicable to liquids and solids, depending on the mode of propagation (discussed below). In the MKS system, density is measured in units of kilograms per m³, whereas its units are grams per cm³ in the CGS system (see Chapter 1).

Substances are made up of particles,

that is, atoms or molecules, that naturally have mass. The more particles existing in a given volume or the more mass of each particle in that volume, the greater is the (volume) density of that substance. However, a force acting on a medium can cause the density of that medium to change. If the force causes a gas, such as air, to be compressed into a smaller volume, an effect called **condensation**, the density of air increases. On the other hand, the density of the air will decrease when it is forced to expand, a condition known as **rarefaction**. Densities of some common substances are given in Table 2.1.

Compression and expansion of the particles of the medium also cause its pressure to change. Pressure ($p$), another very important physical quantity, is force density: $p = F/area$. For example, the pressure exerted on a floor by a person wearing very narrow high-heeled shoes is much greater than the pressure exerted by the same person wearing tennis shoes. Although this person will apply the same amount of force with each shoe, that force is spread over a larger surface in the case of the tennis shoes. Pressure has dimen-

sions of $MLT^{-2}L^{-2}$, and it is measured in units of newtons per m$^2$ (MKS) or dynes per cm$^2$ (CGS). One newton per m$^2$ is called a *pascal* (Pa), named after the physicist Blaise Pascal. (Note: The reader should verify that the MKS unit is 10 times larger than the CGS unit; that is, 1 d/cm$^2$ = 0.1 N/m$^2$.)

Media for sound waves, as noted above, also must have elasticity. The compression and expansion of the medium will be opposed by its elasticity, much as is the spring in a simple mechanical vibratory system. The internal stiffness of air is responsible for its elasticity. As in the case of mass, here too the relevant measure is not total stiffness of the medium. Rather, the medium is characterized by its **bulk modulus** of elasticity ($\kappa$). Analogous to Young's modulus in mechanical systems, a parameter reflecting the relation between stress and strain (see Chapter 1), the bulk modulus is a measure of the change in pressure of the substance when a force is applied to it or its opposition to a fractional change in its volume. Its dimensions and units are identical to those of pressure. Bulk moduli of some common substances

TABLE 2.1.
**Characteristics of Solid, Liquid, and Gaseous Media for Sound**[a]

| Solid | Density ($kg/m^3$) | Bulk Modulus ($N/m^2$) | Characteristic Impedence (MKS rayls) | Speed of Sound ($m/sec$) |
|---|---|---|---|---|
| Aluminum | 2700 | $7.5 \times 10^{10}$ | $17.0 \times 10^6$ | 6300 |
| Iron (cast) | 7700 | $8.6 \times 10^{10}$ | $33.5 \times 10^6$ | 4350 |
| Steel | 7700 | $17.0 \times 10^{10}$ | $47.0 \times 10^6$ | 6100 |
| Rubber (soft) | 950 | $0.1 \times 10^{10}$ | $1.0 \times 10^6$ | 1050 |
| *Liquid*[b] | ↓ | ↓ | ↓ | ↓ |
| Water (fresh) | 998 | $2.18 \times 10^9$ | $1.48 \times 10^6$ | 1481 |
| Mercury | 13600 | $25.30 \times 10^9$ | $19.70 \times 10^6$ | 1450 |
| *Gas*[b,c] | ↓ | *Ratio of Specific Heats* | ↓ | ↓ |
| Air | 1.21 | 1.402 | 415 | 343 |
| Oxygen | 1.43 | 1.400 | 453 | 317 |
| Hydrogen | 0.09 | 1.410 | 114 | 1270 |

[a] Abridged version of table by L. E. Kinsler and A. R. Frey: *Fundamentals of Acoustics.* John Wiley & Sons, New York, 1962.

[b] All measurements at 20°C.

[c] All measurements at a pressure of $1.013 \times 10^5$ N/m$^2$.

are given in Table 2.1. In contrast, substances such as the one-dimensional medium of strings or the two-dimensional medium of membranes attain their elasticity from tension that occurs when they are stretched.

The properties of a medium, as stated earlier, determine how a sound wave travels through that medium. This can be appreciated by envisioning a finite volume (thus the medium is three dimensional), made up of minute masses connected to one another by minute springs. The springs represent the elastic property or restoring force of the medium. Because of this, a disturbance, such as the abrupt displacement of one small part of the medium, can be transmitted or *propagated* to adjacent parts of the medium by means of a chain reaction. That is, the motion of one particle or mass is passed on to the next, because they are "connected" together by a spring. Thus, the motion that started at a discrete place in the medium can be dispersed in all directions throughout the entire medium. Because of elasticity, however, the particles of the medium return to their original sites after the wave passes through. The important point here is that *the medium as a whole does not move*, because the net change in the displacement of each particle of the medium actually will be zero over time. Only the wave of disturbance is passed along. Saying it another way, *only the energy in the wave moves* through the medium.

## C. SOUND PROPAGATION

The fact that it is the disturbance that moves, not the entire medium, is eloquently described by Herman von Helmholtz in his famous treatise, *On the Sensations of Tone*:

> This is a peculiarity of all so-called *undulatory motions*. Suppose a stone is to be thrown into a piece of calm water. Round the spot struck there forms a little ring of wave, which, advancing equally in all directions, expands to a constantly increasing circle. . . . The waves of water,

therefore, continually advance without returning. But we must not suppose that the particles of water of which the waves are composed advance in a similar manner themselves. The motion of the particles of water on the surface can easily be rendered visible by floating a chip of wood on it. Now, such a chip is not carried on by the rings of wave. It only bobs up and down and finally rests on its original spot. The adjacent particles move in the same manner. When the ring of wave reaches them they are set bobbing; when it has passed over them they are still in their old place, and remain there at rest, while the ring of wave continues to advance towards fresh spots on the surface of the water, and sets new particles of water into motion. Hence the waves which pass over the surface of the water are constantly built up of fresh particles of water. What really advances as a wave is only the tremor, the altered form of the surface, while the individual particles of water themselves merely move up and down transiently, and never depart far from their original position. (Helmholtz, H. L. F., 1954, p. 9 (ca. 1885).

As described by Helmholtz, the wave on the surface of water is the result of a combination of **longitudinal** and **transverse propagation**. (This has been called *trochoidal propagation*.) In transverse propagation, the motion of the particles of the medium is basically perpendicular to the direction of travel of the disturbance. Thus, the wood chip moves up and down, following the water particle motion (transversely), whereas the wave in the water forms expanding circles (longitudinally) in its travel at right angles to this particle motion. Sound waves in strings show transverse propagation as well. Sound waves in solids may be either longitudinal or transverse.

The disturbance propagated in air as a sound wave is similar to the undulatory motion on the surface of water, because, in both cases, energy is propagated away from the source, but the analogy is limited. The compressional waves of sound in air are strictly longitudinal. Again, in the longitudinal propagation pattern, the particle motion is along the axis of the movement of the disturbance. Thus, sound in air is a disturbance involving an undulatory motion of the particles such that they vibrate back and forth along the axis of propagation. At least, that is the way it would be if the particles always occupied the same locations in the absence of sound. The molecules of air, however, are in constant random motion as a result of their thermal energy. This thermal agitation, called Brownian motion, results in an air pressure at sea level of approximately $1 \times 10^5 \text{N/m}^2$, a quantity called *ambient or atmospheric air pressure*. Sound thus may be further defined as an orderly change in air pressure above and below this ambient value (and in the ambient density of air), which is caused by a vibrating source.

To provide a blow-by-blow description of the propagation of sound in air would be rather tedious. Nevertheless, what happens to the particles of this medium can be appreciated by resorting to a hypothetical experiment. Assume that a conventional loudspeaker[2] is driven by a sinusoidal voltage, setting up a forced harmonic vibration of the speaker cone, as illustrated in Figure 2.1. Consequently, the cone of the speaker is set into back-and-forth motion according to the timetable dictated by the equation for the general sinusoid (refer to Eq. 1.10, Chapter 1). Furthermore, suppose that by some magic it would be possible to visualize the particles of a small slice of the air medium

directly in front of the speaker. The following would be observed. As the speaker cone is driven to move to the right by the source, the air particles in the vicinity of the speaker are pushed closer together. According to the gas law, when a volume of air is compressed, and thereby made more dense (also known as condensation), there is an increase in pressure above the ambient or static atmospheric pressure. Thus, with the movement of the speaker cone to the right, a momentary local high-pressure area is created in this slice of air. The peak of this condensation phase is called a *crest*. But, as the cone starts moving back to the left, driven by the next half-cycle of the sinusoidal voltage, an area of lower-than-atmospheric pressure will be created. Thus, a local low pressure area (also known as rarefaction) will occur in this same slice of air. The peak of this lower-than-normal density is called a *trough*. Subsequently, the air particles will be free to fill in this void, and the original density of the particles in the vicinity of the speaker will be reestablished. This causes the pressure at this point in space to return to its static pressure.

In this manner, the right-to-left and left-to-right movement of the speaker cone initiates an alternating change in the air density, thus initiating alternating intervals of *condensation* and *rarefaction*. In the application of these terms to sound, condensation represents the time during which density is increased above the static pressure value, whereas rarefaction is the time during which density is decreased below this static value. The time it takes for the completion of one condensation and one rarefaction defines the period of the sound. Recall that period is inversely related to frequency ($T = 1/f$). Period (or, for that matter, frequency), it should be noted, is not affected by the properties of the medium.

Changes in density, again, cause pressure changes. During condensation, pressure thus increases above the ambient value, whereas during the rarefaction

---

[2] Technically speaking, a loudspeaker is an electroacoustic transducer. It transforms electrical to acoustical energy. The details of this process depend on the specific type of speaker involved. The most common type is the electromagnetic speaker. The speaker cone is attached to a permanent magnet, which is surrounded by coils of wire. The speaker cone and magnet are suspended by a flexible diaphragm, which is relatively free to move in and out. Alternating electric current passing through the coil induces alternating electromagnetic fields that, in turn, alternately push and pull on the magnet (because it is polarized). Thus, movement is conveyed directly to the speaker cone and creates disturbances in the air surrounding the cone.

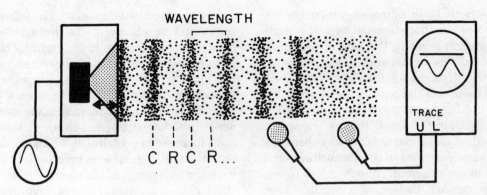

**Figure 2.1.**   Longitudinal propagation of a sound wave generated by a loudspeaker driven (electrically) by a sine-wave generator. The sound pressure is being monitored by microphones connected to the upper (*U*) and lower (*L*) channels of a dual-trace oscilloscope. Peaks of condensation (*C*) and rarefaction (*R*) phases are indicated.

phase, pressure decreases below atmospheric values. The time course of these pressure changes can be plotted, as shown in Figure 2.1 (how this is accomplished is explained below), yielding yet another perspective on the disturbance called sound—propagated pressure waves. That is, waves of *sound pressure* fluctuations are set up by the loudspeaker and propagated away from it. Sound pressure, incidentally, is the most practical measure of the magnitude of a sound, because microphones are inherently pressure detectors, but more on this matter momentarily.

Visualization of particle motion in a small slice of air initiated by the motion of the speaker cone—a sort of two-dimensional view—is useful for heuristic purposes and yields a relevant perspective in some acoustic situations (for example, sound waves in pipes, as discussed later in this chapter). More generally, though, the sound source causes changes in density and pressure of the medium over space, that is, in three dimensions and often in all directions. To illustrate, assume the motion of the speaker terminates after executing only one cycle. The condensation half-cycle that initially occurs in the air in front to the speaker cone, again, represents a high-density and high-

pressure area of the medium. The energy in this area of the medium will be passed on via the motion of adjacent air particles, thereby creating a high-density and high-pressure area in them as well. They, in turn, will pass on this energy to air particles adjacent to them. Thus, a wave of high pressure travels to the right in space. Of course, each condensation half-cycle is followed by a rarefaction half-cycle, and in a given direction, longitudinally, this is seen, at a given instant in time, as alternating regions of high and low pressure (Fig. 2.1).

This all takes time, that is, to pass along these condensations and rarefactions. The disturbance is displaced progressively away from the source. By definition (see Chapter 1), the change in displacement per unit time equals velocity or, ignoring direction, speed. Consequently, sound waves travel through a medium at a particular speed. Consider once more the sort of sound generation and measurement setup illustrated in Figure 2.1 and the observations that might be made with a single microphone. As hinted above, the purpose of the microphone is to pick up the pressure changes in the acoustical signal delivered by the loudspeaker and transform them into elec-

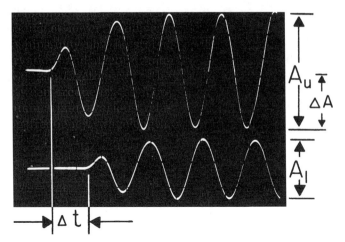

**Figure 2.2.** Difference in time of arrival ($t$) of the sound wave at the two microphones positioned as in Figure 2.1. An amplitude difference between the sounds represented by the *upper* and *lower traces* of the oscillograph is also evident, wherein the difference in amplitude ($\Delta A$) equals $A_u - A_l$ ($A_u$ and $A_l$ being the respective peak-to-peak amplitudes).

tricity,[3] thereby permitting the pressure fluctuations of the sound to be measured or even visualized via tracings on an oscilloscope. The oscilloscope is a device that measures voltage (the magnitude of an electrical signal) and instantaneously plots the voltage as a function of time. Particularly noteworthy at this juncture is that the microphone, regardless of how close it is to the loudspeaker, will still be separated from it by a certain distance. The electrical signal driving the loudspeaker now is turned on abruptly, initiating a sound wave. Simultaneously, the oscilloscope trace is initiated. However, as shown in Figure 2.2 (*upper trace*), the oscilloscope trace, at first, shows no change in the ambient pressure, signaling that the sound wave has not yet reached the microphone. After a period of time, though, depending on the distance between the loudspeaker and microphone, the oscilloscope finally begins to register pressure changes.

From the definition of (average) speed, if the distance between the loudspeaker and microphone and the time gap between the sound onset and the beginning of the trace in Figure 2.2 (*top*) are measured, the speed of sound[4] travel ($c$) can be calculated as follows:

[3] A microphone may be thought of as a loudspeaker used backward. Indeed, in some intercommunication systems (intercoms), speakers are used for both functions. The difference is that the microphone transforms acoustic into electrical energy, the reverse function of the loudspeaker (see Footnote 2). The exact transduction process depends on the type of microphone. Some of the simplest microphones use piezoelectric elements. The oldest types are crystal microphones, but these have been replaced largely by microphones using synthetic crystalline (ceramic) elements. In either type of piezoelectric microphone, the diaphragm is attached to the element, which, when bent, causes an electrical potential to be created. Other types of microphones include electrodynamic (electromagnetic), condenser, and electret. Although the transduction mechanisms are different among these, the results are the same. Sound pressure waves strike the diaphragm and cause it to move in and out. This motion causes a voltage to be generated, which follows (within limits) the amplitude and frequency of the sound. Incidentally, a microphone can be used as a speaker, but its small diaphragm, and consequently small excursions, limit its usefulness for most practical applications; it is just too small to do the job.

[4] Speed and velocity (of sound wave propagation) are terms that are often used synonymously. Speed is preferable and avoids confusion with particle and volume velocity. The speed of sound refers specifically to the rate at which the sound wave moves (generally treated as a scalar quantity), whereas the particles themselves are in constant motion with certain velocities that are independent of the propagation speed.

$$c = x/t \qquad (2.1)$$

The speed of sound at 20° Celsius (C), or room temperature, is approximately 343 m/sec. That sound does not travel instantaneously from one point to another is vividly demonstrated by a common experience, simply using one's own senses. The sound of thunder is always heard some time after lightning is sighted. This happens because sound travels much more slowly than light. Indeed, an estimate of the distance of the lightning from the point of observation can be made simply by counting the number of seconds elapsing between seeing the lightning and hearing the thunder and multiplying this time by the speed of sound in air. By algebraic manipulation of Eq. 2.1, $x = ct$.

Following from the statement made earlier that period (and thus frequency) of the sound is independent of the medium, it can be stated that sound waves of all frequencies travel at the same speed in air. Nevertheless, it seems intuitive that the two physical properties of the medium, density and elasticity, must somehow affect the sound. In fact, these properties influence the speed of sound. The speed of sound in solids, such as strings, membranes, and bars, is determined by density ($\rho$) and the elastic modulus ($\kappa$) of the medium:

$$c = (\kappa/\rho)^{1/2} \qquad (2.2)$$

This expression is reminiscent of the expression for the natural frequency in the simple spring-mass system ($f \propto (k/m)^{1/2}$). More dense or massive media thus tend to propagate sound more slowly, analogous to the lowering of the natural frequency when mass is increased in the simple harmonic oscillator. Stiffer media propagate sound at greater speeds, just as increased stiffness in the simple spring-mass system causes the natural frequency to increase. Among media, there is a trade-off between these two characteristics. This is demonstrated by comparing the properties of various materials and the speeds at which

sound is propagated in them, as shown in Table 2.1. Of particular note are the speeds of sound in solids for which Eq. 2.2 is the most applicable.

In the case of fluids and gases, thermodynamics play a substantial role in determining the speed of sound, so the effects of temperature also must be considered. If the temperature of the medium is increased, the speed of sound is increased. For example, the speed of sound in air at 0°C is 331 m/sec, whereas again, at 20°C it is 343 m/sec. The speed of sound in gases and fluids is proportional to the square root of temperature, specifically the Kelvin temperature ($\tau$), as follows:

$$c \propto \tau^{1/2} \qquad (2.3)$$

As a rule of thumb and sticking with Celsius temperature, the speed of sound is altered approximately 0.6 m/sec for each degree. However, even after taking the factor of temperature into account, Eq. 2.2 must be substantially rewritten when it comes to air and other gaseous media. This, again, is a reflection of thermodynamic considerations, particularly the *gas law*. Fortunately, only a couple of factors prove to be critical in the final analysis, and the speed of sound in gases may be computed from the following expression:

$$c = (\gamma p_o/\rho_o)^{1/2} \qquad (2.4)$$

where $p_o$ and $\rho_o$ are the static pressure and density, respectively, and $\gamma$ is the constant known as the *ratio of specific heats*. This parameter characterizes the particular gas of interest.

Despite the appearance of $p_o$ in Eq. 2.4, atmospheric pressure, interestingly, does not influence the speed of sound in air, because density varies directly with atmospheric pressure. In other words, the effect of increasing $p_o$ in the numerator of Eq. 2.4 is counterbalanced by a corresponding change in $\rho_o$ in the denominator of the expression. Consequently, sound travels at the same speed in the mountains as it does at sea level if there is no change in temperature or composition of the air (such as water content, as indicated by the humidity index). The molecular weight of a particular gas (on which density is dependent), however, is an important determinant. The lighter the gas, the faster the speed of sound, as seen in Table 2.1, comparing, for instance, hydrogen to oxygen.

Thus there are two important temporal aspects of sound. The first, *period*, is the time it takes for one complete condensation-rarefaction cycle. The second is the *speed of propagation* of the sound in the medium. Period is independent of the physical properties of the medium but is dictated by the sound source—the frequency of vibration. Speed of sound, as just described, is determined by the properties of the medium. Now, the upshot of the propagation of sound is that sound waves occupy space as well as take up time. It should be expected, then, that there exists a spatial corollary of the period of the sound. In fact there is, and this parameter is called **wavelength** ($\lambda$). Wavelength is the distance in meters or centimeters covered by one complete cycle of density change, that is, one condensation and one rarefaction of the total wave and, therefore, one period in time. Analogous to the measurement of period, the wavelength of a sound is measured as the distance covered by the wave from any starting point to the same point on the next cycle, for example, from crest to crest (see Fig. 2.3). Because period and frequency are related, wavelength is also dependent on the frequency of the sound, as follows:

$$\lambda = c/f \qquad (2.5)$$

Table 2.2 gives the wavelength of some sounds, many of which are frequently used in hearing assessment, and Figure 2.3 illustrates the relationship between frequency and wavelength.

Referring back to Figure 2.2, the bottom trace shows what happens when the microphone is moved farther from the loudspeaker. Naturally, it takes even longer (by an interval of $\Delta t$) before the tracing

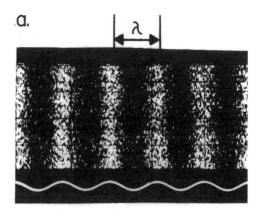

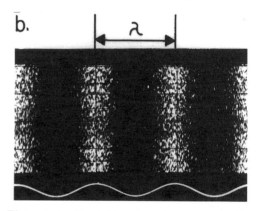

**Figure 2.3.** Simulation of sound wave propagation showing dependence of wavelength on frequency. The sound in **b** is lower in frequency (longer wavelength, $\lambda_o$) than the sound in **a**. The pressure variation over distance is shown at the bottom of each oscillograph. (Adapted from Durrant, J. D. [1975]. Simulation of sound waves on the oscilloscope. *J. Acoust. Soc. Am.* 57:1558–1559.)

**TABLE 2.2.**
**Wavelength in Air at 20°C Versus Frequency**

| Frequency in Hz | Wavelength | |
|---|---|---|
| | (m) | (cm) |
| 100 | 3.43 | 343 |
| 250 | 1.37 | 137 |
| 500 | 0.685 | 68.5 |
| 1000 | 0.34 | 34.2 |
| 2000 | 0.17 | 17.1 |
| 4000 | 0.086 | 8.58 |
| 8000 | 0.043 | 4.29 |

starts to show some action. Indeed, without knowing the actual distance between the speaker and the microphone, the speed of sound could be determined by simply measuring the difference in distance between the two points of observation ($\Delta x$) and this time difference ($\Delta t$). But there is another effect suggested by Figure 2.2; namely, there is a phase difference between the top and bottom traces. Consequently, there also is an interaction between phase and distance from the source at which the sound is sampled. This effect is demonstrated further in Figure 2.4. To obtain this figure, a continuous tone was generated by driving the loudspeaker with a sinusoidal voltage. The measuring microphone was first positioned, arbitrarily, such that the oscilloscope registered the start of a condensation half-cycle (designated 0° [relative] phase; Fig. 2.4, *top*). Then, with the sound continuing in time, the microphone was moved farther and farther from the source. Note the phase changes with the change in position of the microphone. Inasmuch as one wavelength is the distance covered by the sound wave in one period, which in phase terms is 360°, a change of phase of 360° shows that the microphone was moved one wavelength. As illustrated in Figure 2.3, the

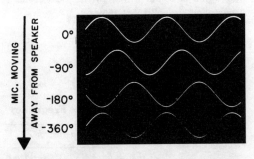

**Figure 2.4.** Changes in phase of the sound wave recorded by a microphone (*MIC*) at increasingly greater distances from a sound source continuously driven by a sinusoidal electrical signal. The sign of the indicated relative phase (in degrees) reflects the increasing phase lag with distance, namely caused by the increasing time of arrival of the wavefront at the microphone.

distance between sample points would be greater for a sound of lower frequency. Several relationships may now be stated from these observations and algebraic manipulations of Eq. 2.5, together with the relationship between frequency and period, thereby summarizing various relationships among frequency, wavelength, and period:

$$c = \lambda F$$
$$F = c/\lambda$$
$$T = \lambda/c$$
$$c = \lambda/T$$
$$\lambda = cT$$

## D. SOUND WAVES AND THEIR PROPERTIES

The sound source, the medium in which sound waves exist, and other factors (discussed below) determine the form of these waves. For example, assume a string is fixed at both ends and under tension; it now is plucked. This disturbance causes a wave of motion to move up and down the string in a one-dimensional mode. A similar pattern would be observed for a sound wave in a tube filled with air (as will be discussed in more detail later). Surface waves in water, as described previously, show motion of the medium in two dimensions. In large media, such as that of air in a room, sound waves can propagate in three dimensions, that is, in all directions. These are *free progressive sound waves*. Whether their propagation is equal in all directions depends on the directionality of the source and whether objects are placed in the path of the sound waves. Examining, for now, only the case in which sound waves freely propagate away and equally in all directions from the source, these waves can be envisioned as spheres of expanding radii with increasing distance from the source (Fig. 2.5). The sound source in this case is relatively small, sometimes referred to as a ***point source***. (A more precise definition is given below.)

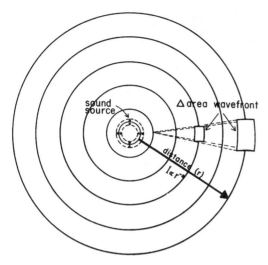

**Figure 2.5.** Cross-sectional drawing of spherical waves radiated by a simple (or point) source. The change in the surface of the wavefront (Δ *area wavefront*) with distance is indicated. *I*, Acoustic intensity.

For a continuous sound, connecting the crests of the waves in adjacent areas with lines, as in Figure 2.5, provides a useful means of defining **wavefronts**. It is obvious that these wavefronts are curved and, in turn, define what is known as **spherical waves**.

At relatively large distances from the source, however, a given area of the spherical wavefront will seem to be straight, just as the world seemed to be flat to Christopher Columbus's skeptics. Therefore, distant from the source, a **plane wave** is approximated. The importance of this approximation lies in the fact that the acoustics of plane waves are simpler. It is at times advantageous in solving acoustic problems to be able to assume plane-wave propagation and related behavior, despite the fact that the sound waves in question are actually spherical or other types of waves with curved wavefronts.

Examining Figure 2.2 once more, there is yet another observable effect when the microphone is moved farther from the loudspeaker; the sound pressure decreases, as demonstrated further in Fig-

ure 2.6. This is an observation that also is verifiable by daily experience and one's own senses. For instance, a person talking while standing across the street from a listener is usually more difficult to hear than a person standing nearby. It thus is a familiar experience that the greater the distance from the source of the sound, the less is the observed magnitude of the sound.

In any given situation, the relationship between the magnitude of sound and distance is based on many factors. However, to determine this relationship in its most basic form, consider once more the example of a relatively small or *point source*. The ideal point source, specifically, is a pulsating sphere of smaller dimensions than the wavelength of the sound being emitted (Fig. 2.5). Such a source, again, will give rise to spherical waves. Because energy was necessary to create the waves, what will determine how much sound pressure appears at a given distance is the power produced by the sound source, that is, the rate at which energy is transferred from the source to the medium. The power produced by the sound source is constant over time in the total wavefront at any distance in space, assuming that the source produces a constant signal. Therefore, in any one sphere, the total power equals that of any other sphere. Because the spheres expand with distance from the source, this amount of power is spread increasingly thin as the wavefront grows (see Fig. 2.5).

The average rate at which energy is transferred by the same unit area of the wavefront, that is, the rate at which work is done by a unit area of the wavefront, is an important physical quantity called **acoustic intensity** (*I*). Acoustic intensity thus diminishes with distance from the source. Acoustic intensity is power density and is measured as the amount of power in a circumscribed area of the wave: $I = (W/t)/L^2 = P/L^2$. The unit of measure of acoustic intensity is the watt (w) per $m^2$ in the MKS system and is the watt per $cm^2$ in the CGS system. One $w/cm^2 = 10^4$

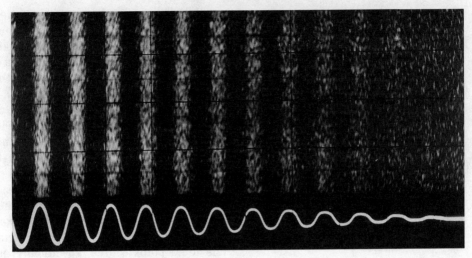

**Figure 2.6.** Decay of sound pressure with increasing distance from the source (propagation to the right). (Adapted from Durrant, J. D. [1975]. Simulation of sound waves on the oscilloscope. *J. Acoust. Soc. Am.* 57: 1558–1559.)

$w/m^2$. (Note: this is not a misprint. The CGS unit really is larger than the MKS unit, because the unit of power—1 watt—is the same in both systems and thus is focused into a much smaller unit area, the $cm^2$, in the CGS system.)

Acoustic intensity is considered the most basic way in which sound magnitude can be quantified. It follows from the foregoing discussion that the relationship of acoustic intensity to distance $(r)$ for a freely progressive plane wave is given by the equation:

$$I = P/4\pi r^2 \qquad (2.6)$$

where $P$ is the total power in the wavefront, and $4\pi r^2$ is the expression for the area of the surface of a sphere with radius $r$. For a given sound power, ignoring the constants in Eq. 2.6, the relationship between acoustic intensity and distance from the source can be simplified, as follows:

$$I \propto r^{-2}$$

In words, acoustic intensity is inversely proportional to distance squared from the source. This relationship, consequently, is known as the *inverse (square) law*. As

pointed out previously, however, sound pressure is the more convenient way to quantify sound magnitude. To link the two measures, it first is necessary to define an impedance-like parameter to characterize the medium.

As emphasized in Chapter 1, impedance is determined by the mass, elasticity, and damping acting within a system and the frequency of the vibratory force used to drive the system. A vibratory system thus is characterized by its impedance. Coincidentally, the term *characteristic impedance* $(Z_c)$ is applied to that measure of particular applicability in describing a large, virtually unbounded medium. Because the speed of sound is also intimately dependent on the properties of the medium, it should not be surprising that the characteristic impedance and the speed of sound are directly related, as defined by the following equation:

$$Z_c = \rho_o c \qquad (2.7)$$

Characteristic impedance applies for a dispersive medium, meaning that sounds of all frequencies travel at the same speed. In other words, the medium does not discriminate against sounds on the basis of frequency. In such media, the resonant frequency approaches 0 Hz because the overall mass of the medium is very large. It follows that the characteristic impedance is considered purely resistive; this, in turn, implies that sound pressure and particle velocity are always in phase with one another. That characteristic impedance is purely resistive, however, does not mean that the loss in intensity with increasing distance is caused by dissipation. Indeed, the heat loss involved in sound propagation is essentially negligible.

Characteristic impedances are measured in units called *rayls* (after Lord Rayleigh), rather than ohms[5]. The characteristic impedances of various media are given in Table 2.1. These values can be verified by plugging into Eq. 2.7 the density and sound speed of the particular medium of interest. For example, for air at room temperature, $\rho_o$ is 1.21 kg/m$^3$, and $c$ is 343 m/sec. Therefore,

$$Z_c = 1.21 \times 343 = 415 \text{ rayls (MKS)}$$

(Note: it is left to the reader to verify that the characteristic impedance of air in CGS units is 41.5 rayls or, more generally, that 1 CGS rayl = 10 MKS rayls.)

So, where does sound pressure come in? Right here. Recall from Chapter 1 the relationship between power, force, and impedance, as expressed by Eq. 1.19: $P = F^2/Z$. A similar relationship can be derived for acoustic intensity, sound pressure, and characteristic impedance, as follows:

$$I = p^2/\rho_o c = p^2/Z_c \qquad (2.8)$$

where $p$ is the effective sound pressure, a static pressure equivalent of the alternating pressure of sound (to be defined more precisely in Chapter 3). That Eq. 2.8 and

1.19 are analogous becomes particularly compelling when it is borne in mind that acoustic intensity is a power-based term, and sound pressure is force per unit area. Most importantly, Eq. 2.8 clearly indicates that acoustic intensity and sound pressure are interdependent. If one is known, given the characteristic impedance, the other may be derived. A numerical example will be useful at this juncture, as follows:

Find the acoustic intensity of a sound that has a sound pressure of $2 \times 10^{-5}$ N/m$^2$, given that the characteristic impedance of air is 415 rayls (MKS):

$$I = (2 \times 10^{-5})^2/415$$

$$= (4 \times 10^{-10})/(4.15 \times 10^2)$$

$$\approx 10^{-12} \text{ w/m}^2$$

This acoustic intensity and the corresponding sound pressure were not chosen randomly. They have particular significance as the most common MKS reference values in use today in acoustics and hearing science, as discussed in Chapter 3. These values represent approximately the smallest sound detectable by the human ear. Their CGS equivalents can be derived by acknowledging the differences in size of the MKS and CGS units that are, respectively, $2 \times 10^{-4}$ d/cm$^2$ and $10^{-16}$ w/cm$^2$.

From Eq. 2.8, the relation between acoustic intensity and sound pressure can be simplified, as follows:

$$I \propto p^2$$

Conversely,

$$p \propto I^{1/2}$$

because, for any given medium and condition, $Z_c$ is constant. Based on the latter proportionality, the inverse law now can be restated in terms of sound pressure:

$$p \propto I^{1/2} \propto (r^{-2})^{1/2} \propto r^{-1}$$

Stated simply, sound pressure is inversely related to distance from the source. In fact, as long as unobstructed spherical-wave

---

[5] There is also such a thing as *acoustic impedance*, which is directly analogous to mechanical and electrical impedance, as described in Chapter 1. It is defined as the complex ratio of sound pressure to volume velocity, or $Z_a = p/u$, and it is measured in (acoustic) ohms. This is a parameter that is perhaps more appropriate in describing certain acoustic systems, such as an acoustic resonator, rather than a medium.

propagation can be assumed, using the inverse law, it is possible to predict the sound pressure at any distance from the sound source based on a single sound pressure measurement taken at a known distance from this source. Unfortunately, at least for the sake of simplicity, the assumption of freely propagated spherical waves cannot be assumed in all situations, a topic that will be covered later in the discussion of sound fields.

## 2. Sound Wave Phenomena

If all sound waves were radiated in a simple and predictable manner, as in the case of freely propagated spherical sound waves, there would be no point in going further in this treatment of acoustics. In reality, however, sounds are generated and must travel under less than ideal conditions. Consequently, there are several other phenomena associated with sounds waves that must be considered, particularly those that are associated with the behavior of sound waves when they encounter boundaries of the medium, barriers, or other obstructions. Generally, one of four things, or a combination of these things, may happen: *transmission, reflection, absorption*, and/or *diffraction* of the sound. In the treatment of these phenomena here, unless stated otherwise, the assumption will be made that the waves under consideration are plane waves, rather than spherical waves. (Again, adopting this assumption simplifies the explanation.)

### A. TRANSMISSION VERSUS REFLECTION

It is common experience that boundaries of a room—walls, floors, and ceilings—impede the passage of sounds out of the room. In some cases, such as a room with thick concrete walls, a negligible amount of sound energy may be *transmitted*, whereas in other cases, such as rooms with thin plaster-board walls, a substan-

tial amount of sound may be propagated through the wall. To determine what proportion of the sound energy will be transmitted through a given barrier, the concept of impedance once again must be brought to the forefront. At the heart of the matter is the problem of transferring sound energy from one medium to another, because the walls of the room themselves constitute a separate medium. There are situations in which transmission of sound through a wall may not seem like much of a problem, for instance, when the neighbor's stereo is on the other side of the wall, blasting away. Yet, the transmission of sound in this example is not without difficulty. The sound must be transmitted from air to the wall material and then back to air again. As loud and annoying as the neighbor's stereo may seem, this is a situation that actually is not conducive to efficient sound energy transfer.

The transfer of energy from one medium to another is optimal only when the impedances of the two media are the same. The sound wave encountering the wall is called the *incident sound wave*. In the simplest situation (illustrated in Fig. 2.7), incident sound waves encounter a barrier head on. In other words, the waves are parallel to the barrier; this is called *normal incidence*. As stated above, the waves themselves are assumed to be plane waves, that is, the wavefronts are essentially flat. The proportion of transmitted sound energy is predicted by the equation:

$$H = 4Z_b Z_a / (Z_b + Z_a)^2 \qquad (2.9)$$

where $Z_b$ and $Z_a$ are the characteristic impedances of the two media in question, and $H$ is the proportion, or fraction, of energy transmitted from the first $(a)$ to the second $(b)$ medium. Similar but more complex formulas could be written for situations involving more than two media, sound waves encountering a barrier at grazing angles (rather than normal incidence), or spherical and other wavefronts.

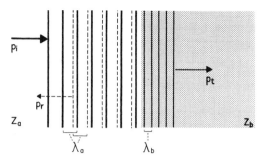

**Figure 2.7.** Transmission and reflection of sound at the boundary between two media with characteristic impedances of $Z_a$ and $Z_b$. Incident $(p_i)$, transmitted $(p_t)$, and reflected $(p_r)$ sound pressure waves are represented. Note that the transmitted wave has a different wavelength $(\lambda_b)$, than that of the incident wave $(\lambda_a)$. This occurs anytime the impedances of the two media differ, because of the correspondingly different speeds at which sound travels through the two media, as in the case of air and water (see Table 2.1).

In addition, the assumption is made that the influence of damping in the medium is negligible.

Despite the numerous assumptions involved, Eq. 2.9 will suffice here, because it yields respectable, ball-park predictions of transmission for various problems of practical interest. It is evident from this equation that if the two media do not have the same characteristic impedances, the proportion of energy transmitted from one to the other will be less than 1. An example that will find particular relevance in later discussions of hearing mechanisms (Chapter 5) is that of sound traveling from air to water. Table 2.1 shows that the characteristic impedance of air is 415 rayls, whereas that of water is 1,480,000 rayls. Therefore:

$$H = (4 \times 4.15 \times 10^2 \times 1.48 \times 10^6)$$
$$/(4.15 \times 10^2) + (1.48 \times 10^6)^2$$
$$= (2.46 \times 10^9)/(2.19 \times 10^{12})$$
$$= 1.12 \times 10^{-3}$$
$$\approx 0.001$$

In other words, only 0.1% of the sound en-

ergy will be transmitted across the air-water boundary! If only 0.1% of the sound energy is transmitted from air to water, this means that $100 - 0.1\% = 99.9\%$ of the energy is lost or, more precisely, is not transmitted. Of course, the energy is not really lost, because the law of conservation of energy dictates that it must be conserved. In the case of the air-water boundary, nearly all of the other 99.9% of the energy is reflected from the surface of the water. In other words, the portion of the sound that is not transmitted bounces back as a reflected sound wave traveling in the opposite direction of the incident wave.

Reflected waves are illustrated in Fig. 2.7. The reflection of sound waves from the surface of water, from a wall, or from other media and barriers is analogous to the reflection of light waves from a shiny surface. A mirror, for example, is designed to provide nearly perfect ($\approx$100%) reflection. Reflected sound waves thus carry energy given to them by the incident wave back into the medium from which the incident wave originated.

Scrutiny of Eq. 2.9 reveals that the greater the differences in the impedances of the two media, the greater the amount of energy reflected and the less transmitted. The proportion of sound energy reflected can be calculated using Eq. 2.9 and subtracting $H$ from 1.0 or can be calculated directly using the following equation:

$$D = [(Z_b - Z_a)/(Z_b + Z_a)]^2 \quad (2.10)$$

where $D$ is the proportion of energy reflected from the barrier. (Note: it is left to the reader to verify that $D = 1 - H$ or, in other words, to derive Eq. 2.10 from Eq. 2.9.) Returning to the example of air-to-water transmission:

$$D = [(1.48 \times 10^6 - 4.15 \times 10^2)$$
$$/(1.48 \times 10^6 + 4.15 \times 10^2)]^2$$
$$= (1.479 \times 10^6/1.481 \times 10^6)^2$$
$$= 0.9992 \approx 0.999 \text{ or } 9.99\%$$

The quantity $H$ is sometimes called the *transmission coefficient* and the quantity $D$ the *reflection coefficient*. It is important to note that Eq. 2.9 and 2.10 are applicable only in cases in which neither significant absorption nor diffraction occur. (Absorption and diffraction are described below.) Incidentally, it does not matter whether the sound is being propagated from a medium of greater impedance to one of lesser impedance or vice versa; Eq. 2.9 and 2.10 state that the same proportion of transmission and reflection will occur.

## B. ABSORPTION

Continuing with the consideration of the transmission of sound from air to water, it is clear that this problem is somewhat special in that, again, most of the sound energy is reflected. However, not only are there no appreciable losses of the energy of the incident sound waves because of transmission, there also is no significant loss of energy because of *damping*. In the parlance of acoustics, however, it is said that no significant sound energy is *absorbed*. Absorption thus is the acoustical equivalent of damping in mechanical systems. Consequently, absorption causes sound energy to be dissipated in the form of heat.

Some materials are better absorbers than others. As a general rule, materials that are hard, dense, and/or have smooth surfaces are poor absorbers. Most of the sound energy that is not transmitted through these materials is reflected. In contrast, materials that are soft, porous, and/or have rough surfaces are good absorbers. Certain types of ceiling tile, often referred to as acoustic tile, are designed to be good absorbers. This material thus is placed on ceilings to reduce reflections and to minimize transmission.

A useful specification in designing the acoustical characteristics of lecture rooms, therapy rooms, music practice rooms, studios, etc., is the *absorption coefficient* of wall-, ceiling-, and floor-covering mate-

**TABLE 2.3.**
**Representative Absorption Coefficients**[a]

| Material | $\alpha$[b] |
| --- | --- |
| Acoustic paneling | 0.50 |
| Brick wall, unpainted | 0.03 |
| Draperies, light | 0.11 |
| Draperies, heavy | 0.50 |
| Floor, concrete | 0.02 |
| Floor, wood | 0.06 |
| Floor, carpeted | 0.37 |
| Glass | 0.05 |
| Glazed tile | 0.01 |
| Plaster | 0.05 |

[a] Abridged version of table by L. E. Kinsler and A. R. Frey: *Fundamentals of Acoustics*, John Wiley & Sons, New York, 1962.

[b] Values of coefficient specifically at 500 Hz; also dependent on mounting and thickness of material.

rials. The absorption coefficient ($\alpha$) is an index of the absorbing power per unit area of a particular material. Cloth, fiberglass (insulation), and the like have high absorption coefficients; this explains the usefulness of draperies and rugs in reducing sound wave reflection. Absorption coefficients for some familiar materials are listed in Table 2.3. An absorption coefficient of 0 indicates a perfect reflective material, whereas a coefficient of 1 characterizes a material that allows neither reflection nor transmission. Often a material will absorb high-frequency sounds, which have short wavelengths, better than low-frequency, long-wavelength sounds (Eq. 2.5). Thus the net effect of absorption is to decrease the energy in reflected sound waves or to reduce the amount of energy transmitted through a barrier.

## C. INTERFERENCE

Rooms containing both incident and reflected sound waves, typical of the real world, present a much different acoustic environment than rooms that contain only incident waves. To appreciate this point, it is necessary to understand sound wave *interference*. Although two people or two objects cannot occupy the same space simultaneously, two sound waves can. Consider the situation of an incident sound wave striking (at normal incidence) a boundary that allows some of the energy in the incident wave to be transmitted through it but reflects the rest (Fig. 2.7). The reflected waves travel in a direction opposite that of the original incident wave. If the source generates sound continuously, new incident waves will exist in the room coincident with reflected waves. As shown in Figure 2.7, the two waves will be superpositioned on one another. What happens then depends on details of the situation, such as the distance of the sound sources from the barrier versus wavelength and the point of observation. At any

given point, this interaction may lead to an increase or decrease in sound pressure. This effect is known as interference.

Interference also can occur between two (or more) incident sound waves and perhaps is easiest to understand in this context, as illustrated in Figure 2.8. Here, two sound sources are illustrated (in this case, generating hemispheric waves) that are producing the same amplitude and frequency of sinusoidal sounds, within a few wavelengths of one another. The sound pressure observed at any point of superposition will be the algebraic sum of the instantaneous sound pressures of each sound at the point of observation. When the *crests* or *troughs* of the two wavefronts

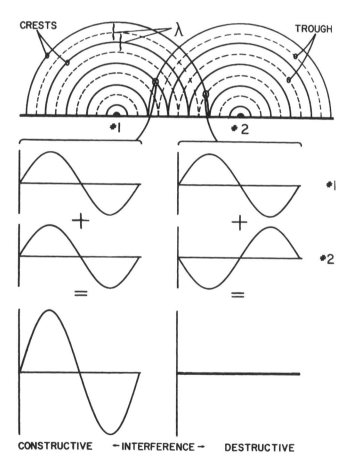

**Figure 2.8.** Constructive and destructive interference between two sound waves. The space between two *solid lines*, that is, between crests, or between two *broken lines*, that is, between troughs, is one wavelength ($\lambda$).

precisely overlap one another, *constructive interference* will occur (Fig. 2.8*a*), and the sound pressure there will be greater than that of either of the two sounds. In this example (two sounds of equal sound pressure), the resulting sound pressures will be double. Under this condition, the two sounds completely reinforce one another, thus an example of perfect constructive interference. However, when the crests of one and the troughs of another sound wave overlap, cancellation will occur (Fig. 2.8*b*). This is an example of perfect *destructive interference*. As the sound waves from the two sources propagate and expand, if one were to walk across the paths of the two sounds, one would walk in and out of regions of changing sound pressure. Partial interference, by the way, results when amplitude and/or phase differences exist between incident waves, reflected waves, or incident and reflected waves.

Interference resulting from the superposition of reflected and incident waves can be used to achieve particular acoustic objectives. For example, assume that a microphone is mounted in a dish-shaped reflector, known as a parabolic reflector. When the microphone is placed at the focus of the parabola, all of the sound striking the dish is reflected to the same point and at the same time, so constructive interference occurs. The result is a dramatic increase in the sound pressure appearing at the microphone, relative to what the microphone would pick up without the reflector. However, its effective area of pickup also is more restricted, so this apparatus is called a *spot* microphone. This device is often seen at televised sporting events (along the sidelines of football games, for example) or in advertisements in curio catalogs, billed (in effect) as "spy" microphones.

## D. REVERBERATION

Reflected sound waves arrive at a given point of observation, for example, at the ear of a listener, delayed in time compared with the arrival of the incident waves at the same point. Whether this arrival time disparity is important is, in part, dependent on the size of the time delay. The delay, in turn, is dependent on the distance between the reflective surface and the listener. The sound wave must travel to the reflective boundary and return to the listener, making its time of arrival longer than that of the incident wave. If the distance is substantial, and thus the delay is perceptually noticeable, the reflected sound wave is perceived as an **echo**. In effect, two (or more) separate sounds are heard. The echo is an exaggerated form of a phenomenon known as **reverberation**. Therefore, reverberation is an acoustic phenomenon resulting from multiple reflected sounds that, in turn, arrive at a point of observation with minimal time delays between the incident and reflected waves.

In reverberation, the delays among the times of arrival of the sound reflections often are small enough so that only one sound is perceived, but the observed sound effectively is extended in duration compared with the incident sound. For a brief incident sound, the result is a decaying sound as the energy of the reflected waves are absorbed. Reverberation is thus quantified as the time necessary for the sound pressure at the observation point to decay to a certain level, typically 0.001 of its initial value (established by convention). This index is called **reverberation time** ($T_{60}$).

Reverberation time is a useful index for characterizing the acoustics of rooms and auditoriums and depends directly on room volume. Therefore, the greater the room volume, the greater the reverberation time. This is because the sound waves must traverse larger distances between boundaries in larger rooms, and thus more time elapses before the sound can be absorbed or transmitted by these boundaries. Reverberation time thus depends also on absorption by the boundaries of the volume or even objects within the environment of the waves. For example, when the walls of a room are covered with highly absorptive material, reverberation time will be very low. People, who naturally are covered with hair and clothing (inherently absorptive materials), also can reduce reverberation time greatly. Consequently, rehearsals in an empty auditorium never sound the same as the actual performance, unless the covering of the seats mimics very well the absorption of an audience. Reverberation time is related to volume and absorption as follows:

$$T_{60} \propto V/\alpha_{total} \qquad (2.11)$$

where $V$ is the volume of the enclosure, and $\alpha_{total}$ is the total absorption of all surfaces in metric sabins (calculated by summing the product of all surface areas and their respective absorption coefficients).

## E. DIFFRACTION

Not all objects or barriers obstructing the free travel of sound waves necessarily disrupt the progression of the entire wavefront. In some cases the sound waves are seemingly able to move around objects. Although perhaps not obvious, a related situation is that in which a sound barrier has a hole in it, providing a small, but otherwise unobstructed, pathway through the barrier. In this case, the sound will seem to spread out on the other side of the barrier, almost as if the barrier were not there. Consequently, sounds readily can be heard behind an object such as a chair or through an opening such as a window. The phenomenon by which this is possible is *diffraction*. Diffraction occurs when the wavefront is bent or distorted. The result of diffraction is that sound waves are scattered. Whether diffraction occurs is dependent on the relationship between the size (dimensions) of the object obstructing the sound wave or the opening in the barrier and the size (wavelength) of the sound. If the wavelength is greater than the dimensions of the barrier, diffrac-

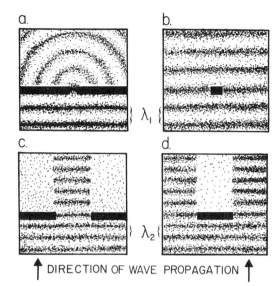

DIRECTION OF WAVE PROPAGATION

**Figure 2.9.** Main effects of sound encountering barriers. **a** and **b**. Diffraction occurs because the wavelength ($\lambda_1$) of the sound is much greater than the dimensions of the hole (**a**) or obstructing object (**b**). **c** and **d**. No diffraction occurs because the wavelength ($\lambda_2$) is much shorter than dimensions of the hole (**c**) or the barrier (**d**). The barrier, in such cases, casts a sound shadow.

tion will occur. Figure 2.9 illustrates the main effects of what happens under four different conditions. In two of these conditions, the wavelength is greater than the dimensions of the hole or object (*a* and *b*); therefore, diffraction occurs. In the other two (*c* and *d*), the wavelength is smaller than the dimensions of the hole or object, and there is no diffraction. It will be worthwhile to consider these situations in some detail.

If a sound wave encounters a hole in a wall, and the size of the hole is very small compared with its wavelength, the sound radiating through the hole will scatter in all directions—an example of diffraction (Fig. 2.9*a*). It is as if there were a new sound source at the location of the hole. The portion of the sound wave front encountering the hole acts somewhat like a piston or the cone of a loudspeaker. Naturally, there will be a loss of energy, because much of the initial sound wave will be reflected and/or absorbed by the barrier. In addition, some of the sound probably will be transmitted through the barrier, but for simplicity it is assumed here that no transmission occurs. The important observation is that it does not matter whether the sound is monitored directly in front of the hole or behind the wall; comparable sound pressures will be observed at the two locations. Even though the incident waves are essentially flat (plane), the sound emerges from the opening scattering in all directions, thus generating hemispherical waves. In contrast, when the opening is very large, compared with the wavelength of the sound, as illustrated in Figure 2.9c, the sound emerges through the opening as a beam of sound. This condition is analogous to a beam of light passing through the mask of a slide via a slide projector; a well-defined rectangular spot of light is projected onto the screen. The lack of sound diffraction is a troublesome matter for engineers responsible for designing high-fidelity speakers. Because of their short wavelengths, very high frequency sounds become highly directional, making proper seating in front of the speaker critical. Indeed, one of the purposes of grille cloth on loudspeaker enclosures (other than for protection and decoration) is to encourage diffraction and thus a wider angle of dispersion.

The effects of obstacles in the pathway of the sound follow the same basic rules as those that govern the effects of a hole in the wall. If the dimensions of an object are much smaller than the wavelength of the sound, the sound waves will bend around the object and fill it behind. It almost is as if the obstacle did not exist, as illustrated in Figure 2.9b. For this reason, the presence of such obstacles may go completely unnoticed acoustically. However, when the wavelength is much smaller than the dimensions of the object, diffraction does not occur, and the object casts a sound shadow (Fig. 2.9d). Again, an analogy to the behavior of light waves is instructive. No diffraction effects are observed when light strikes an opaque object; a shadow is cast. Similarly, there are no sound waves present on the other side of an acoustically opaque barrier (in other words, assuming no transmission of sound through the barrier).

Diffraction may be either a desired or undesired effect. In a lecture room, it is hoped that the sound waves created by the lecturer's voice will diffract around the obstacles in front of listeners seated in the back of the room. On the other hand, barriers that discourage sound diffraction and transmission are sometimes used to separate a large room into smaller working cubicles, as in a typical bank building. In this case, the word **baffle** is often used to describe the barrier. In essence, a baffle decreases sound diffraction and transmission and increases its reflection and/or absorption.[6]

Again, it must be emphasized that the phenomena described in the foregoing paragraphs are the primary, or first-order, effects. Some unrealistic assumptions were made in the interest of simplicity. For example, some sound might in fact be transmitted through a would-be barrier, so some interaction between the diffracted and transmitted waves is expected. In addition, sound waves most likely will be reflected by the barrier, so the incident and reflected sound waves will interact (interference). The distribution of sound energy in practical situations thus may be rather complex and is the subject of the section on sound fields below.

---

[6] As exemplified by the situation illustrated in Figure 2.9c, a sound source also can be highly directional in its radiation pattern. The directional characteristics of a transducer (whether it be used to detect or generate sound) can be quantified by the directivity factor. For instance, in the case of a loudspeaker, the directivity factor is determined by comparing the sound pressure observed directly in front of the diaphragm with that measured off axis, but at the same distance from the source. A loudspeaker approximating a simple or point source produces an omnidirectional pattern (sound radiating equally in all directions) and has a directivity factor approaching 1. Practical loudspeakers have directivity factors greater than 1; the more focused their patterns of radiation, the higher the directivity factor.

## F. WEIRD SOUND WAVE BEHAVIORS

Sound wave propagation can be affected by factors other than physical barriers, and then some really strange things can happen (not that reverberation and diffraction are not a bit on the weird side). For example, it was noted earlier that the physical properties of the medium, including temperature for gaseous and fluid media, influences the speed of sound in that medium. Assume that a sound wave, in its propagation, moves from a warm to a cooler air mass. The speed of propagation will be slower in the cooler than in the warmer medium. So, what is weird about this? The result—the change in temperature causes the path of the sound wave propagation to bend. The bending of the sound wave's path of propagation is known as **refraction** (not to be confused with rarefaction, the low-density phase or half-cycle of a sound [The Sound Medium, above]). Although for simplicity this was not illustrated in Figure 2.7, refraction also occurs when sound energy is transmitted from one medium to another, because the sound speed and characteristic impedance are interrelated (Eq. 2.7).

In all of the previous descriptions of sound wave phenomena, a stationary sound source and observer were assumed. In many cases, one of these moves, and when this happens another strange and interesting acoustic phenomenon occurs, the **doppler effect**. The doppler effect is an apparent frequency change in the sound caused by the motion and is a phenomenon commonly experienced while standing along a road as cars go by. As the car (sound source) moves toward the observer, its sound has a relatively higher pitch than normal. This is caused by the fact that the sound waves are being compressed by the approaching source (the car). Because the distance between two adjacent crests (or troughs) decreases, the wavelength of the sound decreases. Sounds with shorter wavelengths have higher frequencies (Eq. 2.5), leading to the perception of higher pitch (Chapter 7). On the other hand, when the sound source moves past the listener, the frequency decreases, because as the source moves away, the wavelength of the sound is stretched. Virtually the same effect occurs when the sound source is stationary and the listener approaches and then passes it (for example, as experienced while riding in a train and going by the ringing alarm bell at a road crossing).

## 3. Sound Fields

Sound transmission, reflection, absorption, diffraction, and interference all combine to determine the distribution of sound energy in what is called the sound *field*. Despite the complexities that may be created by some of the sound wave phenomena just described, there are several basic and general types of **sound fields** that may be defined. Thus, the focus of this discussion will be shifted from the sound waves themselves to the environment in which they exist. Any area in which sound waves are present may be called a sound field. There are different kinds of sound fields, and in any given realistic situation, the sound field probably will contain some elements of each. It is conventional that theoretical models are used in discussing this topic. The models are rarely even approximated in real life, but they are useful for the sake of explanation and they are approximated and used in laboratory work.

The simplest model is the **free field**. In a free sound field, there are no boundaries or barriers, so sound waves are permitted to travel without obstruction. The net effect is that there will be no reflection, diffraction, absorption, or transmission from one medium to another. Rather, the sound waves are free to propagate indefinitely.

Earlier discussions of the inverse square law assumed a free field because in that case, the sound waves were free, progressive, spherical waves. Although a free field clearly cannot exist without limit in the real world, it can be approximated even within the rather small confines of a room-sized enclosure. Because any sound waves other than those radiating directly from the source will alter the sound pressure distribution in the sound field, the interior of the enclosure must be isolated from sound waves originating from outside the enclosure in which the free field is being established. In short, the enclosure must be **soundproof**. This can be achieved by using thick interior walls of highly absorptive material with highly reflective material covering the exterior of the enclosure. By virtue of this construction, most energy of externally generated sound waves is reflected, and any transmitted energy is completely absorbed. Furthermore, reflected sound waves inside the enclosure cannot be tolerated, because reflections give rise to reverberation. Consequently, such a chamber also must be **anechoic** (without echoes). Anechoic chambers are both anechoic and soundproof, although it is possible to have soundproof rooms that are not anechoic. In an anechoic chamber, thick wedge-shaped panels of acoustically absorbent material (typically glass wool) are used to eliminate reflections inside the room, as shown in Figure 2.10*a*. Even in a room built to be anechoic, maintaining a pure free field is not without difficulty. Objects in the field such as chairs, tables, equipment, and people act as sound diffractors and/or reflectors that thus can contaminate the free field. Nevertheless, even in hearing experiments, in which the head and ears themselves introduce diffraction and reflection (see Chapters 5 and 7), the anechoic environment may be the most appropriate for some kinds of experiments and measurements, namely those in which the only contaminants are those inherent to the structures in question and not further complicated by reverberation.

For subjects who have normal hearing, hearing tests are most accurate when administered in quiet rooms, as illustrated

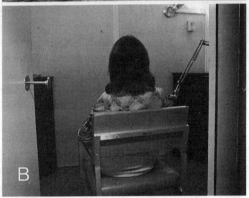

**Figure 2.10.** Anechoic (**a**) and sound-treated (**b**) chambers. (**a**, Courtesy of Industrial Acoustics Company, Bronx, NY; **b**, photograph of a hearing test suite typical of those used for hearing testing by audiologists.)

in Figure 2.10*b*. These rooms are relatively free of extraneous sounds and reflected sound waves, but they are neither soundproof nor anechoic. Rather, they are referred to as **sound-treated** or **sound isolation booths**. In these booths extraneous sounds are reflected and absorbed only partially, although they attenuate ambient noise (sounds from external sources) by specified amounts and have very little reverberation.

As described previously in this chapter, reflective surfaces in the sound field can alter the acoustics appreciably. A sound field in which multiple reflected waves are present is known as a **reverberant field**. Reverberation exists in degrees dependent on the same factors that determine the amount of sound energy that is transmitted, reflected, and/or absorbed by the walls of a particular enclosure and the objects inside it. In an ideal reverberant field, a single impulsive sound, such as that made by a snap of the fingers, would bounce around indefinitely, because of endless reflections off all surfaces. The reverberation time ($T_{60}$) in such an idealistic acoustic environment thus would be infinite. In real-life situations, the sound energy of the reflected waves decays as it is ultimately absorbed by the walls of or structures within the enclosure and/or transmitted outside of the enclosure. Consequently, $T_{60}$ is finite and, indeed, is typically adjusted to specific needs of the particular experiment or measurements at hand (namely, by introducing or removing panels of absorptive material).

A highly reverberant room is often described as being *live*, whereas a room that has very little reverberation is called *dead*. Radio studios and hearing test booths are thus very dead acoustically, with anechoic chambers being the deadest. In contrast, an empty room or apartment with plaster walls and hardwood or tile floors will be quite live. The reverberation time may be controlled by an appropriate choice of building materials and architectural design. Some reverberation is desirable for aesthetic purposes. Indeed, different reverberation times are optimal for ideal listening to different program materials, such as chamber music versus orchestral music, music versus speech, etc. A certain amount of reverberation actually enhances speech intelligibility (that is, the understandability of what is being spoken) and gives the sound of the speech a more pleasant quality. The auditory system apparently benefits from the inherent redundancy of reverberant sound. However, a room also may have too much reverberation, causing sounds to be muddled.

If a continuous sound were produced in the ideal reverberant field—the antithesis of the anechoic chamber—the sound pressure would grow indefinitely. By virtue of the law of conservation of energy, the sound energy being poured into the room must accumulate, because it can neither be transmitted nor absorbed. This obviously is not typical of any realistic situation. The point is, however, that both incident and reflected sound waves are being created continuously and will interfere with one another. The impact of this is that the sound pressure observed at any point in the room will no longer be uniquely determined by the distance from the sound source at which it is measured, as predicted by the inverse square law. Close to the source, nevertheless, the sound pressure will be more dependent on the incident sound waves (in essence, sound energy directly from the source). Closer to the walls, on the other hand, the observed sound pressure will be dominated by reflected sound waves. If, in fact, there are many reflected waves of random incidence—that is, from all directions—an average sound pressure will be attained that will be nearly uniform throughout the room. Such a situation is characteristic of the third model, the ***diffuse sound field***. Like the ideal free and reverberant fields, the ideal diffuse field is difficult to attain in any practical setting. It is best approximated in a large reverberant room at relatively great distances from the sound source.

In the practical sound-treated booth, it is not possible to assume that the field will be either purely free or diffuse, even to a first approximation. As suggested in the preceding paragraph, the situation can change according to how far the point of observation is from the sound source. Furthermore, there is yet another breakdown of the sound field that must be considered: the difference between the ***near*** and ***far fields***. For reasons beyond the scope of coverage here, the inverse law does not hold for distances of less than a few wavelengths from the sound source. In other words, the decrease in sound pressure with distance does not decrease in direct proportion to distance. This is the acoustic

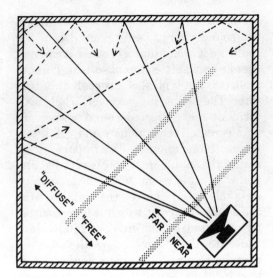

**Figure 2.11.** Regions of the practical sound field that approximate different types of sound fields according to the distance of the observer from a loudspeaker and proximity of the reflecting surface to the boundaries of the room. Some of the possible paths of travel of sound from the speaker are indicated by *solid lines*; some possible paths of reflected sound are indicated by *broken lines*.

*near field*. However, at a sufficient distance from the sound source (typically several wavelengths away), the inverse law will prevail, namely in the *far field*. As shown in Figure 2.11, the far field overlaps the regions of the sound field in which a free and a diffuse sound field predominate. At distances closer to the near field, the sound pressure naturally will be dominated by the incident wave, so a free field fundamentally exists. At greater distances, the influence of reflected waves will become more pronounced, and once more the sound pressure will no longer behave according to the inverse law. In this area, a diffuse (far) sound field is approximated, and the sound pressure, again, will assume a nearly constant value regardless of distance from the source. Which field is desirable for a particular application will depend on which feature is most important for the particular measurements involved, although it is generally desirable

to avoid the near field because of the more radical change of sound pressure with distance from the source.

## 4. Earphone Sound Delivery

**Earphones**, which are merely miniature loudspeakers, (Fig. 2.12) represent a method of delivering sound to the ear(s) directly. It may seen strange to discuss earphones after devoting so much discussion to the acoustics of sound fields. However, with some of the complexities of the sound field in mind, it is easier to appreciate the reasons for the prevalent use of earphones in clinical hearing testing, hearing research, and even everyday applications. The first and most obvious advantage of using earphones is that each ear may be stimulated independently (although not without limits). The sound generated by the earphone transducer is confined primarily to the volume of air between the diaphragm of the earphone and the eardrum. Because of the rather small dimensions of this volume, roughly 2 to 6 cm$^3$, depending on the specific type of earphone, the sound pressure will remain fairly constant throughout this space for much of the audible frequency range. It is technically possible to measure the sound pressure directly in front of the eardrum, using a microphone fitted with a fine *probe* tube. However, the sound pressure can be estimated with reasonable accuracy for a variety of applications by using a dummy cavity—a hole in rigid material simulating the typical ear canal volume. Again, the volume of this cavity depends on the type of earphone used, with the major variable being whether the earphone rests on the ear, a *supraaural earphone* (Fig. 2.12a), or whether it is inserted into the ear canal, an *insert earphone* (Fig. 2.12b). The typical volumes used are 6 cm$^3$ for supraaural earphones and 2 cm$^3$ for insert earphones.

The small volume represented by 2 to 6 cm$^3$ is itself an advantage of earphones;

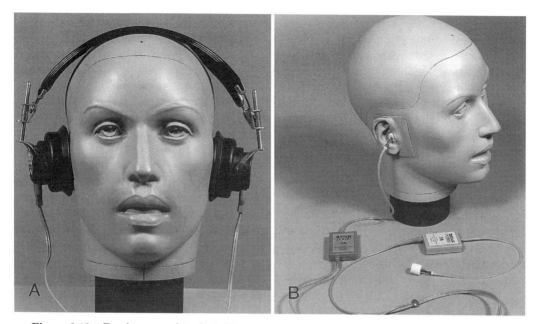

**Figure 2.12.**   Earphones used in clinical hearing testing, supraaural (**a**) and tubal insert (**b**) types.

relatively little acoustic power is required from the earphone to develop substantial, or even intolerably high, sound pressures. The acoustic power produced by the sound source is confined to a fixed-area wavefront, unlike that of spherical waves propagating in a free field. At least this is true for most of the audible frequency range, wherein the sound waves produced by earphones can be assumed to be plane waves. For this reason, the inverse law, by and large, does not apply to sound in the ear canal: the acoustic intensity is not being diminished by the expansion of the wavefront, as it is in the case of freely propagated spherical waves. However, for frequencies of relatively short wavelengths (that is, relatively high frequencies), the acoustics of the ear canal do introduce some complexities here, as discussed in the next section and in Chapter 5.

Finally, earphones provide a degree of isolation from outside sounds. This may even permit hearing testing, for some purposes, in a quiet office, rather than in a sound-treated booth. How much, if any, sound isolation is provided by the ear-

phone also depends on its design. Earphones currently popular for personal listening (high-fidelity) devices, including so-called "ear buds," are not designed to provide any isolation. These are sometimes called "open-air" earphones; they radiate outside the ear as well as inside. Earphones typically used in hearing testing are designed to form essentially a closed acoustic system. Consequently, they leak relatively little sound to the outside world and provide useful amounts of sound isolation, namely fourfold or more reduction in sound pressures of extraneous sounds (although the amount is frequency dependent).

Even with all of these advantages, the use of earphones unfortunately involves a highly unnatural acoustic environment, even if it does seem like every other person on the streets today is wearing personal listening devices (namely, radios, tape players, and compact disc players with earphones). This fact also cannot be overlooked just because of their widespread use in hearing clinics and research laboratories. Natural listening experiences involve the acoustics of sound fields and of the ear itself (Chapter 5), which involves such phenomena as diffraction. It will be seen later (Chapter 7) that, indeed, it is in the sound field that hearing is most sensitive and that the benefit of hearing with two ears, rather than with one, is most vividly demonstrable. It also is important not to assume that, just because earphones are intended for direct sound delivery to the ears, the principles of sound propagation can be discarded. For example, the eardrum does not begin to vibrate at the first instance of vibration of the earphone diaphragm. It takes time for the propagated disturbance initiated by the diaphragm to travel down the ear canal, even if it is only 2.5 cm in length. The precise delay will depend on the type of earphone, which, by its own construction, can add to this delay. Tubal insert earphones (Fig. 2.12*b*), for instance, introduce an additional 8- to 9-msec delay over that produced by supraaural earphones (Fig. 2.12*a*). This is because of the length of the tubing between the transducer and the terminating foam tip inserted into the ear canal. Other types of insert earphones, typically those used with hearing aids, can produce less delay, because they may place the diaphragm closer to the eardrum. Last, earphones, whether supraaural or insert, alter the natural acoustics of the ear, often by shifting or eliminating the *ear canal resonance*. The acoustic principle that makes such resonance possible is the subject of the next section. These details and the importance of this and other acoustic phenomena in hearing will be taken up in Chapter 5.

## 5. Acoustical Resonance and Standing Waves

### A. The Helmholtz Resonator (or Resonate, but Keep It Simple)

Throughout this chapter, emphasis has been placed on the characteristics of the medium that carries sound and on the be-

havior of sound waves in that medium. Although various concepts developed in Chapter 1 concerning mechanics have been applied in this discussion of sound and acoustics, there has been no discussion of the acoustical analog of the simple spring-mass system and the phenomenon of resonance. Indeed, resonance is an important phenomenon in acoustics. Recall that at resonance a system operates with maximum efficiency, meaning that minimum force is required to set it into vibration and to maintain that motion. Alternatively stated, at resonance the maximum motion is achieved with the least applied force.

A series of simple resonating systems is shown in Fig. 2.13. In each of these devices, the air in the open tube constitutes an ***acoustic inertance*** $(m_a)$ that is caused by the mass of the air in the tube. This entire volume of air tends to move back and forth in the tube when the system is driven by a sound source; therefore, it behaves much like the mass in the simple spring-mass system. Similarly, the air enclosed in the cavity itself acts like a spring. Air is compressible, and as it is compressed into a smaller volume, greater opposition develops to the applied pressure. This fact can be appreciated by anyone who has filled a tire with air using a hand pump. It becomes increasingly difficult to pump air into the tire as it inflates, and the air pressure inside the tire builds up like a restoring force. The tire itself

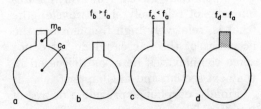

**Figure 2.13.** Helmholtz resonators. The relationship of the resonant frequency of resonators **b** through **d** to that of **a** is indicated in each case: acoustic mass $(m_a)$, acoustic compliance $(c_a)$, and acoustic resistance (*dotted area* in **d**).

does not significantly stretch. Although a spring constant of sorts could be determined for this air spring (namely, the bulk modulus of elasticity), it is often more convenient to deal with elasticity in terms of *acoustic compliance* $(c_a)$.[7] As noted in Chapter 1, compliance is the reciprocal of stiffness. The more compressible the enclosed volume of air, the greater the acoustic compliance, which, in turn, is measured as the volume displacement per unit volume.

The influence of compliance and mass on the resonant frequency in acoustic resonators is identical to that in the (mechanical) simple spring-mass system. This is illustrated by comparing resonant frequencies among resonators *a* through *c* in Figure 2.13. The resonant frequency is directly proportional to the square root of stiffness, which means that it will be inversely proportional to the square root of compliance. Consequently, resonator *b* has a higher resonant frequency than *a*, because it has a smaller acoustic compliance. The resonant frequency is also inversely proportional to the square root of mass. This means that resonator *c* will have a lower resonant frequency than resonator *a*, because it has the greater acoustic mass. It follows that resonator *c* will have a much lower resonant frequency than *b*, because it has both greater inertance and greater compliance. These resonators also have some damping, primarily because of the dissipation of sound energy occurring as sound is radiated into the surrounding medium. Additional damping could be achieved by packing steel wool or other acoustically absorbant material into the tube, as seen in the case of resonator *d*. The effects of damping in these acoustical resonators is the same as in the simple spring-mass system. The natural response of the system decays

more rapidly with increased damping, and its forced response is less frequency dependent, that is, the resonant peak is less sharp, than in the undamped case.

This acoustic analog of the mechanical simple harmonic oscillator is known as a *Helmholtz resonator*. It typically has an additional opening in the cavity with a slightly protruding tube for insertion into the ear. This allows one to hear the resonant effects of the device, a primary tool of observation and measurement before the 20th century. Speech and other environmental sounds may be altered appreciably, because the sound pressure in these sounds, at frequencies in the vicinity of the resonant frequency of the device, will be enhanced. By the same token, at frequencies above and below the resonant frequency, the sounds will be attenuated. Although it may not be obvious from its construction, the roar of the ocean that is heard in sea shells is caused by this form of resonance.

### B. BASIC CONCEPTS OF STANDING WAVES: VIBRATING STRINGS

Acoustical resonance may occur under circumstances other than that depicted by the Helmholtz resonator. An example of particular interest here is the formation of *standing waves*. A vibrating string serves as an excellent vehicle to demonstrate the concept of a stationary wave and the underlying physical principles. It is the formation of standing waves on strings that makes it possible to produce tones by plucking or otherwise vibrating the strings of stringed musical instruments. However, a more visual example will helpful here. Consider a length of highly elastic string, such as stretchy rubber hose often found in chemistry or biology labs, suspended as illustrated in Figure 2.14. The string or hose is affixed to a rigid structure or a wall at one end, and a vibratory pattern is started at the opposite, hand-held, end by jiggling it up and down (Fig. 2.14*a*). This disturbance in the string can be seen to travel away from the

---

[7] Compliance is a particularly appropriate parameter, because it is directly analogous to electrical capacitance. This simplifies modeling of acoustic systems with electrical systems, such as an electrical analog of the vocal tract.

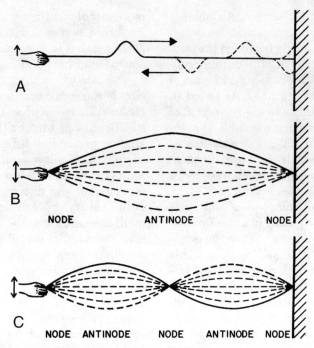

**Figure 2.14.** Standing waves on a vibrating string. **a.** An upward jerk at the end of the string initiates the propagation (transverse) of a pulse down the string, which is reflected at the other end, where it is affixed to the wall. **b** and **c.** First and second modes of vibration, respectively, resulting from sinusoidal, up-down, displacements of the end of the string. The *solid lines* show the displacement along the string at the instant of the peak upward phase of the vibration at the end of the string; the *broken lines* show displacements at various other instants in time.

vibrated end. As a matter of fact, with a quick snap of the string, a single impulse could be imparted to it (Fig. 2.14b) that would initiate an incident wave involving a single upward deflection. However, when this disturbance reaches the far (fixed) end, it will be reflected backward as a wave moving in the opposite direction. More intriguing, as dictated by physical principles, the reflected wave must be inverted, so the wave moving back toward the hand causes the string to move downward.

Now, if a periodic vibratory force is applied to the string, rather than one brief jerk, many incident and reflected waves will be set up along the string. Complicating matters further, waves can be reflected from either end, because, in essence, both are fixed. (The hand-held end can be considered fixed, because the dis-placement amplitude will be much less than that developed elsewhere on the string.) So, a seemingly chaotic superpositioning of incident, reflected, and rereflected waves can be imparted to the string. Yet, with the proper frequencies of applied vibration, the interaction of the incident and reflected waves will constructively interfere, and out of "chaos" will emerge a standing wave.

The lowest frequency at which a standing wave will form on the string is that at which transverse displacement occurs all along the string, except at the ends that constitute displacement **nodes** (Fig. 2.14b). Between the nodes, a single displacement **antinode** occurs. An antinode is a point at which displacement, up or down, is maximal. At the frequency at which this occurs, the wave seems not to move along the length of the string but simply to cause the middle of the string to oscillate up and down. This is why the wave is said to be standing. The frequency at which the standing wave has a single antinode is called the fundamental or first *mode* of vibration. The fundamental mode occurs at a frequency whose wavelength is twice the length of the string, because, in effect, the wave pattern on the string is half a wavelength. Therefore,

$$f_o = c/2L$$

Alternatively,

$$2L = c/f_o = \lambda_o$$

Consequently,

$$L = \lambda_o/2 \qquad (2.12)$$

where $f_o$ is the fundamental, $c$ is the speed of the wave travel, and $L$ is the length of the string.

Now, standing waves may be established at other frequencies as well, and these higher modes will occur at integer multiples of the fundamental mode: $2f_o$, $3f_o \ldots nf_o$. The result will be the formation of two, three $\ldots n$ antinodes (Fig. 2.14c). However, the amplitude of the wave will decrease with mode number and thus with increasing frequency (Fig. 2.14, compare $b$ and $c$). To further emphasize the concept of the standing wave as a seemingly stationary disturbance, it is noteworthy that the nodes of the string (again, the points along the string at which displacement is zero) can be touched without appreciably damping the amplitude of vibratory displacements along other parts of the string.

That the formation of standing waves represents a resonance-like effect (albeit for much different reasons than resonance of the simple harmonic oscillator) can be appreciated from the following. At the frequencies of the modes of a string, relatively little force is required to set and keep the string in motion. The formation of standing waves represents a sort of self-reinforcing system. Consider the first mode. Upward displacement of the string sends a half-cycle of the wave down the string; as this half-cycle is reflected, the next half-cycle of the incident wave is initiated. So, the first half-cycle of the wave is reflected and consequently is inverted as it meets the next half-cycle of the incident wave, which is also negative going. (The vibration was initiated with an upward movement; now the hand holding the string is moving down.) This is how the two constructively interfere. Admittedly, the picture is a bit more complicated at higher modes, but intuitively it makes sense that only at the modal frequencies will the proper phasing of the incident and reflected waves occur such that there will be constructive interference. The tie-in to resonance also is manifest in the efficiency of energy transfer at modal frequencies. Namely, the greatest efficiency will be realized when the frequency of the applied vibration is at one of the modes with the optimal transfer occurring at the fundamental mode. As illustrated in Figure 2.14, again, the hand is moving relatively little compared with the displacement of the string at the antinodes.

## C. ACOUSTICAL STANDING WAVES

Acoustically, the direct analog of the vibrating string with fixed ends is an air-filled tube or pipe with closed (reflecting) ends. Displacement nodes must occur at the closed ends, because the air particles cannot be displaced out of the tube. At the fundamental mode of vibration, a single displacement antinode will occur in the center of the tube, just as it does in the case of the vibrating string. The higher modes of the tube will be integer multiples of this fundamental mode, as calculated for the string (Eq. 2.12). As mentioned previously, sound pressure is usually the amplitude measure of practical importance, and the sound pressure in the tube with closed ends also can be described. Because the ends are closed, air particles cannot be displaced by the sound wave, and the sound pressure reaches its maximum value here. Thus, there will be pressure antinodes at the two closed ends. This

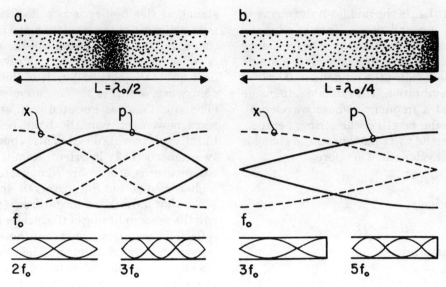

**Figure 2.15.** Standing waves in pipes. The *solid lines* show the pressure variation along the pipes at the condensation or rarefaction peaks, and the *broken lines* show particle displacements. The distribution of particles along the pipes are represented at the instant of peak condensation. The particle density outside the pipe is essentially the same as that at the open ends of the pipes, which is where the pressure nodes occur (see text). **a.** Pipe with both ends open. **b.** Pipe with one end closed. $f_o$, Fundamental frequency; $L$, length; $\lambda_o$, wavelength at the fundamental frequency.

means that there will be one pressure node in the center of this tube.

Actually, the pipe with both ends closed is of limited practical interest, but although it may not be immediately obvious, Eq. 2.12 also applies to a more practical pipe, one with both ends open (Fig. 2.15a). Reflection still occurs at the ends, even though they are open, because of the impedance difference between the air inside versus that outside the pipe. This impedance difference precludes perfect transmission of the wave out of the tube; thus, it forms a reflective boundary. This means that at an open end the particle displacement and sound pressure are just opposite those in the case of a closed end. On the other hand, because the particles may be readily displaced, displacement antinodes must appear at each end of the tube. The result is that a single node appears in the middle. Using the same logic, there will be a sound pressure node at each open end, because the pressure there will be close to ambient pressure.

This is because the particles distribute themselves much as they are outside the pipe. However, there will be a pressure antinode in the middle of the pipe where the particles are not free to be displaced and where the density fluctuation is greatest (Fig. 2.15a). This means also that pressure and displacement nodes are 90° out of phase.

It is a relatively simple matter to go from this case to the situation in which one end is closed and the other is open. At the first mode, there will be a pressure antinode (displacement node) at the closed end where the particle build-up is greatest (Fig. 2.15b). A pressure node (displacement antinode) will occur at the open end. This condition can occur only when the standing wave is one quarter of the wavelength, because the nodes and antinodes are one quarter of a cycle apart. Thus, the first mode of the pipe with one end closed occurs at a frequency that has a wavelength four times the length of the pipe; that is:

$$f_o = c/4L$$

Alternatively,

$$4L = c/f_o = \lambda_o$$

Consequently,

$$L = \lambda_o/4 \qquad (2.13)$$

Furthermore, the higher modes can occur only at odd integer multiples of this frequency: $3f_o$, $5f_o$ ... $n_{odd}f_o$. At $2f_o$ and higher even multiples, nodes would have to occur at each end—an impossible situation.

At this point, a simple numerical example might help solidify the concept of the standing waves and the relationship between the length of the pipe and the frequency of the fundamental mode. The pipe with one end closed will prove to be of most practical relevance in this text, so it will be used in this example. Assume the pipe to have a length of 0.025 m (that is, 2.5 cm or about 1 inch). Given the speed of sound to be 343 m/sec:

$$f_o = 343/(4 \times 0.025) = 343/0.1$$

$$= 343 \times 10^2/1 \times 10^{-1}$$

$$= 3.43 \times 10^{(2-(-1))}$$

$$= 3.43 \times 10^3 \text{ Hz or 3.43 kHz}$$

The length of this hypothetical pipe should be familiar; it is length of the average adult ear canal. Like the pipe in the example, the ear canal is open at one end and closed at the other, namely by the eardrum. Standing waves thus can be set up in the ear canal pipe, affecting the sound pressure at the closed end, that is, at the eardrum. The role of the ear canal, and thus the contribution of its acoustic effect to hearing, will be described in Chapter 5.

Many examples of the standing wave phenomena actually could be cited. The concept is clearly relevant to the acoustics of musical instruments. The pipe organ, flute, and other wind instruments (and, as mentioned earlier, stringed instruments and even percussion instruments such as the piano, harp, and xylophone) all rely on the formation of standing waves when played. One's ability to create a tonal sound by blowing over the mouth of a test tube or bottle is another demonstration of the resonance of a tube, in particular, with one end closed and the other open. The vocal tract also functions basically like a pipe with one end closed (by the vocal folds) and one end opened (the mouth), albeit a more complex example than that of the straight pipe of uniform diameter. Standing waves also may play a role in the determination of the sound pressure distribution in a sound field, especially when a sound enclosure or room has parallel walls. That is, there is such a thing as *room resonance*.

Room resonance represents a bit more complex situation than that exemplified by standing waves in pipes, and the term *resonance* is loosely applied in this case. Unlike the pipes of an organ, rooms are nearly as wide and high as they are long. Sound spreads out in many directions, and reflections often occur over many paths. And other factors than the simple rules governing modes of pipes and strings contribute to the determination of standing waves in rooms. Nevertheless, standing waves can form. The fundamental mode is usually low in frequency (long wavelength), and the upper modes are plentiful. The degree to which standing waves become prominent depends on the exact dimensions of the room and other factors that contribute to reverberation as well, such as the preponderance of reflecting surfaces. It again becomes apparent that the behavior of sound in a given sound field can be complicated. The formation of standing waves may adversely affect the accuracy of sound pressure measurements and, subsequently, the specification of the sound pressure in that field. This, in turn, can compromise the precision with which hearing measurement (in a sound field) can be made. This is another reason for performing sound-field hearing measurements (whether for clinical or research purposes) in sound-treated rooms;

they have relatively low reverberation. Stimuli also are used that are less prone to development of standing waves (random noise, speech, and frequency-modulated tones; see Chapter 3). Acoustics thus plays important roles in hearing science, not only by virtue of how the ear works and what one hears, but also in one's ability to quantify hearing.

## BIBLIOGRAPHY

Backus, J. (1969). *The Acoustical Foundations of Music*. W. W. Norton & Co., New York.

Beranek, L. L. (1988). *Acoustical Measurements*. 2nd ed. American Institute of Physics, New York.

Broch, J. T. (1967). *The Application of the Bruel & Kjaer Measuring Systems to Acoustic Noise Measurements*. Bruel & Kjaer Instruments, Marlborough, MA.

Durrant, J. D. (1975). Simulation of sound waves on the oscilloscope. *J. Acoust. Soc. Am.* 57:1558–1559.

French, A. P. (1971). *Vibrations and Waves*. W. W. Norton & Co., New York.

Hall, D. E. (1980). *Musical Acoustics: An Introduction*. Wadsworth Publishing, Belmont, CA.

Helmholtz, H. L. F. (1954). *On the Sensations of Tone as a Physiological Basis for the Theory of Music*. Dover Publications, New York.

Kinsler, L. E., and Frey, A. R. (1962). *Fundamentals of Acoustics*. John Wiley & Sons, New York.

Knudsen, V. O. (1932). *Architectural Acoustics*. John Wiley & Sons, New York.

Knudsen, V. O. (1963). Architectural acoustics. *Sci. Am.* 209:78–92.

Kock, W. E. (1971). *Seeing Sound*. Wiley-Interscience, New York.

Lindsay, R. B. (1966). The story of acoustics. *J. Acoust. Soc. Am.* 39:629–644.

Lloyd, L. S. (1937). *Music and Sound*. Book of Libraries Press, Freeport, NY.

Lovrinic, J. M., and Durrant, J. D. (1991). Audiologic instrumentation. In *Diagnostic Audiology*, edited by J. T. Jacobson and J. L. Northern, pp. 53–66. Pro-Ed, Austin.

Morse, P. M. (1976). *Vibration and Sound*. American Institute of Physics, New York.

Murray, R. L., and Cobb, G. C. (1970). *Physics: Concepts and Consequences*. Prentice-Hall, Englewood Cliffs, NJ.

Olson, H. F. (1958). *Dynamical Analogies*. 2nd ed. D. Van Nostrand, Princeton.

Peterson, A. P. G., and Gross, E. E., Jr. (1967). *Handbook of Noise Measurement*. General Radio Co., West Concord, MA.

Prout, J. H., and Bienvenue, G. R. (1990). *Acoustics for You*. Krieger Publishing, Malabar, FL.

Rainey, J. T., and Neville, D. G. (1972). Sound field visualization techniques. *Sound Vibr.* 6:10–14.

Rossing, T. D. (1990). *The Science of Sound*. 2nd ed. Addison-Wesley Publishing, Reading, MA.

Speaks, C. E. (1992). *Introduction to Sound: Acoustics for Hearing and Speech Sciences*. Singular Publishing Group, San Diego.

Sonn, M. (1969). *Psychoacoustical Terminology*. Raytheon Co., Portsmouth, RI.

Tonndorf, J. (1980). Physics of sound. In *Otolaryngology: Vol. 1. Basic Sciences and Related Disciplines*, 2nd ed, edited by M. M. Paparella and D. A. Shumrick, pp. 177–198. W. B. Saunders Co., Philadelphia.

## CHAPTER 3

# MEASUREMENT OF SOUND

The generation of sound, behavior of sound, and underlying physical concepts have been presented in the preceding chapters. This chapter will focus on the measurement of sound. Much of hearing research and the clinical assessment of hearing deal with the stimulation of sensation—the presentation of sound to evoke a subjective response to it. The careful quantification of the sound stimulus eliciting a particular sensation is essential in these endeavors. Indeed, sensations are often characterized by the pertinent parameter(s) of the physical stimulus that is sufficient to elicit them. Such questions may be asked as what intensity of sound is required to make it just detectable, how much change in frequency is necessary to produce a noticeable difference in pitch, etc. Indeed, even when absolutely nothing is known about a particular physical or biological system, one at least can characterize the system by determining how the output (response) of the system compares with the input of the system (sound, in this case). This is the "black box approach." Even when one comes to a complete understanding of what is in the black box and how it all works, the function relating the output to the input is still of interest, because it allows characterization of the performance of a particular system.

There are various parameters of sound, which must be determined to permit one to completely specify the stimulus. Princi-

pal among these are measures of amplitude, frequency, and phase. Both the nitty-gritty details of how sound measurements are made and the specific electronic instrumentation required for such measurements are beyond the scope of this text. Of concern here, rather, are the concepts underlying the pertinent procedural matters and the practical units of measure of sound, particularly for the purposes of hearing science. There actually are various ways by which analyses of the physical attributes of sound can be made and by which their measures can be rendered. Additionally, it is important to understand how the change in one parameter of the sound stimulus can affect another, purely on a physical basis. An example is the effect that a change in duration can have on the frequency content of a sound (as described below). Therefore, it is the purpose of this chapter to describe relevant measures of sound, ways in which these measures can be specified, and, indeed, the nature and makeup of various types of sound of particular interest in hearing science.

## 1. Amplitude Revisited and More

The peak displacement of vibration $(A_{o\text{-}p})$ of the simple spring-mass system was defined in Chapter 1 as the amplitude: the difference between the maximum instantaneous value and equilibrium. Displacement, however, is not the most practical measure for quantifying the magnitude of a sound; as revealed in Chapter 2, the most practical measure is that of sound pressure. Peak sound pressure can be measured and is defined as the difference between the peak condensation pressure and the ambient, or atmospheric, pressure. Peak-to-peak amplitude $(A_{p\text{-}p})$ also was defined previously, namely as the difference between the maximum and minimum values—peak condensation and rarefaction, respectively, for sound pressure. For sinusoids, $A_{p\text{-}p} = 2A_{o\text{-}p}$ (see Fig. 3.1). In practical applications, however, neither the peak nor peak-to-peak amplitude may provide the most useful index of the magnitude of a sound or vibration. It often is preferable to obtain a measure that better reflects the overall power of the sound or vibration. A quantity that serves this purpose very well is the **effective** or **root-mean-square (RMS)** magnitude. The RMS magnitude can be explained via a familiar electrical analogy. A light bulb of an appropriate voltage and current rating can be connected to a battery causing it to light. The light emitted is the result of heating of the filament, which, in turn, is caused by the resistance of the filament wire. Thus, electrical energy, driven by the voltage, a forcelike quantity, is dissipated when electrical current is passed through the filament. The battery produces a direct-current (DC) voltage, which is analogous to static pressure in acoustical and mechanical systems. In other words, this electrical force is constant over time. However, electricity of the household variety is alternating current (AC). AC is analogous to sound and other vibratory motion, and it can be equally effective in powering the light bulb. The question is, what measure of the AC voltage yields a value equivalent to the DC voltage, such that the light bulb burns equally brightly? Answer: the RMS voltage. To have the same power dissipation in the lamp with 12 V DC applied, the AC voltage applied would have to be 12 $V_{rms}$. This is nearly 36 $V_{p\text{-}p}$! The basis for this relationship will become apparent momentarily.

The term *root-mean-square* derives from statistics and is an abbreviated way of saying the "square root of the mean of the deviation scores squared." The deviation scores are the values above and below the mean (average). The mean for sinusoids and other functions symmetrical about the baseline is zero. In the case of a sinusoid, the magnitude at each instant during one half-cycle mirrors the corresponding magnitude during the opposite half-cycle, that is, each is equal in value but of opposite sign (Fig. 3.1). (Note: in this chapter, because the physical quantities under consideration may range from displacements of vibration to sound pressures, or even voltages, instantaneous magnitudes will be represented by $a$ in figures such as 3.1 [where $a = f(t)$], namely, to denote the values underlying an amplitude measure.) Now, because the simple average will be zero, it is necessary to remove the sign of the deviations, a process that can be accomplished simply by squaring the instantaneous values. At first glance, this may seem a bit complicated, and, granted, the actual computation of the RMS magnitude of all but the simplest vibratory quantities can be tedious. In practice, however, one simply uses mea-

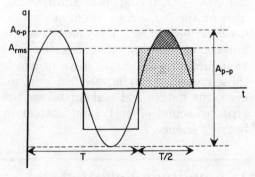

**Figure 3.1.** Comparison of RMS $(A_{rms})$ to peak $(A_{o\text{-}p})$ and peak-to-peak amplitudes $(A_{p\text{-}p})$ of the sinusoid. The period is indicated by $T$. The sinusoid is overlaid with a square wave, which has the same area; the peak amplitude of this square wave equals the $A_{rms}$ of the sine wave.

suring equipment that automatically computes RMS or a reasonable estimate thereof.

Sinusoidal sound (pure tones) are frequently used in hearing science, and it turns out that the computation of the RMS magnitude of a sinusoid is simple. Conceptually, the task involved is akin to trying to fit a round peg into a square hole. In this case, the object is to fit a sine wave into a square wave. Specifically, the task is to determine a single value that best reflects the area under the curves or waveforms of the two. In the case of the square wave (Fig. 3.1), this is no problem. Because the area of one half-cycle of a square wave, shown by the *dotted area* in Figure 3.1, is rectangular, the magnitude at all instants within each half-cycle is constant. Because both positive and negative halves of the function contain the same area, it could be visualized that the negative half is flipped up to the positive side so that the function has a constant value at all instants of time. From the electric light bulb analogy above, this is the DC-equivalent value; it thus is the RMS value in this case. In contrast, the area under the curve of the sine function clearly is not rectangular. Yet, there is an equivalent rectangular area, as illustrated in Figure 3.1. This figure shows that the portion of the dotted area of the half cycle of the square wave falling outside of the half cycle of the sine wave is contained in the *cross-hatched portion* of the sine wave located above the square wave. The magnitude at which this cut though the sinusoid occurs is the RMS amplitude, designated here as $A_{rms}$. Therefore, the RMS amplitude of the corresponding sinusoid and the peak magnitude of the best-fitting square wave are the same and turn out to be about 71% of the amplitude ($A_{o\text{-}p}$) of the sine wave. Specifically, $A_{rms}$ is related to $A_{o\text{-}p}$ by the simple equation:

$$A_{rms} = 1/2^{1/2} \times A_{o\text{-}p}$$

$$= 1/1.414 \times A_{o\text{-}p}$$

$$= 0.707 \, A_{o\text{-}p} \qquad (3.1)$$

Likewise,

$$A_{o\text{-}p} = 1/0.707 \, A_{rms} = 1.414 \, A_{rms}$$

To apply Eq. 3.1 to a numeric example, assume that the peak sound pressure of a particular sinusoidal sound is observed to be 3 N/m². Then the RMS sound pressure is

$$0.707 \times 3 = 2.121 \text{ N/m}^2$$

What this result actually means is that the alternating pressure changes comprising this sound represent the same overall power as that of a constantly applied pressure of 2.121 N/m².

When using a microphone in conjunction with an oscilloscope to measure sound pressure (see Chapter 2, Fig. 2.1), it actually is more convenient to measure peak-to-peak amplitude. Although the oscilloscope provides a graphical display of the waveform of the sound, it is difficult to visually locate the zero axis of a sinusoid with accuracy. As long as the waveform is symmetrical around the zero axis, as it is in the sinusoid, $A_{o\text{-}p}$ may be determined by first measuring $A_{p\text{-}p}$, because, again, $A_{p\text{-}p} = 2 \, A_{o\text{-}p}$. Consequently,

$$A_{o\text{-}p} = A_{p\text{-}p}/2 = 0.5 \, A_{p\text{-}p} \qquad (3.2)$$

Even more difficult to obtain from measurements on the oscilloscope is an accurate estimate of RMS, at least by eye. However, using Eq. 3.1 and 3.2, this task is fairly simple, given $A_{p\text{-}p}$. Substituting $0.5 \, A_{p\text{-}p}$ (from Eq. 3.2) into Eq. 3.1,

$$A_{rms} = 0.707 \times 0.5 \, A_{p\text{-}p}$$

$$= 0.354 \, A_{p\text{-}p} \qquad (3.3)$$

Likewise, $A_{p\text{-}p} = A_{rms} \times 2.828$. From Eq. 3.3, an even simpler, although only approximate, equation can be written relating RMS and peak-to-peak values:

$$A_{rms} \approx 1/3 \, A_{p\text{-}p}$$

Conversely,

$$A_{p\text{-}p} \approx 3 \, A_{rms}$$

Thus, a pure tone with a peak-to-peak

sound pressure of 3 N/m² has an RMS sound pressure of approximately 1 N/m². Again, these relationships hold only for sinusoids.

## 2. Decibel Notation

### A. SOUND LEVELS

As important as the physical quantities of acoustic intensity and sound pressure are, the units of measure of these quantities, watts per m² or Newtons per m², respectively, are not frequently encountered in day-to-day work, whether in the research laboratory, the hearing clinic, industry, or the acoustics and hearing science literature. More often than not, the *decibel (dB)* is used. The decibel is simply the logarithm of the ratio of two quantities, as will be described in more detail momentarily. Ratios of like quantities are dimensionless; that is, the dimensions of the quantities cancel one another in the process of calculating a ratio. Therefore, the representation of sound magnitude in decibels has physical meaning only when there is an accompanying reference quantity, such as $2 \times 10^{-5}$ N/m² for sound pressure, unless the reference is clearly understood. Furthermore, an adjustment must be made in terminology to clearly flag the use of such a relative index of magnitude as the decibel. The measurement of acoustic intensity in decibels yields the *acoustic intensity level (IL)* of the sound, whereas the measurement of sound pressure in decibels yields the *sound pressure level (SPL)*. So, the flag is the word *level*. This may seem to complicate matters unnecessarily, yet the most common sound measuring device, known as the *sound level meter* (see Fig. 3.2), indicates sound magnitude in dB SPL, not units of sound pressure per se. The sound level meter thus detects the sound, measures it, compares it with a reference (generally, $2 \times 10^{-5}$ N/m² or 20 μPa [see below]), and then computes the decibel value. Incidentally, the specific measure-

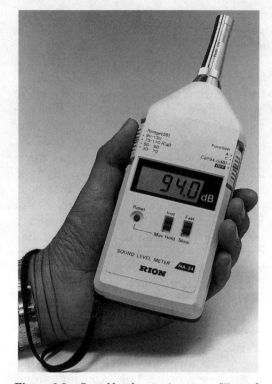

**Figure 3.2.** Sound level meter (courtesy of Scantek Inc., Silver Spring, MD).

ment performed in this process, more often than not, is that of the RMS magnitude of the sound. However, some types of sound level meters provide readouts of peak SPL, if not other measures (for example, impulse SPL, an RMS estimate for very brief sounds known as impulses, discussed in Section 10 below). Without specific knowledge of the reference measure, the "consumer" of the SPL or IL data would have no real sense of the actual magnitude of the sound. This will become apparent in the following three sections.

The use of decibel notation is widely accepted in acoustics, hearing science, and other disciplines, and it does offer some advantages over working with actual acoustic intensities, sound pressures, or other physical units of measure to which decibel notation has been applied (for example, voltage in electronics). Because of its widespread use, including in the clinical setting, it is worthwhile to consider the virtues of the decibel, its history of development, and the numeric transformation on which it is based—the logarithm.

The range of sound pressures over which the sense of hearing is operative is truly awesome. The greatest sound pressure that can be tolerated is greater than 10,000,000 times that of the least detectable sound pressure. This range is even more impressive when expressed in terms of acoustic intensity, namely $10^{14}$:1. (Recall, from Chapter 2, that $I \propto p^2$; more on this point below.) In addition to working with a range of sound pressures of $10^7$:1 or acoustic intensities of $10^{14}$:1, one frequently encounters very small numbers. The smallest sound pressure detectable by the normal human listener is about 0.00002 or $2 \times 10^{-5}$ N/m$^2$; the smallest acoustic intensity detectable is $10^{-12}$ w/m$^2$! Coping with such a wide range of numbers and numbers with so many decimal places generally has been perceived as simply too mind boggling. In decibels these awkward numbers often can be represented for practical purposes by integer values on a scale from 0 to 140. To make use of decibel notation and, indeed, to fully comprehend its meaning, it is necessary first to gain a basic understanding of the logarithm and an ability to transform numbers into logs. It is from its logarithmic origin that yet other advantages of the decibel emerge.

## B. THE LOGARITHM: FRIEND OR FOE?

For readers who have already encountered the logarithm, perhaps in high school or college math, and who may not remember the experience as a particularly pleasant one, this subsection could be entitled "The Wretched Logarithm." However, logs are not really all that bad, once you get to know them. This is especially true when one has a working knowledge of scientific notation. The reason is that the logarithm of a number, specifically the **common logarithm**, is the exponent to which the base 10 must be raised to equal

that number. Consequently, once the value of interest is translated into scientific notation, the exponent—the most significant part of the logarithm—is already known. For some numbers, that is all that is necessary. For example, the $log_{10}$ of 100 is 2, because $100 = 10^2$. Naturally, it is often necessary to deal with numbers that are not integer powers of 10, such as 120, 2,550, 897,000, etc.; correspondingly, the logs of such numbers are not integers, that is, whole numbers such as 1, 2, 3, etc. For this reason, the logarithm is traditionally described as having two parts—the **characteristic** and the **mantissa**; these parts are separated by a decimal point. The characteristic is always located to the left of the decimal point, whereas the mantissa is always to the right. For example,

$$log_{10}260 =$$

$$characteristic \rightarrow 2.4150 \leftarrow mantissa$$

In words, the log to the base 10 of 260 equals 2.4150. This is the same as saying that 260 equals $10^{2.4150}$.

Because the characteristic of the log and the power to which 10 must be raised (that is, the exponent) are the same, the process of finding the log of a number is greatly simplified if that number is first translated into scientific notation. This point is further illustrated by the examples presented in Table 3.1. It is easy to obtain the log of such numbers as 10, 100,

**TABLE 3.1.**

**Common Logarithms Compared to Numbers in Scientific Notation**

| Number | Scientific Notation | Logarithm[a] |
|---|---|---|
| 1 | $10^0$ | 0 |
| 10 | $10^1$ | 1 |
| 100 | $10^2$ | 2 |
| 1,000 | $10^3$ | 3 |
| 10,000 | $10^4$ | 4 |
| 100,000 | $10^5$ | 5 |
| 1,000,000 | $10^6$ | 6 |

[a] Specifically, the characteristic. For these examples, the mantissa is zero; that is, the logs are 0.0000, 1.0000, 2.0000, etc., when properly stated.

1000, and others involving positive whole powers of 10. But what of numbers between 1 and 10, 10 and 100, etc.? Take, for instance, a relatively simple number such as 20. Logic dictates that the log of this number must lie between 1 and 2, because 20 lies between 10 and 100, or $10^1$ and $10^2$, respectively. Enter the mantissa. The mantissa is the logarithm of the coefficient of the number in scientific notation. The mantissa assumes values from 0.0000 . . . to 0.9999 . . . ; these values are listed in Appendix C, along with a more detailed discussion of transforming numbers into logarithms. So, in the example of the number 20, written as $2 \times 10^1$ in scientific notation, the coefficient is 2.0. The mantissa is found by looking up this value in Appendix C (or any table of common logarithms) and is 0.30. (Note: the values in Appendix C are only approximate, because they have only two-place precision; however, this table will be adequate for the purposes of this text.) Because the characteristic of the log of 20 is 1, the log of 20 is $1 + 0.30 = 1.30$.

Herein lies one of the mysterious advantages that derive from the logarithmic basis of the decibel, alluded to earlier. The logarithm simplifies division and multiplication of long numbers, turning the calculation merely into addition and subtraction, respectively. Because logarithms are exponents, the laws of exponents apply here. Multiplication, for instance, requires that the logs of the numbers involved be added; in division, they are subtracted like the mathematical manipulation of exponents in scientific notation. (These computational rules are reviewed in more detail in Appendix C.) For example, the log of $5,500 \times 7,900,000$ is $3.74 + 6.90 = 10.64$. (Note: It is left to the reader to verify this. Lest one be gluttonous for punishment, the first step, again, is to convert each number into scientific notation.)

It is important to keep in mind that logarithmic transformation is not one of merely adding or even multiplying by a constant. Adding just shifts a value along the number scale; multiplying magnifies the number scale, as when converting from centimeters to millimeters, wherein 1 cm = 10 mm. After logarithmic transformation, the original number scale is "warped." As illustrated by Figure 3.3a, when the log is plotted against the number being transformed, the graph obtained is a curved line. For small numbers, say 1 to 10, the logarithmic value grows dramatically. For large numbers, such as 100 to 1000, the function levels off appreciably. Consequently, on a logarithmic scale, differences between two relatively small numbers are expanded, whereas differences between two relatively large numbers are compressed. The reason for this is also evident in Figure 3.3a; on a logarithmic scale, the interval from 50 to 100 is the same as the interval from 500 to 1000 (or 5,000 to 10,000, 50,000 to 100,000, etc.). Constant ratios on the "regular" or linear number scale, in this case 1:2, thus yield constant intervals on the log scale. Furthermore, a straight line graph in log coordinates (log-log) or semilog coordinates (log-linear), will not yield a straight line if graphed in linear coordinates or vice versa. Indeed, a completely different picture of the data may be obtained, as illustrated by Figure 3.3b. There can be advantages to such manipulations. For example, an otherwise curvilinear function could be reduced to a straight-line function, permitting more accurate interpolation between individual data points on a graph or perhaps even extrapolation to values beyond the available data. As long as logarithmically (or otherwise) transformed data are presented with full cognizance of the effects and implications of the transformation, these alterations can be applied justifiably and can be useful. The important point is that logs and other logarithmic numbers, such as the decibel, are fundamentally different from the numbers from which they were derived and must be treated accordingly. For example, the addition or subtraction of logarithmic numbers clearly

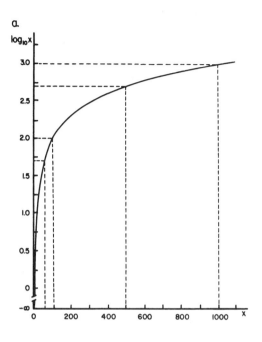

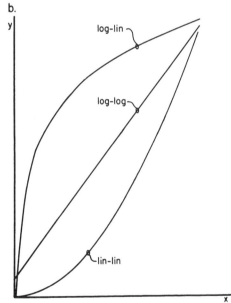

**Figure 3.3.** **a.** The graph of the common logarithm ($log_{10} x$) as a function of the number $x$. For $x < 1$, the log is negative and approaches negative infinity as $x$ approaches zero. **b.** Comparison of full logarithmic (*log-log*), semilogarithmic (*log-lin*), and linear (*lin-lin*) plots of the function, $y = x^2$. Each graph has been arbitrarily scaled to permit direct comparisons of their characteristic configurations.

implies something different from the addition or subtraction of regular numbers. Similarly, the relationship between two logarithmic numbers must be viewed in the proper perspective—additive increments in logarithmic units ($1 + 1 + 1 + \ldots [n$ times$] = n$) translates into multiplicative leaps and bounds along the underlying linear number scale ($10 \times 10 \times 10 \times \ldots [n$ times$] = 10^{[1 + 1 + 1 + \ldots]} = 10^n$)!

## C. THE HISTORIC DECIBEL

The history of the decibel can be traced to the early days of telephone communication. Telephone engineers quickly learned that the longer a telephone cable, the weaker is the signal at the output end. A measure of this attenuation effect of the cable subsequently was established and called the mile of standard cable, which was defined as the ratio of the power measured at the output of a cable $n$ miles long ($W_n$) to the power at the input ($W_r$):

$$log_{10}(W_n/W_r) = -0.1\, n \qquad (3.4)$$

By multiplying the log of the power ratio by 10, measurements of attenuation could be expressed directly in terms of $n$ miles of standard cable (rather than 10ths of miles). (Note: because the signal is being attenuated, the power ratio is inevitably less than 1. The log thus is always negative—hence the minus sign on the right-hand side of Eq. 3.4.) Although the name of this measure was changed and another unit of measure vied for acceptance on a world-wide basis,[1] the mile of standard cable, in essence, became firmly established and, ultimately, came to be known as the Bel in honor of Alexander Graham Bell. (Never mind that it is not spelled correctly; after all, it's the thought that counts.) However, in practice it was deemed to be more practical to use smaller units, leading to the emergence of the pop-

---

[1] A competitor of the decibel is the ***neper***, which is based on the natural or Naperian logarithm (*ln*, log to the base $e$) of the power ratio: $N = 1/2\, ln(I/I_o)$. (Note: $e \approx 2.7183$.) One neper equals about 8.7 dB. However, the neper has received little, if any, use by the hearing science community.

ular decibel (dB). 1 Bel = 10 dB; conversely, 1 dB = $10^{-1}$ Bel.

In addition to the issues of size and ranges of numbers encountered in practice and the computational advantages afforded by its logarithmic origins, the broad appeal of the decibel notational system in hearing science has yet another basis, stemming in part from a well-known law of psychophysics, a subarea of the discipline today known as sensory psychology (see Chapter 7). Equation 3.5 below reveals the basis for this seemingly innate "bonding" between the psychophysics of hearing and the decibel. This is Fechner's law:

$$R = C \, log \, S \qquad (3.5)$$

where $R$ is the magnitude of the response or sensation (such as hearing), $S$ is the magnitude of the stimulus (such as sound), and $C$ is a constant of proportionality. Because the decibel expresses stimulus magnitude in log units, Eq. 3.5 predicts a direct proportionality between the magnitude of hearing sensation (loudness) and acoustic intensity or sound pressure in decibels. As discussed later (Chapter 7), this is not exactly true, but Eq. 3.5 better approximates the relationship of loudness to sound intensity than does a direct proportionality. Furthermore, the decibel turns out to be approximately the smallest change in sound intensity that is discriminable by a listener with normal hearing. Although the prudence of using such an indirect measure as the decibel is always subject to debate, the decibel remains in common usage today.

## D. THE DECIBEL EQUATIONS

*The single most important aspect of decibel notation for understanding how to compute its value and the combining of decibel values is that the basic definition of the decibel is made from a reference of power (recall Eq. 3.4).* In the case of sound, the appropriate parameter is acoustic intensity. Again, acoustic intensity in decibels yields the measure known as the

(acoustic) intensity level (*IL*). In words, the IL of a sound in decibels is equal to 10 times the common log of the ratio of the measured or observed acoustic intensity ($I$) to the reference intensity ($I_r$). The factor of 10, again, simply changes Bels into decibels. The equation for computing IL thus is,

$$IL = 10 \, log_{10}(I/I_r) \text{ dB} \qquad (3.6)$$

Suppose that a given sound has an acoustic intensity of $10^{-6}$ w/m$^2$, and that it is desirable to state the IL of the sound in reference to $10^{-12}$ w/m$^2$ ($I_r$), the commonly used MKS reference. Entering these values into Eq. 3.6,

$$IL = 10 \, log_{10}[10^{-6} \text{ w/m}^2)/(10^{-12} \text{ w/m}^2)]$$
$$= 10 \, log_{10} 10^6$$
$$= 10 \times 6$$
$$= 60 \text{ dB}$$

Properly stated, the magnitude of the sound in question is 60 dB IL re $10^{-12}$ w/m$^2$.

It is important to underscore the fact that the decibel is a dimensionless number. It is merely a ratio. In fact, the term decibel ratio may be encountered from time to time, although it clearly is redundant to say "ratio" in the same breath as "decibel." In the above example, the units of measure, watts per m$^2$, in the numerator were canceled out by the same units in the denominator, leaving a ratio of $10^{-6}$: $10^{-12}$ or simply $10^6$. One might just as well, and with equal validity, express the quantity of jelly beans in one jar to that of a reference jar, for instance 20 dB re $10^2$ jelly beans (Note: It is left to the reader to verify that the observed jar contained 10,000 jelly beans.) In other words, there is nothing sacred about transforming numbers into ratios, taking the log of the ratio, and then multiplying the resultant by a constant. This is exactly what the computation of the decibel involves and nothing more. Again, the actual physical magnitude is preserved only by virtue of the stated reference. A 60-dB IL noise referenced to an acoustic intensity of $10^{-12}$ w/m$^2$ would clearly be more tolerable, indeed more "survivable," than one referenced to 1 w/m$^2$! Therefore, to say that a sound is 60 dB is totally meaningless unless the reference is given or understood. Fortunately, reference intensities (and sound pressures) have become fairly standard over the years. Nevertheless, it is advisable, and just good science etiquette, to state explicitly the reference intensity used at least once in any given situation. It also should be noted that in hearing science the word *level* implies decibel values and should not be used in the context of direct measures of acoustic intensity (watts per m$^2$) or sound pressure (Newtons per m$^2$).

Now, the measure of interest for most practical applications is not IL but, rather, SPL. At first glance, it might seem reasonable to simply plug the observed and reference sound pressures into Eq. 3.6 to obtain SPL. However, it is here that a certain physical lawfulness creeps into the situation, even though the decibel is a dimensionless number. In Chapter 2, it was learned that acoustic intensity is equal to the square of the effective sound pressure divided by the characteristic impedance (Eq. 2.7). Consequently, $I \propto p^2$. From this relationship, it follows that it is the sound pressures squared, and not the sound pressures per se, that must be entered into Eq. 3.6 to compute SPL. On the other hand, squaring numbers is somewhat computationally intensive, so it is useful to derive a more convenient equation for computing SPL. The derivation commences, again, by giving deference to the relationship between acoustic intensity and sound pressure, but for both the observed and reference values, as follows:

$$I = p^2/Z_c$$

and

$$I_r = p_r^2/Z_c r$$

However, the reference and observed

sound pressures would presumably be measured over the same specific impedance, that of air, under the same conditions. It thus may be assumed that $Z_c = Z_c r$. Therefore,

$$I_r = p_r^2/Z_c$$

Consequently, the intensity ratio may be translated into a pressure ratio, as follows:

$$I/I_r = (p^2/Z_c) / (p_r^2/Z_c)$$
$$= p^2/p_r^2$$
$$= (p/p_r)^2$$

Substituting the sound pressure ratio into Equation 3.6:

$$SPL = 10 \: log_{10} \: (p/p_r)^2$$
$$= 2 \times 10 \: log_{10} \: (p/p_r) \quad (3.7)$$
$$= 20 \: log_{10} \: (p/p_r) \: \text{dB}$$

This solution calls on the law of logarithms (Appendix C) that states that the log of a number raised to a power is equal to the log of that number multiplied by the power (that is, $log x^n = n log x$).

Suppose that a sound pressure of 2 N/m$^2$ is observed. To determine the SPL in reference to $2 \times 10^{-5}$ N/m$^2$ (again, the basic MKS reference sound pressure), the appropriate values are entered into Eq. 3.7:

$$SPL = 20 \: log_{10} \: [(2 \times 10^0 \: \text{N/m}^2)$$
$$/(2 \times 10^{-5} \: \text{N/m}^2)]$$
$$= 20 \: log_{10} \: (1 \times 10^5)$$
$$= 20 \: log_{10} \: 10^5$$
$$= 20 \times 5$$
$$= 100 \: \text{dB}$$

(bearing in mind that the units of measure cancel out). Stated completely, the observed sound pressure is 100 dB SPL re $2 \times 10^{-5}$ N/m$^2$. It is worth mentioning again, at this juncture, that 1 N/m$^2$ = 1 Pascal (Pa). It thus could be stated that this sound is 100 dB SPL re $2 \times 10^{-5}$ Pa.

Alternatively, $2 \times 10^{-5}$ Pa can be expressed as 20 $\mu$Pa. In either case, the same decibel value is obtained.

The MKS reference sound pressure translates in the CGS system into $2 \times 10^{-4}$ d/cm$^2$. (This is because 1 N/m$^2$ = 10 d/cm; consequently, 1 d/cm$^2$ = 0.1 N/m$^2$.) The CGS reference is frequently encountered in the older literature and for many years was the most widely used reference. An even older term is the *microbar*, which is equivalent to the dyne per cm$^2$. Thus 2 $\times 10^4$ d/cm$^2$ = $2 \times 10^{-4}$ microbars.

Another example of decibel calculation might be helpful at this point. A sound is observed to have a sound pressure of 3 $\times 10^{-2}$ d/cm$^2$. What is the SPL re $2 \times 10^{-4}$ d/cm$^2$? (Note: it hopefully is vividly clear by now that the decibel is a dimensionless number and that this is because the units of measure cancel out; from here on, the units of measure will not be shown in the equations for the sake of simplicity.) Using Eq. 3.7 once more,

$$SPL = 20 \ log_{10} \ (3 \times 10^{-2})/(2 \times 10^{-4})$$

$$= 20 \ log_{10} \ (1.5 \times 10^2)$$

$$= 20 \times 2.18$$

$$= 43.6 \approx 44 \ dB$$

Another useful exercise, both for purposes of gaining direct experience with computing SPLs and for use when studying some of the early hearing science literature, is to determine what SPL 1 microbar represents in reference to: 1) 2 $\times 10^{-4}$ d/cm$^2$, and 2) $2 \times 10^{-5}$ N/m$^2$. Answer: 1) 74 dB, and 2) 94 dB. (The details of the computation and the mystery of the difference of 20 between the two values are left to the reader to discover).

At this juncture, ILs and SPLs are likely to be abstract. A sense of the size of any given decibel value can be grasped only through experience with measured ILs or SPLs. For purposes of orientation, then, Table 3.2 provides a list of various sounds in the environment and their typical sound levels. By *typical*, it is meant

**TABLE 3.2.**
**Sound Level of Some Environmental Sounds**

| Sound Level (dB SPL[a] or dB IL[b]) | Sound |
|---|---|
| 0 | Softest sound human can hear |
| 10 | Normal breathing |
| 20 | Leaves rustling in a breeze |
| 30 | Very soft whisper |
| 40 | Quiet residential community |
| 50 | Department store |
| 60 | Average speaking voice |
| 70 | Inside moving car |
| 80 | Loud music from a radio |
| 90 | City traffic |
| 100 | Subway train in Philadelphia |
| 110 | Loud thunder |
| 120 | Amplified rock 'n roll band in discotheque |
| 130 | Machine gun fire at close range |
| 140 | Jet engine at takeoff |
| 180 | Space rocket at blastoff |

[a] re: $2 \times 10^{-5}$ N/m$^2$ or Pa [MKS]; 20 $\mu$Pa [MKS]; $2 \times 10^{-4}$ d/cm$^2$ [CGS].
[b] re: $10^{-12}$ w/m$^2$ [MKS]; $10^{-16}$ w/cm$^2$ [CGS].

that these values are average levels based on measurements made under conditions in which these sounds are usually encountered unless otherwise specified.

## E. Decibel SPL Versus Decibel IL

Much, indeed too much, is often made of the fact that if the same ratio is entered into Eq. 3.6 and 3.7, the decibel SPL obtained will be twice the decibel IL. Care must be taken that this fact is not misinterpreted to mean that $n$ dB IL = $2n$ dB SPL. The 1:2 numerical difference in the two equations does not mean that a certain sound of 60 dB IL has an SPL of 120 dB. The SPL actually will be the same, given corresponding references; for example, in the MKS system, $10^{-12}$ w/m$^2$ and $2 \times 10^{-5}$ N/m$^2$, and in the CGS system, $10^{-16}$ w/cm$^2$ and $2 \times 10^{-4}$ d/cm$^2$.

It must be borne in mind that sound pressure is not independent of acoustic intensity. It takes energy to produce force. Similarly, it takes acoustic intensity to develop sound pressure. Therefore, as discussed in Chapter 2, an acoustic intensity of $10^{-12}$ w/m$^2$ in air produces a sound pressure of $2 \times 10^{-5}$ N/m$^2$. Because acoustic intensity is proportional to sound pressure squared, then, conversely, $p \propto I^{1/2}$. For example, if the ratio $I/I_o$ were $10^4$, then the ratio of $p/p_o$ would have to be $(10^4)^{1/2} = 10^2$. (Note: The square root of an exponent equals the exponent divided by 2.) Entering the ratio $10^4$ into Eq. 3.6 for decibel IL,

$$10 \, log_{10} \, 10^4 = 10 \times 4 = 40 \text{ dB } IL$$

Entering the pressure ratio of $10^2$ into Eq. 3.7 for decibel SPL,

$$20 \, log_{10} \, 10^2 = 20 \times 2 = 40 \text{ dB } SPL$$

In other words, $n$ dB IL = $n$ dB SPL! This is true, again, as long as the respective IL and SPL references correspond. Once more, the importance of remembering that the decibel is defined in terms of the power ratio (Eq. 3.6) is manifest. Because the computational equation for SPL was derived from this fundamental definition, the 20 in the decibel SPL equation (vs. 10 in the decibel IL equation) again merely spares the user from squaring the sound pressures during the computation, compliments of the law of logarithms! Therefore, the fact that the same ratio plugged into the SPL equation (Eq. 3.7) yields a number twice that obtained using the IL equation (Eq. 3.6) is of no practical consequence.

## F. The Decibel in Reverse and Other Considerations

On occasion, it may be desirable to determine the observed sound pressure, or acoustic intensity, given the SPL, or IL of the sound. This requires working back through the appropriate decibel equation (Eq. 3.7 or 3.6, respectively) to solve for the observed sound pressure ($p$) or acoustic intensity ($I$), as the case may be. Given an SPL of 80 dB (re $2 \times 10^{-5}$ N/m$^2$), for example, the observed sound pressure is obtained by plugging the known values into Eq. 3.7 and solving for $p$:

$$80 = 20 \, log_{10} \, [p/(2 \times 10^{-5})]$$

Dividing both sides of the equation by 20,

$$4 = log_{10} \, [p/(2 \times 10^{-5})]$$

Finding the antilog of both sides of the equation,

$$antilog \, 4 = 10^4 = p/(2 \times 10^{-5})$$

Multiply both sides by the reference $SP$,

$$p = (2 \times 10^{-5}) \times 10^4$$
$$= 2 \times 10^{-1} \text{ or } 0.2 \text{ N/m}^2$$

Similarly, it is possible to solve for the observed acoustic intensity. For example, given an IL of 80 dB (re $10^{-12} \, w/m^2$),

$$80 = 10 \, log_{10} \, [I/(10^{-12})]$$
$$8 = log_{10} \, [I/(10^{-12})]$$
$$antilog \, 8 = 10^8 = I/(10^{-12})$$

Therefore,

$$I = 10^{-12} \times 10^8 = 10^{-4} \, w/m^2$$

Such problems underscore the necessity of knowing the reference. To say that the sound is 80 dB, for instance, is only to say that it was $10^4$ times larger in sound pressure, or $10^8$ times larger in acoustic intensity, than some other sound—that "phantom" sound is the reference. Once more, it is evident that the decibel level of a sound alone provides no concrete information concerning the real magnitude of that sound!

This is not to say that the decibel, as a ratio, cannot be informative. It, indeed, may be the ratio that itself is of primary interest for some purposes. As noted earlier, the decibel can be used to specify increases or decreases in the magnitude of a signal or sound regardless of the absolute values involved. An increase is called **gain**. Take the example of a sound picked up by a microphone and amplified by a public address system to yield a 100-fold increase in sound pressure. This increase could be expressed as a sound pressure gain of 40 dB. This figure is obtained by simply entering the ratio of 100:1 (which is the same as 100/1, or simply 100) into Eq. 3.7:

$$20 \, log_{10} \, 100 \, = \, 40 \text{ dB}$$

Also, as noted earlier, when a decrease is observed at the output of a certain system, it is called a **loss** or attenuation. Had the sound pressure in the example above been decreased by a factor of 100, as might happen when measuring sound on the opposite side of a wall from the source, then it could be stated that the sound pressure was attenuated 40 dB or that there was a 40-dB attenuation. Consequently, a basic specification of a hearing aid is its gain, in decibels. Similarly, ear muffs and ear plugs, used for ear protection against excessive exposures to sounds that may be hazardous, are characterized by their attenuation values, specified in decibels.

Now, were a gain or loss measured in acoustic intensity (more generally, a power gain or power loss, respectively), then Eq. 3.6 would be used. It is true that a power gain or loss of 100:1 would represent a change of only 20 dB. However, a power gain (for example) of 100:1 does not yield a pressure gain of 100:1; rather, the corresponding pressure gain would be $100^{1/2} = 10$. Plugging this value into Eq. 3.7 for the pressure ratio yields a result of 20 dB.

The subject of attenuation raises the possibility that it may be necessary to work with sound pressure or acoustic intensity ratios that are less than 1. This occurs if the observed value is less than the reference. If the ratio is less than 1, the logarithm of that ratio will be negative yielding a negative decibel value. Such an outcome is expected for attenuation, reflecting a decrease in sound magnitude. For example, assume the observed sound pressure is 0.5 N/m² and the reference sound pressure is 1 W/m²:

$$20 \, log \, (0.5/1) \, = \, 20 \, log \, (5 \times 10^{-1})$$
$$= \, 20 \times -0.3 \, = \, -6 \text{ dB}$$

Working with negative logarithms is a bit cumbersome, and it is possible to avoid this problem by inverting the ratio to put the larger value in the numerator. By doing so, the ratio will be a number larger than 1, yielding a positive logarithm. The only catch is that once the result is obtained, that is, the decibel value is computed, a minus sign must be placed in front of the equation:

$$-20 \, log \, (1/0.5) \, = \, -20 \, log \, 2$$
$$= \, -20 \times 0.3 \, = \, -6 \text{ dB}$$

The important point that should emerge from this discussion is that a negative decibel value does not indicate a nonsensical situation. It simply means that the observed value was less than the reference. Indeed, a value of 0 dB would be calculated if the observed and reference values are identical. So, 0 SPL or 0 dB IL does not mean that there was no sound. It simply implies the log of the ratio of the observed and reference values was 0, or saying it differently, that the ratio of these two values was 1. Furthermore, the fact that sounds less than 0 dB SPL (re 2 × $10^{-5}$ N/m²) or 0 dB IL (re 1 × $10^{-12}$ w/m²) may be inaudible is irrelevant and does not alter the fact that sound energy is still present. Once more, the importance of the reference sound pressure (or acoustic intensity) is manifested. Clearly, a reference could be chosen such that a 0-dB SPL sound would be infinitesimally small or excruciatingly loud! It is simply a matter of convention or preference.

## 3. Octave Notation

Frequency also may be scaled or transformed. In fact, rather than plotting frequency in linear coordinates, the usual practice is to use a logarithmic frequency scale. The result of this transformation may be appreciated when one considers that, on a logarithmic scale, 1 kHz falls approximately in the middle of the range of human hearing of roughly 20 to 20,000

Hz. This is in sharp contrast with where the arithmetic center of this range would fall, namely at approximately 10,000 Hz. Just as the magnitude of a sound can be expressed in decibels, there are notational systems for frequency. A common one, whose origin is found in music, is **octave notation**. The audiogram, that is, the chart on which measures of hearing sensitivity are plotted for clinical purposes, is scaled along the frequency axis in terms of octave intervals or, simply, octaves. For any frequency, $f_o$, the frequency that is one octave above it, is equal to $2f_o$. The frequency that is two octaves above it is equal to $2 \times 2f_o = 4f_o$. The frequency three octaves above is $2 \times 2 \times 2f_o = 8f_o$, etc. This scheme represents a progression in powers of 2. In general,

$$f_n = 2^n f_o \qquad (3.8)$$

where $f_n$ is the $n$th octave frequency, $n$ is the number of the octave, and $f_o$ is the reference frequency. For instance, the fourth octave frequency of 500 Hz (that is, the frequency that is four octaves above 500 Hz) is

$$f_4 = 2^4 \times 500$$
$$= 2 \times 2 \times 2 \times 2 \times 500$$
$$= 16 \times 500$$
$$= 8000 \text{ Hz}$$

Equation 3.8 is equally valid for finding octave frequencies below the reference frequency. In this case, the octave number, $n$, is negative. For example, the frequency that is two octaves below 500 Hz is

$$f_{-1} = 2^{-2} \times 500 = 1/4 \times 500 = 125 \text{ Hz}$$

Furthermore, Eq. 3.8 can readily accommodate fractional octaves, such as finding the frequency that is half an octave above 1000 Hz:

$$f_{1/2} = 2^{1/2} \times 1000 = 1.414 \times 1000$$
$$= 1414 \text{ Hz}$$

Fractional octaves can be troublesome unless there is strict adherence to Eq. 3.8. In the example above, it is tempting to assume that 1500 Hz must be the frequency half an octave above 1000 Hz, because the frequency that is one whole octave above 1000 Hz is 2000 Hz, and half the difference is 500 Hz. Clearly, this is not the case. It also may be tempting to multiply the reference by the octave number. This, for example, would suggest that the frequency five octaves above 100 Hz is 500 Hz when, in fact, it is $2^5 \times 100 \text{ Hz} = 3200 \text{ Hz}$. The errors in computation that would accrue if one gives way to these temptations, can be averted only with faithful use of Eq. 3.8, bearing in mind that the number of the octave is an exponent of 2 and not merely a coefficient (or multiplier) of the reference frequency. Similarly, the frequency which is half an octave below 1000 Hz is not 750 Hz, but rather is 707 Hz:

$$f_{-1/2} = 2^{-1/2} \times 1000$$
$$= (1/2^{1/2}) \times 1000$$
$$= (1/1.414) \times 1000$$
$$= 0.707 \times 1000$$
$$= 707 \text{ Hz}$$

Using Eq. 3.8, the octave interval between two frequencies also may be determined. For example, the octave interval between the frequencies of 2000 and 3000 Hz can be calculated by entering the known values into Eq. 3.8,

$$3000 = 2^n \times 2000$$

The object is to solve for $n$. Transposing the equation above:

$$2^n \times 2000 = 3000$$
$$2^n = 3000/2000 = 1.5$$

Now, things get a bit rough. Solving for $n$ means finding the 1.5th root of 2. This can be done with some pocket calculators or mathematical tables; otherwise, the easiest solution is to use logarithms. Given $2^n = 1.5$, it is also true that $log\ 2^n = log\ 1.5$. Invoking the laws of logarithms (Appendix C),

$$n \ log \ 2 = log \ 1.5$$

$$n = (log \ 1.5)/(log \ 2) = 0.18/0.30 = 0.6$$

Therefore, 3000 Hz is 0.6 an octave above 2000 Hz, whereas one octave above 2000 Hz is 4000 Hz.

It should be evident that octave intervals of frequency do not represent equal frequency intervals. To explain, the arithmetic difference between 1 and 2 kHz and that between 2 and 3 kHz are equal: $2k - 1k = 3k - 2k = 1k$. Although, these three frequencies are separated by 1-kHz intervals, they are not separated by equal octave intervals. The interval between 1 and 2 kHz is one octave, but between 2 and 3 kHz there is only 0.6 octave, as was demonstrated above. Intervals on the octave scale, on the other hand, represent equal ratios: 0.5 to 1.0 kHz = 1 octave and 5 to 10 kHz = 1 octave, etc. Clearly, the arithmetic differences between 1.0 and 0.5 kHz and between 10 and 5 kHz are not equal. Herein lies the relationship between the decibel and octave notational systems. Both are logarithmic.[2] The critical point is that, like the decibel, the octave is a dimensionless number!

It is worth noting that there is also a notational system for frequency that uses a base of 10—the **decade**. For instance, the frequency that is 1 decade above 1 kHz is $10^1 = 10$ kHz; 2 decades above is $10^2 = 100$ kHz; or $n$ decades above, $10^n$ kHz. Still, for most applications in hearing sci-

ence, the octave, which obviously is a much smaller unit, provides more practical intervals with which to work. Indeed, fractional octave intervals are common, such as one third of an octave.

## 4. Types of Sounds

With these preliminary matters concerning the quantification of sound out of the way, it is possible to consider the characteristics of various kinds of sound. Thus far, most of the discussion has focused on the simplest type of sound, the **pure tone**—the sound that results from sinusoidal disturbances in the medium. However, one is bombarded daily by a myriad of sounds; a variety of sounds can be created in the laboratory, as well. Yet, in the simplest system, all sounds might be classified as either **tones** or **noises**. However, it soon will become apparent that this distinction is not always easy to make. There are other classification schemes that lend themselves to fewer ambiguities and more rigorous definitions, although no system is likely to be perfect or completely adequate for all applications. One approach is to classify sounds as either periodic or aperiodic. Another is to use the categories of periodic, transient, or random. Here, a combination of all these schemes will be used.

As learned in Chapter 1, periodic quantities repeat themselves at regular and equal intervals in time. For a signal to be periodic, it must be (for reasons that will become more apparent below) effectively continuous. But, there are (effectively) continuous signals and sounds that are **aperiodic**—nonperiodic—and thus do not demonstrate a fundamental period. One class of sounds that are aperiodic are random noises. The concept of **random** will be elaborated in Noises below; the general idea is that from instant to instant the magnitude is a chance occurrence and is predictable only in a statistical sense, as exemplified by the prediction that one

---

[2] Whereas the decibel is based on a logarithmic transformation using the base 10, the octave uses the base 2. From the laws of logarithm, $log_a x = q$, which means that $a^q = x$. In other words, the log of a number is the exponent to which the base must be raised to equal that number, in this case $x$. Equation 3.8 may be rewritten as follows: $2^n = f_n/f_o$. Therefore, $log_2(f_n/f_o) = n$, or $n = log_2(f_n/f_o)$. The latter expression bears an unmistakable resemblance to the decibel equation, although it is more directly comparable computationally to the Bel. Although there is no "decioctave," there is the semitone, which is 1/12th octave. The semitone is a division of the musical scale; on the piano, for example, it is the interval represented by adjacent keys (black or white). Of course, the decibel is 1/10th of a Bel. Because $1/12 = 0.125 \approx 0.1$ (or 1/10), the semitone thus represents a comparable ratio interval in the frequency domain to that of the decibel in the intensity domain.

has a 50/50 chance of observing heads on the toss of a coin. This is in contrast to a periodic quantity, such as sinusoid, for which the time history is directly and entirely specified. A periodic sound thus is completely predictable. **Transients** also are completely predictable (that is, in a literal sense), but they are signals and sounds that are not continuous. They also are aperiodic, although they may be produced by turning a periodic signal on and off (forming a tone burst, as discussed in Section 9 below). Some familiar transients are speech consonants, such as [t], [k], or [p], and a snap of the fingers. These examples also underscore the fact that everyday sounds tend to be transient or otherwise time varying and, often, impulsive.

The subject of transient sounds will be discussed extensively in Sections 9 and 10. For the moment, however, attention will be directed toward steady-state sounds and, initially (once more), to the sounds commonly called tones. Although not the most representative of sounds in the environment, they are of keen interest in the environments of the laboratory and clinic. It is on the foundation of understanding of the synthesis and analysis of these simpler sounds that an understanding of the nature and makeup of the other types of sounds can be built.

## A. TONES: PURE VERSUS COMPLEX

Tonal sounds, or simply **tones**, represent a broad class of sounds, of which the **pure tone** is the simplest example. The pure tone, again, is characterized by the sinusoidal function, which clearly qualifies as a periodic waveform. As noted in Chapter 1, however, a function need not be sinusoidal to be periodic (see Chapter 1, Fig. 1.10, and Fig. 3.4b and other examples below). More to the point here, the sound need not be characterized by a single sinusoidal function to be a tone. Tones also may be complex. **Complex tones** contain more than one frequency component

and may be either periodic or aperiodic.[3] The resultant waveform appears remarkably different from the sinusoidal functions of the individual frequency components comprising the complex tone. When a (pure) tone of one frequency is added to one of another frequency, the waveform obtained is the sum of the magnitudes of the components at each instant in time. Figure 3.4a illustrates the addition of pure tones of 100 and 300 Hz. In this case, both sounds start at a phase of 0° and the 300-Hz component has half the amplitude of the 100-Hz tone. The phases of the different constituents of a complex sound are very important in determining its waveform. Figure 3.4b shows the result of adding the same two components as in Figure 3.4a, but the 300-Hz tone is started at a phase of −90° relative to the starting phase of the 100-Hz tone. A familiar example of a complex tone frequently encountered in the environment is the dial tone of the telephone, whose waveform is shown in Figure 3.5. It is composed of two pure tones (350 and 440 Hz in this case) of the same amplitude.

As complex tones go, those illustrated

---

[3] Many complex tones encountered are periodic. Thus, regardless of how complex such sounds may be, there is always an inherent, fundamental periodicity in the magnitude-versus-time function. The individual components of periodic complex tones have frequencies such that one divided by another forms a rational fraction; namely, there are integer numbers in the numerator and denominator. The signal illustrated in Figure 3.4 is periodic (300/100 or 3/1). Any sound similar in form and genesis to a sustained vowel or that produced by a string and wind instrument is periodic, because there is a fundamental frequency that excites the other frequencies. All frequency components of such sounds also are harmonically related.[4] (See also Section 3.11.) On the other hand, real-world events are not limited to neat numbers. Two components, for instance, may come together to form a complex wherein the ratio of their frequencies is not rational, and the waveform will never repeat itself precisely. The gist of what an aperiodic complex tone (two frequency components) might look like is provided by the dial tone, illustrated in Figure 3.5, even though it is, in the strictest sense, periodic (440/350 or 44/35 is rational). Nevertheless, within the analysis window of the figure, it does not repeat itself exactly or in detail. An example of a truly aperiodic two-tone complex would be one whose frequencies divided by one another equals $\pi$ (3.141 . . .). The familiar fraction, 22/7 (which is rational), is merely an approximate to $\pi$ (which, again, is irrational).

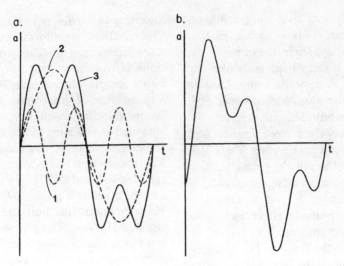

**Figure 3.4.** Addition of two pure tones, represented by curves *1* and *2*, to form a complex tone (curve *3*). The frequency of tone *1* is three times that of tone *2*, for example, 300 and 100 Hz, respectively. **a.** Both tones are initiated at a phase of 0°. **b.** The higher tone (*1*) has a starting phase of −90° in reference to that of the lower tone (*2*). All other parameters are the same.

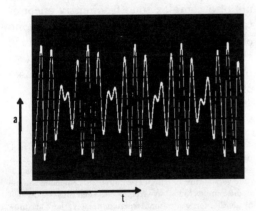

**Figure 3.5.** Oscillograph of the dial tone of a telephone.

in Figures 3.4 and 3.5 are fairly simple. Less-simple examples could be cited, such as sustained vowel sounds (Chapter 1, Fig. 1.9) and the sounds produced by string and wind (musical) instruments. Nevertheless, a complex tone, regardless of its complexity, can be broken down into its pure tone constituents. This process is called ***Fourier analysis*** (attributed to the physicist and mathematician Jean Fourier). Fourier analysis is a very powerful method and will be elaborated on in the section to follow. The inverse process of analysis is ***synthesis***. It follows from Fourier's principle that a tone of any complexity may be produced or synthesized by the appropriate combination of discrete pure tones. It thus could be stated that the complex tones shown in Figure 3.4, *a* and *b*, were synthesized by combining tones of 100 and 300 Hz. Consider for a moment what might happen if a sound were synthesized by the addition of many tones together, for instance, one every 100 Hz from 100 to 10,000 Hz. Although intuitively the resultant sound might not be expected to have a tonal quality, it indeed would be a complex tone. It would even be periodic (repeating itself every 1/100 sec = 10 msec).

## B. NOISES

The term ***noise*** and sounds judged as being noise can be only broadly defined. Psychologically speaking, noise is any undesirable sound or signal. The whine of an airplane engine, a "blood-curdling" scream, or a blaring auto horn all would be considered noise, yet they all meet the definition of complex tones. Many complex

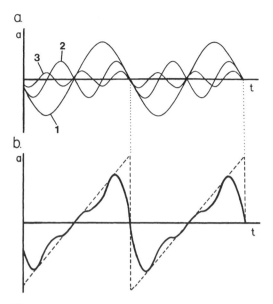

**Figure 3.6.** Rudiments of the synthesis of the sawtooth wave. **a.** Three lowest frequency components of the sawtooth (*dashed line graph* in **b**). Curve *1* is the graph of the fundamental, whose period and amplitude are twice that of curve **2** and three times that of curve *3*. **b.** Sum of the components *1-3* (*solid curve*). Adding more and more components of the appropriate amplitude, frequency, and phase, the resulting function increasingly approaches the sawtooth waveform, yet the overall shape is well established merely with the addition of just the first three components. The period of the sawtooth is clearly that of the fundamental frequency component.

3.6*b*. Therefore, the basic definition of noise and the common usage of this word make this classification a rather subjective business. However, in acoustics and hearing science there are sounds of particular interest that can be defined rather precisely. By equating these sounds with the term *noise* (and by any standard they would be considered noise), then a reasonably straightforward operational definition of noise is possible.

A specific kind of noise that has proved to be very useful in hearing science is ***white noise***. Just as white light contains all colors, white noise contains all tones, in a manner of speaking. The graph of a white noise is shown in Figure 3.7. To the listener, it has a hissing quality, which can be roughly simulated by making a sustained [s] sound. White noise also can be analyzed in terms of its constituent fre-

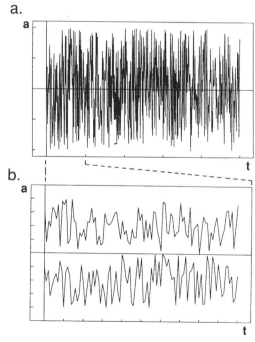

**Figure 3.7. a.** White noise. **b.** Time-expanded "slices" of the noise at beginning (*top panel*) and end (*bottom panel*) of the epoch graphed in **a**, demonstrating random and aperiodic nature of this noise. (Note: magnitude scale in **b** is ½ with respect to [full-blown] tracing in **a**.)

tones may be deemed noises by virtue of their perceived quality. ***Sawtooth noise***, once widely used for masking in clinical hearing measurement (see Chapter 7), is actually a complex tone. This sound is produced by driving an earphone with an electrical signal known as the sawtooth wave, the function of which is graphed in Figure 3.6*b*. The sound produced has a buzz-saw quality. Despite the rugged characteristic of its waveform, it can be synthesized by successively adding the appropriate pure tones at the proper amplitude and phases. Indeed, the sawtooth waveform is approximated merely by the addition of the first three components, as shown in Figure

quency components. A white noise can be generated covering the same range of frequencies as the hypothetical complex tone mentioned previously, namely 100 to 10,000 Hz. However, white noise is made up of components at every frequency and is not periodic. It thus does not contain equal intervals at which the magnitude as a function of time (Fig. 3.7) assumes equal values, beyond that which occurrs purely by chance.

One way to obtain white noise is to generate *Gaussian noise* (sometimes called thermal noise). In the ideal Gaussian noise, there is an infinite number of frequency components that are, on the average (that is, in the long run), equal in amplitude. However, phase varies randomly across frequency, causing the magnitude to fluctuate randomly from instant to instant. The term *Gaussian* refers to the underlying distribution of instantaneous magnitudes over time; namely, it follows the normal probability density function (the familiar bell-shaped curve in statistics). This means that the occurrence of a given magnitude at a given instant in time is strictly a matter of chance. This noise is produced constantly in air by the random bombardment of the molecules of the medium against one another, a phenomenon known as *Brownian movement*. Although Brownian motion is inaudible, it can be detected by a sensitive microphone. This type of noise also is usually evident in electronic equipment, such as the hissing sound produced by an FM receiver when it is tuned to a frequency at which there is no station broadcasting. It should be noted here that *Gaussian* and *white* are not synonymous terms, although they are often used interchangably. White noise is a more generic term; Gaussian noise is a specific term. The only underlying assumption about white noise is that within a specified frequency range the magnitudes of the individual frequency components of the noise are independent of frequency (again, in the long run).

Gaussian noise thus is a specific type of noise; there are other forms of random noise. If the sinusoid represents a pure tone, then Gaussian noise might be thought of as pure noise. Neither sound occurs naturally, although there are sounds, both in nature and man made, that are reasonable approximations of these ideal sounds. More typically, though, sounds in the environment tend to be more erratic and complex in their frequency composition and less easy to describe precisely.

## 5. Intensity and SPLs of Complex Sounds

### A. Adding Sound Levels: When 2 and 2 May Not Equal 4

When two or more sounds are combined, one obviously can simply calculate the resultant magnitude, given the acoustic intensities (watts per $m^2$) or sound pressures (Newtons per $m^2$) of the individual sounds. When dealing with decibel values, though, the determination of the resultant level must conform to the fact that the numbers involved here are logarithmic! Specifically, simple addition of intensity or SPLs will not work. Remember, when logarithmic numbers are added, the underlying numbers on the linear scale multiply. Here, so to speak, 2 plus 2 does not equal 4! Two sounds of 60 dB SPL thus do not form a sound of 120 dB SPL. The implication of such a result would be that combining the two sounds involved the multiplication of the intensity of the first sound by that of the second. This just is not the case. Consequently, the calculation of the resultant level for (specifically) uncorrelated sounds, must reflect the actual sum of the acoustic intensities of the individual sounds. By uncorrelated it is meant, in effect, that the individual sounds are independently generated, such as in the case of traffic noise or the sound of a group of musicians playing, etc.

The principle here is very important and bears restatement: *the resultant of the summation of uncorrelated sounds is the sum of the acoustic intensities of the sounds.* This means that to find the resultant sound level, given two or more sounds, it is necessary to work back through the decibel equation to solve for the observed acoustic intensity ($I$), given the IL and reference intensity ($I_r$). The acoustic intensities of the individual sounds can be added and this sum used to determine the total IL. Assume two sounds of 60 dB IL re $10^{-12}$ w/m$^2$ are added. The acoustic intensity of each sound would be:

$$60 = 10 \: log \: (I/10^{-12} \text{ w/m}^2)$$

$$6 = log \: (I/10^{-12} \text{ w/m}^2)$$

$$10^6 = I/10^{-12} \text{ w/m}^2$$

$$I = 10^{6 \times 10 - 12} \text{ w/m}^2 = 10^{-6} \text{ w/m}^2$$

Now adding two of these sounds:

$$1 \times 10^{-6} \text{ w/m}^2 + 1 \times 10^{-6} \text{ w/m}^2$$
$$= 2 \times 10^{-6} \text{ w/m}^2$$

and converting this sum back into IL:

$$IL = 10 \: log \: [(2 \times 10^{-6} \text{ w/m}^2)$$
$$/(1 \times 10^{-12} \text{ w/m}^2)]$$
$$= 10 \: log \: (2 \times 10^6)$$
$$= 10 \times 6.3$$
$$= 63 \text{ dB}$$

Thus, two sounds each of 60 dB IL yield a total sound of 63 dB IL. The total SPL will be the same. However, when starting with SPLs, it will be necessary to solve for the sound pressure of each component ($p$) and to compute the total sound pressure as follows:

$$P_{total} = (p_1{}^2 + p_2{}^2 + ...p_n{}^2)^{1/2}$$

where $p_1{}^2, p_2{}^2$, etc. are the individual RMS sound pressures. The reason for this rigmarole is that, again, $I$ is proportional to $p^2$, not to $p$. (It is left the reader to prove that, using the equation for $p_{total}$, the total SPL of two 60-dB SPL sounds is, indeed, 63 dB.)

Fortunately, when combining two sounds of equal ILs or SPLs, a much simpler approach is possible. The resultant acoustic intensity must be twice the acoustic intensity of either sound alone ($I + I = 2I$). It follows that the decibel increase from combining the two sounds can be computed by simply entering 2 into Eq. 3.6. In other words, the ratio of the intensities is 2:1. Therefore,

$$\varDelta L = 10 \: log_{10} 2 = 10 \times 0.301 \approx 3 \text{ dB}$$

where L is the change in the level resulting from the addition of the two sounds. Consistent with the finding in the example above, therefore, the addition of two sounds of 60 dB IL would yield 60 + 3 = 63 dB IL. The same would be true for two sounds of equal SPL, because the addition of uncorrelated sounds is intensity based. For example, were two sounds of 45 dB SPL being combined, the total SPL then would be 45 + 3 = 48 dB SPL. In general,

$$L_t = L + \varDelta L \qquad (3.9)$$

where $L_t$ is the total IL or SPL, and $L$ is the level of the individual sounds in decibels.

But what if there were three or more sounds? No problem! For the addition of (uncorrelated) sounds of equal level, $L$ is simply obtained by plugging the number of sounds into the equation

$$\varDelta L = 10 \: log_{10} n \qquad (3.10)$$

where $n$ is the number of components involved. For example, if 12 sounds of 75 dB SPL each were being added together, the resulting level would be determined using Eq. 3.10 and then 3.9, as follows:

$$\varDelta L = 10 \: log_{10} 12$$
$$= 10 \times 1.08$$
$$= 10.8$$
$$\approx 11 \text{ dB}$$
$$L_t = 75 + 11$$
$$= 86 \text{ dB SPL}$$

In other words, because the change in sound level for uncorrelated sounds is dictated by the resultant change in acoustic intensity, and the total acoustic intensity is 12 times the acoustic intensity of one sound, the total SPL (or IL) must be 11 dB higher. Using the decibel clearly simplifies the calculation here. The multiplier (12) is handled merely by finding the decibel equivalent and adding it to the level of the individual sounds being combined.

When working with two sounds of different levels, life is a bit more complicated, but it need not be burdensome if the chart provided in Appendix D is used. In this situation, $L$ is the more intense of the two sounds, and $\Delta L$ is read from the chart following the procedure given in Appendix D. When more than two sounds are being added, $L_t$ can be determined by sequentially combining them; that is, find the total level of the first two, combine it with the next, then this total to the next, etc. Alternatively, the calculation could be accomplished working directly with the acoustic intensities or sound pressures, as described earlier in this section.

The discussion, thus far, has focused on what happens to the overall IL or SPL when sounds are combined. It is possible that the situation could arise wherein component sounds are removed or the number of sound sources decreased. For example, traffic noise is more intense during peak traffic hours. During lighter periods, there are fewer sound sources, so the overall level decreases. The subtraction of ILs or SPLs abides by the same basic rules as addition. Therefore, the determination of the resultant level after the removal of some sound components cannot be accomplished by arithmetic subtraction, because subtracting logarithmic numbers actually represents division. Rather, the approach necessary will use the same logic as does the addition of sounds. For example, if at first there were 20 sound sources of 80 dB IL and now there is only one, the change in acoustic intensity is 20:1, and $\Delta L$ can be computed

using Eq. 3.10 but is subtracted from $L$ because the original overall acoustic intensity is being reduced by a factor of 20. The resultant level ($L_t$) is 80 − 13 dB = 67 dB SPL. If the sounds involved are not of equal levels, then one must bite the bullet and work directly with the acoustic intensities or sound pressures of the individual sounds. (Appendix D is of no practical value in this case.)

## B. SPECTRUM LEVEL AND RELATED CONCEPTS

A problem related to subtracting sound levels is encountered in the analysis of white noise, wherein it is desirous to determine the magnitude of each component frequency of the noise, or what is called the *spectrum level* or *level per cycle* ($L_{pc}$). The latter term is a bit of a truncation of what would be the more precise term level per cycle per second or level per hertz, but it is the one most commonly used. (The term *spectrum* will be given considerable discussion in the section to follow, and its relevance to hearing science will be elaborated in Chapter 7.) Whereas it is a fairly simple matter to determine the overall level of a noise, using a sound-level meter, determining the level at each frequency requires more complicated methods of analysis and instrumentation. However, if the noise can be considered to have reasonably constant energy across the band of frequencies that it occupies (as is the case for white noise), the spectrum level can be calculated, given the overall level and the *bandwidth*—the range of frequencies spanned by the noise. The spectrum level then can be computed via the formula:

$$L_{pc} = OAL - 10 \, log_{10}BW \quad (3.11)$$

where *OAL* is the overall level or *band level*, specified in decibels SPL (or IL), and *BW* is the bandwidth. Technically, *BW* is divided by a reference bandwidth, which, in practice, is always assumed to be 1 Hz, called the unit bandwidth. As a numerical example, assume a white noise of 10 kHz bandwidth (for example, a noise containing frequencies from 0 to 10 kHz) to have an *OAL* of 100 dB SPL; the spectrum level would be computed, as follows:

$$L_{pc} = 100 - 10 \ log_{10}10^4 = 100 - 40$$

$$= 60 \ dB \ SPL$$

In other words, each frequency component is effectively 60 dB SPL. It is as though the noise were created by adding individual (uncorrelated) tones, namely 10,000 of them, each at 60 dB SPL at random phases and randomly varying instantaneous magnitudes.

It is also noteworthy that, if somehow the spectrum level were known, it would be possible to predict the overall SPL (or IL) for a given bandwidth by solving for $L_t$ in Eq. 3.11, yielding

$$OAL = L_{pc} + 10 \ log_{10}BW$$

This should not be too surprising at this juncture, especially if the similarity between this equation and Eq. 3.9 is recognized. By way of analogy, determining the *OAL* of a noise that has a bandwidth of 100 Hz is just like predicting the overall level of traffic noise produced by 100 automobiles, given the level per car. In the case of the former, each frequency is treated like one packet of sound energy, in effect, one sound source. The addition of more and more frequencies or packets must cause an increase in the overall level.

Finally, it also is possible to use Eq. 3.11 to predict the bandwidth of a noise, given the band and spectrum levels:

$$BW = [antilog_{10}(OAL - L_{pc})]/10$$

With the assistance of the logarithm, the number of packets are found by dividing the overall SPL by the SPL at each cycle (or the respective acoustic ILs). Notice that before taking the antilog, an $\Delta L$ is computed, $(OAL - L_{pc})$; that is, the difference in level between the band and spectrum levels is calculated. This is exactly what the BW determines! It must be iterated that the underlying assumption in all

cases in which Eq. 3.11 is applied, in whatever form, is that the long-time average intensity of the noise is constant across its bandwidth.

## 6. Special Considerations in the Determination of Sound Levels

As a sort of interlude before getting into a subject such as spectrum analysis, coming up in the next section, attention should be drawn to a couple of situations that do not follow the addition-by-intensity (or power) rule of thumb implicit in the foregoing discussions. First there is a circumstance under which two or more sounds, even from different sound sources, may interact and their sound pressures add directly. This occurs when the sounds are of identical amplitude, frequency, and phase; this situation will be recognized as one of complete constructive interference. In this case, the instantaneous sound pressures summate directly to produce twice the sound pressure, if there are two sounds involved. The increase in SPL then will be 6 dB (not 3 dB). This change in level is computed using the computational equation for SPL (Eq. 3.7) and entering a sound pressure ratio of 2:1. Again, the sound pressure in this case is literally doubling. This clearly is a special condition. Specifically, it is one in which the two sounds are perfectly correlated. A simple example of correlated sounds is incident and reflected sound waves. More typically, however, sounds in the environment arise from various independent sources and thus are rarely correlated. This is why the collective level of the sounds will depend on the average of their powers (acoustic intensities, in practical terms), rather than their sound pressures. Consequently, addition by power is the rule, whereas addition by sound pressure is the exception.

The second point of special consideration is that there are applications wherein it is appropriate to directly add (or subtract) decibel values using simple arithmetic. For example, assume that outside noise is attenuated 40 dB by the walls of a sound-treated booth and, furthermore, noise reaching a subject's ear is attenuated by an additional 6 dB, because of the effects of wearing earphones. The total attenuation of the extraneous noise reaching the subject's ears would then be 40 + 6 = 46 dB. This is true because the isolation-booth and earphone-cushion attenuators are effectively cascaded; consequently, the combined effects of these two attenuators are, in fact, multiplicative! The wall reduces the sound pressure of the noise by 100-fold (40 dB), and this decremented noise is further reduced by half (6 dB). Thus there is a total reduction of $1/100 \times 1/2 = 1/200 = 0.005 = 5 \times 10^{-3}$. This ratio can be shown to be $-46$ dB. (Note: to keep your decibel ciphering well honed, verify this result.) The same principle could be applied in the case of cascading two amplifiers such that the output of the first is magnified by the second. If the first amplification stage had a gain of 20 dB, and the second had a gain of 15 dB, the total gain would be $20 \times 15 = 35$ dB. Similarly, if the second stage of amplification were removed, the resulting gain would be $35 - 15 = 20$ dB.

Consequently, whether decibels are combined arithmetically or according to the power rule discussed above, is a matter of whether the particular problem involves a process that is multiplicative (such as when combining amounts of attenuation) or additive (such as when combining sound levels). Now, on with some serious sound analysis.

## 7. Spectrum Analysis— Determining the Makeup of a Sound

### A. BASIC CONCEPTS AND LINE SPECTRA

To this point, vibratory motions and sounds have been graphically represented

in terms of their magnitude-versus-time functions. This is the *time analysis* of the vibration and sound, wherein magnitude is plotted at each instant of time ($a$ vs. $t$). When characterizing a sound as having a certain waveform, such as sinusoidal, what thus is being described is the time history of the sound. This is what was displayed on the oscilloscope screen in Figures 2.1 and 2.2 (Chapter 2); the graphs in Figures 3.4–3.6 are other examples of time analyses. However, as revealed above, the amplitude of the individual frequency components comprising a sound may be of interest, and this may not be evident from the time analysis of the sound. The magnitude-versus-frequency function ($a$ vs. $f$) is more to the point in such cases and is obtained by means of *spectrum analysis*. The graph of this function is called the *spectrum* (*spectra*, plural). The spectrum, specifically the amplitude spectrum, of a pure tone is shown in Figure 3.8, along with its time analysis for reference. Pure tones are characterized

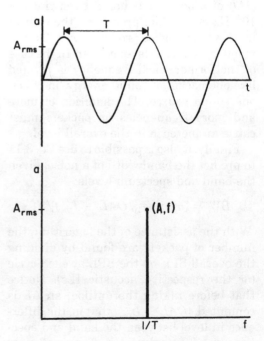

**Figure 3.8.** Spectrum analysis of a pure tone with the time analysis (waveform) shown above, for comparison.

by only one frequency, equal to the reciprocal of the period $T$, that is, $f = 1/T$. Consequently, the spectrum of a pure tone is the simplest result possible from spectrum analysis. The spectrum of the pure tone is represented graphically by a single point—in Cartesian coordinates, $(A, f)$, where $A$ and $f$ represent specific values of amplitude (typically an RMS value, $A_{rms}$) and frequency, respectively. Rather than merely plotting this one point, however, it is customary to represent the amplitude by a line dropped from point $(A, f)$ to the abscissa. The spectrum analysis of a pure tone thus yields a single line located at frequency $f$ along the abscissa with a height equal to the RMS sound pressure (or, with appropriate calibration, SPL). The spectrum of a pure tone thus is an example of what is known as a *line spectrum*.

The spectrum of a complex tone is largely predictable from that of a pure tone. Because a complex tone can be synthesized by adding two or more discrete, pure tones together, it should not be surprising that the complex tone also has a line spectrum. In other words, its amplitude spectrum appears as a series of two or more lines. An example of a spectrum for a complex tone is shown in Figure 3.9. The time analyses for these tones were shown previously in Figure 3.4. All naturally occurring complex periodic tones are

characterized by line spectra wherein the components appear only at frequencies that are whole-integer multiples of some fundamental frequency, $1/T$ ($T$ being the period about which the complex tone repeats itself): $1/T, 2/T, 3/T \ldots n/T$ or $f_o, 2f_o, 3f_o \ldots nf_o$, where $f_o$ is the fundamental frequency. Consequently, the spectral components are said to be harmonically related and themselves are called ***harmonics***. Which harmonics are present and their individual amplitudes depend on the exact nature of the complex tone.[4] Some familiar examples of complex sounds that are very rich in their harmonic structure are the tones produced by wind and string musical instruments.

## B. CONTINUOUS SPECTRA AND OTHER CONCEPTS

The spectra of many sounds are not made up of individual components, such as 100 Hz, 500 Hz, etc., as in the case of complex tones. Rather, the energy of these sounds is not concentrated at discrete frequencies, although it may be concentrated with a certain band(s) of frequencies. Instead of consisting of a series of vertical lines, as characteristic of line spectra, the spectra of these sounds are ***continuous***, at least within certain ranges of frequencies. Such spectra appear as more-or-less continuous lines (see Figs. 3.10$a$ and 3.12). Intuitively, the "prime candidates" for sounds with continuous spectra are noises, but they are not the only candi-

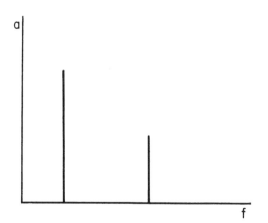

**Figure 3.9.** Spectrum analysis of the complex tone for which the time analyses were shown in Figure 3.4.

[4] Other terms used in discussing frequency components of complex tones, in addition to harmonics, are partials and overtones. ***Partial*** is the broadest term of the three and can be applied to any frequency component of a complex sound at or above the fundamental. ***Overtones*** are partials above the fundamental (or upper partials). The term *harmonics* refers specifically to upper partials or overtones that are integral multiples of the fundamental (or very nearly so). Specific attention is sometimes given to "even" (for example, $2f_o$, $4f_o$, etc.) versus "odd" harmonics (for instance, $3f_o$, $5f_o$, etc., where $f_o$ is the fundamental). That a distinction is made between the even and odd harmonics reflects the fact that one or the other may dominate the makeup of a complex tone or in the production of distortion products (see Section 3.11 below). Incidentally, there also are such things as subharmonics—submultiples of the fundamental ($f_o/2$, $f_o/4$, etc.).

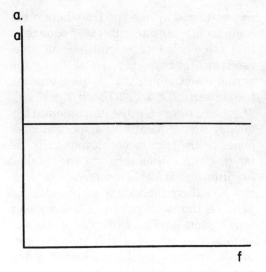

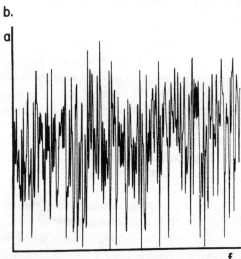

**Figure 3.10.**   **a.** Ideal, long-time average spectrum of Gaussian noise. **b.** Essentially, the instantaneous spectrum of the same noise (obtained from a single sweep with a noise generator connected to the input of a digital spectrum analyzer; resolution was 50 Hz).

sian noise is the simplest example of a continuous spectrum. As might be expected from the earlier description of Gaussian noise, its spectrum is represented by a straight horizontal line (Fig. 3.10*a*), indicating equal magnitude at all frequencies. However, the spectrum shown here and the conditions under which it was obtained must be understood, because an analysis of the spectrum using only a single brief sampling or "snapshot" of this noise (the spectrum in real time) presents a strikingly different picture, as demonstrated by Figure 3.10*b*. Magnitude is seen to vary erratically across frequency. At the next instant this entire picture would change, a fact expected from the definition of Gaussian noise. The spectrum in Figure 3.10*b* might be thought of as an "instantaneous" (amplitude) spectrum, as opposed to that which is shown in Figure 3.10*a*. The latter is the result of long-term averaging of spectral samples; it is actually a graph of the power spectral densities or, simply, the ***power spectrum***. It shows the average amplitude contribution of each frequency to the total power in the signal, and it is this average contribution that is constant across frequency for Gaussian noise.

Although a distinction is made between time analysis and spectrum (or frequency) analysis, it is clear that the two are not independent. In fact, the same information is contained in the two forms of analyses; only the domain has changed (from time to frequency).[5] Given one, the other may be derived. The mathematics by which this is possible, and indeed the basic

dates, as will be demonstrated later in this chapter. Nevertheless, the concepts of line and continuous spectra provide yet another basis for distinguishing tones from noises. Simply stated, tones have line spectra, whereas noises and transients have continuous spectra.

Just as the spectrum of the pure tone is the simplest example of a line spectrum, the long-time average spectrum of Gaus-

[5] There is a term that may be encountered, when dealing with spectrum analysis, and that may create some confusion: ***real-time analysis***. This is not a form of time analysis per se. Technically, the more correct term would be "real-time spectrum analysis," because real-time analysis is just that (spectrum analysis). Until the more recent advances in computer technology, spectrum analysis was a slow process and was often limited to essentially continuous sounds. This was so because it was necessary to measure the magnitude of one frequency or band of frequencies, then the next, and so on, in a sequential fashion. The point is that the different parts of the spectrum were not sampled simultaneously. Therefore, such spectrum analyses were not made in real time. Today, instrumentation is readily available that per-

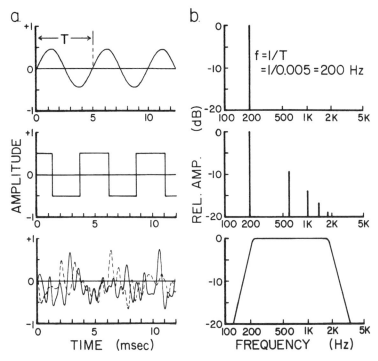

**Figure 3.11.** Time (**a**) and spectrum (**b**) analyses of a 200-Hz sinusoid (*top*), 200-Hz square wave (*middle*), and 200- to 2000-Hz filtered noise (*bottom*). Two epochs of the noise are shown to demonstrate the lack of periodicity in its waveform; the spectrum shown in **b** is the average. (Adapted from Durrant, J. D. [1983]. Fundamentals of sound generation for auditory evoked responses. In *Bases of Auditory Brain Stem Evoked Responses*, edited by E. J. Moore. Grune & Stratton, New York).

notion of breaking sounds down into their constituent components, is attributed to Fourier, as noted earlier. Spectrum analysis is often called Fourier analysis, but the Fourier transforms (the mathematics in question) permit one to go in either direction. Given the time history of a signal, the spectrum can be determined. Conversely, given the spectrum, the time history can be derived. However, only the *amplitude spectrum* has been considered thus far, and, by itself, it does not provide enough information to permit the reconstruction of the time history. For example, based on the amplitude spectrum alone, it is impossible to distinguish between the two com-

plex tones shown previously in Figure 3.4, namely between the case in which the 300-Hz tone is started at a phase of 0° (Fig. 3.4*a*) and that in which it has a phase lag of 90° (Fig. 3.4*b*). To retain all of the information that is necessary to reconstruct the time history or waveform, knowledge of the phase-versus-frequency function also is required. In other words, the *phase spectrum* also must be determined. The phase spectrum is often ignored in the measurement of sound; indeed, some (electronic) spectrum analyzers provide only for the determination of the amplitude spectrum. This is acceptable for a broad range of applications, and the practice here will be to show only amplitude spectra. Still, the phase spectrum clearly provides information that cannot be ignored in the final analysis.

Figure 3.11 is offered as a sort of visual

mits spectrum analysis in real time. The spectrum of Gaussian noise shown in Figure 3.10*b* is an example of a spectrum obtained via a real-time spectrum analyzer (in this case, using a device that samples the waveform and computes the Fourier transform).

summary to this section. It provides a comparison between three different waveforms and their spectra. It should be pointed out that square wave sounds are impossible to come by environmentally, but when an electronically generated square wave is applied to an earphone or loudspeaker, a complex tone is produced whose spectrum is much like that shown in this figure. Still, the exact weighting of the spectral component and overall bandwidth depends on the nuances of the transduction system (amplifier and earphone). For the noise, time analyses over different time intervals are shown to underscore the lack of periodicity that characterizes random noises. The noise in this case actually started out as white noise whose spectrum would be a flat horizontal line throughout the range of frequencies shown along the abscissa, but it has been "shaped" to provide a different noise. That spectra can be modified in this manner and how this may be done are the subjects of the next section.

## 8. Shaping of Spectra

### A. TYPES OF FILTERS

Sunglasses are often fascinating to children, not because they make it easier on the eyes to be in the bright sun, but because they make people and things look kind of funny. If the lenses are blue, purple, red, yellow, or another vibrant color, all the better, because now Grandma has a blue face or Fido appears all red, for example. Sunglasses, fundamentally, are designed to attenuate light, but they also filter light, freely passing one wavelength or wavelength range while reducing light at other wavelengths, thereby enhancing a particular color. Sunlight and many artificial light sources are "broad band" —comprising a wide range of colors more or less equally represented within the visible range. The tinted glass of the sunglasses thus reshapes the light spectrum. Likewise, it is possible to influence the spectrum of a sound using filters to selectivity pass some frequencies while rejecting others. Filters are named for the type of spectral change that they cause. A filter that passes only frequencies below a certain designated "corner" or cut-off frequency $(f_u)$ while rejecting, or more precisely attenuating, higher frequencies is called a *low-pass filter*. Thus, a low-pass filter can be thought of as a high-reject filter. Conversely, a *high-pass filter* passes only frequencies above the cut-off frequency $(f_l)$. If only frequencies within a certain range, or bandwidth, are passed, (namely, between $f_l$ to $f_u$), this function or device performing this function is called a *band-pass filter*.

To illustrate the three basic types of filters, the spectra of low-, high-, and band-pass filtered white noise are shown in Figure 3.12. In practice, band-pass filtering often is obtained by cascading (that is, connecting in tandem) high- and low-pass filters. For instance, to obtain the spectrum shown in Figure 3.11c (0.2- to 2.0-kHz band of noise) broad-band white noise was first low-pass filtered with a corner frequency of 2 kHz. This low-pass-filtered noise was then high-pass filtered with a cut-off frequency of 0.2 kHz. The order of these operations actually is not critical; the same results would have been obtained if the filtering was done in reverse order. The resulting noise is often called *narrow-band noise* (or band-limited noise) whereas the original noise is called *wideband noise*. Similarly, low- and high-pass filters can be combined to reject frequencies within a certain band, often an extremely narrow band, by low-pass filtering below a certain frequency, and high-pass filtering above a higher frequency. This produces what is known as *stopband* or *band-reject filtering*. A common example is a device intended to reject 60 Hz (or 50 Hz in some countries), which is the line noise or hum that derives from AC power sources. A stop-band filter intended to reject a specific frequency is known specifically as a *notch filter*.

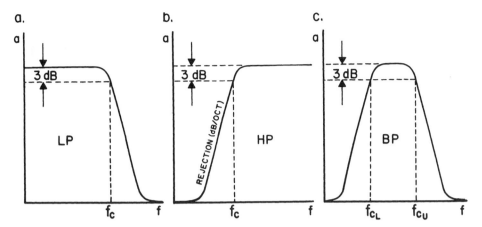

**Figure 3.12.**  Frequency response plots of low-pass (*LP*), high-pass (*HP*), and band-pass (*BP*) filters. Cut-off frequencies ($f_c$), that is, half-power or 3-dB down points, are indicated; *U* and *L* indicate upper and lower cut-offs, respectively, for the band-pass filter. Both coordinates are logarithmic, namely, decibel units versus log frequency.

## B. FILTER SPECIFICATIONS

The specification of the cut-off (corner) frequency(ies) is important. Discrete cut-off frequencies are attainable only by an ideal filter. Such a filter would yield a perfectly rectangular spectrum, given Gaussian noise at its input. In reality, the ideal filter can only be approximated, although essentially ideal filters can be implemented via digital signal processing (that is, using digital circuitry or a digital computer). For less-than-ideal filters, a compromise is usually necessary. A convenient and widely accepted way of specifying cut-off frequencies is to determine that frequency at which the power output of the filter has been attenuated to 50% of its maximum—the **half-power point**. In terms of sound pressure, this is the point along the frequency axis at which the signal magnitude drops to 70.7% of the maximum, in other words, the square root of 50% (50% = 0.50; $0.50^{1/2} = 0.707 = 70.7\%$). At 50% power or acoustic intensity or 70.7% sound pressure, the relative output is decreased 3 dB. ($10\ log\ 0.5 = 20\ log\ 0.707 = 3$ dB.) For this reason, the half-power point is often called the 3-dB-down point. Because a band-pass filter has two cut-off frequencies ($f_l$ and $f_u$), the span

**TABLE 3.3.**
**Coefficients for Computing Frequency Limits of Octave and Fractional Octave Bandwidths (BW)**

| *Desired BW* *(Octaves)* | *Center-Frequency* $f_l$—*Multiplier*—$f_u$ | |
|---|---|---|
| 2 | 0.500 | 2.000 |
| 1 | 0.707 | 1.414 |
| ½ | 0.841 | 1.189 |
| ⅓ | 0.891 | 1.122 |
| ⅙ | 0.944 | 1.059 |
| ⅒ | 0.966 | 1.035 |

Example: to determine the frequency limits of a ⅓ oct. band centered at 2,000 Hz:

$$f_l = 0.891 \times 2,000 = 1,782\ \text{Hz}$$
$$f_u = 1.122 \times 2,000 = 2,244\ \text{Hz}$$

of frequencies between the half-power points (Fig. 3.12c) is called the **half-power bandwidth** or nominal bandwidth. Sound that has been band-pass filtered can be described by its corner frequencies or by its center frequency ($f_c$) and its bandwidth, typically stated in octaves or fractional octaves. Some filters are designed to provide constant bandwidths (for example, 10 Hz), whereas others provide constant percentage bandwidths (such as 10%, one third of an octave, half an octave, etc.). Table 3.3 provides computational equations for cut-off frequencies of several bandwidths, most of which are used commonly in hearing science.

The use of half-power points or bandwidth to specify the response characteristics of a filter, or the resulting sound spectrum, is somewhat akin to the determination of the RMS amplitude. In a nutshell, it is an attempt to demarcate the area under the graph of the frequency-response curve of a filter or the graph of the resulting sound spectrum which best approximates the ideal filter (a rectangular area). Also, the implication of the nonideal filter is that not all of the energy in the spectrum of the filtered sound is confined to the frequency range indicated by the corner frequency(ies). For instance, if a low-pass filter is used and the cut-off frequency is set to 1 kHz, this does not necessarily mean there will be no energy passed at frequencies of 1001 Hz and above. Of course, the magnitude of the sound will be reduced more than 3 dB above 1 kHz, and the further above the corner frequency, the greater the amount of attenuation. How much attenuation occurs at these frequencies (conversely, how much sound "leaks" through) depends on the rejection rate or rolloff of the filter. This parameter of filters usually is stated in decibels per octave (dB/oct). For example, if a low-pass filter attenuates the SPL at a rate of 6 dB/oct above the corner frequency, this means that above the half-power point the sound pressure decreases by twofold each time the frequency is doubled (or acoustic intensity is decreased by $2^2$ or fourfold). To more completely specify the response characteristics of a particular filter, thus, both the corner frequency(ies) and the rolloff(s) of the filter must be stated. Incidentally, if two filters with rejection rates of 6 dB/oct are cascaded, the net rejection rate will be 12 dB/oct. In other words, the rejection rates are multiplicative. This occurs because the first filter will attenuate the sound pressure by a factor of 1/2 per octave, whereas the second filter does the same (1/2 × 1/2 = 1/4; in decibels, 20 $log$ 1/4 = 20 $log$ 0.25 = −12 dB).

Although the cut-off frequencies and rejection rate give a fairly good indication of what the response characteristics of a specific filter are, there are other parameters that may be of interest. The phase-response characteristics have been ignored in the description thus far and only the amplitude response considered. However, many filters (especially nondigital or analog filters) alter the phase of the signal at the output, and, in some cases, this may be a critical factor. For instance, phase changes may be intolerable when temporal features, such as waveform peaks, must be precisely reproduced at the output. Whether phase is altered does not depend on filter type (low-pass, etc.); rather, it depends on how the filter is designed. Digital filters can be, and typically are, designed to be zero phase shift.

## C. ACOUSTIC VERSUS ELECTRONIC FILTERS

From some of the foregoing discussion, it may be deduced that in hearing science, or acoustics in general, filtering is not necessarily performed directly on the sound itself. In fact, although there are acoustic filters, electronic filters are often used. A noise or signal is generated electronically (microphone, electronic oscillator, function generator, etc.), filtered electronically, and then transduced via an earphone or loudspeaker to produce the actual filtered sound. The reason is that electronic filters are easier to build, easier to design for specific response characteristics, and easier to adjust. There are numerous electronic circuits that can be used for filtering, each with its own detailed amplitude and phase response characteristics. In a given application, the type of filter circuit used is important; its response characteristics, if not known, must be determined, especially if phase distortion is intolerable (see Section 11 below). When essentially ideal filter characteristics are required and no phase distortion is tolerable, then again, digital and computer signal processing methods are required.

The emphasis on electronic means of filtering should not be construed as devaluing the practical use of acoustic filters. One common application is in the venting of an earmold of a hearing aid. The earmold fits into the entrance of the ear and serves to efficiently couple sound produced by the hearing aid to the ear. A vent in the mold, essentially a small hole that can vary in length and diameter, serves to allow excessive and unneeded low-frequency sound to leak out. The vent, therefore, is designed to serve as a low-pass filter. If designed appropriately, high frequency energy does not pass or leak out because of the relatively high mass (and consequently high mass reactance) of the column of air in the vent. Like other filters, the vent can be characterized by its effective corner frequency and roll-off.

The use of filters to shape noise spectra represents only one of numerous applications of filtering and the concepts and terminology presented here. It often is desirable to filter speech or other sounds (for instance, to determine the relative importance of different frequency ranges for the recognition of the material presented). Furthermore, not all applications are output oriented or concerned with signal production or reproduction. Adjustable narrow-band-pass filters can be used to measure the contribution of each component of a complex sound, a form of spectrum analysis. An example of such devices is the wave analyzer, a tunable band-pass filter. However, filtering also may occur inadvertently. The telephone band-pass filters the voice, permitting only frequencies from between about 300–3000 Hz to get through. This is a limitation in the telephone design imposed by economic constraints; a high-fidelity telephone system would be too expensive. Similarly, filter concepts and terminology can be used to describe any system, including the auditory system, that alters the spectrum of the input signal. For example, in Chapter 5 the case will be made that sound is bandpass filtered in the peripheral auditory system. It will be shown how the auditory system analyzes complex sounds through, in effect, the use of a bank of bandpass filters. Stay tuned!

## 9. Spectral Influence of Temporal Factors

### A. GATING—TEMPORAL WINDOWING

For the sake of simplicity, sounds have been assumed to be continuous; therefore, their durations have been considered to be effectively infinite. This is because it simplifies matters to be able to assume that the spectra of sounds are determined from analyses of samples taken at a relatively long time after their beginning, or onset, and far in advance of their termination, or offset. This is so, in turn, because as soon as a time window is introduced, the spectrum obtained will no longer be that of just the sound that is being manipulated. The time window, or gating function, is the transformation describing how the sound is turned on and off, or for that matter by which it is sampled. This process, particularly from the sampling viewpoint, can be thought of as looking at an otherwise continuous sound through a window in time. Alternatively, the process may be viewed much like the opening and closing of a gate on an otherwise free-running sound, analogous to light shining through the shutter of a camera. (Note: in practice, it is the input signal to the sound transducer that actually is gated.) The resultant spectrum will reflect contributions of the gating function itself. In other words, the function controlling the onset and offset and duration of the sound has a spectrum of its own. For instance, as will be elaborated momentarily, the spectrum of a burst of tone has a remarkably different spectrum than that of a continuous tone. ***Any*** *change in the time domain thus leads to a change in the frequency domain!* The two effects are inseparable! Of course, sounds in the environment are rarely continuous and unchanging, that is, steady state. Not only do their spectra change from instant to instant, but also the manner in which they change contributes to their spectra. Consequently, it is necessary to consider the influence of the temporal characteristics of a sound on its spectrum. These temporal characteristics are time-dependent amplitude, frequency, and/or phase variations or *modulations* that represent fluctuations in the waveform. Such fluctuations also can be created intentionally and in a precisely controlled manner in the laboratory. Some rather standard modulation paradigms and their spectral influences are worthy of attention here and are of broad interest in hearing science.

The results of modulation can be more or less complex. For example, the result of modulation of a pure tone can be the generation of a complex tone, a sound whose spectrum (again) is discrete. A common example is sinusoidal *amplitude modulation* (AM) of a pure tone (often called the carrier). In other words, the amplitude of a sinusoid is itself varied sinusoidally, as illustrated in Figure 3.13a. The rate at which the amplitude of the carrier changes is called the *modulation rate* or *modulation frequency*. The amplitude of this change is called the *depth* and is measured as percent of peak carrier amplitude. The spectrum of such a sound is composed of three components—one at the carrier frequency $(f_c)$ and one above and one below the carrier separated by a distance equal to the difference between the carrier and modulation frequencies $(f_c + f_m$, where $f_c = 1/T_c$, the period of the carrier, and $f_m = 1/T_m$, the period of the modulator). For instance, if the carrier frequency is 4000 Hz and the modulation frequency 200 Hz, the components in the spectrum will be 4000, 4200, and 3800 Hz. The 4-kHz component, that is, the carrier,

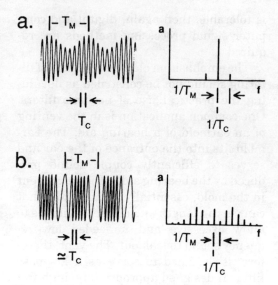

**Figure 3.13.** Examples of amplitude- (**a**) and frequency (**b**)-modulated sinusoids (carriers). $T_m$ and $1/T_m$, period and frequency, respectively of the modulator (also sinusoidal); $T_c$ and $1/T_c$, period and frequency, respectively, of the carrier.

will have the largest amplitude; the amplitude of the two "side tones" will depend on the depth of modulation.

It is also possible to create a complex tone by sinusoidally modulating the frequency of a carrier, a process known as *frequency modulation* (FM). Sidebands of energy thus will be created with FM, too (see Fig. 3.13b). The spectral details will depend on the rate of frequency change or modulation frequency (FM) and depth of modulation (range over which frequency is changed). Even sinusoidally frequency-modulated sinusoids can have complicated spectra, particularly when the modulation and carrier frequencies are not greatly separated (as in Fig. 3.13b). *Phase modulation* is another possibility, although of greater interest in radio communications. Although in practice frequency and phase modulation may be performed separately, these two forms of modulation actually are inseparable; signal frequency cannot be varied without altering phase and vice versa.

## B. THE BELOVED TONE BURST AND ITS NUANCES

An extreme form of amplitude modulation of special interest in hearing science is generated by switching a pure tone completely on and off to create what is called a *tone burst* (fundamentally, a sinusoidal pulse). The tone burst is probably the most frequently used stimulus for hearing science and constitutes the standard stimulus for baseline clinical audiometry (see Chapter 7). It may come as a surprise that the spectrum of a tone burst is continuous! This is because the tone burst obtained by gating even a single sinusoid (that is, one frequency component) is a transient and thus is inherently aperiodic![6] The details of its spectrum depend upon the length of its plateau duration (the steady-state part) and the gating function governing its onset and offset. An important parameter of the latter is the duration of the onset and offset; this is known as the *rise and fall (or rise and decay) time*. Therefore, the creation of a tone burst can be viewed as a process like opening and closing a gate on a free-running sinusoid.

From the spectra shown in Figure 3.14 it can be seen that the effects of the gating function, or what is frequently called the *envelope*, can be dramatic, indeed. When the sinusoid is turned on abruptly for a relatively short time (Fig. 3.14*a*), the spectrum analysis reveals that energy is

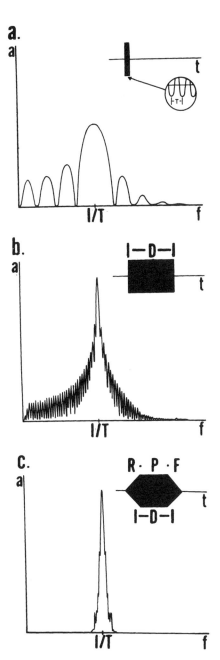

**Figure 3.14.** Examples of spectra of tone bursts with different durations and rise and fall times (rectilinear envelopes). The amplitude axes are is scaled logarithmically (as is the case, effectively, when amplitude is plotted in decibels). *Insets*, Envelopes of the tone bursts, determined by time analyses. The frequency of the sinusoid being gated is $1/T$. Other parameters are effective duration ($D$), plateau duration ($P$), and rise and fall times ($R$ and $F$).

---

[6] The relationship between duration, $t$, and bandwidth, $f$, is expressed by the following: $\Delta t \times \Delta f > 1$. This is an adaptation of what is known in quantum mechanics as the Heisenberg uncertainty principle. This principle addresses the behavior of subatomic particles and the uncertainty involved in specifying their positions and velocities. The situation here is analogous; there is uncertainty, so to speak, in specifying time and frequency. The uncertainty principle above may be rewritten as follows: $f > 1/t$. Thus, as duration decreases, bandwidth increases. One can view decreasing duration as an attempt to more precisely specify the time of occurrence of the sound, namely by confining it to one brief instant. The shorter the duration of the sound, however, the less certain the specification of frequency, hence a broader bandwidth. The converse is also true. The more certain the frequency, the less certain the time, in the sense that the duration must approach infinity. In other words, the duration must be indefinite!

"splattered" widely above and below the center or main lobe of the spectrum, although the center frequency equals the frequency of the sinusoid itself. Tone bursts are often referred to as *frequency-specific* stimuli, but it can be seen that frequency specificity is a matter of degree and "central tendency" of the spectrum. In the case illustrated in Figure 3.14a, the rise and fall time is nil, and the duration equals three periods of the sinusoid. The result is a rather robust splatter. The splattering is effectively reduced in the long-term spectrum by increasing the duration of the tone burst, say 10-fold (Fig. 3.10b). Relatively more energy is concentrated at the center frequency. Still, the quality of this tone burst is that of a brief tone accompanied by a "clicking" noise; the latter is caused by the sharp rise and decay characteristics of the envelope. Substantial improvement in frequency specificity, and consequently tonality, is achieved by turning the tone on and off more gradually, as illustrated in Figure 3.10c. With sufficiently long durations of the rise and decay and plateau portions of the tone burst, depending also on the choice of the gating function (that is, shape of the envelope), the spectral characteristics of a tone burst may be made very close to those of a continuous tone. What is sufficiently long depends on the specific situation. For example, in hearing testing these conditions are generally met with durations of 200 milliseconds or more and rise and fall times of 10 to 25 milliseconds for tone bursts of the type illustrated in Fig. 3.14c (see Chapter 7).

There are other factors that are also influential in determining the final signal spectrum but that will be considered here only briefly. First, less high-frequency spectral splatter will occur when the sinusoid is gated at the zero-crossings of the sinusoid, turning the sinusoid on and off at points in time at which the instantaneous magnitude is zero. In contrast, low-frequency splatter is minimized by gating at a 90° phase.

Second, the envelope need not be rectilinear, as in Figure 3.14. There are numerous other windowing functions, as hinted above, some of which cause even less energy spread. Figure 3.15 illustrates the differences between spectra of sinusoidal pulses obtained via several different gating functions. The curvilinear windows (cosine and Blackman) reduce sideband splatter appreciably compared with the rectilinear windows of comparable temporal parameters, although at the risk of a broader main lobe.

Third, the specification of the total duration of a tone burst with other than exceedingly short rise and fall times bears a resemblance to the determination of the RMS amplitude and half-power bandwidths, especially if it is the total energy in the tone burst that is of major importance. For tone bursts with rectilinear envelopes, the effective duration ($D$) is given by the equation:

$$D = 2R/3 + P$$

where $R(=F)$ is rise and fall time, and $P$ is plateau duration (See Fig. 3.14c). The approach here is like asking, "Given a tone burst with a rise and fall duration greater than 0 milliseconds, what is the duration of a tone burst with a rectangular envelope (rise = fall = 0 milliseconds) with the same energy?." In practice, especially for tone bursts with nonrectilinear envelopes, simpler rules often are adopted, such as defining overall duration as the time between the points at which amplitude rises and falls to 50% of the maximum amplitude. Similarly, rise and fall times might be defined as the interval from 10% to 90% full on.

Finally, everything discussed in this section applies to complex tones and noises, as well as to pure tones. Likewise, their spectra will be enriched in ways determined by the manner in which they are gated. The emphasis on gated single sinusoids here is simply in deference to the ease with which one can visualize the ef-

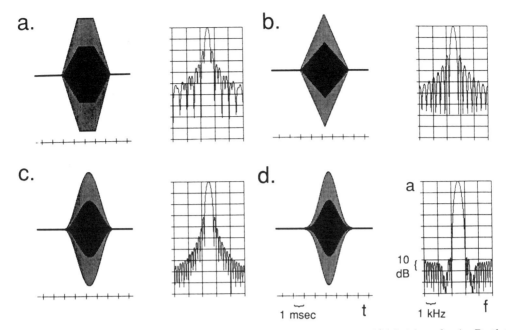

**Figure 3.15.** Effects of gating function (time window) on spectrum: trapezoid (**a**), triangular (or Bartlett) (**b**), cosine squared (or Hanning) (**c**), and Blackman (**d**). Time base, 1.33 msec/div.

fects of modulation on the sinusoid, compared with more complex sounds.

## 10. Spectra of Impulses

Some insight into why there is such a spread of energy in the case of the shorter and more abruptly switched tone burst is provided by examining the spectra of *impulses*. At the same time, the impulse has special interests and utility in hearing science. The impulses of interest here are created electronically by rapidly switching direct current and so are referred to as DC pulses, in contrast to tones, tone bursts, random noises, and various other types of impulses (such as the damped sinusoidal pulse) that are oscillatory in nature and are generated electronically using AC. The time histories (waveforms) and spectra of DC pulses of two different durations are illustrated in Figure 3.16, *a* and *b*. These spectra are clearly continuous, but particularly notable are the nulls that occur in the spectra at frequencies equal to the reciprocal of the pulse duration

(1/D). As would be expected, given the relationship between period and frequency, the shorter the duration of the pulse, the higher is the frequency of the first null. This means that with decreasing duration, each lobe is increasingly broader. Therefore, if the duration were infinitely short, producing what might be thought of as the ideal impulse, the main (and only) lobe would have an infinite bandwidth. Consequently, duration of the pulse and bandwidth of the spectrum are, essentially, reciprocals.[6] There is a catch, though; the magnitude of the main lobe is proportional to the pulse duration. Less on time means less energy present!

Returning to Figure 3.14, *a* and *b*, it now should be evident that the spectra of these tone bursts depend substantially on the spectra of the envelopes themselves. Specifically, the spectra of sinusoidal pulses are the result of multiplying the sinusoid by the envelope or gating function used—DC pulses for the functions illustrated in Figure 3.14, *a* and *b*. Consequently, the spectra appear like those of

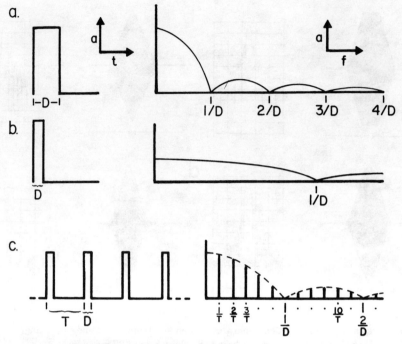

**Figure 3.16.** Spectra of DC pulses. **a** and **b**. Spectra of single pulses of two different durations, wherein the duration of pulse **a** is three times that of **b**. **c**. Spectrum of pulses repeated at intervals of $T$ duration, that is, $1/T$ pulses/sec. (Based on figures from Pfeiffer, R. R. [1974]. Consideration of the acoustic stimulus. In *Handbook of Sensory Physiology: Vol. V/1-Auditory System*, pp. 9–38, edited by W. D. Keidel and W. D. Neff. Springer-Verlag, Berlin.)

DC pulses, although shifted to the right along the abscissa to the frequency of the sinusoid. The fact that there is spectral splatter below this frequency as well as above it does not detract from this comparison, for this also happens in the case of the DC pulse. However, the center frequency for the DC pulse is zero, which, in turn, means that the spectrum extends to negative as well as to positive frequencies. The concept of negative frequency is rather abstract; such details are ignored for practical purposes, and the spectra of DC pulses generally are shown as in Figure 3.16. (As an aside, this discussion should add further meaning and credibility to an assumption made in Chapter 1 regarding simple harmonic motion. There it was assumed that the abrupt release of the mass of the simple harmonic oscillator from the starting position imparted no specific frequency to the system. Because

the simple harmonic oscillator was started by an impulse, in effect, this assumption is entirely reasonable!)

Although the spectrum of a single DC pulse is continuous, a line spectrum is obtained when such pulses are repeated at regular intervals, as shown in Figure 3.16c. This should not be too shocking, for a periodic signal indeed has been created by the repetition rate. Therefore, these repetitive pulses form a complex tone. Nevertheless, the amplitudes of the spectral components still trace the outline of the spectrum of the single pulse (Fig. 3.16c).

That impulsive sounds are characterized by rather broad spectra is easily appreciated from experience, for many common sounds are impulses: clapping, gunshots, a door slamming, etc. However, a sound whose time history is identical to that of the DC pulse does not occur natu-

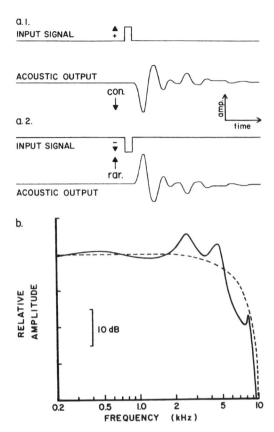

**Figure 3.17.** **a.** Acoustic clicks produced by driving an earphone (Telephonics TDH-39) with DC pulses of positive (*a1*) and negative (*a2*) polarity, thus producing condensation (*con.*) and rarefaction (*rar.*) clicks, respectively. (Note: the relationship between pulse polarity and click phase depends on the combined characteristics of the specific sound production and monitoring systems used; therefore, in any given situation, a positive pulse will not necessarily produce a condensation click, etc., as illustrated here.) **b.** Spectrum of the input signal (*dashed curve*) versus that of the acoustic output (*solid curve*). (From Durrant, J. D. [1983]. Fundamentals of sound generation for auditory evoked responses. In *Bases of Auditory Brain Stem Evoked Responses*, edited by E. J. Moore. Grune & Stratton, New York.)

rally. If a DC pulse is used to drive an earphone or loudspeaker, a rather different waveform results, as shown in Figure 3.17. Nevertheless, the transduced sound is still impulsive and has a fairly broad spectrum, as seen in Figure 3.17*b*. By virtue of its quality, this sound is referred to

as an ***acoustic click***. The reason for this remarkable transformation of the DC pulse is that transducers, such as earphones, do not have response characteristics with infinite bandwidths. Rather, they act like band-pass filters. In other words, they fail to operate efficiently at very low and very high frequencies. Such transducers may have some substantial resonances that reveal themselves as peaks in the sound spectrum (Fig. 3.17*b*, *solid line*).

The spectrum of the DC pulse thus is altered by the response characteristics of the transducer, as illustrated by Figure 3.17*b*. This is another example in which the response of a vibratory system is seen to be the combination of its natural response and the forced response discussed in Chapter 1. The response characteristics of the transducer that give rise to the click will similarly influence the reproduction of tone bursts. As shown in Figure 3.18, just as the earphone cannot perfectly transduce a DC pulse, neither can it perfectly follow the waveform of a sinusoidal pulse with a rectangular envelope. The "overshoot" at the onset and the persistent waves at the offset of the tone burst are evidence of this inadequacy and are examples of what is often referred to as ***ring-***

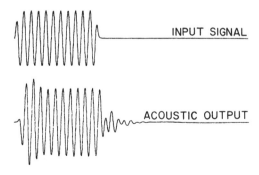

**Figure 3.18.** Time analysis of the acoustic output of an earphone (as in Fig. 3.17) versus that of the gated sinusoidal voltage driving it—an example of ringing. (From Durrant, J. D. [1983]. Fundamentals of sound generation for auditory evoked responses. In *Bases of Auditory Brain Stem Evoked Responses*, edited by E. J. Moore. Grune & Stratton, New York.)

*ing*. Again, it is evident that changes in the time domain, such as switching the sound on and off, influence the spectrum; conversely, changes in the frequency domain such as filtering influence the waveform.

Finally, attention should be drawn to the fact that in Figure 3.16 only one polarity of pulse is illustrated, but it is evident in Figure 3.17 that the starting phase of the click is directly linked to the polarity of the DC pulse being transduced. Which polarity is actually used in the generation of the click thus depends on whether it is desirable to initiate the sound with a condensation or rarefaction phase. With respect to stimulation of the auditory system, this difference amounts to one of initiating stimulation with an inward or outward movement, respectively, of the eardrum. The phase difference is evidenced in the electrical activity of the auditory nervous system, yet, perceptually, the condensation and rarefaction clicks sound the same. This is because their spectra are identical. Now, this assumes that pulses of each polarity themselves are identical and that they are transformed with equal fidelity. However, sound systems are not flawless in their reproduction, again as evidenced by the response characteristics of transducers shown in Figures 3.17 and 3.18. Other "perversions" of the input signal are possible, leading to the topic of the next and final section of this chapter: distortion.

## 11. Distortion

### A. FUNDAMENTAL TYPES OF DISTORTION

When a sound, vibration, or electrical signal is passed through any physical system, the spectrum of the signal inevitably undergoes some degree of change. The signal at the output of the system is not a faithful representation of the signal at the input; rather, it is changed or distorted in some manner. There are three basic forms

of **distortion** that may be introduced by the system. One type, which is familiar by now, is frequency distortion, wherein the output is characterized by some change in frequency response. In effect, filters cause frequency distortion, albeit sometimes desirable. One common device that causes frequency distortion is the telephone with its limited frequency response (nominally 300 to 3000 Hz). Another example is the AM radio; most listeners prefer the superior fidelity of a high-quality FM stereo receiver. The latter has a much wider bandwidth and, therefore, less frequency distortion.

Also familiar from earlier discussion is phase distortion. The output signal may be shifted in phase relative to the input signal. In practice, frequency distortion is usually accompanied by phase distortion, and vice versa. There are absolute phase shifts and frequency-dependent phase shifts. At least in the area of filtering, phase distortion can be averted by using zero-phase (shift) filters. It is difficult to exemplify phase distortion in terms of everyday experience. It is not that phase distortion is uncommon, but rather that it may go undetected. When the components of a complex tone are differentially affected by phase distortion, the waveform of the tone will clearly change (Fig. 3.4). How significant such changes are perceptually is another matter and also is beyond the scope of the current discussion.

The last general form of distortion is amplitude distortion, the form of distortion most commonly associated with the term *distortion* and the coupling of this term with the concept of **nonlinearity**. In the simple spring-mass system, amplitude distortion occurs when the limits of elasticity of the spring are exceeded and the restoring force is no longer proportional to the displacement of the spring. This is called a nonlinearity because the input-output function of the system, that is, the graph of the output versus input, is not a straight line. Naturally, such distortion impacts the waveform, an example of

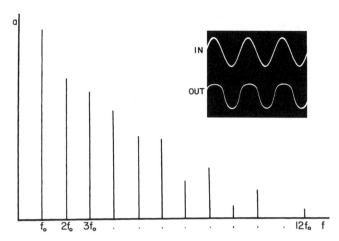

**Figure 3.19.** Effects of amplitude nonlinearity in the reproduction of a sinusoidal signal (*IN*) and demonstration, specifically, of harmonic distortion. The fundamental of the output signal (*OUT*), $f_o$, is the frequency of the input signal. The distortion products have frequencies of $2f_o$, $3f_o$, etc., and, thus, are harmonically related. (The 11th, 13th, and higher components are not measurable.) The amplitude axis is logarithmic, whereas the frequency scale is linear. (OUT obtained electronically using an asymmetric peak-limiting circuit.)

which is shown in the *inset* of Figure 3.19 (tracing labeled "out"). The nonlinearity illustrated in Figure 3.19 is, specifically, an example of peak clipping, wherein the output is limited to a particular positive and/or negative value. A severely and symmetrically peak-clipped sine wave would approximate a square wave (see Fig. 3.11).

### B. HARMONIC VERSUS INTERMODULATION DISTORTION

The result of amplitude distortion is that oscillation(s) no longer occurs at just the driving frequency(ies). In other words, the presence of amplitude distortion is characterized by the production of frequency components in the spectrum of the output signal that are not present at the input (Fig. 3.19). The frequencies, phases, and amplitudes of the distortion products themselves depend upon the exact nature of the nonlinearity involved and the driving signal. If a single sinusoidal signal is fed into the input of a system (such as a hearing aid), ***harmonic distortion*** can be seen by comparing input and output signals. An example of an amplitude-distorted signal and its spectrum are shown

in Figure 3.19. The salient characteristic of harmonic distortion is that the distortion products appear at frequencies that are integer multiples of the fundamental. Because integer multiples of a fundamental frequency are called *harmonics*, these distortion products are often called harmonics. They are numbered according to multiples of the fundamental: $2f_o$, second; $3f_o$, third; etc. harmonics. The greater the amount of amplitude distortion present, the greater the amplitude of these components compared to the fundamental and, generally, the greater the number of harmonics present. Although the presence of amplitude distortion is clearly evident in the output signal shown in the *inset* of Figure 3.19, it would be misleading to suggest that the presence of amplitude distortion—specifically harmonic distortion—will be evident to the naked eye in all cases. Small amounts of distortion can escape visual detection on the oscilloscope or other measurement devices and require more critical methods of observation, for instance, a distortion, wave, or spectrum analyzer. Even a high-quality sine wave generator will produce some harmonic distortion, although negligible for most practical purposes.

Now, if two pure tones or sinusoidal signals are fed into an amplitude-distorting system, interactions between the two will occur. Not only will this interaction occur between the two fundamentals (or primaries), but also between their harmonics. This particular manifestation of amplitude nonlinearity is referred to as *intermodulation distortion*. The spectrum of a complex tone that has been subjected to intermodulation distortion will contain components that equal the sums and differences of the fundamentals, as well as the sums and differences of the higher harmonics and all combinations thereof. The more pronounced the intermodulation distortion, the more prevalent will be these components and the more complex the spectrum of the signal produced at the output of the system.

Amplitude nonlinearities, like other forms of distortion, are unavoidable in real physical systems. Amplitude distortion is probably the major cause of displeasure with the sound produced by a cheap radio or hi-fidelity system that is blaring. Interestingly, intermodulation distortion products are generally considered more strident and displeasing than harmonics. Still, it is possible to produce acceptably clean sounds, that is, to reduce distortion to negligible levels. This is what one is paying for when spending sizable amounts of money on high-end hi-fidelity systems. What are negligible levels depends on the application and/or the limits of the measuring apparatus. Amplitude distortion is typically measured in percent computed from the ratio of the total energy in the distortion components to that of the total sound—20% in the case of the signal analyzed in Figure 3.19. This is what is known specifically as the total harmonic distortion. Alternatively, it may be sufficient to specify only the relative amplitude or percentage of a specific distortion product. This is certainly the most practical approach in analyzing intermodulation distortion. In the case illustrated in Figure 3.19, it could be stated that the second harmonic was 16 dB down from or below the fundamental. In other words, the SPL of $2f_o$ was 16 dB less than the amplitude of $f_o$. Clearly, the measurement of amplitude distortion fundamentally involves spectrum analysis.

It should be evident that distortion is another way, usually an undesirable one, in which the spectrum of a sound may be altered with respect to the input signal used to create it. Amplitude distortion also provides yet another demonstration of how changes in the time domain (waveform) are "echoed" in the frequency domain (spectrum), and vice versa. Last, distortion is not only characteristic of practical physical systems but also of biological systems, including the auditory system. Indeed, in later chapters, it will be shown that distortion of one form or the other is evident at the most basic levels of sound pickup, transmission, and neural encoding in the auditory system.

## BIBLIOGRAPHY

Békésy, G. v. (1974). Introduction. In *Handbook of Sensory Physiology: Vol. V/1. Auditory System: Anatomy, Physiology (Ear)*, pp. 1– 8, edited by W. D. Keidel and W. D. Neff. Springer-Verlag, Berlin.

Beranek, L. L. (1988). *Acoustical Measurements*, 2nd ed. American Institute of Physics, New York.

Bickel. H. J. (1971). Real-time spectrum analysis. *Sound Vibr* 5(3):14–20.

Blackman, R. B., and Tukey, J. W. (1958). *The Measurement of Power Spectra*. Dover Publications, New York.

Botsford, J. H. (1971). Sound without decibels. *Sound Vibr* 5(10):11.

Durrant, J. D. (1983). Fundamentals of sound generation for auditory evoked responses. In *Bases of Auditory Brain Stem Evoked Responses*, pp. 15–49, edited by E. J. Moore. Grune & Stratton, New York.

Gabor, D. (1947). Acoustical quanta and the theory of hearing. *Nature* 159:591–594.

Huntley, R. (1970). A bel is ten decibels. *Sound Vibr* 4(1):22.

Ladefoged, P. (1962). *Elements of Acoustic Phonetics*. University of Chicago Press, Chicago.

Lee, Y. W. (1960). *Statistical Theory of Communication*. John Wiley & Sons, New York.

Licklider, J. C. R. (1951). Basic correlates of the auditory stimulus. In *Handbook of Experimental Psychology*, pp. 985–1039, edited by S. S. Stevens. John Wiley & Sons, New York.

Lovrinic, J. M., and Durrant, J. D. (1991). Audiologic instrumentation. In *Diagnostic Audiology*, pp. 53–66, edited by J. T. Jacobson and J. L. Northern. Pro-Ed, Austin, TX.

Moody, R. C. (1971). The duality of time and frequency, a Fourier transform pair. *Sound Vibr* 5(1): 4.

Moody, R. C. (1971). Properties of periodic waves. *Sound Vibr* 5(2):5.

Moody, R. C. (1971). Properties of random waves. *Sound Vibr* 5(4):12–14.

Peterson, A. P. G., and Gross, E., Jr. (1967). *Handbook of Noise Measurement*. General Radio Co., West Concord, MA.

Pfeiffer, R. R. (1974). Considerations of the acoustic stimulus. In *Handbook of Sensory Physiology: Vol. V / 1. Auditory System: Anatomy, Physiology (Ear)*, pp. 9–38, edited by W. D. Keidel and W. D. Neff. Springer-Verlag, Berlin.

Rossing, T. D. (1990). *The Science of Sound*, 2nd ed. Addison-Wesley Publishing, Reading, MA.

Sonn, M. (1969). *Psychoacoustical Terminology*. Raytheon Co., Portsmouth, RI.

Speaks, C. E. (1992). *Introduction to Sound: Acoustics for Hearing and Speech Sciences*. Singular Publishing Group, San Diego.

*Standards, Formulae and Charts: Excerpts from International Standardization on Acoustical and Mechanical Measurements*. Brüel & Kjær Instruments, Cleveland, OH.

*Theory and Applications of Wave Analyzers*. Hewlett-Packard Applications Note 126. Hewlett-Packard Co., Loveland, CO.

Tonndorf, J. (1980). Physics of sound. In *Otolaryngology: Vol. 1. Basic Sciences and Related Disciplines*, ed. 2, pp. 241–260, edited by M. M. Paparella and D. A. Shumrick. W. B. Saunders, Philadelphia.

Wever, E.G., and Lawrence, M. (1954). *Physiological Acoustics*. Princeton University Press, Princeton, NJ.

## CHAPTER 4

# ANATOMY OF THE EAR

To understand how one hears, it is essential to understand more than the physical principles underlying sound, the stimulus of hearing. And although various physical principles established in the preceding chapters will be applied in the next chapter to a description of how the hearing system or *auditory mechanism* actually works, some important groundwork first must be laid. The auditory mechanism is a biological system, and, like all biological systems, it is described by the science known as **anatomy**. Anatomy is based on the principle that to understand how something functions, it first is necessary to understand how it is built. Indeed, the most fundamental premise of anatomy as a scientific discipline is that structure dictates function.

The hardware of the auditory mechanism, in the common vernacular, is the ear and the brain. Commonly, the **ear** is viewed merely as one of the conspicuous flaplike appendages found on the sides of the head. Yet, the ear is much more. Technically, the term *ear* refers to the entire **peripheral auditory system** (or *peripheral auditory apparatus*). This involves everything from the readily visible outer ear (of which the above-mentioned flaplike appendage is a part) to the intricate structures of the inner ear, located deep in the skull, and the nerve connecting it to the brain. The portions of the brain most directly involved in hearing, on the other hand, are called collectively the **central auditory system**. Its anatomy will be presented in Chapter 6.

The peripheral auditory system consists of three major subdivisions referred to classically as the **external, middle, and internal ears**. In more common terms, although somewhat less precise, these portions are known as the *outer, middle*, and *inner ears*, respectively (Fig. 4.1). Although these divisions are anatomically and functionally arbitrary, they are useful for descriptive purposes, so this partitioning scheme will be used here. The outer ear, much as its appearance suggests, "collects" the sound and directs it to the more internal parts. The middle ear is a cavity, and its major contents are three small bones known collectively as the *ossicular chain*. The external and middle parts of the ear together are frequently referred to as the **conducting apparatus**, because they provide the means by which sound energy is transformed into mechanical vibration and, thereby, conducted to the inner ear. The inner ear, which contains the sensory or *end organ* of hearing, has the task of converting this energy into an effective stimulus for the end organ. The final product of end organ function is the initiation of a message to the brain signaling the presence of the sound and providing detailed information about it. Incidentally, the inner ear also includes the end organs of balance, that is, the *peripheral vestibular system*.

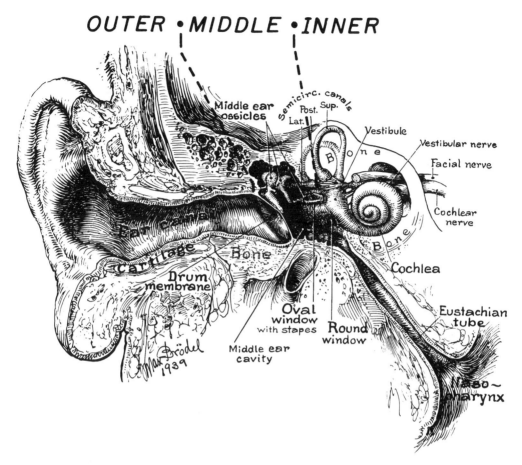

**Figure 4.1.** Drawing of the outer, middle, and inner ear based on a frontal section of the head. (Adapted from Brodel, M. [1946]. *Three Unpublished Drawings of the Anatomy of the Human Ear.* W. B. Saunders Co., Philadelphia.)

## 1. Anatomical Terminology

It is difficult to provide a reasonably in-depth treatment of the anatomy of the peripheral auditory system without first presenting a basic understanding of anatomical methodology and terminology. Most scientific fields use specialized methods and associated vocabularies. Consequently, to be able to read and understand the literature in those fields, it is essential to gain at least a cursory understanding of these methods and terms.

As noted above, in effect, ***anatomy*** is the science of structures of the body. Although modern-day anatomists use var-

ious sophisticated devices, such as the electron microscope, all anatomical study relies on the classical technique of ***dissection***. In dissection, organs or whole specimens are cut or sliced systematically to provide an internal view of their structure. They are then observed with the naked eye or, after suitable preparation, with a microscope. Of necessity, the dissection of a structure requires that certain things be cut away to provide the desired view. Furthermore, the anatomist often is obliged to discern the organization and orientation of a three-dimensional structure from a cross-sectional, two-dimensional, view (as in Fig. 4.1). Consequently,

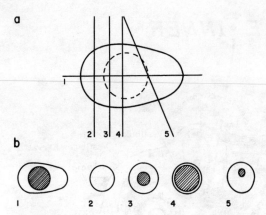

**Figure 4.2.** Dissection of an egg. **a.** The *lines* indicate the planes of the section. The *broken circle* indicates the position of the yolk. **b.** Sections resulting from slices through the egg in the corresponding planes in **a.**

the view obtained from a given section may be misleading if not considered in the proper perspective. This concept can be illustrated by taking a familiar object, such as a boiled egg, and observing it after dissection (Fig. 4.2). In effect, the egg takes on different shapes and sizes according to how it is sliced or sectioned. For example, cutting through the egg longitudinally (Fig. 4.2*a1*), as is typically done in preparing deviled eggs, reveals a light elliptically shaped outer structure with a dark round inner structure—the egg white and yolk, respectively (Fig. 4.2*b1*). Sectioning perpendicular to this cut in the middle of the egg (Fig. 4.2*a4*), the inner structure appears unchanged, but the outer structure now assumes the appearance of a thin ring (Fig. 4.2*b4*). Other sections (Fig. 4.2, *a2, a3,* and *a5*) may miss the inner structure entirely (Fig. 4.2*b2*) or place it in different positions within the outer structure (Fig. 4.2, *b3* and *b5*). Similarly, anatomical structures may take on different appearances depending on how the specimen is prepared. Only with knowledge of the orientation of the plane of section, in relation to the remainder of the body, can one clearly understand where these structures are, their makeup, and their relationship to other structures.

In anatomy there are standard **planes of reference** and terms to describe direction with respect to these planes. In describing human anatomy, these planes, and thus directions, are defined presuming the body to be erect with the head straightforward. The major planes of section are illustrated in Figure 4.3. Because the interest here is confined to structures within the head, only the head is shown in these rather schematic drawings, but the terms used apply equally to the whole body. A slice through the head that divides it into front and back portions is said to be a section in the *frontal (or coronal) plane*. A section dividing the head into left and right portions represents a cut in the *sagittal plane*. A section in the plane projecting specifically through the middle of the head is said to be in the *median* or *midsagittal plane*. Frontal and sagittal planes of section are thus vertical sections and perpendicular to one another. On the other hand, a slice in the *horizontal plane* divides the head into upper and lower portions and is sometimes referred to as a *transverse section*.

The **anatomical directions** by which the location of some structure, or a part of it, may be described are summarized in Table 4.1 and are supplemented by Figure 4.3. *Anterior* and *posterior* are seen to be synonymous with front and back. *Inferior* and *superior* refer to the bottom and top, or above and below, respectively. *Lateral* and *medial*, however, are slightly more complicated. The term *lateral* means away from the median plane, whereas *medial* means toward it. For example, the eyes are located laterally to the nose, whereas they are situated medially to the outer ears (as well as anteriorly). Other terms frequently used in anatomy are *ventral* and *dorsal*, which are referenced to the vertebral column. In the human, these terms are synonymous with anterior and posterior, respectively. *Caudal* and *cranial* (*rostral* or *cephalad*) are directions away from or toward the head, respectively and, in the human, generally corre-

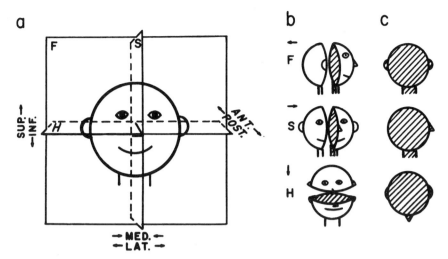

**Figure 4.3.** Anatomical planes and directions with respect to the human head. **a.** Frontal (*F*), sagittal (*S*), and horizontal (*H*) planes; superior (*SUP*), inferior (*INF*), medial (*MED*), lateral (*LAT*), anterior (*ANT*), and posterior (*POST*) directions are indicated. **b.** Frontal, sagittal, and horizontal sections of the head. **c.** Corresponding views of these sections from the directions indicated by the *arrows* in **b**.

TABLE 4.1
**Description of Anatomical Directions**

| Term | General Anatomical Meaning | Anatomical Meaning re Human |
|---|---|---|
| Anterior | Toward the front of a structure or organ | Toward the belly surface or toward the face |
| Posterior | Toward the back of a structure or organ | Toward the back |
| Lateral | Toward the side of a structure or organ; away from the midline | Toward the side of the body or side of the head |
| Medial | Toward the middle or midline of a structure or organ | Away from the side of the body or head and toward the median plane |
| Ventral | Away from the backbone | Synonymous with anterior |
| Dorsal | Toward the backbone | Synonymous with posterior |
| Superior | Toward the upper surface of a structure or organ | Toward the head or cranium (in head and neck anatomy, the terms "cephalad" or "rostral" may be used) |
| Inferior | Toward the bottom or lower surface of a structure or organ | Toward the feet or lower part of the body (in head and neck anatomy, the term "caudal" may be used) |

spond to inferior and superior. Two other terms that are useful are *superficial* and *deep*, referring to locations away from or near the center of the body. In general, these terms are also applied in describing the detailed anatomy of organs or even substructures within the body.

Finally, there are numerous terms, largely of Latin or Greek origin, that are used by the anatomist to describe certain types or shapes of structures. A dictionary often reveals that an exotic sounding anatomical term really means something common. This occurs because most anatomical terms are of a descriptive nature. For instance, *fenestra rotunda* translates to "round window." Obviously, the simplest approach would be to describe the anatomy of the peripheral auditory system in the common vernacular. There are two reasons why such an approach would be ill advised. First, anatomical texts and other literature are replete with the standard anatomical terms. Second, the standard anatomical terms are often more efficient; they simply are not widely accepted terms in the common vernacular. For example, to describe the area of the eardrum known as the *umbo*, one would have to say, "the most depressed portion of the tympanic membrane when viewed laterally." In any event, the terms used here will be those that seem to be the most common in the hearing literature.

## 2. Gross Anatomy of the Temporal Bone

The human skull is composed of a number of individual bones connected to one another at sutures (Fig. 4.4*a*). The ***tem-***

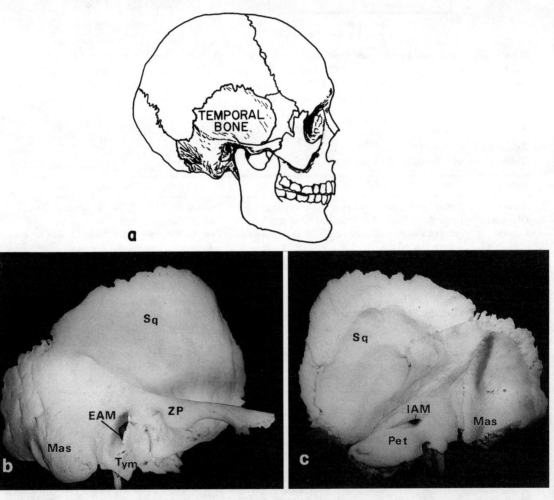

**Figure 4.4.** Human temporal bone (right ear). **a.** Relation of the temporal bone to the rest of the skull. (Based on a drawing by Gardner, E., Gray, D. J., and O'Rahilly, R. [1963]. *Anatomy*. W. B. Saunders Co., Philadelphia). Lateral (**b**) and medial (**c**) views show the external auditory meatus (*EAM*), mastoid (*Mas*), squamous (*Sq*), zygomatic process (*ZP*), tympanic (*Tym*) and petrous portions (*Pet*), and internal auditory meatus (*IAM*).

*poral bones*, constituting major portions of the lateral surface of the skull, contain the organs of hearing and balance. Each temporal bone is divided into four parts known as the *squamous, mastoid, tympanic*, and *petrous* portions. In a lateral view of the temporal bone (Fig. 4.4*b*), the **squamous portion** appears as a fanlike projection superior and anterior to the opening of the **external auditory meatus**, or *external canal*. In other words, the squamous portion lies above and in front of the ear canal. (Note: from this point on, you are on your own. Refer to Fig. 4.3 as often as necessary, but the only way to really master anatomical terms is to use them.) On the opposite side of the external canal, which is located posteriorly and inferiorly, is a bulky structure known as the **mastoid** portion. This is the slight bulge that is felt just behind the *auricle* (the ear as defined in the common vernacular). Whereas the squamous portion is a thin bony plate contributing to the lateral wall of the cranium, the mastoid is fairly thick but has numerous air-filled spaces or **air cells**. The **tympanic portion** of the temporal bone forms the floor and part of the anterior and posterior walls of the external auditory meatus and is only partially visualized in the lateral view (Fig. 4.4*b*). The **petrous portion** is almost totally obscured in this view, because it projects medially from the other three parts. Consequently, the temporal bone specimen must be turned around to completely reveal its structure, as shown in Figure 4.4*c*. The sensory organs of the peripheral auditory system are found deep in the petrous portion of the temporal bone.

There are numerous anatomical details of the temporal bone that are of significance. The various ridges and crevices on the surface of the temporal bone reflect important underlying structures, and there are various openings that form passageways for blood vessels and nerves. A particularly important example is the **internal auditory meatus**, through which the *acoustic nerve* (cranial nerve VIII)

passes. The internal auditory meatus can be seen as an opening on the posterior surface of the petrous portion of the temporal bone in Figure 4.4*c*. The temporal bone thus contains the most significant parts of the peripheral auditory mechanism.

## 3. The Outer Ear

The most familiar structure of the ear is, of course, the aforementioned flaplike appendage, which anatomists call the **auricle** or **pinna**. (Note: the former term seems most prevalent in anatomical descriptions of the human, whereas the latter is most often encountered in the animal hearing literature.) Except for its most inferior part, the auricle is built on a framework of cartilage. It is provided with some musculature, but this is of negligible functional value in man. Even the mastery of wiggling one's ears is more a matter of training the surrounding muscles than those of the auricle itself. Often the auricles are considered to be as much of cosmetic value in humans as they are of functional value, except perhaps for eyeglass wearers for whom they are essential. It

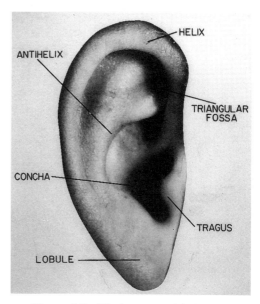

**Figure 4.5.**  The human auricle (pinna).

will become apparent in Chapter 5 that, in fact, the auricle plays an important role in the hearing of humans.

Although auricles come in assorted sizes and shapes and seem to be idiosyncratic, there are still a number of distinctive, but common, landmarks associated with their structure. The major structures are shown in Figure 4.5. The prominent ridge, which begins just superior to the opening of the external auditory meatus and runs around much of the edge of the auricle, is called the **helix** (Fig. 4.5). Just inside the helix, following a similar course, is the ridge known as the **antihelix**. Anteriorly and superiorly, the antihelix splits to form a depression called the **triangular fossa**. The most inferior aspect of the auricle is the **lobule** or *ear lobe* (the frequent site of puncture wounds for earrings). Lying just above the lobule is a deep depression similar to the sides of a funnel—the **concha**. The concha forms the mouth of the external auditory meatus. Located on the anterior wall of the ear canal is a small cartilaginous flap called the **tragus**.

It is evident from a frontal section of the outer ear (Figs. 4.1 and 4.6) that the auricle is the lateral extension of the soft and cartilaginous tissue of the external auditory meatus. The external canal appears as a tube leading medially into the deeper parts of the temporal bone and is terminated on its medial aspect by the **tympanic membrane** or *eardrum*. The

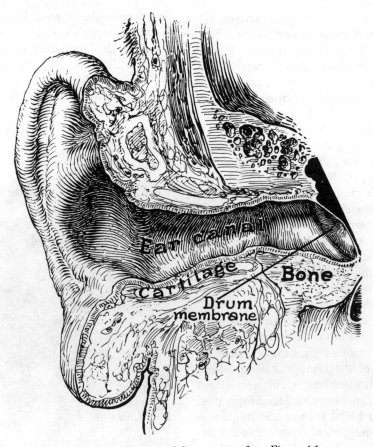

**Figure 4.6.** Close-up of the outer ear from Figure 4.1.

medial half of the tube is formed of squamous and tympanic portions of temporal bone, lined with skin, whereas the lateral half is formed of skin-lined cartilage. As might be expected, the diameter of the cartilaginous portion of this tube can be changed by such things as jaw movement. The tube is not perfectly straight; rather, there are slight bends in it, which seem to serve a protective function for the tympanic membrane. Of clinical importance is the limited visibility of the eardrum imposed by the canal's shape and the slight downward bend that the canal takes near it (Fig. 4.6). Clear visualization of the eardrum, even with the physician's otoscope, requires manipulation of the auricle (a gentle tug superiorly and posteriorly, in adults), whereas the downward bend at the end of the canal makes it easy for debris or fluid to be trapped there.

Another nuance of the external auditory meatus is that it is slightly elliptical in shape. Furthermore, the tympanic membrane does not form a perfectly flat end for the canal (Fig. 4.7). Rather, the membrane is concave, curving inwardly or medially, with its inferior aspect anchored more medially than its superior aspect. Consequently, the observed length of the external canal depends on where it is measured, that is, along the anterior, posterior, superior, or inferior wall. These factors result in a great deal of variability in canal dimensions. The average human adult canal, which is somewhat oval in cross-sectional shape, is approximately 5 to 9 mm in diameter and 23 to 25 mm in length.

The skin of the cartilaginous portion of the external auditory meatus contains glands that secrete *cerumen* (earwax). Along with shape of the canal (and in some people the hairs at the entrance of the canal), the secretion of cerumen helps keep foreign objects out of the canal and aids in self-cleansing it. In general, the outer ear affords considerable protection for the middle and inner ear and maintains a fairly stable environment (particu-larly constancy of temperature) for these more delicate parts.

## 4. The Middle Ear

### A. THE MIDDLE EAR CAVITY

The structure of the middle ear is shown in Figure 4.1 and, in more detail, Figure 4.7. As stated previously, the middle ear, first of all, is a cavity. This cavity is rather small and irregular in shape, consisting of several interconnected air-filled spaces that can be divided into three regions. The region of most direct interest here is the *tympanic cavity* or *tympanum*, lying directly between the tympanic membrane and the inner ear. Above the tympanic membrane is the region known as the *epitympanic recess* or attic. These two regions (approximately 2 cm$^3$ in volume) vary in lateral-to-medial width from 2 to 6 mm and about 15 mm in height (superior to inferior) and depth (anterior to posterior). Extending posteriorly from the epitympanic recess and connected via and opening called the *aditus* is the *mastoid antrum*, an enlarged space in the mastoid portion of the temporal bone. The air cells in the mastoid open into the antrum. The final air-filled chamber associated with the middle ear is the *auditory* or *Eustachian tube*. These chambers are shown schematically in Figure 4.8.

Although the tympanic cavity is irregular in shape, it can be described as though it were a box, having six surfaces or walls. The lateral wall of the box is largely formed by the tympanic membrane (Fig. 4.7) and so is referred to as the *membranous wall*. If the tympanic membrane were removed, it would be possible to look into the middle ear and examine the other sides of the box, as illustrated in Figure 4.9. The anterior wall of the middle ear cavity is often referred to as the *carotid* wall, because the internal carotid artery lies just anterior to it. Some important

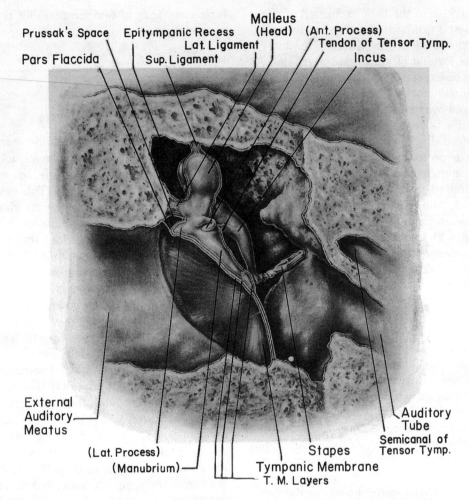

Prussak's Space     Epitympanic Recess     Malleus (Head)     (Ant. Process)
                                                              Tendon of Tensor Tymp.
                         Lat. Ligament
Pars Flaccida       Sup. Ligament                             Incus

External
Auditory
Meatus

(Lat. Process)                          Stapes          Auditory Tube
(Manubrium)                 Tympanic Membrane            Semicanal of Tensor Tymp.
                         T. M. Layers

**Figure 4.7.** Close-up of the middle ear. (Based on Deaver, J. B. [1926]. *Surgical Anatomy of the Human Body*. Blakiston Co., Philadelphia.)

openings also are present in this wall.[1] The most superior of these is the **semicanal of the tensor tympani**; the tensor tympani is one of the two muscles of the middle ear. Just below is the mouth of the *auditory tube*, mentioned above. The auditory tube is a canal of about 35 mm, which connects the middle ear cavity to the naso-pharyngeal cavity. It permits air to get into the middle ear to provide pressure equalization with the atmosphere outside. The portion of this canal connecting directly to the tympanic cavity is a channel though the temporal bone, opening near the top of the tympanic membrane, whereas the walls of the end of the tube, which opens into the nasopharynx, are cartilaginous. This end of the tube is not open continuously but opens only during such activities as swallowing, chewing, or yawning by virtue of the action of naso-pharyngeal musculature (*tensor veli pa-*

---

[1] A small opening not indicated in Figure 4.9 is one through which the *chorda tympani* (nerve) exits from the middle ear. En route, the chorda crosses just above and behind the eardrum (that is, medially). The chorda is a small sensory branch of the VIIth cranial nerve (or facial nerve), which innervates taste receptors of the tongue.

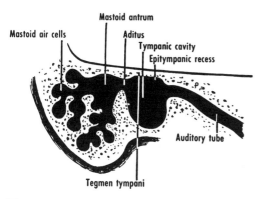

**Figure 4.8.** Air spaces of the human middle ear. This view is essentially the result of a frontal section of the temporal bone, although no single frontal section actually can show all of the indicated spaces simultaneously. (From Gardner, E., Gray, D. J., and O'Rahilly, R. [1963]. *Anatomy*. W. B. Saunders Co., Philadelphia.)

*latini,* aided by *levator veli palatini*) or in a passive manner by positive middle ear pressure. Closure of the auditory tube at this end generally prevents infections of the middle ear (from mucus, etc., from the nasopharynx) and attenuates one's own voice. The functioning of the nasopharyngeal opening of the auditory tube thus is very important in the normal physiological functioning of the middle ear.

Opposite the anterior wall is the posterior or ***mastoid*** wall. One of the most notable features of this wall is an opening in the epitympanic recess that leads to the mastoid air cells, the aditus (Fig. 4.9). There are two other anatomical landmarks of particular interest. Located near the middle of the mastoid wall is a pyramid-shaped prominence, the ***pyramidal eminence***, which contains the body of the

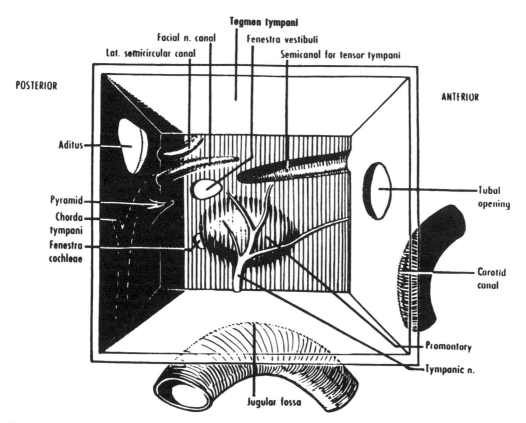

**Figure 4.9.** Lateral view of the right middle ear illustrated via a schematic representation of the middle ear, as if it were a box. The tympanic membrane has been removed to permit a view of the contents of the box. (From Gardner, E., Gray, D. J., and O'Rahilly, R. [1963]. *Anatomy*. W. B. Saunders Co., Philadelphia.)

other muscle of the middle ear—the **stapedius**. The stapedius tendon projects through a small opening in the apex of the pyramid to attach to the ossicular chain (specifically, the stapes, described below). Just lateral and slightly above the pyramidal eminence is a recess known as the **fossa incudis**. It forms a depression into which is fitted one "leg" of the middle bone of the ossicular chain—the *short crus of the incus* (described below). This recess is thus important in the suspension of the ossicular chain.

The inferior wall (floor) of the middle ear cavity, the **jugular wall**, derives its name from the jugular fossa, holding the jugular vein, lying just beneath it. The superior wall (ceiling) or **tegmental wall** is formed by a thin plate of bone from the petrous and squamous portions of the temporal bone called **tegmen tympani**. This bone separates the middle ear cavity from the cranial cavity.

The medial or **labyrinthine wall** is, with regard to hearing, the most remarkable of the six sides of the cavity. It is termed *labyrinthine* because it is largely formed by the bony wall of adjacent parts of the inner ear or *labyrinth* (described extensively in the next section). The two most important features of the medial wall are two openings or windows (Fig. 4.9). The window located most superiorly is the **oval** or **vestibular window** (or *fenestra vestibuli*). As its names imply, it is somewhat oval in shape and opens into the **vestibule** of the labyrinth. This is the part of the inner ear where the *semicircular canals* and the *cochlea* connect; these are the major vestibular and auditory parts of the inner ear, respectively. Located inferiorly is the smaller window, the **round** or **cochlear window** (*fenestra rotunda*). It too derives its names from its shape and by virtue of its opening into the cochlea. Another noteworthy feature of the medial wall is the bony prominence separating the two windows—the **promontory**. This bulge is actually the wall of the cochlea (Fig. 4.1). Now, the windows are not

"open" to the middle ear. The oval window is "closed" by a portion of one of the ossicles (the stapes footplate, see below), which is held in place by the **annular ligament**. The round window is covered by the thin *round window membrane*, sometimes called the *secondary tympanic membrane*. There are other prominent features of the medial wall, of which only one will be noted here. This is the prominence of the *facial canal*. It contains the *facial nerve* (cranial nerve VII), whose primary functions are to provide motor innervation to the muscles of facial expression and to transmit sensory information from the soft palate and tongue to the brain. The facial nerve also innervates the stapedius muscle.

## B. THE TYMPANIC MEMBRANE

The tympanic membrane (eardrum), again, terminates the external auditory meatus and thus, as described previously, forms the major portion of the lateral wall of the middle ear cavity. The largest portion of the tympanic membrane (Fig. 4.10a), known as the **pars tensa**, is formed of four layers of tissue. The most lateral layer is simply skin and is continuous with the lining of the meatus. The most medial layer is a part of the mucous lining that covers the inner surfaces of the middle ear cavity. Between these two layers are dense fibrous layers, composed of circular and radial fibers, that give the membrane some stiffness. The periphery of pars tensa is thickened into a fibrocartilaginous ring—the *annulus*—which, in turn, fits into the tympanic sulcus of the temporal bone. However, a small portion of the membrane, located superiorly, lacks the dense fibrous layers and, consequently, is more compliant or flaccid. Hence, this part of the tympanic membrane is called the **pars flaccida** (Fig. 4.10a).

The **malleus**, the lateral-most bone of the ossicular chain, is attached to the medial surface of the tympanic membrane. Its handle—the **manubrium**—extends

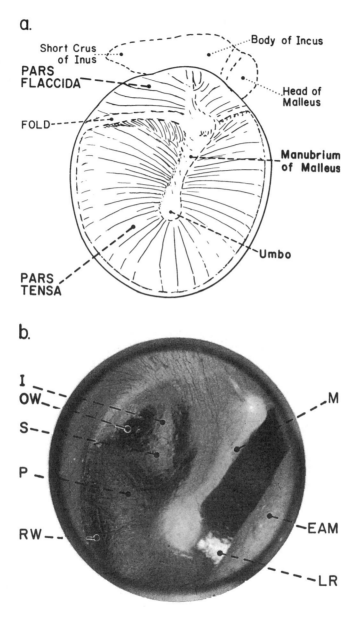

**Figure 4.10.** Lateral view of the tympanic membrane (right ear). **a.** The positions of the malleus and incus are shown by the *broken line* behind the eardrum. (Based on a drawing by Anson, B. J., and Donaldson, J. A., [1973]. *Surgical Anatomy of the Temporal Bone and Ear*. W. B. Saunders Co., Philadelphia.) **b.** Right tympanic membrane as seen through an otoscope. The semitransparent quality of the tympanic membrane permits the visualization of parts of the ossicular chain and the medial wall of the middle ear cavity: manubrium of the malleus (*M*), long crus of the incus (*I*), head of the stapes (*S*), niche of the oval window (*OW*), niche of the round window (*RW*), promontory (*P*), and portion of the anterior wall of the external auditory meatus (*EAM*). The bright cone-shaped spot near the umbo is a light reflection (*LR*). (Black-and-white print from color transparency, courtesy of Dr. R. A. Buckingham, University of Illinois College of Medicine, Chicago, IL.)

from just below the middle of the tympanic membrane to the upper part of pars tensa, angled in an anterosuperior direction (Fig. 4.10, *a* and *b*). As shown in Figure 4.7, when viewed in a frontal cross-section, the tympanic membrane is conical in shape, like a loudspeaker diaphragm. The tip of the cone coincides with the tip of the manubrium and is called the ***umbo*** (Fig. 4.10*a*).

Through the otoscope (Fig. 4.10*b*), the healthy tympanic membrane often appears nearly transparent, having a pearly gray hue. Under normal circumstances, some of the structures of the middle ear can be seen through the membrane. For example, the manubrium appears as a whitish streak, resembling the hour hand of a clock that is pointing to about 1:00 (that is, just to the right of 12:00) in the right ear and to about 11:00 (just to the left of 12:00) in the left ear. As might be expected from the diameter of the external canal, the eardrum is quite small—approximately 8 to 9 mm in diameter or about 81 mm$^2$ in area. It is approximately 0.1 mm thick and weighs in at about 14 mg. The tympanic membrane clearly is a delicate structure, underscoring again the importance of the protective role of the external auditory meatus.

## C. THE OSSICULAR CHAIN

As a matter of necessity, the bones of the ossicular chain already were identified in the foregoing paragraphs. Nevertheless, it is worth iterating that the three ossicles of the chain are the ***malleus, incus,*** and ***stapes***; perhaps more familiar are their common names: *hammer, anvil*, and *stirrup*, respectively. There also are various details of the anatomy of the ossicular chain that deserve discussion. As noted above, the malleus attaches to the tympanic membrane along the manubrium. It articulates with the incus posteriorly, as shown in Figures 4.7 and 4.11. Both the head of the malleus and the body of the incus, comprising the bulk of the mass of the ossicular chain, are located

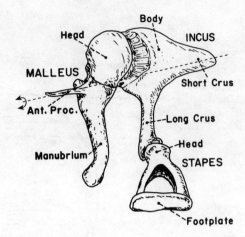

**Figure 4.11.** Medial view of the ossicular chain of the right ear, that is, from the center of the head (specifically from a position slightly anterior and superior to the ossicles) looking out. The axis of rotation (see text) is indicated by the *dashed line*. (Based on a drawing by Anson, B. J., and Donaldson, J. A. [1973]. *Surgical Anatomy of the Temporal Bone and Ear.* W. B. Saunders Co., Philadelphia.)

above the tympanic membrane in the epitympanic recess (Figs. 4.1 and 4.7). The incus has two legs or ***crura*** (*crus*, singular), one longer than the other. The short crus fits into the *fossa incudis*, whereas the long crus attaches to the stapes, the most medially located bone in the chain. The base of the stapes, called the *footplate*, fits into the oval window. Compared with the tympanic membrane, the stapes footplate is small, typically measuring only 1.3 × 2.5 mm (area, 3.2 mm$^2$).

The ossicles are suspended by a number of ligaments. The joints and attachments of these bones do not permit quite the same form of motion as seen in arms and legs, namely flexion and extension. The ossicular chain is designed to transmit the minute vibrations of the tympanic membrane to the inner ear efficiently over a very wide range of frequencies. Consequently, the chain tends to move as a whole in a rocking motion. The pivotal point of this motion, viewing the ossicular chain as a lever (see Chapter 5), is formed by the short crus of the incus and the *ante-*

*rior process* of the malleus. Therefore, the axis of rotation is located essentially at the center of mass of the chain.

The motion of the ossicular chain is further influenced, to varying degrees, by the muscles of the middle ear. From an anatomical point of view, the muscles seem to be antagonists, in that they pull in opposite directions and on opposite ends of the ossicular chain. The stapedius attaches near the head of the stapes, whereas the tensor tympani attaches to the manubrium. Functionally, they act more as synergists, as will be discussed later in Chapters 5 and 6. They are not activated by the same nerve; the tensor tympani is innervated by a motor branch of the trigeminal nerve (Vth cranial nerve), whereas the stapedius is innervated by the facial nerve, as noted earlier. It is important not to attribute to the middle ear musculature the same sort of action associated with other skeletal muscles. Although the muscles of the middle ear can cause movements of the eardrum and the ossicles, their primary function derives more from their resting tone (tonus) and increased tension under activation, thereby modifying motion that has been imparted to the ossicular chain by sound.

# 5. The Inner Ear

## A. THE LABYRINTHS

A series of interconnecting canals is found in the petrous portion of each temporal bone (Fig. 4.12a). Collectively they are called the *labyrinth*, which befits their complex shape. The terms *labyrinth* and *inner ear* often are used synonymously, although the latter term is commonly associated with only the auditory portion of the labyrinth, the cochlea. It will be recalled, however, that the inner ear contains the end organs of two sensory systems, the vestibular and auditory. If the bone of the petrous portion were cut away carefully, it would be possible to isolate the osseous labyrinth itself. This is, by no means, a

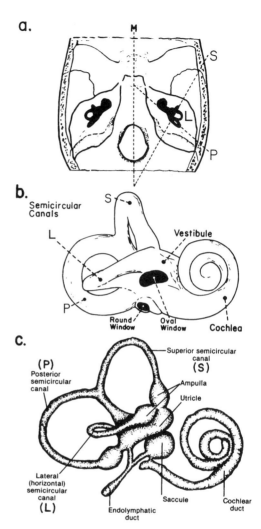

**Figure 4.12.** **a.** Location of the labyrinths in the skull. The median plane (*M*) and the planes of the superior (*S*) and posterior (*P*) semicircular canals are indicated by the *dashed lines*. *L*, Lateral semicircular canal. **b.** Osseous labyrinth (right ear), view from lateral and slightly anterior directions. (Based on drawings by Sobatta, J. [1954]. *Atlas of Descriptive Human Anatomy*, vol 3, ed 5, translated and edited by E. Ehlenhuth. Hafner Publishing Co., Inc., New York; and based on Schuknecht, H. F. [1974]. *Pathology of the Ear*. Harvard University Press, Cambridge.) **c.** Membranous labyrinth (right ear, comparable view to that of the bony labyrinth in **b**). (Adapted from Durrant, J. D., and Freeman, A. R. [1982]. Concepts in vestibular physiology. In *Dizziness and Vertigo*, p 16, edited by A. J. Finestone. John Wright-PSG, Boston.)

trivial task in humans and other primates! The isolated labyrinth would appear as a bony shell, as shown in Figure 4.12*b*. Major divisions of the labyrinth are the three semicircular canals, the vestibule, and the cochlea. The illustration in Figure 4.12*b* provides a lateral view of a right labyrinth, that is, the right inner ear as it would appear in an unobscured view from the ear canal.

Now, if the bony or **osseous labyrinth** could be cut away without destroying its contents, another labyrinth would be found! However, this "new" labyrinth would not be made of bone, but rather of soft tissue. It thus is called the **membranous labyrinth** (Fig. 4.12*c*). It resembles the bony labyrinth in overall shape, but it is much smaller in cross-sectional area. The space between the bony and membranous labyrinths is filled with a fluid called **perilymph**. The membranous labyrinth itself is filled with another fluid known as **endolymph**. The composition of these fluids will be discussed later in this chapter.

## B. THE VESTIBULAR APPARATUS

The vestibular apparatus comprises three bony **semicircular canals** and the bulk of the space joining this channel system to the cochlea—the vestibule—and the contents therein. Inspection of the membranous labyrinth in Figure 4.12*c* reveals that each of the three **membranous semicircular ducts** has a bulge at one end, just before the canals enter into the saclike structure called the **utricle**, lying in the vestibule. The bulged part is called the **ampulla**, and it is here that the sensory receptor organ of the semicircular canal is located. Because there are three canals, there are three membranous ducts, and, therefore, three semicircular receptor organs, known as **cristae ampullares** (*crista ampullaris*, singular). The cristae ampullares contain *sensory epithelia*, that is, patches of sensory and supporting cells, related to that of the cochlea, as described below. This system is de-

signed to respond only to angular motion (rotation), as is experienced when one turns his or her head. The three semicircular canals lie in three different planes that are perpendicular to one another. The *superior canal* is oriented at right angles to the *posterior canal*, and both are perpendicular to the *horizontal* or *lateral* canal. This scheme provides for detection of rotational movements in any direction. The three semicircular canal organs together thus act as a vectorial analyzer to break down a given accelerative force into component forces (vectors) in each plane.

The vestibule (Fig. 4.12*b*) houses the utricle (into which the semicircular canals open) and another saclike structure known as the **saccule** (Fig. 4.12*c*). The sensory epithelia in the utricle and saccule are termed **maculae** (*macula*, singular). They are composed of a relatively flat plate of sensory cells, covered by a gelatinous material containing calcium carbonate crystals or **otoliths**. The maculae are responsive to linear acceleration such as experienced in locomotion. Because of its anatomical orientation, the utricular macula is particularly responsive to the accelerative force of gravity, which is experienced during body or head tilt. The mechanisms by which this is possible are beyond the scope of coverage here. The intent is only to underline the important role of the nonauditory parts of the labyrinth and the anatomical relation between these structures and the auditory portion of the inner ear.

In addition to forming part of the vestibular system, the vestibule has the added significance of being the site of the oval window, as was shown in Figure 4.12*b*. The perilymphatic fluid freely communicates throughout the osseous labyrinth, so functionally it may be of little consequence that the oval window does not open directly into the cochlea. It also should be mentioned that endolymph communicates throughout the membranous labyrinth, because the vestibular and auditory portions of the membranous labyrinthine system are connected by a small duct (see Fig. 4.12c)—the *ductus reuniens*. Furthermore, the manner in which the membranous labyrinth is situated in the bony cochlea creates three essentially separate fluid spaces, as described below.

## C. THE AUDITORY APPARATUS

The auditory portion of the inner ear is the **cochlea**. It derives its name from its snail-shell shape; it has a structure that appears somewhat like a coiled hose. In humans, the cochlea has two and three quarters coils or turns. Other mammalian species (of which all have coiled cochleae) have more or less numbers of cochlear turns. The bony shell of the cochlea coils around a central bony canal known as the **modiolus** (Fig. 4.13). The modiolus contains blood vessels and nerve fibers that are described in detail below and in Chapter 6. A favored histological approach is to orient the temporal bone specimen so that

the cochlea seems to be resting on its broad **base**, the largest coil. Sections are cut through the cochlea in planes that are parallel to the modiolus. A section through the middle of the modiolus, called a *midmodiolar section*, yields the view shown in Figure 4.13. The midmodiolar section provides a particularly vivid cross-sectional view of the cochlea. A better understanding of why the cochlea appears as it does in this section can be obtained by referring to Figure 4.14. Panel *a* shows a drawing of a coiled tube of uniform diameter. When a slice is made through the coil, dividing it into halves, two vertical rows of holes are seen (when viewing one of the halves). Now, suppose that a tube, whose diameter diminishes toward one end (that is, a tapered tube) is used to make the coil. Furthermore, suppose a flexible rod is pushed through the tube. Because it is somewhat stiff, the rod will conform to the outside of the coiled tube (Fig. 4.14b). A section of

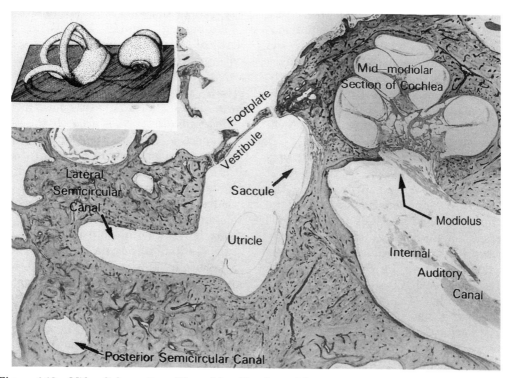

**Figure 4.13.** Midmodiolar section of the cochlea. The plane of the section is indicated in the *inset*. (Adapted from Schuknecht, H. F. [1974]. *Pathology of the Ear*. Harvard University Press, Cambridge.)

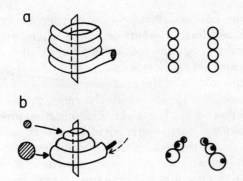

**Figure 4.14.** Sectioning a coiled hose. (See text for discussion.)

this "specimen" would resemble the mid-modiolar section of the cochlea (Fig. 4.13). In fact, the diameter of the bony cochlea does diminish toward the top or **apex**. The membranous labyrinth, similar to the behavior of the flexible rod, also attaches to the outer wall, that is, the wall opposite the modiolus. On the other hand, the membranous labyrinth also attaches to the modiolus, partitioning the space within the cochlear coils effectively into three channels (more on this point momentarily). And, unlike the rod, the cochlear membranous labyrinth changes in its transverse dimensions with length. Surprisingly, it is narrowest at the base, at which the coils of the cochlea are widest, and widest at the apex, at which the cochlea is narrowest (Fig. 4.15b).

The midmodiolar and comparable parallel sections provide one of two general views commonly used in describing the anatomy or functional anatomy of the cochlea; this view might be called "radial" (versus "longitudinal," the other view, described below). The radial perspective is particularly revealing of how the structures within each coil are situated relative to one another (Fig. 4.15a). Terms typically used to discuss location are referenced to the modiolus, for example, inner (toward the modiolus) and outer (away from the modiolus). "Medial" and "lateral," respectively, also are used, although not in a rigorous application of these ana-

tomical directions (that is, according to the definitions given in Anatomical Terminology). It is also important to keep in mind, as demonstrated earlier, that how the structures appear is very much a product of how the specimen is sliced.

An enlarged view of the cross-section of one cochlear coil, as shown in Figure 4.15a, reveals more details of the structure of the cochlear membranous labyrinth. As mentioned previously, not only is the membranous labyrinth attached to the outer cochlear wall, but it also attaches to a bony shelf projecting from the modiolus—the **osseous spiral lamina**. If the bony cochlear wall were stripped down and the membranous labyrinth removed, leaving just the osseous spiral lamina and the modiolus, the result would be a specimen appearing much like the "business end" of a wood screw. This can be appreciated by inspection of Figure 4.16; this figure provides further insight into the coiled structure of the cochlea, the nature of the modiolus, and the relationship between the cochlea and the vestibular apparatus.

Examining Figures 4.13, 4.15, and 4.16a, it is apparent that indeed the space within each cochlear coil is effectively divided into three channels—the **scala vestibuli, scala media,** and **scala tympani**. The scala media, also known as the *endolymphatic space*, is actually the interior space of the cochlear portion of the membranous labyrinth or **cochlear duct**. It is filled with endolymph. By virtue of its attachment to both the bony wall of the cochlea and the modiolus, it partitions the remaining space within the cochlear osseous labyrinth into two channels—the scala vestibuli and scala tympani. These scalae are filled with perilymph and communicate via an opening at the apex known as the **helicotrema** (Fig. 4.17).

In the conventional cross-sectional or radial view of the cochlea (Fig. 4.15), the scala vestibuli appears as the uppermost channel. It is via the scala vestibuli that perilymph directly and freely communicates between the vestibule and the coch-

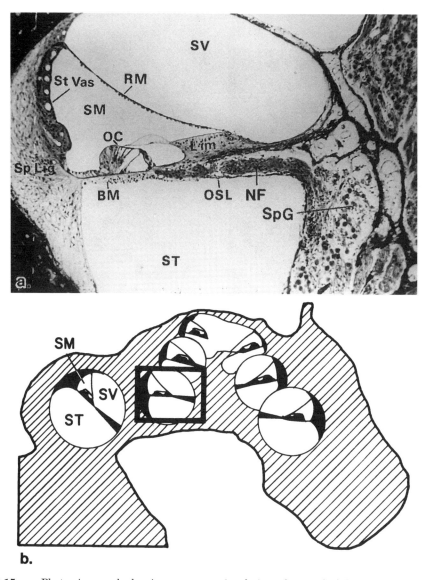

**Figure 4.15.** **a.** Photomicrograph showing a cross-sectional view of one coil of the cochlea, as indicated in **b**. Shown are the scala vestibuli (*SV*), scala media (*SM*), scala tympani (*ST*), Reissner's membrane (*RM*), stria vascularis (*St Vas*), organ of Corti (*OC*), spiral ligament (*Sp Lig*), basilar membrane (*BM*), spiral limbus (*Lim*), osseous spiral lamina (*OSL*), nerve fibers (*NF*), and spiral ganglion (*Sp G*). **b.** Highly schematic view of a section through the cochlea illustrating scalae and locus of the section in **a**. (Based on photographs by Mizoguti, H. *Color Slide Atlas of Histology*. Maruzen Co., Tokyo.)

lea. Because the scala vestibuli opens directly into the vestibule, and the oval window is in the vestibule, the oval window effectively opens into the scala vestibuli. In other words, it is the scala vestibuli that first receives the vibrations of the stapes footplate in the oval window, as a result of sound stimulation. On the other hand, the scala tympani, appearing as the lowermost channel, ends blindly at the round window, which "looks" into the middle ear cavity. These anatomical details explain the basis of the other, albeit more schematic but functional, view of the coch-

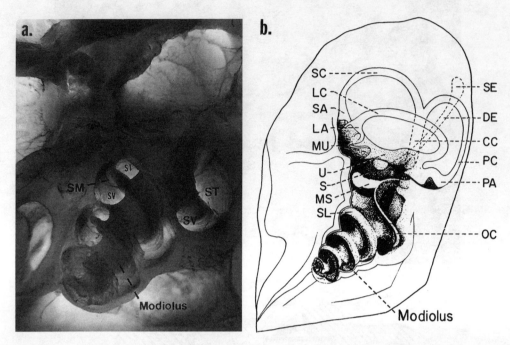

**Figure 4.16.** **a.** Dissection of the temporal bone, in this case the left ear of a guinea pig, to reveal the channels of the cochlea: scala vestibuli (*SV*), scala media (*SM*), and scala tympani (*ST*). Note: in this animal the cochlea is nearly free standing, rather than being embedded in the temporal bone, and has approximately four turns. (Courtesy of Dr. J. E. Hawkins, Kresge Hearing Research Institute, University of Michigan, Ann Arbor.) **b.** Drawing of the membranous labyrinth and the osseous spiral lamina essentially corresponding to the photograph in **a.** *SC, PC,* and *LC,* superior, posterior, and lateral semicircular canals, respectively; *SA, PA,* and *LA,* corresponding ampullae; *CC,* common crus; *U,* utricle, and *MU,* utricular macula; *S,* saccule, and *MS,* saccular macula; *DE* and *SE,* endolymphatic duct and sac, respectively; *SL,* spiral ligament; and *OC,* organ of Corti. (Adapted from a drawing by J. Wersall in Hawkins, J. E., and Johnsson, L.-G. [1976]. Microdissection and surface preparations of the inner ear. In *Handbook of Auditory and Vestibular Research Methods*, p 21, edited by C. A. Smith and J. A. Vernon. Charles C. Thomas, Springfield, IL.)

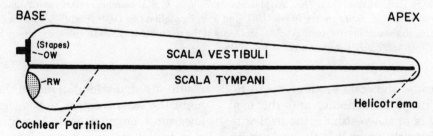

**Figure 4.17.** Schematic drawing of the uncoiled cochlea. *OW,* Oval window; *RW,* round window.

lea mentioned above—the longitudinal view (see Fig. 4.17). This view is typically used to illustrate how the cochlea works mechanically (see Chapter 5). In this perspective, the cochlea is shown as though it has been uncoiled. For simplicity, the scala media often is represented as a single membrane or partition—the *cochlear partition*. This picture obviously is an abstraction, but it is much easier to visualize mechanical events in the cochlea from this schema. Although the number of cochlear coils (two and three quarters in humans) and the length of the cochlear partition (about 36 mm in humans) are species specific, all cochleas seem to work along the same principles. Thus, the detailed dimensions are of secondary importance from a functional viewpoint.

It is easy to become a bit confused by what seem to be several aliases for the cochlear membranous labyrinth—scala media, cochlear duct, and cochlear partition. However, each term has its special meaning. *Scala media* is perhaps applied best in a geographical sense, such as viewing the three channels of the cochlea; it is more of a place than a structure. *Cochlear partition* is a term that is useful in describing cochlear mechanics, because it draws attention away from the anatomical details of the cochlear membranous labyrinth and presents it as a simple barrier. *Cochlear duct* is perhaps the most anatomical term, in that it underscores the reality of what this part of the cochlea actually is, a soft-tissue tube or duct—a structure, rather than a place or a simple barrier.

The cochlear duct is by no means a simple structure! As shown in Figure 4.15, it has somewhat a triangular shape in cross-section, with each side being composed of different tissues. Two of these sides define the boundaries of the scala media. First, *Reissner's membrane* separates the scala media from the scala vestibuli, and as seen in this figure, it attaches to the osseous spiral lamina and projects obliquely to attach to the outer wall of the cochlea. The cochlear duct is affixed to the outer wall of the cochlea by means of the *spiral ligament*, a band of connective tissue. On the side of the spiral ligament facing the modiolus lies a highly vascularized strip of tissue—the *stria vascularis*. The boundary between the scala media and the scala tympani is formed by another membrane—the *basilar membrane*, which spans the space between the osseous spiral lamina and the scala tympani side of the spiral ligament. As alluded to earlier, there is a systematic variation in the width of the basilar membrane from the base to the apex of the cochlea. The membrane is narrowest at the base and widest at the apex, but, curiously, it is thickest at the base. These anatomical changes cause a gradient of stiffness of the membrane, on the order of 100:1, from base (most stiff) to apex (least stiff). The functional ramifications of this feature will receive much attention in Chapter 5. For the time being, in the context of this predominantly anatomical description of the auditory apparatus, this membrane perhaps holds more interest for what it holds than for its own (albeit important) role. On the basilar membrane lies the hearing organ—the *organ of Corti*.

## 6. Fine Structure of the Organ of Corti

If the cochlear duct were examined under high magnification, a number of distinctive structures would become apparent, as illustrated by Figure 4.18. The *organ of Corti* is composed of both sensory and supporting cells. To understand the manner in which the hearing organ is constructed, it is useful to consult both idealized representations, such as the drawing in Figure 4.18, and photomicrographs of actual specimens, such as the two types in Figure 4.19. In Figure 4.19*a*, a section through the organ of Corti has been prepared using conventional histological techniques and photographed

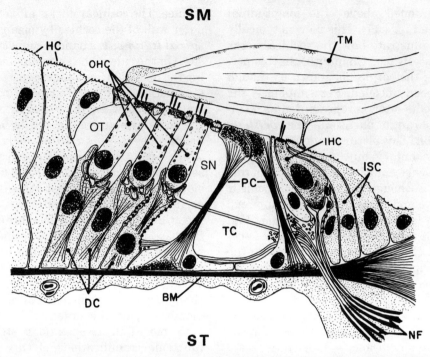

**Figure 4.18.**   Drawing of the cross-section of the organ of Corti, based on histological data, including electron microscopy, as well as electrophysiological data and theoretical considerations. Shown are the scala media (*SM*), tunnel of Corti (*TC*), scala tympani (*ST*), tectorial membrane (*TM*), inner supporting cells (*ISC*), Deiter's cells (*DC*), Hensen's cells (*HC*), pillar cells (*PC*), nerve fibers (*NF*), space of Nuel (*SN*), outer tunnel (*OT*), OHCs, and IHCs. (Adpated from Ryan, A., and Dallos, P. [1984]. Physiology of the cochlea in hearing disorders. In *Communicative Disorders: Hearing Loss*, 2nd ed, p 256, edited by J. L. Northern. Little, Brown & Co., Boston.)

through the light microscope (as also was the case for the specimen shown in Fig. 4.15*a*). The drawing in Figure 4.18 is based on this sort of histological preparation. The view is clearly two-dimensional. For a more three-dimensional view of this organ, Figure 4.19*b*—a photomicrograph obtained with the scanning electron microscope—is very useful. The specimen was cut to reveal the same cross-sectional view as in Figure 4.19*a*, but this technique allows observation of the rest of the specimen beyond the plane of section and conveys a greater sense of the actual shape of the organ. The drawing (Fig. 4.18), nevertheless, is perhaps the most useful picture for seeing the basic characteristics of a particular structure and where it is located.

The sensory cells of the hearing organ are called **hair cells**. Their name derives from the hairlike structures—**stereocilia**—that project from their tops or apical ends. The stereocilia are not really hair, but rather microvilli, which are extensions of the cell membrane. The stereocilia are stiffened substantially by their high actin content. Actin is a protein complex that is a major component in the makeup of muscle tissue and that is principally responsible for the ability of muscle cells to contract. This detail will be found later to be important in the working of this cell. There actually are two types of hair cells in the mammalian organ of Corti, **inner hair cells** and **outer hair cells** (IHCs and OHCs, respectively). There is a single row of IHCs running longitudinally

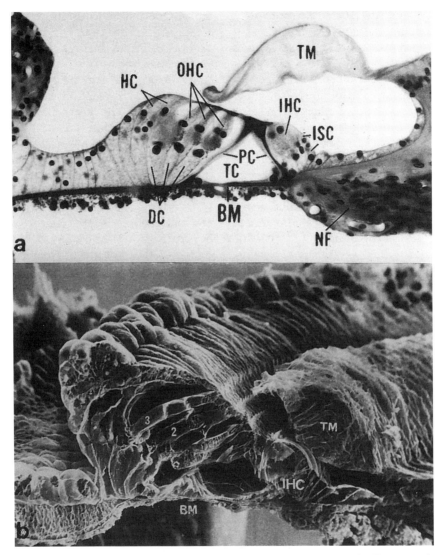

**Figure 4.19.** Cross-section of the organ of Corti. **a.** Conventional photomicrograph. The tectorial membrane is somewhat retracted from its normal position because of fixation artifact. Abbreviations are as in Figure 4.18. **b.** Scanning electron micrograph. OHCs are indicated by the *numbers* of their rows, 1–3; other abbreviations as above. (From Bredberg, G., Ades, H. W., and Engstrom, H. [1972]. Scanning electron microscopy of the normal and pathologically altered organ of Corti. *Acta Otolaryngol. [Suppl.] [Stockh.]* 301:3–48.)

along the extent of the basilar membrane. In humans, there are approximately 3,500 IHCs lined up side by side along the entire length of the organ of Corti. Recalling that the length is about 36 mm, the number of IHCs reveals just how small in diameter are they are, namely about 10 $\mu$m (or $10^{-2}$ mm) in diameter. These flask-shaped cells are called IHCs because they lie on the side of the organ that is closest to the modiolus or core of the cochlea. In contrast, there are usually three, and occasionally four or five, rows of OHCs. Thus there are more than three times as many OHCs as IHCs; specifically, there are approximately 12,500 OHCs in the human cochlea. Although of similar diameters as the IHCs, OHCs have a shape reminiscent of a test tube and are located farther away from the modiolus than IHCs. OHCs also vary in length from base (shortest) to apex (longest).

Not only do the two types of hair cells differ with regard to the shapes of their cell bodies and their numbers, they also differ in the configurations of their bundles of stereocilia. As shown in Figure 4.20, the stereocilia on the IHCs are lined up such that the hairs form an almost continuous line along the organ of Corti. On each hair cell, the stereocilia, numbering about 60 per cell, form a very shallow crescent (Fig. 4.20). The bundle of stereocilia atop each OHC, however, forms a very distinctive pattern, which typically is described as a W. As seen in Figure 4.20, the base of the W points away from the IHCs and radially away from the modiolus. The number of stereocilia atop each OHC changes with location, varying from 20 to 100 per cell from the first and second rows in the base (most) to the third row in the apex (least). As can be seen in Figure 4.21a, several rows of stereocilia are found on each OHC. The stereocilia diminish in length by row within the bundles with the shortest hairs in the row nearest the IHCs and modiolus (inside the W pattern). The overall lengths of stereocilia of both types of hair cells increase from base to apex.

Overlying the organ of Corti, and thus the stereocilia, is the **tectorial membrane** (Figs. 4.18 and 4.19). Being approximately 90% water, the tectorial membrane has a gelatinous consistency and is nearly transparent, even in heavily stained specimens. The tectorial membrane projects radially from the **spiral**

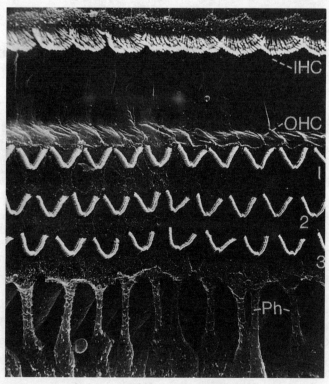

**Figure 4.20.** Surface of the organ of Corti. Stereocilia belonging to IHCs, the different rows of OHCs, and the phalangeal processes (*Ph*) are indicated. (Adapted from Bredberg, G., Ades, H. W., and Engstrom, H. [1972]. Scanning electron microscopy of the normal and pathologically altered organ of Corti. *Acta Otolaryngol.* [Suppl.] [Stockh.] 301:3–48.)

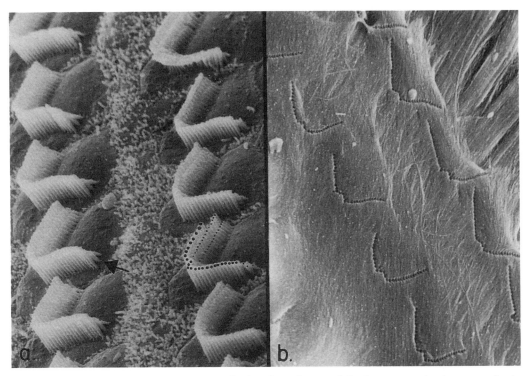

**Figure 4.21. a.** Scanning electron micrograph of surface of organ of Corti encompassing two rows of outer hair cells; view is slightly oblique, looking somewhat into the tufts of hairs atop each cell. Each cell has three rows of stereocilia of different lengths (*arrow*). Tops of stereocilia on one cell have been *dotted* for emphasis, the larger dots having been placed on the tallest hairs. (Micrograph courtesy of Dr. I. M. Hunter-Duvar, The Hospital for Sick Children, Toronto, Ontario, Canada.) **b.** Micrograph showing an imprint of outer hairs on the underside of the tectorial membrane. Note that imprints occur only for the tallest stereocilia, namely those in the most radially located row). (Adapted from Hunter-Duvar, I. M. [1978]. Electron microscopic assessment of the cochlea. *Acta Otolaryngol. [Suppl.] [Stockh.]* 351:3–23.)

*limbus*, which consists of a mound of connective tissue resting on the osseous spiral lamina (Fig. 4.15). The tectorial membrane is firmly attached at its origin, that is, along its inner edge, to the spiral limbus. It attaches on its outer edge primarily to the outer supporting cells of the organ of Corti, namely *Hensen's cells* and/or *Deiters' cells*, and secondarily to the inner supporting cells (Fig. 4.18). (The supporting cells are described in more detail below.) However, these latter attachments usually cannot withstand the conventional procedure used to prepare the tissue for histological examination, so the tectorial membrane often seems to hang freely over the organ (Fig. 4.19*a*). As will be discussed later (Chapter 5), it is of func-

tional importance that the attachment of the tectorial membrane on its outer border allows the membrane to move somewhat independently from the underlying organ of Corti. In other words, it forms a relatively loose connection to the body of the organ. On the other hand, the longer stereocilia of the OHCs are embedded in the undersurface of this membrane. As mentioned earlier, the hairs of the OHCs are not of uniform length (the longest stereocilia being found at the base of the W), so some are embedded more deeply than others. It is unclear whether the stereocilia of the IHCs are embedded in the tectorial membrane at all, although the bulk of the evidence suggests not. As shown in Figure 4.21, when the undersurface of the tectorial membrane is examined microscopically, imprints of some of the outer hairs are clearly evident, whereas no such imprints are seen for the stereocilia of the IHCs.

Lending structural stability to the hair cells are a variety of supporting cells, the most distinctive of which are the *pillar cells*. There are both *inner* and *outer pillars* (or *rods*) whose bases rest on the basilar membrane but whose heads lean toward one another, ultimately joining at the top of the organ of Corti (Figs. 4.18 and 4.19). The triangular space formed by the pillars extends longitudinally throughout the organ and is called the *tunnel of Corti*. It is also notable that there are spaces between the outer pillars and the first row of OHCs (the *spaces of Nuel*), the last row of OHCs, and the Hensen's cells (the outer tunnel), and even between the OHCs themselves (see Fig. 4.18). These spaces and the tunnel of Corti are filled with fluid that at one time was thought

to be significantly different than the other two fluids of the cochlea and referred to as *cortilymph*, although it was generally acknowledged that this fluid was much more like perilymph than endolymph. It now seems that the basilar membrane acts like a sieve, permitting free communication between the intercellular and tunnel spaces and the scala tympani. The hair cells thus are bathed in perilymph.

There are three other major types of cells that provide support specifically for the OHCs, some of which were mentioned above: *Deiters', Hensen's,* and *Claudius's cells*. Deiters' cells have two major parts. The main bodies of these cells rest on the basilar membrane and cradle the bottom of the OHCs in cuplike depressions at their apexes. Emanating from the cell body of each is a finger-like extension, called the *phalangeal process*, which projects to the surface of the organ of Corti to hold the top of a different OHC than the one resting on it (Figs. 4.20 and 4.22). In

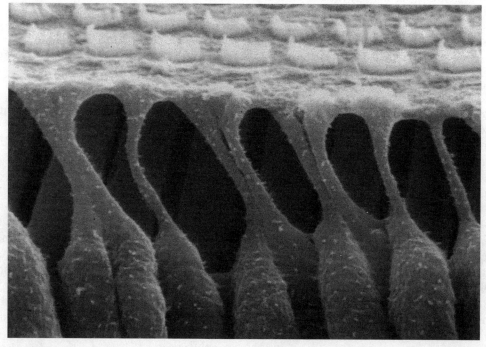

**Figure 4.22.** Scanning electron micrograph of a fractured organ of Corti specimen revealing orientation of the phalangeal processes of Deiters' cells in relation to OHCs (From Hunter-Duvar, I. M. [1977]. Morphology of the normal and the acoustically damaged cochlea. *Scan Electron. Microsc.* 2:421–428.)

other words, each Deiters' cell connects to an OHC at only two places, at the base and apex, but not of the same OHC. Otherwise, the OHCs are virtually free standing (Fig. 4.22), hence the spaces noted above.

It is noteworthy that the architecture of the organ of Corti clearly is based on the structurally sound geometric shape of the triangle. The most obvious element of this structural design is the tunnel of Corti formed by the "walls" of pillar cells, as described above (Figs. 4.18 and 4.19). But even longitudinally, a sort of triangular design is evident (Fig. 4.22). The phalangeal processes act like diagonal struts or braces by virtue of the fact that the phalangeal process adjoining a given OHC arises from a Deiters' cell located several cells more basally! This complex is reinforced by still other supporting cells. In particular, the *Hensen's* and *Claudius's* cells provide a supporting network, shoring up the OHCs on the opposite side of pillars (Fig. 4.23). The IHCs, on the other hand, receive additional support by the cells that make up the ***inner sulcus*** (Fig. 4.23), lying along the outer surface of the spiral limbus.

Even the hair cells themselves contribute, in effect, to the structural support complex. Each hair cell has a thickened membrane at its apex known as the ***cuticular plate***. Collectively, the phalangeal processes, tops of the pillars, and cuticular plates of the hair cells form the continuous surface on the endolymphatic side of the organ called the ***reticular lamina*** (or *reticular membrane*), as shown in Figure 4.23. Tight junctions are found between sensory and supporting cell processes at the level of the reticular lamina. These junctions prevent intermixing of endolymph in scala media and perilymph within the organ of Corti. (Of course, Reissner's membrane has the same role, namely, to keep the perilymph and endolymph separate between the scala media and the scala vestibuli.) Consequently, although the bodies of the OHCs are surrounded by perilymph, their stereocilia are surrounded by endolymph (a controversial issue over the years).

The robust structural support provided to the hair cells by the supporting cells and accessory structures apparently is intended to ensure the ability of the sensory cells to withstand a wide range of vibrations. At the same time, the structure of the organ of Corti must provide the means by which unbelievably minute vibrations can be translated into effective stimuli for the hair cells. The various anatomical and microanatomical details presented previously will be ramified in the next chapter, in which they indeed will be shown to be critical to the workings of hair cells and, especially, the contribution of the OHCs to the mechanics of the hearing organ. In fact, the OHC-IHC dichotomy will be found to take on a rather unexpected twist. Recall the various manifestations of this dichotomy: different "body types," patterns of stereocilia, and modes of engagement of the tectorial membrane. Then there is the most obvious fact, the greater than three-to-one majority of OHCs. Even the support systems are different. As just discussed, the IHCs seem to be held rather snugly in place, completely surrounded by supporting cells, whereas there are spaces around OHCs. Could it be that the OHCs need some elbow room? If so, why? Stay tuned!

## 7. General Physiology of the Cochlea

It may be a bit surprising that physiology is being discussed in a chapter otherwise dedicated to anatomy. Actually, quite a bit of anatomy will be found herein. The term *general physiology* also may seem strange, but it is used here (for lack of a better term) to clearly distinguish the sort of physiology under discussion from that which pertains directly to how the ear functions as a sensory mechanism (the topic of Chapter 5). The present section deals first with the neural "wiring" of the

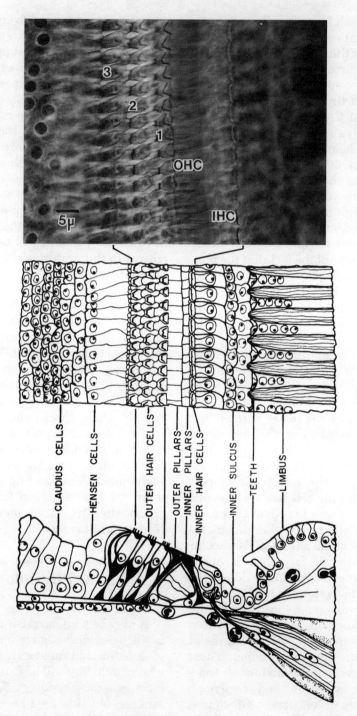

**Figure 4.23.** Photomicrograph and drawings of surface (*middle*) and cross-sectional views (*bottom*) of the organ of Corti. OHCs are of rows 1–3. (Photomicrograph: phase contrast, surface view of organ of Corti, courtesy of Dr. B. A. Bohne, Washington University School of Medicine, St. Louis, MO. Drawings adapted from Hawkins, J. E., and Johnsson, L.-G. [1976]. Microdissection and surface preparations of the inner ear. In *Handbook of Auditory and Vestibular Research Methods*, p 23, edited by C. A. Smith and J. A. Vernon. Charles C. Thomas, Springfield, IL.)

hearing receptor organ and then the circulatory "plumbing" of the inner ear.

## A. INNERVATION OF THE COCHLEA

Communication between organs in the periphery and the central nervous system is made possible by nerves that form the peripheral nervous system. The brain has both *ascending* (to convey messages to the higher centers) and *descending* tracts (to convey messages from the higher centers). The nerves communicating with the ascending and descending pathways of the brain are referred to as ***afferent*** and ***efferent***, respectively. The inner ear is innervated by the ***VIIIth cranial nerve*** (the ***statoacoustic nerve*** or, in more common parlance, simply the *acoustic nerve*). The VIIIth nerve has two major divisions, one *vestibular* and the other *auditory*, both of which are afferent. However, there is also a small efferent bundle, which subserves both the vestibular and auditory apparatuses but which "travels" within the vestibular nerve. On its way to the brain, the VIIIth nerve passes through the ***internal auditory meatus*** (Fig. 4.13), a canal that extends from the base of the cochlea to the posterior surface of the petrous portion of the temporal bone where it opens into the cranial cavity. The cell bodies of the individual ***neurons*** or ***nerve fibers*** that make up the auditory nerve are contained as a group in the ***spiral ganglion*** (Fig. 4.15), located in the modiolus. (Note: a collection of cell bodies in peripheral nervous systems, such as the auditory and vestibular systems, is called a *ganglion* [*ganglia*, plural].) The peripheral processes of these neurons enter the organ of Corti via small openings in the edge of the osseous spiral lamina (Fig. 4.18)—the ***habenulae perforata***. Consequently, the osseous spiral lamina is not solid; it is hollowed out to accommodate the nerve fibers on their way to the hair cells (Figs. 4.15 and 4.18). There are some 30,000 or more auditory nerve fibers in humans, yet, surprisingly enough, only a small percentage of the neurons (10% or

less) go to OHCs. (Another OHC-IHC dichotomy; the plot thickens!) Consequently, each of the fibers innervating an OHC branches extensively, so one neuron receives input from numerous OHCs (perhaps as many as 10). In addition, each OHC receives terminals from several neurons. The remainder of the neurons (about 90%) innervate the inner hair cells, which, of course, are much fewer in number than OHCs. So, one IHC communicates with multiple neurons, typically 11 or 12 in humans, and, on the whole, IHCs do not even share! This "wiring scheme" is illustrated in Figure 4.24, and its significance will be considered in Chapter 6, in which other detailed differences in the innervation of the two types of hair cells, both afferent and efferent, will be presented. Suffice it to say here that the IHCs and OHCs are not innervated by the same type of neurons, and not all of the neurons innervating the cochlea carry sensory information

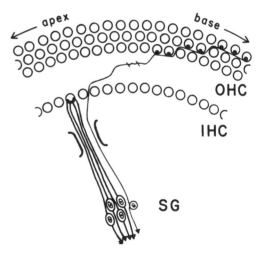

**Figure 4.24.** Schematic diagram of the basic pattern of afferent innervation of the organ of Corti. The break of the dendritic fiber leading to the OHCs indicates that it may travel a considerable distance (at least more than indicated by the number of OHCs pictured) before terminating. The direction of travel of this fiber is basalward. *SG*, Spiral ganglion. (Modified from a drawing by Spoendlin, H. [1966]. The organization for the cochlear receptor. *Biblio. Otorhinolaryngol.* 13:1–227.)

from the hair cells to the brain. As noted above, there is a small efferent bundle within the VIIIth nerve. These neurons may influence responsivity of the hair cells or neurons innervating hair cells, or perhaps even the mechanics of the hearing organ!

Of more immediate interest, for the time being, are efferent neurons that are not at all associated with sensory function but rather are concerned with autonomic or visceral functions. Sympathetic neurons arise in the central nervous system and innervate cochlear blood vessels via the sympathetic chain. *Parasympathetic* innervation is much less well known; indeed, even its existence is debatable. The extent to which the autonomic system influences cochlear function also has yet to be determined.

## B. COCHLEAR BLOOD SUPPLY

The blood supply to the cochlea is intricate. The arterial supply is provided by the ***common cochlear artery***. The origin of this artery stems from the anterior inferior cerebellar artery, which, in turn, derives from the basilar artery. The common cochlear artery passes through the internal auditory meatus along with the VIIIth, as well as the *VIIth (facial)*, nerve. This presents both the surgeon and researcher with problems when it is desirable to manipulate the acoustic nerve while preserving the cochlear blood supply and the integrity of facial function (innervation of muscles of facial function, etc.). Venous drainage of the cochlea is provided by the ***common modiolar vein***. Once in the cochlea, the common cochlear artery and common modiolar vein branch to form intricate beds of minute vessels called *arterioles* and *venules*, which supply and drain, respectively, capillary beds in the cochlea. The stria vascularis, spiral limbus, and spiral ligament are major areas of concentration of vessels. A limited number of vessels also run beneath the organ of Corti on the scala tympani side of the basilar membrane (Fig. 4.25).

The vascular network of the stria vascularis reflects the high level of metabolic activity believed to be primarily associated with the maintenance of the ionic composition of endolymph in scala media, as well as an associated electrical potential or voltage (the *endocochlear potential*; see Chapter 5). However, the stria does

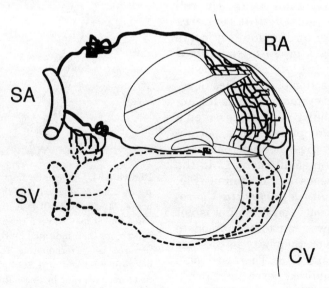

**Figure 4.25.** Blood supply of the cochlea: radiating arterioles (*RA*), collecting venules (*CV*), the spiral artery (*SA*), and the viral vein (*SV*).

not seem to provide life support, per se, to the organ of Corti. At least, there does not seem to be any major movement of materials or transfer of oxygen across the reticular lamina from the scala media. Although much controversy exists in the literature, there is evidence to suggest that nutrients and oxygen are supplied to the cells of the organ of Corti by perilymph. Indeed, it is assumed that perilymph is relatively free to move into the spaces of the organ of Corti. Whatever might be the actual details, the life support of the organ, particularly the hair cells, is clearly not a direct process. The nutrients and oxygen must be carried from blood vessels to the hair cells via the surrounding fluid, because there is no direct blood supply for the hair cells.

## C. COCHLEAR FLUID SYSTEMS

Two issues must be addressed when discussing the cochlear fluids: the chemical differences between perilymph and endolymph and their production, and fluid pressure regulation within the cochlea. These are not entirely independent issues, but the discussion will be simplified by treating them somewhat separately.

Recall that perilymph is found in the scala vestibuli, the scala tympani, and the spaces within the organ of Corti, whereas endolymph is confined to the scala media space above the reticular lamina. Perilymph thus is the more abundant fluid and is characterized by a high concentration of sodium ($Na^+$) and calcium ($Ca^{++}$) ions and a low concentration of potassium ($K^+$).[2] Namely, there is about 30 times as much $Na^+$ as $K^+$ in perilymph. By virtue of this ionic composition, it closely resembles the fluid typically found outside of all cells in the body, known as *interstitial fluid*. There are basically two theories concerning the origin of perilymph. One is that it is a filtrate of blood serum, which is produced by capillaries in the spiral ligament, specifically the part of the spiral ligament that protrudes into the scala vestibuli, and in the walls of the scala tympani. The other theory is that perilymph is nothing more than *cerebrospinal fluid (CSF)*. In fact, CSF and perilymph are nearly identical in their ionic composition, but there is controversy regarding whether they are as similar in other regards, particularly in terms of their protein content. As shown in Figure 4.26a, there is definitely a route by which CSF could be supplied to the cochlea—a small channel in the temporal bone near the round window known as the ***cochlear aqueduct***. This duct connects scala tympani with the subarachnoid space of the cranium. In children and in lower mammals this passageway seems to be open or patent. However, in adult humans and other primates, it seems to be occluded by a membranous network. At the heart of the controversy then is whether the aqueduct is functionally patent in the adult, that is, whether a truly free exchange of fluid is permissible via this channel.

It is generally assumed that if perilymph can be shown to be significantly different from CSF in its makeup, it would have to be produced within the cochlea. This logic seems sound enough. The burden of proof lies on the acquisition of uncontaminated samples of the two fluids in question and a reliable (artifact-free), comprehensive comparison between them. This has proved to be a difficult task. On the other side of the argument is the assumption that if perilymph and CSF are alike and/or materials in CSF can be shown to appear in the cochlea, perilymph must be CSF. Unfortunately, the logic here is not so ironclad. Demonstrated similarities between perilymph and CSF simply might mean that the inner ear produces fluid the same way it is produced in the subarachnoid spaces. After all, CSF is also a blood serum filtrate! So, the cochlea

[2] Ions are electrically charged particles made up of an atom or groups of atoms (molecules) that have an electron deficiency (positive ions or *cations*) or an electron surplus (negative ions or *anions*). Other discussions of ions are incorporated in Chapters 5 and 6.

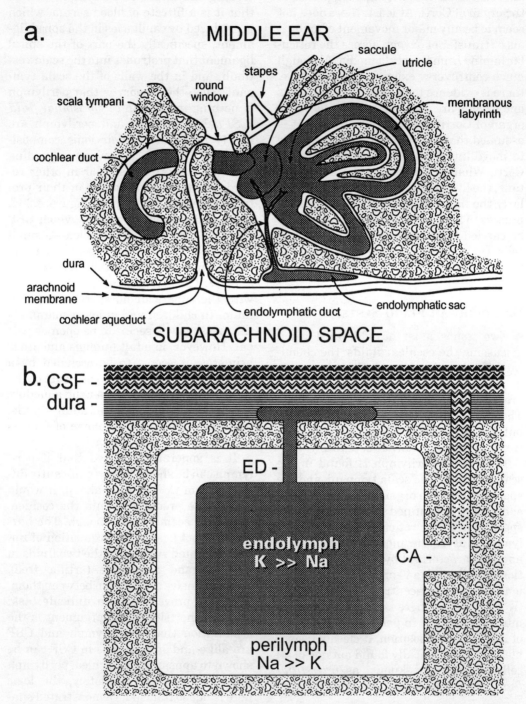

**Figure 4.26.**   **a.** Fluid spaces of the inner ear. **b.** Schematic representation of the relationship between the fluid spaces of the inner ear and the central nervous system. *ED*, Endolymphatic duct; *CA*, cochlear aqueduct.

still could be responsible for producing the bulk of the perilymph, whereas the "CSF connection" could subserve another role (one that will be suggested momentarily) or might become involved in certain pathological conditions, as in the case of a meningitic infection of the inner ear. Thus, the two theories of perilymph production are not necessarily mutually exclusive.

Endolymph, in contrast, is most unusual, not so much for its composition, which is remarkably different from perilymph, but rather for where it is found. Endolymph has a high concentration of $K^+$ and a low concentration of $Na^+$. Indeed, the sodium-potassium mix of endolymph is opposite that of perilymph; therefore, there is about 30 times as much $K^+$ as $Na^+$. Endolymph actually resembles more closely the fluid found inside, rather than outside, living cells. So what is so unusual about endolymph and just how unusual is it? Well, it of course is an extracellular, not intracellular, fluid; again, it fills the scala media (indeed, the entire membranous labyrinth). A high-potassium fluid in an extracellular space is found in only one other part of the body—the kidney! The specific mechanisms of endolymph production remain to be described completely, and such details are beyond the scope of coverage here. The most salient and well-established fact is that the production of endolymph directly involves the stria vascularis. Current thinking on the matter suggests the existence of potassium-sodium exchange pumps in the stria, through which ions are moved across Reissner's membrane. The chemical balance between endolymph and perilymph seems to be maintained by local circuits or loops operating all along the cochlear duct that keep and/or replenish potassium in the scala media while pumping sodium out.

The cochlear fluid system seems to have a mechanism for regulating the overall fluid pressure within the inner ear. Again, the issue of freedom of flow of CSF through the cochlear aqueduct notwithstanding, it seems likely that there could be sufficient fluid movement to provide a mechanism of pressure control for perilymph (Fig. 4.26b). Similarly, endolymph may be slowly absorbed by a specialized portion of the membranous labyrinth known as the **endolymphatic sac** (Figs. 4.12c and 4.26a). The sac itself is situated in a subdural space and communicates with the remainder of the membranous labyrinth via the endolymphatic duct. Although endolymph does not flow into CSF spaces, the location of the sac effects the completion of a hydraulic circuit, as illustrated schematically in Figure 4.26b. Therefore, the inner ear appears as an intricate system of fluid-filled spaces connected, in turn, to the fluid spaces of the central nervous system (Fig. 4.26b). The result is a mechanism by which a balance of pressure can be maintained between the two cochlear fluids and between the cochlear fluids and the CSF. The overall cochlear fluid pressure, furthermore, can affect cochlear perfusion or blood flow (analogous to the effects of CSF pressure on cerebral perfusion); an increase in inner ear pressure reduces blood flow. So, the fluid balance of the inner ear is intimately involved in its own homeostasis.

## 8. Comparative Study of the Ear

From anatomical considerations alone it is evident that the cochlea is an intricate sensory structure. By virtue of its fairly distinct anatomical (and functional) separation from the rest of the inner ear, it is tempting to view the structures of the cochlea as being unique to the auditory system. There are certain details of these structures that are undeniably unique to the cochlea, but there also are underlying common elements between the cochlea and the vestibular apparatus. Not only are there similarities in the sensory epithelia of the organ of Corti, otolith organs, and organs of the semicircular canals, but also between these organs and a more primi-

tive structure known as the ***lateral line
organ***. Lateral line organs are found on
the skin of lower vertebrates such as amphibians (for example, frogs), fish, and
even more primitive species (such as lam-
preys). It is in the lateral line organ that
the organs of both hearing and balance
find their ancestry. Collectively, the lateral line organs, organs of balance, and the
organ of hearing are referred to as the
***acousticolateralis organs***. Although
each type of organ has its distinctive characteristics, all acousticolateralis organs
share the common features (as illustrated
by Fig. 4.27): 1) the distinctive hair cell
type of sensory cell; 2) a superstructure
overlying the hair cells; and 3) a substratum of supporting cells. Because all these

organs are fundamentally similar in structure and function, a basis is thus provided
by which one particular organ may be
studied through a comparative analysis of
the others. Although the lateral line organs are not present in higher vertebrates, they are of great interest to the
hearing scientist because they have more
readily permitted the direct study of hair
cell function by virtue of the greater size
and accessibility of their sensory cells
compared with the hair cells of the inner
ear.

As the hair cell migrated during evolution from the surface of the body (namely,
from the lateral line organ) to the confined
spaces of the vestibular apparatus in
primitive vertebrates, and ultimately to
the hearing organs of higher vertebrates,
significant changes occurred in the sensory structures. These changes were necessary so that a given end organ might be
able to detect the appropriate physical
stimulus. Although the lateral line organ
is responsive to vibratory stimuli and the
saccule subserves the role of a hearing
organ in fish, it was not until the emergence of the amphibian that a distinct
hearing organ developed. Yet, the amphibian's organ of hearing is contained within
the vestibule. At the reptilian level the
cochlea began to develop, and in birds a
hearing organ emerged that rests in a
slightly curved projection from the vestibule. Only in mammals is the coiled cochlea observed (Fig. 4.28). The coiling of the
sensory organ provides a means to contain
a longer organ within the limited confines
of the temporal bone.

The evolution of the cochlea did not
come about in an isolated manner. The
middle and outer ears have undergone notable changes as well. The primitive middle ear is the swim bladder in fishes. In
amphibians, reptiles, and birds, the middle ear has only one or two ossicles, which
form, in essence, a rod or *columella* between the tympanic membrane and the
inner ear (Fig. 4.29). The combined evolution of the middle ear and the cochlea has

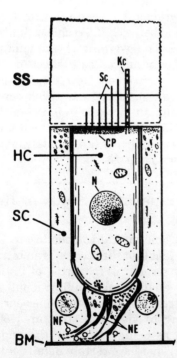

**Figure 4.27.** Generalized hair cell receptor. Shown
are the basement membrane (*BM*), cuticular plate
(*CP*), hair cell (*HC*), kinocilium (*Kc*), cell nucleus (*N*),
nerve ending (*NE*), nerve fiber (*NF*), stereocilia (*Sc*),
and superstructure (*SS*). (Inspired by H. Spoendlin
from Durrant, J. D., and Freeman, A. R. [1982]. Concepts in vestibular physiology. In *Dizziness and Vertigo*, p 21, edited by A. J. Finestone. John Wright-
PSG, Boston.)

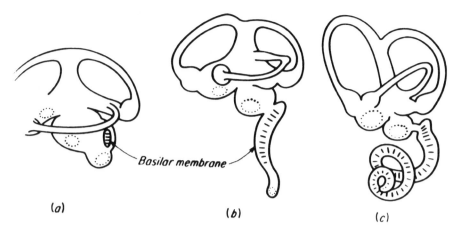

**Figure 4.28.** The membranous labyrinths of a turtle (**a**), a bird (**b**), and a mammal (**c**). (From Bekesy, G. V. [1960]. *Experiments in Hearing*, translated and edited by E. G. Wever. McGraw-Hill, New York).

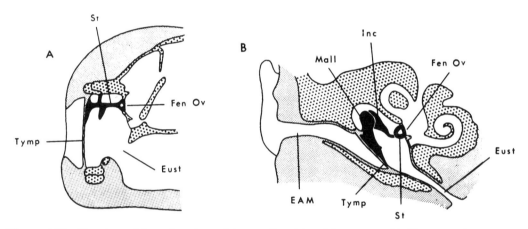

**Figure 4.29.** Drawings of frontal sections of the reptilian (**a**) and human ear (**b**). Shown are the tympanic membrane (*Tymp*), stapes (*St*), fenestra ovalis (*Fen Ov*), Eustachian tube (*Eust*), external auditory meatus (*EAM*), malleus (*Mall*), and incus (*Inc*). (From Hopson, J. A. [1966]. The origin of the mammalian middle ear. *Am. Zool.* 6:437–450.)

been essential in developing a sensory system that can respond to airborne sounds and accurately analyze sounds over a wide range of intensities and frequencies. Outer ears are found primarily in mammals, and they take on a wide range of sizes and shapes within that phylum, especially where the auricle is concerned. The outer ear has undergone change under a dichotomy of needs—one being acoustical (improvement of the collection of sound and directional hearing afforded by the auricle) and the other for protective purposes (protection of the delicate inner structures from the elements). All of these changes, across and within phyla, suggest delicate adjustments on the part of nature to provide each organism with ample capabilities to respond to an important aspect of its environment—sound.

This cursory description of the evolutionary basis of hearing hardly does justice to the subject, considering the millions of years of evolutionary engineering, but should serve to introduce the reader to the use of comparative study in hearing science, even though the major concern of this text is human hearing. But humans obviously cannot be used for most anatomical and physiological research needed to address the many mysteries, both past and present, surrounding the workings of this fascinating sensory system. Furthermore, the human ear does not lend itself to the degree of experimental manipulation available in other species. Therefore, the hearing scientist is obliged to work on the animal that provides a practical basis for interfacing and interacting with the desired structures and carrying out the needed observations. The relatively freestanding cochleas of rodents, for example, provide direct access to the fluid spaces of the cochleas for purposes of physiological or electrophysiological study. The cochleas of higher mammals are almost completely buried in temporal bone, severely limiting the scope of such studies in these animals. Naturally, structural and functional differences exist among the species, but the scientist must operate on the assumption that the similarities between the peripheral auditory mechanisms, at least within phyla, outweigh these differences. Even across phyla, it is possible to demonstrate basic mechanisms of hearing that are common to all species with acousticolateralis organs. In Chapter 5, as well as in Chapter 6, descriptions of how the auditory system functions will be based extensively on data obtained from subhuman species, especially the guinea pig and the cat. In some cases, it will be beneficial to fall back on data from the hearing organ's phylogenetically older relatives: the vestibular and lateral line organs. It is only through the integration of such a variety of data that a reasonably complete picture of the workings of the ear is possible. Herein lies the importance of the comparative study of the auditory system and hearing.

# BIBLIOGRAPHY

Ades, H. W., and Engstrom, H. (1974). Anatomy of the inner ear. In *Handbook of Sensory Physiology,* *Vol V/1. Auditory System: Anatomy, Physiology (Ear)*, vol V/1, pp 125–158, edited by W. D. Keidel and W. D. Neff. Springer-Verlag, Berlin.

Anson, B. J., and Davies, J. (1980). Embryology of the ear. In *Otolaryngology: Basic Sciences and Related Disciplines*, 2nd ed, vol 1, pp 3–25, edited by M. M. Paparella and D. A. Shumrick. W. B. Saunders Co., Philadelphia.

Anson, B. J., and Donaldson, J. A., (1973). *Surgical Anatomy of the Temporal Bone and Ear*. W. B. Saunders Co., Philadelphia.

Axelsson, A. (1974). The blood supply of the inner ear in mammals. In *Handbook of Sensory Physiology. Auditory System: Anatomy, Physiology (Ear)*, vol V/1, pp 213–260, edited by W. D. Keidel and W. D. Neff. Springer-Verlag, Berlin.

Axelsson, A., and Ryan, A. F. (1988). Circulation of the inner ear. I. Comparative study of the vascular anatomy in the mammalian cochlea. In *Physiology of the Ear*, pp 295–315, edited by A. F. Jahn and J. Santos-Sachi. Raven Press, New York.

Békésy, G. V. (1960). *Experiments in Hearing*, translated and edited by E. G. Wever, McGraw-Hill, New York.

Bohne, B. A. (1978). *Microscopic Anatomy of the Inner Ear*. Available from the Department of Otolaryngology, Washington University School of Medicine, St. Louis, MO.

Bredberg, G., Ades, H. W., and Engstrom, H. (1972). Scanning electron microscopy of the normal and pathologically altered organ of Corti. *Acta Otolaryngol. [Suppl.] (Stockh.)* 301:3–48.

Brodel, M. (1946). *Three Unpublished Drawings of the Anatomy of the Human Ear*. W. B. Saunders Co., Philadelphia.

Donaldson, J. A., and Miller, J. M. (1980). Anatomy of the ear. In *Otolaryngology: Basic Sciences and Related Disciplines*, 2nd ed, vol 1, pp 26–62, edited by M. M. Paparella and D. A. Shumrick. W. B. Saunders Co., Philadelphia.

Durrant, J. D., and Freeman, A. R. (1982). Concepts in vestibular physiology. In *Dizziness and Vertigo*, pp 13–43, edited by A. J. Finestone. John Wright-PSG Inc., Boston.

Engstrom, H., and Engstrom, B. (1976). *Structure and Function of the Inner Ear*. Widex, Topholm, and Westermann, Vaerlose, Denmark.

Felix, H., Fraissinette, A. D., Johnsson, L. G., and Gleeson, M. J. (1993). Morphological features of human Reissner's membrane. *Acta Otolaryngol.* 113:321–325.

Gardner, E., Gray, D. J., and O'Rahilly, R. (1963). *Anatomy*. W. B. Saunders Co., Philadelphia.

Glasscock, M. E., and Shambaugh, G. E. (1990). *Surgery of the Ear*, 4th ed. W. B. Saunders Co., Philadelphia.

Gulley, R. L., and Reese, T. S. (1976). Intracellular junctions in the reticular lamina of the organ of Corti. *J. Neurocytol.* 5:479–507.

Hawkins, J. E. (1965). Cytoarchitectural basis of the

cochlear transducer. *Cold Spring Harbor Symp. Quant. Biol.* 30:147–158.

Harrison, R. V., and Hunter-Duvar, I. M. (1989). An anatomical tour of the cochlea. In *Physiology of the Ear*, pp 159–171, edited by A. F. Jahn and J. Santos-Sachi. Raven Press, New York.

Hawkins, J. E., and Johnsson, L.-G. (1976). Microdissection and surface preparations of the inner ear. In *Handbook of Auditory and Vestibular Research Methods*, pp 5–52, edited by C. A. Smith and J. A. Vernon. Charles C. Thomas, Springfield, IL.

Hopson, J. A. (1966). The origin of the mammalian middle ear. *Am. Zool.* 6:437–450.

Hunter-Duvar, I. M. (1978). Electron microscopic assessment of the cochlea. *Acta Otolaryngol. [Suppl.] (Stockh.)* 351:3–23.

Hunter-Duvar, I. M. (1977). Morphology of the normal and the acoustically damaged cochlea. *Scan. Electron Microsc.* 2:421–428.

Iurato, S. (1967). *Submicroscopic Structure of the Inner Ear.* Pergamon Press, Oxford.

Lawrence, M. (1980). Inner ear physiology. In *Otolaryngology: Basic Sciences and Related Disciplines*, 2nd ed, vol 1, pp 216–240, edited by M. M. Paparella and D. A. Shumrick. W. B. Saunders Co., Philadelphia.

Lawrence, M. (1980). Control mechanisms of inner ear microcirculation. *Am. J. Otolaryngol.* 1: 324–333.

Marchbanks, R. J., and Reid, A. (1990). Cochlear and cerebrospinal fluid pressure: their inter-relationship and control mechanisms. *Br. J. Audiol.* 24: 179–187.

Morgenstern, H., Miyamoto, H., Arnold, W., and Vosteen, K.-H. (1982). Functional and morphological findings of endolymphatic sac. *Acta Otolaryngol.* 93:187–194.

Nadol, J. B. (1993). Hearing loss. *N. Engl. J. Med.* 329:1092–1102.

Nadol, J.B. (1990). Synaptic morphology of inner and outer hair cells of the human organ of corti. *J. Electron Microsc. Tech.* 15:187–196.

Nadol, J. D. (1979). Intracellular fluid pathways in the organ of Corti of cat and man. *Ann. Otol.* 88: 2–11.

Naftalin, L., and Harrison, M. S. (1958). Circulation of labyrinthine fluids. *J. Laryngol. Otol.* 72: 118–136.

Nakashima, T., Suzuki, T., and Yanagita, N. (1991). Cochlear blood flow under increased inner ear pressure. *Ann. Otol. Rhinol. Laryngol.* 100: 394–397.

Palmer, J. M. (1993). *Anatomy for Speech and Hearing.* Williams & Wilkins, Baltimore.

Palva, T., Raunio, V., Karma, P., and Ylikoski, J. (1979). Fluid pathways in temporal bones. *Acta Otolaryngol.* 87:310–317.

Pickles, J. O. (1979). An investigation of sympathetic effects on hearing. *Acta Otolaryngol.* 87:69–71.

Ritter, F. N., and Lawrence. (1965). A histological and experimental study of the cochlear aqueduct patency in the adult human. *Laryngoscope* 75: 1224–1233.

Ryan, A. F. (1988). Circulation of the inner ear. I. Comparative study of the vascular anatomy in the mammalian cochlea. In *Physiology of the Ear*, pp 317–325, edited by A. F. Jahn and J. Santos-Sachi. Raven Press, New York.

Ryan, A., and Dallos, P. (1984). Physiology of the cochlea in hearing disorders. In *Communicative Disorders: Hearing Loss*, 2nd ed, pp 253–266, edited by J. L. Northern. Little, Brown & Co., Boston.

Salvinelli, F., Maurizi, M., Calamita, S., et al. (1991). The external ear and the tympanic membrane. *Scand. Audiol.* 20:253–256.

Santi, P. A. (1988). Cochlear microanatomy and ultrastructure. In *Physiology of the Ear*, pp 173–199, edited by A. F. Jahn and J. Santos-Sachi. Raven Press, New York.

Salt, A. N., and Thalmann, R. (1988). Cochlear fluid dynamics. In *Physiology of the Ear*, pp 341–357, edited by A. F. Jahn and J. Santos-Sachi. Raven Press, New York.

Schuknecht, H. F. (1974). *Pathology of the Ear.* Harvard University Press, Cambridge.

Smith, C. A. (1973). Vascular patterns of the membranous labyrinth. In *Vascular Disorders and Hearing Defects*, pp 1–21, edited by A. J. D. deLorenzo. University Park Press, Baltimore.

Sobatta, J. (1954). *Atlas of Descriptive Human Anatomy. Blood Vessels, Nervous System, Sense Organs, Integument and Lymphatics*, 5th ed, vol 3, translated and edited by E. Ehlenhuth. Hafner Publishing Co., Inc., New York.

Spoendlin, H. (1988). Neural anatomy of the inner ear. In *Physiology of the Ear*, pp 201–219, edited by A. F. Jahn and J. Santos-Sachi. Raven Press, New York.

Spoendlin, H. (1966). The organization for the cochlear receptor. *Biblio. Otorhinolaryngol.* 13: 1–227.

Spoendlin, H. (1966). Ultrastructure of the vestibular sense organ. In *The Vestibular System and Its Diseases*, pp 39–68, edited by R. J. Wolfson. University of Pennsylvania Press, Philadelphia.

Spoendlin, H. (1976). Neural connections of the outer hair cell system. *Acta Otolaryngol.* 87:381–387.

Takagi, A., and Sando, I. (1989). Computer-aided three-dimensional reconstruction: a method of measuring temporal bone structures including the length of the cochlea. *Ann. Otol. Rhinol. Laryngol.* 98:515–522.

Valvassori, G. E., Buckingham, R. A., Carter, B. L., et al. (1988). *Head and Neck Imaging.* Thieme Medical Publishers, Inc., New York.

Wever, E. G. (1974). The evolution of vertebrate hearing. In *Handbook of Sensory Physiology, Auditory System: Anatomy, Physiology (Ear)*, vol V/1, pp 423–454, edited by W. D. Keidel and W. D. Neff. Springer-Verlag, Berlin.

## CHAPTER 5

# PHYSIOLOGICAL ACOUSTICS OF THE AUDITORY PERIPHERY

As the old saying goes, "It looks good on paper, but will it work?" The anatomy of the peripheral auditory system reveals an intricate conglomeration of structures. The functions of these structures, which were previously described only in the most general terms, now will be considered in detail. The objective of this system is to translate the physical stimulus of sound into a suitable physiological signal that is capable of being transmitted to and within the central nervous system (CNS) and, ultimately, analyzed by the cortex. The result of the brain's analyses is a psychological response—the sensation of hearing. The purpose of the peripheral auditory system, then, is not only to pick up sound but also to condition properly the information borne by sound so that the brain can process it. This is somewhat like working with a computer; one must have the proper means of talking to it. The physical principles discussed earlier will provide the bases on which an understanding of the workings of the peripheral auditory system can be developed. However, these principles must be merged with concepts from physiology, namely those governing the functioning of sensory mechanisms, the nervous system, and their component structures. Consequently, some basic concepts from sensory physiology must be established before proceeding to the specific issue of how the peripheral auditory system works.

## 1. Some Basic Sensory Physiology

The detection of sound and the encoding of information that it contains is a complex process involving various stages. It is easy to become overwhelmed by the details of this process and to lose sight of the objectives that must be met by this or any other sensory system. Although the exact details of how the hearing mechanism works, as yet, are not fully understood, and although no two sensory systems are alike, there are some well-established principles governing the operation of sensory systems in general. Sensory organs are concerned with three processes: 1) absorbing the energy of the stimulus, 2) using the energy absorbed to bring about some change in the state of the sensory cell, and 3) initiating electrical impulses in the nerve leading from the sensory organ to the CNS.

Nerves are composed of a multitude of individual fibers. Each fiber arises from an individual nerve cell. The nerve fiber thus is a part of what is commonly referred to as a **neuron**. (The structure and function of neurons will be discussed in Chapter 6.) The neuron that is specifically excited by the action of the stimulus on the sensory organ and that bears the responsibility of conveying sensory information to the CNS is called the **sensory neuron**. Sensory systems are classified according to whether the sensory neuron is acted on directly by the stimulus or via a separate cell—the **receptor cell**—which absorbs the energy of the stimulus and excites the sensory neuron. The former, wherein the receptor mechanism is a part of the sensory neuron, characterizes a primary sensory system. The latter, composed of separate receptor and nerve cells, is a secondary system. There are even tertiary sensory systems in which an additional (intermediary) neuron is found between the receptor cell and the sensory neuron. Regardless of which class of sensory system is involved, there must be both a receptive structure and, naturally, a neural structure to do the job.

To understand what the job is, the sensory system can be treated as a black box in which the output signal recorded from the box is compared with the signal fed into its input (Fig. 5.1a). The contents of the box and the details of what might actually be going on inside are unknown (or treated as such), so attention is focused on what the box does, not exactly how it works. The input signal of ultimate interest here is sound, but, for the moment, a simple mechanical force can be envisioned. The question is, "what is the desired output?" The answer is a train of pulses that represents the magnitude of the input signal. In sensory systems this is made possible by virtue of the all-or-none nature of neural discharges. In other words, the output signal consists of electrical impulses that arise due to the rapid discharge, and subsequent recharging, of the excited sensory neuron. Basically, the neuron assumes one of two states: on or off. Neither the height nor the duration of the neural impulses carry meaningful information; indeed, these dimensions are rather uniform (as discussed in more detail in Chapter 6). Consequently, the pri-

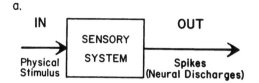

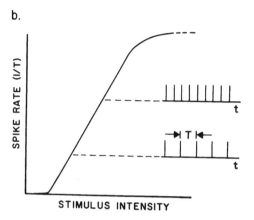

**Figure 5.1.** **a.** Black-box representation of sensory systems in general. **b.** Hypothetical plot of spike rate as a function of stimulus intensity.

mary information-bearing aspect of these pulses is how often they occur, namely, their frequency or **spike rate**. (These pulses have very short durations, about 1 msec, so they look like spikes when recorded and monitored with an oscilloscope.) As shown in Figure 5.1b, the spike rate increases as the stimulus intensity increases, so intensity is encoded essentially as frequency. It also should be noted in Fig. 5.1b that there are two regions of the spike rate function that bracket the range of stimulus intensities within which the stimulus is faithfully represented by the neural code (wherein spike rate changes in proportion to intensity). Stimuli of low intensities, that is, those to the extreme left of the intensity axis in Fig. 5.1b, are inadequate to excite discharges in the neuron. At the opposite extreme, intensities can be reached such that no substantial increase in spike rate is realized (saturation). In other words, any given sensory system has an upper, as well as a lower, limit to its response, hence the saturation of the function at high stimulus intensities.

On peering into the black box, one would find that there are still other electrical signals that are generated at stages preceding the actual excitation of neural impulses. Initially, the physical stimulus is changed into an electrical signal, which is some facsimile or *analog* of the stimulus. The magnitude of this signal follows the amplitude of the physical stimulus and, thus, mimics the stimulus waveform, that is, in cases of time-variant input signals such as vibration or sound. Consequently, a transduction process is required to transform the energy of the stimulus into electricity. In primary systems this electrical analog signal is generated in the receptor region of the sensory neuron, whereas in secondary or tertiary systems this signal is generated in the receptor cell and is called the ***receptor potential***.

At this juncture, a bit of a digression is necessary to discuss briefly another physical law—***Ohm's electrical law***—and to define the basic electrical quantities involved. Consider the common flashlight, consisting of a battery, light bulb, and on-off switch. The battery has energy stored in it, and this energy can be used to force charge, borne by free electrons, to flow through a conductor, such as copper wire (as commonly used in house wiring). The rate at which charge flows is called ***current (I)*** (measured in amperes, or amps for short), and the force is ***voltage (E)*** (measured in volts). The conductor, however, tends to oppose this flow of current and dissipates some of the energy; consequently, some of the electrical energy is converted to heat. In other words, the conductor has ***resistance (R)***. Like frictional resistance in mechanical systems, some resistance is inevitable in all electrical systems.

The light bulb of the flashlight is fundamentally a wire that can be heated by the conduction of current, thereby producing light. The resistance of the wire limits the amount of current, just as friction limits velocity in mechanical systems. According to Ohm's law,

$$I = E/R \text{ or } E = IR$$

So, knowing any two quantities, the third can be derived. For example, to obtain a current of 0.1 amp through a resistance of 15 ohms, there must be a voltage of $0.1 \times 15 = 1.5$ volts impressed across the resistance. (This is often called a *voltage drop* or *IR drop*). In other words, a 1.5-volt battery (one D cell, or what is commonly called a flashlight battery) would be required to light up a bulb rated at 0.1 amp. Doubling the voltage would double the current, given the same resistance (because $I = E/R$). Incidentally, the switch in the flashlight, which of course merely provides a convenient means of disconnecting the battery when not in use, also can be characterized in terms of its resistance—infinite when open (off) and zero when closed (on).

All living cells are like small batteries. If their interiors are compared with the surrounding (fluid) environment, a negative voltage, typically tens of millivolts in magnitude, is measured. The reason for this is as follows. First, all living cells contain fluid, the ***intracellular fluid***, which is separated from the ***extracellular*** or ***interstitial fluid*** outside by virtue of the cell's outer covering or ***cell membrane***. Second, in biological systems, electrical charge is carried by ***ions*** rather than electrons. Ions are atoms or molecules that are enriched with (*anions*) or depleted of a certain number of electrons (*cations*), so they may take on a net negative or positive charge, respectively. Chloride, sodium, and potassium are some of the more common ion species and are found in both the intracellular and extracellular fluids. However, the intracellular and extracellular fluids differ in their ionic content, so the cell membrane keeps some ion species relatively segregated. Without pursuing the details at this juncture, the manner in which these ions are distributed on either side of this membrane causes a voltage to be developed across it—the *resting (membrane) potential*. As long as the cell membrane offers sufficient resistance to the appropriate ion species, there is negligible ionic current passing through it, and the cell just sits there like a battery on a shelf. This is typical of many cells of the body, for example, epithelial cells of the skin. On the other hand, receptor and nerve cells have membranes whose properties can be changed to allow one ion or the other to flow across it. The resulting current flow through the membrane will be accompanied by a change in the resting potential of the cell. In the case of the receptor cell, it is the physical stimulus that can cause a change in the cell membrane, and it is in this manner that the energy of the stimulus is transformed into an electrical signal called the receptor potential.

The receptor potential may lead directly to the initiation of neural impulses or to some other event(s) that, in turn, is (are) responsible for triggering the spike discharges in the sensory neuron. The electrical signal that itself is directly responsible for triggering the spikes traditionally has been called the *generator potential*. Although perhaps passé, the term is used here to highlight the fact that, in secondary (such as the hearing organ) and tertiary sensory systems, graded potentials occur in the sensory neuron separate and distinct from the receptor potential. The nature of the electrical events elicited in the sensory neuron will be discussed in detail in the next chapter. The point of importance at this juncture is simply that, in the final analysis, several steps and various structures or substructures are required in the process of encoding the physical stimulus into neural impulses (Fig. 5.2a). First, the energy of the stimulus must be coupled to the receptor, either via a specialized substructure, a specialized external structure, or a combination of both. The manner by which this is done can affect the code that is ultimately established in the sensory neuron. For instance, will the receptor's response follow the stimulus perse, as characteristic of what are defined classically as *tonic* receptors? Or will the receptor respond only when there is a change in the stimulus, as characteristic of *phasic* receptors. Still another possibility is that the response can be a little of both, as in Figure 5.2b.

In this manner, the stimulus is transduced, producing the receptor potential. The receptor potential subsequently leads to the production of the generator potential, which, in secondary or higher systems, usually involves a chemically mediated transmission process (see Chapter 6) between the receptor cell and the sensory neuron. Finally, spike discharges are triggered in the sensory neuron. The nuances of the latter stages also have much to do with the formulation of the final neural code, which typically introduces a time delay (Fig. 5.2b).

Interestingly, many neurons (in the auditory system nearly all) exhibit spontaneous activity, that is, discharges in the absence of a physical stimulus, as suggested by Figure 5.2b. In such cases, the presence of the stimulus (more precisely, a stimulus with an intensity that exceeds a certain minimum or threshold) causes a significant increase in the spike rate above the spontaneous rate. This assumes the presence of an *excitatory* stimulus. Conversely, the stimulus might be *inhibitory*, causing the spike rate to decrease below the neuron's spontaneous rate. In Figure 5.2b inhibition occurs during the negative "overshoots" in the receptor and generator potentials. Therefore, in various sensory systems, and in the nervous system in general, the purpose of stimulation is not so much a matter of turning a neuron completely on or off but, rather, to modulate the spike rate and perhaps even organize patterns of neural discharges in the time domain.

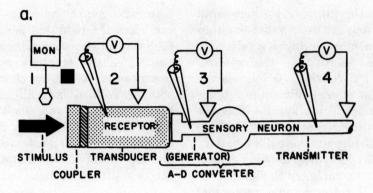

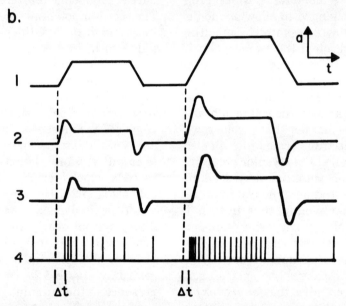

**Figure 5.2.** **a.** Schematic representation of a sensory system (in this case a secondary system). **b.** Signals recorded at positions indicated in **a**. Presuming an intermediate chemical process between the receptor and the sensory neuron, there will be a time delay in the response of the sensory neuron ($\Delta t$).

For now, it is desirable to concentrate only on the initial stages of the sensory encoding process involved in hearing, that is, the events leading to the effective stimulation of the hair cells and the production of receptor potentials by the auditory mechanism. The details of the final stages alluded to in the preceding paragraph will be left for discussion in the next chapter. Hence, the excitation of activity in the auditory nerve will be used simply as an indicator that the hearing organ, in fact, has been successfully stimulated.

## 2. Excitation of Hair Cells

### A. THE GENERIC HAIR CELL

The hair cells of acousticolateralis organs are mechanoreceptors. They are designed to sense mechanical stimuli, such as vibration, and to transduce the energy of such stimuli into a receptor potential, thereby initiating the chain of events outlined in the foregoing section. Present knowledge of hair cell physiology and function rests heavily on the known char-

acteristics of the hair cells of the phylogenetically more primitive vestibular and
lateral line organs rather than those of the
(mammalian) organ of Corti. The hair cells
of the organ of Corti make direct observation very difficult by virtue of their small
size, their location, and the delicate structure of the organ itself.

It is now widely accepted that the *physiological* or *effective stimulus* of hair cells
is the bending of the stereocilia. This is
not a bending over of the hairs, so as to
bow the hairs, but rather a sideways bending or ***shearing displacement*** of the
hairs (Fig. 5.3). If they could be viewed
from the side during such displacement,
the hairs probably would appear perfectly
stiff, much like levers, and simply would
lean to and fro with back-and-forth displacements. Indeed, relatively recent experiments have shown the hairs to be brit-
tle; they tend to break before bending over.
This rigidity is attributed to the fact that
each hair is made up of actin filaments.
Actin is one of the two main molecules of
which muscle cells are composed (myosin
being the other) and is a molecule commonly found in the microvilli lining the
wall of the intestine. The cuticular plate
in which the hairs are rooted also contains
actin. The presence of actin in the hairs
makes for some intriguing possibilities;

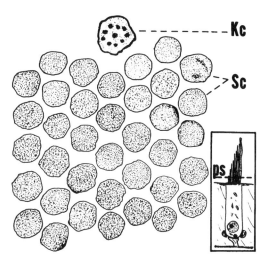

**Figure 5.4.** Kinocilium (*Kc*) and stereocilia (*Sc*) of
one generalized hair cell. Drawing of cross-sectional
view; *inset*, the plane of section (*ps*). (Based on photomicrographs from Spoendlin, H. [1966], from Durrant, J. D., and Freeman, A. R. [1982]. Concepts in
vestibular physiology. In *Dizziness and Vertigo*, pp
13–43, edited by A. J. Finestone. John Wright-PSG,
Boston.)

for instance, the stereocilia might be active, rather than passive, elements of the
"coupler."

The nice thing about the hair cell of lateral line or vestibular organs is that the
direction in which the shearing force must
be applied for optimal stimulation is
clearly indicated by the cell's structure
(Fig. 5.3). It has an extra hair, which
stands out from the stereocilia and differs
structurally from them. This special hair
is called a ***kinocilium***. As seen in Figure
5.4, it appears on one side of a group of
stereocilia; it is, so to speak, the leader of
the pack. As illustrated in Figure 5.5*a*, displacements toward the kinocilium, that is,
from the back of the pack (of stereocilia),
are ***excitatory***. Such displacements are
most effective in terms of the magnitude
and direction of the change elicited in the
membrane resting potential of the cell.
Specifically, the membrane potential decreases, an event known as ***depolarization***. It is this change in the membrane
potential that constitutes the receptor po-

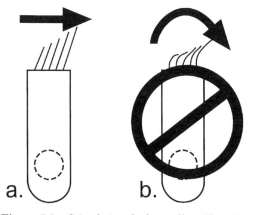

**Figure 5.3.** Stimulating the hair cell. **a.** The right
way—shearing displacements of the stereocilia. **b.**
the wrong way—bending over the stereocilia.

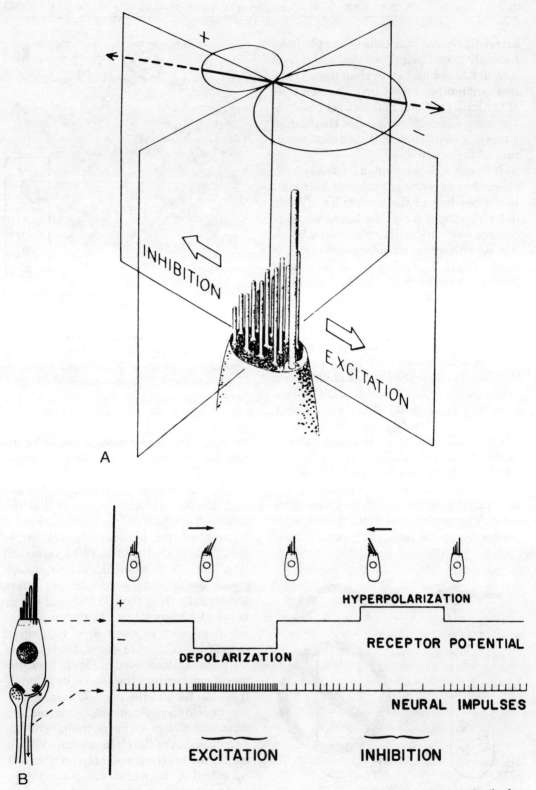

**Figure 5.5.** **a.** Diagram illustrating the directional sensitivity of the hair cell. **b.** Relationship of spike frequency to direction of shearing of the hairs. (Adapted from Flock, A. [1965]. Transducing mechanisms in lateral line canal organ receptors. *Cold Spring Harbor Symp. Quant. Biol.* 30:133–146.

tential and that leads to the chain of events, culminating in the production of spike discharges in the sensory neuron—an increased spike rate—as shown in Figure 5.5*b*.

Displacements in other directions also can excite the hair cell, but the effectiveness of the stimulus diminishes as the direction of displacement increasingly deviates from the main axis of the hair bundle, as defined by the location of the kinocilium (Fig. 5.5*a*). Thus, side-to-side shearing (that is, displacements at right angles [$\pm 90°$] from this axis) is expected to be ineffective regardless of the magnitude of stimulation. On the other hand, displacement of the hairs in the opposite direction (approaching 180°) from that which is optimally excitatory does have an important effect. Such displacements are called *inhibitory*, because they cause the membrane potential to increase or *hyperpolarize*. In other words, a receptor potential, opposite in polarity to that elicited by excitatory stimulation, is generated. The term *inhibitory* is applied here because the spike rate decreases (see Fig. 5.5*b*).

The process of shearing the hairs requires the involvement of structures that themselves are not part of the receptor cell. As discussed in Chapter 4, *superstructures* in all acousticolateralis systems are found overlying the hair cells and, to some degree, in contact with their stereocilia. Thus, the *cupulae* of lateral line and semicircular canal organs, the *otolithic membranes* of the saccule and utricle, and the *tectorial membrane* of the organ of Corti are significant components of the shearing mechanisms in their respective sensory systems. These structures influence the manner by which the energy of the stimulus is absorbed by the hair cell and determine whether it behaves more like a tonic or phasic receptor. Specifically, the superstructure, in conjunction with the stereocilia, determines whether a given hair cell is primarily a displacement, velocity, or acceleration detector. Therefore, these

structures substantially influence the encoding of the stimulus.

During evolution, fine adjustments apparently have been made in the development of energy-coupling mechanisms of the different acousticolateralis organs. This is evident from the comparison of the superstructures of various organs illustrated schematically in Figure 5.6. For example, in lateral line organs the cilia are embedded in the cupula, whereas stereocilia of inner hair cells (IHCs) barely contact the tectorial membrane in the mammalian hearing organ. (More on this point momentarily.) It seems that the energy-coupling mechanism has been critically designed to meet the specific needs of the system in question. Biochemical factors also are likely to be involved.

## B. THE COCHLEAR HAIR CELL

The exact relationship between the stereocilia of the auditory hair cells and the tectorial membrane has been a subject of considerable debate over the years. The fine structure of the tectorial membrane and its attachment to the rest of the organ of Corti are a bit complicated, as illustrated in Figure 5.7, but the single most controversial aspect concerns the attachment of the tectorial membrane to the stereocilia. The bulk of the evidence suggests that only the tallest stereocilia of outer hair cells (OHCs) have their tips firmly embedded in the bottom of the membrane. As was shown in Chapter 4 (Fig. 4.21), small indentations in the underneath side of the membrane have been observed forming the familiar W pattern of the stereocilia. So, the coupling of the tectorial membrane to the OHC stereocilia is believed to be "tight." Indentations corresponding to stereocilia of IHCs have yet to be demonstrated unequivocally. Consequently, only "loose" coupling is assumed to exist between the IHC stereocilia and the tectorial membrane. It might be asked, "If the IHC stereocilia are not embedded in the tectorial membrane, why should there be any coupling at all?" Well,

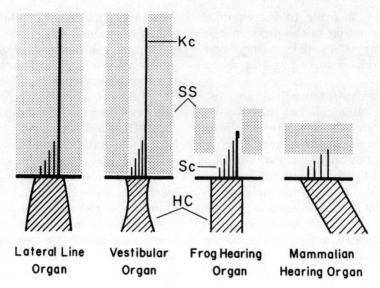

**Figure 5.6.** Modes of attachment of sensory hairs to the superstructure in different acoustico-lateralis organs. *Kc*, Kinocilium; *SS*, superstructure; *Sc*, stereocilia; *HC*, hair cell. (Based on Flock, A. [1971]. Sensory transduction in hair cells. In *Handbook of Sensory Physiology, Principles of Receptor Physiology*, vol 1, pp 396–441, edited by W. R. Lowenstein. Springer-Verlag, Berlin.)

given the presence of fluid in the space between the tectorial membrane and the reticular lamina and given the smallness of this space, some degree of coupling must be effected. Still, histologists are not unanimous in their findings, and the possibility of contamination of many of the histological findings by artifacts must be considered. The tectorial membrane, as already learned (Chapter 4), is adversely affected by fixation, which involves dehydration of the specimen. Because the tectorial membrane is more than 90% water, shrinkage is unavoidable. However, observations of unfixed frozen sections of the organ of Corti have yielded compelling evidence that the tectorial membrane normally fits snugly over the surface of the organ of Corti, from which it would be assumed that the stereocilia of all hairs cells are well embedded in the membrane. Nevertheless, the regular observation of pits in the belly of the tectorial membrane corresponding to OHC stereocilia and the irregular appearance or total absence of such imprints for IHC stereocilia still suggests differential coup-

ling between the membrane and the hairs of the two types of cells, fixation artifacts or not. The notion of the existence of such differences is supported by considerable physiological evidence (some of which will be discussed later), such as electrical recordings from hair cells and from auditory neurons.

Of course, the hair cells of the hearing organ do not have kinocilia, so there is no glowing sign of the direction for optimally excitatory stimulation of these cells. It seems that the base of the *W* pattern of the hair bundle of the OHC, which points radially away from the modiolus, is the indicator of the excitatory direction of shear for both IHC and OHC stereocilia. Also, a small structure, believed to be a rudimentary kinocilium, is sometimes seen at the top of cochlear hair cells. When observed, it too points in a radial direction. Perhaps the most compelling morphological signposts of direction of depolarizing shear of auditory hair cells, and among the most interesting morphological findings in recent years, are the fine linkages between the stereocilia, called ***cross-links and tip***

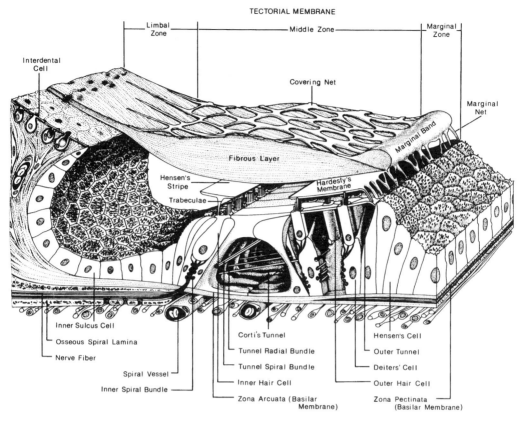

**Figure 5.7.** Artist's conception of structure of the organ of Corti based on scanning electron micrographs. (From Lim, D. J. [1980]. Cochlear anatomy related to cochlear micromechanics. A review. *J. Acoust. Soc. Am.* 67:1686–1695.)

*links*. The cross-links are horizontally oriented (with respect to the hair-bearing surface of the cell) and are thought to subserve stiffening of the hair bundle. Tip links (Fig. 5.8*a*) are nearly vertically oriented and believed to be significant components in the transduction process (Fig. 5.8*b*), as will be discussed momentarily. The point of interest here is that these links are also aligned radially. Each stereocilium in the shortest rows of hairs is linked to a stereocilium in the next tallest row (Fig. 5.8, *a* and *b*, *1* and *2*); the progression of height, again, is itself oriented radially from shortest to tallest.

The shearing displacement of the stereocilia of auditory hair cells also depends on the mode of attachment of the tectorial membrane to the rest of the organ of Corti.

Although it is attached on both sides, that is, along the spiral limbus and in the vicinity of Hensen's cells (see Fig. 5.7), the latter attachment is considered sufficiently loose to permit the tectorial membrane to slide back and forth, subsequently creating a shearing displacement of the stereocilia. For this to happen, an upward or downward displacement of the basilar membrane must occur. How this is effected is illustrated in Figure 5.9. The organ of Corti is viewed as though it has a pivot point in the vicinity of the lip of the osseous spiral lamina. Because the tectorial membrane is hinged at a different point (at the lip of the spiral limbus), upward displacement of the basilar membrane will cause a relative shift between the tectorial membrane and the surface of

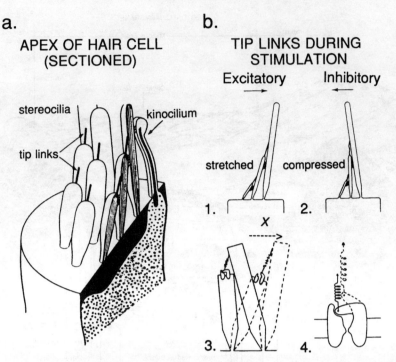

**Figure 5.8.** Tip links of stereocilia. **a.** Anatomy arrangement (semi–cross-sectional view). **b.** Theoretical states of tip links under excitatory (*1*) and inhibitory (*2*) displacements, presumptive opening of ionic gate with excitatory displacement (*3*), and mechanical model of channel (*4*; *dashed line*, excitatory state). (Based on figures from Pickles et al., 1984, and Pickles and Corey, 1992.)

the organ of Corti, which results in shearing the hairs in a radial direction. Downward displacement causes a relative movement between the tectorial membrane and the rest of the organ of Corti, resulting in shearing motion in the opposite direction. Consequently, upward displacements, or, more specifically, movement of the basilar membrane toward scala vestibuli, generally are the most effective and are excitatory, leading to depolarization of the hair cells (similar to that illustrated previously in Fig. 5.5). Movements in the opposite direction, that is, toward scala tympani, are inhibitory, leading to hyperpolarization of the hair cells.

To recap, the up-and-down motion of the basilar membrane is translated into back-and-forth shearing displacements of the hairs by virtue of the relative motion between the tectorial membrane and the organ of Corti proper. A simple self-dem-

onstration can be made to show how this works. Obtain a pencil or similar object; this will be used to represent a stereocilium. Fully extend your right arm with your hand open, palm up. This extremity will represent the body of the organ of Corti, supported by the basilar membrane (your right arm). Take the "stereocilium" in your left hand, fully extend your left arm, and hold the stereocilium vertically between your hands. Your left arm and hand represent the tectorial membrane. The pivot points are the shoulders. Admittedly, they are not aligned vertically, but they are displaced from each other. For this demonstration, that is all that counts. Now, moving your hands and arms together in an up-and-down motion will cause the stereocilium to rock back and forth, because of the resulting shearing motion between the two hands. So, it does work. But, what of the case of loose coup-

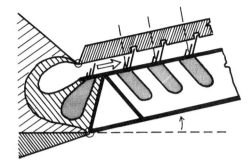

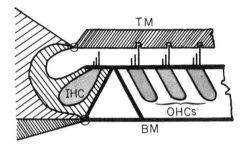

**Figure 5.9.** Schematic representation of the organ of Corti illustrating how shearing displacements of the stereocilia can result from displacement of the basilar membrane. *BM*, Basilar membrane; *TM*, tectorial membrane. (Adapted from Ryan, A., and Dallos, P. [1975]. Physiology of the inner ear. In *Communicative Disorders: Hearing Loss*, pp 80–101, edited by J. L. Northern. Little, Brown & Co., Boston.)

ling between the tectorial membrane and the stereocilia of the IHCs? A back-and-forth flow of the fluid in the space under the membrane presumably is induced by the up-and-down movement of the basilar membrane, as noted earlier. The stereocilia will then be dragged along with the flow, that is, because of this pumping action. Consequently, the displacement of the IHC stereocilia is expected to follow the velocity, as well as the up-and-down displacement of the organ. Although the specifics are beyond the scope of the present discussion, there is experimental evidence that this, in fact, is the case.

# 3. Cochlear (Macro) Mechanics

The next problem to be confronted in the chain of events leading to the excita-

tion of auditory (sensory) neurons is that of getting the basilar membrane to vibrate up and down, which, again, is needed to set up the shearing motion of the hairs. This is where the mechanical properties of the cochlea—as a vibratory system—come into play.

## A. MOTION OF THE COCHLEAR PARTITION—THE "BIG PICTURE"

The discussion thus far has focused on cellular-level events or a level of operation of the transduction system that later will be referred to as *micromechanics*. To avoid a well-known problem of conceptualization, commonly expressed by the analogy of failure to see the forest for the trees, it will be beneficial at this juncture to examine the **macromechanics** of the system, to get the big picture first. As discussed in Chapter 4, the structure of the cochlea, for purposes of a functional analysis of the system, can be simplified considerably. The cochlea can be treated as if it were uncoiled and the whole cochlear partition were a single membrane separating scala vestibuli from scala tympani (see Fig. 5.10). Furthermore, in terms of how sound energy ultimately is used by the cochlea, the properties of the basilar membrane are dominant, to the extent that it is generally equated with the cochlear partition in the simplified cochlea (Fig. 5.10). Consider what must happen to this membrane as the stapes is set into vibratory motion. As the stapes is pushed inward, a difference in pressure, or *pressure gradient*, develops across the cochlear partition. Because the fluids of the cochlea are incompressible, something has to give, so the basilar membrane is deflected toward scala tympani. The displaced fluid, in turn, causes the outward displacement of the round window. As the stapes moves outward, the opposite happens. The basilar membrane is deflected upward, and the round window is pulled inward. Thus, as the stapes moves in and out of the oval window, the basilar membrane, indeed the entire contents of the cochlear parti-

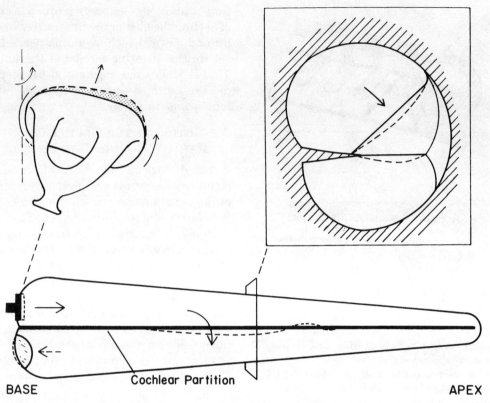

**BASE**

**Cochlear Partition**

**APEX**

**Figure 5.10.** Illustration of the manner in which displacement of the stapes leads to displacement of the cochlear partition (the basilar membrane, in particular). *Inset* drawings indicate in more detail the actual modes of displacement of the stapes and, subsequently, the cochlear partition. Note: the stapes seems to move about an axis defined by the ligament along the posterior aspect of the footplate, although a certain amount of its motion is also piston-like in the truest sense, namely an in-out motion. (Based on Békésy, G. v. [1960]. *Experiments in Hearing*, translated and edited by E. G. Wever. McGraw-Hill, New York.)

tion, is set into an up-and-down motion following the alternating pressure gradient across it. Consequently, most of the vibratory energy delivered by the stapes to the cochlear fluids is coupled to the basilar membrane.

It might be tempting to assume that the helicotrema offers an alternative route for the fluid displaced by stapes motion, such that displacement of the stapes causes perilymph to flow back and forth through this opening. But were this to happen without opposition, then there would be no displacement of the cochlear partition! Fortunately, the dynamics of cochlear mechanics are such that for most audible frequencies the helicotrema acts mechani-

cally as though it were closed. Only at very low frequencies (less than about 100 Hz in man) does significant fluid motion occur via this route. The helicotrema thus seems to be involved primarily with the essentially static balance of fluid pressure within the cochlea, so the helicotrema permits only relatively slow fluid motion through it. In terms of vibratory motion, this means relatively low frequencies, so the helicotrema may serve to filter out very low frequency noise. Now, perilymph itself is a perfectly suitable medium for the propagation of sound (similar to sea water), but sound waves set up in the fluid of scala vestibuli, because of the motion of the stapes, are propagated up the cochlea nearly instantaneously in comparison to the much slower events happening on the basilar membrane. Therefore, it is not the propagation of sound through the cochlear fluids per se that is the important event, but, rather, it is the subsequent *coupling* of this energy to the basilar membrane, by virtue of the chain of events just described. By the same token, it matters very little how sound energy is delivered to the perilymph; the basilar membrane reacts the same. Although the middle ear provides the most efficient route of communication, the basilar membrane also can be set into motion by vibrating the skull, as will be discussed in more detail in Chapter 7.

Once energy has been coupled to the basilar membrane, it is used in a highly characteristic manner. For any given frequency of sound impinging on the ear, the up-and-down displacement of the basilar membrane will vary in amplitude along its length. However, except for the most intense and very low frequency sounds, the whole membrane will not be set into motion simultaneously. As shown in Figure 5.11*a*, the peak-to-peak amplitude gradually increases until a certain distance is reached, after which there is a rapid diminution in the displacement. In Figure 5.11*a*, amplitudes are shown at only a few discrete points, but it is clear that a pattern of peak-to-peak displacements can be outlined (*dashed line* in Fig. 5.11*a*). In other words, all possible instantaneous values of displacement are contained within this pattern or what might be called the *envelope*.

Examining now in detail the displacement pattern along the basilar membrane (still for one frequency), as illustrated in Figure 5.11*b*, a wave is observed that moves from the base to the apex. This pattern of motion is called the ***traveling wave***. It always progresses from one end of the cochlea to the other, again from base to apex. As illustrated by Figure 5.11*b*, it is as if the basilar membrane were a string affixed at one end (apex) and shaken at the other (base). At one point along the

string, it may be moving upward; a short distance away, it may be displaced downward. In the next instant the whole picture changes. But this is where the vibrating string analogy ends. Along the basilar membrane the waves are never stationary, as would be the case were the string vibrated at a modal frequency (see Chapter 2, Acoustical Resonance and Standing Waves, in reference to standing waves). That is why the waves in the cochlea are called *traveling waves*. A familiar example of traveling waves is the waves of the ocean, particularly as seen along the shore. The waves start slowly as they move in toward the shore, build up to a peak, and then break off dramatically. Here, too, the analogy is limited by virtue of the strikingly different conditions under which waves are created in the ocean versus the cochlea. The cochlear waves actually have their highest propagation velocities at the base, progressively slowing as they move toward the apex. Additionally, as may be seen in Figure 5.11*c*, a more three-dimensional view of the cochlear traveling wave at one instant in time, there are remarkably different constraints in the cochlea. The medium (the basilar membrane) is severely limited in width, so the traveling wave envelope can be envisioned as an oblong bulge in the membrane.

Scrutiny of the time course of the traveling wave (Fig. 5.11*b*) reveals several important characteristics of this form of motion. It is notable that the wavelength is constantly changing with distance, becoming shorter as the wave approaches the apex. Recall that the speed of propagation is directly proportional to wavelength (see Eq. 2.5 and manipulations thereof in Chapter 2). Again, the wave literally slows down as it approaches the apex. This, in turn, leads to a progressively increasing phase lag of the motion of the basilar membrane in reference to the motion of the stapes, because of the increasing travel time of the wave. Intuitively, these factors suggest that the medium of this

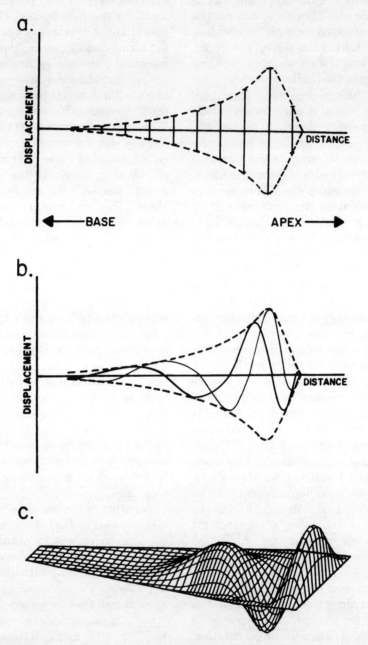

**Figure 5.11.** Traveling waves of the cochlea. **a.** Peak-to-peak displacements of the basilar membrane observed at discrete points along the cochlea. **b.** Instantaneous patterns of displacement. (Based on Békésy, G. v. [1960]. *Experiments in Hearing*, translated and edited by E. G. Wever. McGraw-Hill, New York.) **c.** Three-dimensional view of displacement pattern at one instant. (From Holmes, M. H. [1980]. An analysis of a low-frequency model of the cochlea. *J. Acoust. Soc. Am.* 68:482–488.

wave, the basilar membrane, must have properties that are changing with distance. This is not entirely surprising, given the anatomy of this membrane; its width varies from the base to the apex, suggesting variations in stiffness. The result of all this is that different frequencies optimally activate different regions of the basilar membrane, because these factors are expected to have frequency-dependent effects on the motion of the membrane.

It was the late Nobel laureate Georg von Békésy who first demonstrated traveling waves in the cochlea and to whom the traveling wave theory is attributed. In cadaver specimens of human cochleae, he observed that, indeed, low-frequency sounds elicit traveling waves that have their maxima near the apex, and, as frequency increases, the maximum of displacement moves toward the base. This scheme is illustrated in the *top panel* of Figure 5.12, wherein the peak amplitude is plotted as a function of distance along the basilar membrane. From all indications, it is not the instantaneous maxima

that are of ultimate importance (for purposes of encoding the stimulus); rather, it is the maximum of the traveling wave envelope. In particular, it is the location at which the peak of the envelope occurs that is believed to be the primary basis for the brain's decision as to the pitch of a sound (although not the only basis, as it turns out; see Chapter 6). In effect, the cochlea performs a spectrum analysis on the sound entering the ear, wherein it translates the frequency(ies) of the sound into distance(s) along the basilar membrane—a frequency-to-place or ***tonotopical*** transformation. Within certain limits (which will be covered later), each frequency contained in a sound creates its own traveling wave. For complex sounds, such as speech, the resulting pattern of vibration along the cochlear partition is also complex, because the component traveling waves are all superimposed. Consequently, the brain still has its work cut out for it in the analysis of spectrally rich stimuli, as discussed in Chapter 6. Still, the tonotopicity established on the basilar

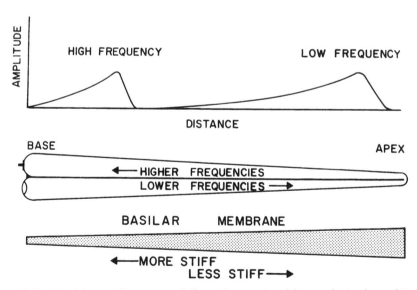

**Figure 5.12.** Behavior of the traveling wave at different frequencies of the sound stimulus and its dependence on the stiffness gradient of the basilar membrane. (Based on drawings and data of Békésy, G. v. [1960]. *Experiments in Hearing*, translated and edited by E. G. Wever. McGraw-Hill, New York; also data of Rhode, W. S. [1973]. An investigation of post-mortem cochlear mechanics using the Mossbauer effect. In *Basic Mechanisms in Hearing*, pp 39–63, edited by A. R. Moller. Academic Press, New York.)

membrane will be found to be a pervasive feature of the organization of the central auditory pathways and pivotal in determining limits of frequency resolution of the system.

The primary determinant of the frequency-to-place transformation is, again, the stiffness of the basilar membrane. The variation in its width, thickness, and composition from base to apex brings about more than a 100:1 change in stiffness, based on measurements in human cadaver specimens (perhaps $10^4$:1 or $10^5$:1 in live human and/or infrahuman cochlear specimens). The basilar membrane is stiffest in the base of the cochlea, where it is narrowest, and least stiff in the apex, where it is widest (Fig. 5.12). As was noted in Chapter 4, the change in the width of the basilar membrane is directly opposite to the change in cross-sectional area of the cochlea itself. As shown in Figure 5.12, the cochlea itself is skinniest at the apex, ironically, where the basilar membrane is the widest. Of course, the friction and mass of the membrane and all the structures resting on it cannot be ignored, any more so than in any other vibratory system. The viscosity of the fluids surrounding the basilar membrane and its own internal friction determine the damping of the motion of the traveling wave. The cochlear partition seems to be critically damped (or very nearly so), but here, not only is the expedient decay of magnitude of motion over

time important, but also decay over distance along the basilar membrane. That is, after reaching the place of maximum, the traveling wave dies out very quickly and over a relatively short distance (reflecting in part, again, the progressively shortening wavelength).

Regardless of the mechanical complexities of the real cochlea, the simplest working model of the cochlea that sustains the kind of traveling wave motion observed by Bekesy requires only a membrane of varying stiffness separating two channels of fluid—essentially water (Fig. 5.13). In such a system the membrane is virtually massless, and the viscosity of the fluid alone provides most of the friction involved. In this simple model, these parameters do not vary significantly along the length of the cochlea. To reiterate, it is the *gradient of stiffness* along the basilar membrane that can be singled out as the key factor determining the tonotopical transformation. Just how it is possible for stiffness to change as a function primarily of the width may seem puzzling at first but can be appreciated by another simple self-demonstration. Obtain a rubber band, and cut it to form an elastic string. Now, cut this string into several pieces of differing lengths. Experiment with the different lengths of the rubber band, suspending them without tension. For the same amount of displacement, the shortest piece affords the most opposition. Thus,

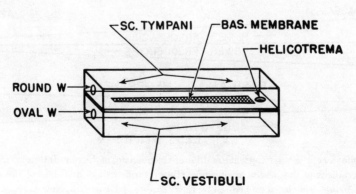

**Figure 5.13.** Drawing of a working model of the cochlea. (From Tonndorf, J. [1958]. The hydrodynamic origin of aural harmonics in the cochlea. *Ann. Otol. Rhinol. Laryngol.* 67:754–774.).

the shorter the length, the greater the stiffness.

## B. COCHLEAR MODELS AND OTHER THINGS

The use of models, both physical and mathematical, has been very important in establishing the existence of traveling waves in the cochlea as a fact, rather than just another theory. Although it is fundamentally possible to make a model do whatever one desires, carefully constructed models can, and indeed have, revealed problems with interpretation of experimental data or conceptual flaws in theories of cochlear mechanics. They can even suggest possible underlying mechanisms overlooked or not readily observed in the real cochlea. They also can allow the researcher to extrapolate beyond the limits of empirical data. The model permits one to play with various structures and parameters in a way that may not be possible in the real cochlea. Models also do not pose the problems inherent in working with biological tissues, particularly the live specimen. Without going into a detailed treatment of any particular model, it will be worthwhile to discuss briefly some of the problems that the model builders have attempted to address.

The early models of the cochlea, physical and mathematical alike, were designed to reduce cochlear mechanics to the bare essentials. This is evident from Juergen Tonndorf's model illustrated in Figure 5.13, which was similar to one studied originally by Bekesy. A membrane of varying width separated two fluid-filled channels. This model was several times the size of the real (uncoiled) cochlea. Corresponding mathematical models, such as Josef Zwislocki's, were unidimensional and behaved best for input frequencies with wavelengths that were relatively long compared with the cross-sectional dimensions of the cochlea. Overall, the traveling waves produced in these relatively simple models mimicked acceptably the phenomena observed by Bekesy in real human-cadaver cochleae. However, the past several decades of research have clearly demonstrated that postmortem changes in the cochlear tissues have substantial effects on the mechanics of the cochlear partition. In the live cochlea a resonance-like effect is now thought to occur in the vicinity of the peak of the traveling wave, as evidenced by the sharpness of the peak of the displacement pattern. Because the basilar membrane in the model illustrated in Figure 5.13 is virtually massless, resonance of the type observed in simple harmonic oscillation is not possible. So, neither observations on the early cochlear models nor Bekesy's observations on cadaver specimens could describe adequately the motion of the basilar membrane in the living cochlea. Indeed, the consensus these days is that the vibratory patterns of the living cochlea cannot be fully explained by completely passive mechanisms.

One of the motivations for keeping things as simple as possible in mathematical models, nevertheless, is to keep the equations involved within the realm of solvability. Furthermore, before computers became commonplace, the testing of numerical solutions was practical only for relatively simple models. Although the problem of finding solutions has not changed per se, advances in mathematics, engineering, and computer science have provided the modern model builder with much greater flexibility. More recent modelers have been able to examine, for example, two- and three-dimensional models wherein both long- and short-wave phenomena can be accommodated. Recall that the wavelength of the traveling wave constantly changes as the wave progresses up the cochlea, so in reality a single long- or short-wave model cannot completely emulate hydrodynamics in the real cochlea. It also has been possible to address factors traditionally ignored, in the interest of simplicity, such as the influence of coiling of the cochlea. Indeed, modern modelers experiment with active elements and/or components representing various micromechanical details of how the real cochlea may work in all its complexity (not simplicity). Some of the more compelling issues involved will be discussed momentarily and include, for example, nonlinearities.

## 4. Cochlear Micromechanics

The term cochlear mechanics, or *macromechanics*, again, generally connotes the hydrodynamics of the cochlea, of which the traveling wave motion of the basilar membrane is the major outcome. ***Micromechanics*** pertains primarily to mechanical events at the hair cell level. How the tectorial membrane interfaces with the stereocilia, the mode of action of the hairs, and mechanical influence of the hair cells are aspects of micromechanics.

Research and work with models during the past two decades have concentrated increasingly on the fine details of the structure and function of the organ of Corti and the hair cells. This interest has been stimulated, first, by a desire to understand the actual way in which the system works and, second, by earlier perceived discrepancies among measures of basilar membrane displacement, response selectivity of the hair cells, response selectivity of auditory neurons, and perceptual limits of auditory frequency discrimination (discussed further in Chapters 6 and 7). For years, the impression from such empirical data was that the frequency analysis performed in the cochlea, by virtue of the tonotopic transformation, was not precise enough to account for the frequency resolution ability, that is, frequency selectivity, of the auditory system, as demonstrated by electrophysiological and psychoacoustical measurements. Even the displacement patterns observed using modern techniques in live preparations, although sharper than those observed by Bekesy using light microscopy in cadavers, did not seem sharp enough, at least not initially. Thus, hearing scientists pursued ways in which frequency resolution might be improved, beyond the (ma-

cro)mechanics of the cochlea. Initially, it seemed that this improvement was effected by the central auditory system. It thus was assumed that the central auditory system somehow would have to sharpen the mechanical response pattern, as reflected in the neural code. Then, it was discovered that the auditory sensory neurons, even in the periphery, already show great selectivity (see Chapter 6). Finally, the responses of hair cells themselves were found to be highly selective. So, the search for the site of the elusive enhancement in frequency resolution—what had come to be known as the "second filter"[1]—moved progressively toward the end organ.

Interestingly, even cochlear micromechanics did not escape Bekesy's relentless query into the mysteries of the auditory system. He studied the nuances of the motion of the tectorial membrane in an effort to determine the direction of bending of the stereocilia relative to the peak of the traveling wave. Although perhaps not as a matter of micromechanics, as such, he also considered whether the hair cells actually respond to the displacement wave or to the spatial derivative of the traveling wave. (The derivative, a mathematical operation, reflects the slope at each point along a given function.) The spatial derivative of the traveling wave yields an envelope with a sharper peak. However, the real source of enhancement of frequency selectivity would prove to be lurking under the tectorial membrane and to be intimately related to the role and contribution of the hair cells themselves.

### A. THE ESSENTIAL NONLINEARITY

Although it is now widely accepted that the shearing displacement of the ste-

---

[1] The elusive enhancement process in question was called the second filter by virtue of the view that the traveling-wave place mechanism makes the cochlea behave like a bank of band-pass filters. (In Chapter 7, this concept will be shown, indeed, to be manifest in a psychoacoustic phenomenon known as the *critical bands*. Therefore, the cochlear macromechanics were considered to constitute the first filter.)

reocilia is the effective stimulus for cochlear hair cells, this notion has been surrounded by controversy over the years. Earlier estimates had suggested that, at just detectable levels of sound, displacement of the basilar membrane must be on the order of the diameter of the hydrogen atom ($10^{-12}$ m or 1 millionth of a micron), perhaps even less! It was difficult to conceive of such minute displacements, let alone how they could be translated into any significant movement of the stereocilia. The need for amplification was evident, but this raised only more questions. Would not a tremendous amount of amplification be required, and would not the useful gain of such an amplifier itself be limited inherently by internal noise of the system from the cochlear blood supply (if not by thermal noise)?

The prediction of atomic, if not subatomic, displacements was based on displacement measurements made at high sound pressure levels and extrapolated assuming a linear relationship between displacement and sound pressure. But, what if the motion of the basilar membrane were nonlinear (see Fig. 5.14b)? Evidence of nonlinearities in the auditory system abounds in the literature and dates from some of the earliest published studies of audition! Interestingly, only during the past couple of decades of research has the nonlinearity of basilar membrane displacement become firmly established, thanks to incredible technical advances that have permitted the necessary measurements to be made over an adequate dynamic range. This is not to say that there was not already plenty of evidence strongly suggesting nonlinear components in cochlear mechanics and/or hair cell transduction. However, the foci of such phenomena were perceived to be associated mostly with issues of overloading the system, that is, problems arising at relatively high levels of stimulation. Even the finest stereo high-fidelity system produces distortion, especially when driven hard. But now, nonlinearity was being recognized as an inherent characteristic of sound transduction by the hearing organ for sounds falling more in the middle to lower end of the dynamic range, that is, for moderate to soft sounds, rather than just for extremely loud sounds.

Now, the idea that the hearing organ is inherently nonlinear may put the high-fidelity enthusiast ill at ease—but remember the decibel? If the decibel, which represents a logarithmic transformation, better scales the dynamic range of hearing than a linear quantity (see Chapter 3), then the amplifier in the transduction system must be, by definition, nonlinear! More specifically, it must be *compressive*. By compressive it is meant that a large range of input signal magnitudes is crammed into a much smaller range of output signal magnitudes (see Fig. 3.3). Theoretically, a compression function could be introduced anywhere in the auditory system. As it turns out, the displacement of the basilar membrane itself *is* nonlinear and, more specifically, compressive. But this is not the case everywhere along the traveling wave envelope, for a given frequency, or, for a given place of observation, at all frequencies! As illustrated in Figure 5.14a, the compression occurs predominantly around the best or *characteristic frequency*. At relatively lower frequencies, displacement is linear (Fig. 5.14b). This is also the behavior of the dead cochlea at all frequencies.

What was becoming increasing apparent with each new observation was that the hearing organ is an even more incredible piece of biological engineering than ever imagined. Only during the past decade of hearing research has the mystery of how the additional frequency selectivity is achieved (beyond that of the cochlear macromechanics) begun to unravel before the scientists' eyes. The central character in this mystery is none other than the OHC. It now is clear that the OHCs are responsible for the most sensitive range of hearing, but not because of some form of summation of the responses of these cells,

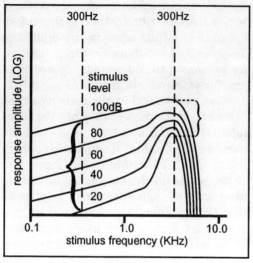
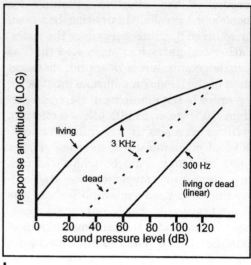

**a.**        **b.**

**Figure 5.14.** **a.** Characteristic patterns and growth of basilar membrane displacement versus stimulus frequency as a function of the SPL. **b.** Dependence of magnitude of basilar membrane response as a function of SPL in the living versus dead cochlea and high- versus low-frequency stimuli. (Courtesy of Dr. Jonathan Siegel, Northwestern University, Evanston, IL.)

as once thought. In fact, its role as a receptor is now being deemphasized in favor of another role—that of a motor!

## B. The Schizophrenic OHC and Other Mysteries of the Universe

This all may begin to sound like some riddle: "When is a receptor cell really an effector cell?" Answer: when it is an OHC. The OHC certainly seems to have a dual personality. It will become more apparent in Chapter 6 just why its motor function has begun to be viewed as the dominant personality; it is there that the neural wiring of the hair cells and the response characteristics of auditory neurons (versus the mechanical response of the cochlea) will be considered in detail. For now, what is of interest is the nature and molecular bases of what has come to be known as the *motile response* of OHCs. As noted earlier, the protein actin is found not only in the fibrous-like structure of the stereocilia, but also throughout the hair cell structure, suggesting contractile proper-

ties or the potential for other actions and reactions of the hairs or the hair cell.

Certainly one of the most exciting observations in hearing science was the recent demonstration that isolated OHCs are capable of reacting by a change in cell length to an applied electric field. On a more jocular note, this phenomenon has been dubbed "dancing hair cells," because, when observed while stimulating with musical signals, the hair cell rhythmically contracts to the beat. The experimental methods leading to this historic observation characterize the incredibly innovative applications of methods of cellular biology that have emerged during the past decade or so of hearing research, particularly the trick of isolating viable individual hair cells. Observing the response of these isolated cells under electric stimulation has demonstrated that depolarization of the OHC is associated with a contraction, and hyperpolarization with an elongation, of the cell body. The OHC thus is indeed capable of reacting mechanically to sound, perhaps even moving in situ; such motion and reaction are assumed to facilitate the vibration of the basilar membrane. A useful analogy is what happens when one person swings another. For the same effort on the part of the person doing the pushing, the person in the swing will go higher, with a kick on the initiation of each swing cycle. This is because the person in the swing is adding to the energy imparted by the individual doing the pushing. However, proper timing is important; kicking out of sync is counterproductive!

"So, what causes the cell to move or otherwise mechanically react?" is the next logical question. The fine details are still subject to debate and are the foci of a wealth of ongoing research, well beyond the scope of this text. However, the general principles seem to have been sorted out, once more as a product of work on both mammalian auditory and other nonmammalian or nonauditory hair cells. The driving voltage presumably is the receptor potential—the product of depolarization or hyperpolarization of the cell on displacement of the stereocilia (Fig. 5.15). After all, the OHC is still a receptor cell.

Recall the tip links? These seem to play a major role in controlling the depolarization of the cells via gating (opening and closing channels) of ionic current flowing through the stereocilia. The receptor potential then activates motor units distributed throughout the OHC's structure. The electromotility of the OHC thus represents the evolutionary culmination of some impressive molecular engineering.

The discussion in this section was initiated on the premise of a mismatch between macromechanics, specifically as suggested by von Békésy's work on cadaver ears and various observations from living ears, pointing to the sharpened mechanical response of the living ear. Various possible sharpening mechanisms have been postulated, all contingent on the precise details of the coupling of the stereocilia to the tectorial membrane. But it is the revelation of the motile response of OHCs that, by far, has given the theoreticians the most food for thought, leading to the currently popular theory that the OHCs provide a mechanism of positive feedback. Again, the OHC now is consid-

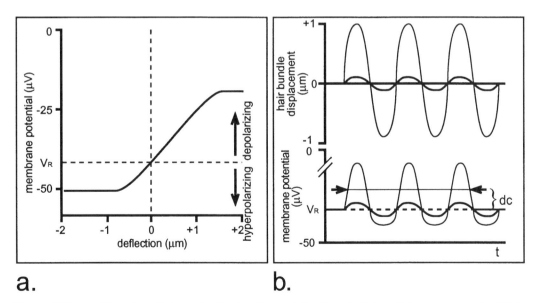

**a.**　　　　　　　　　　　**b.**

**Figure 5.15.** **a.** Characteristic transduction input-output function. **b.** Intracellular receptor potential for relatively low (*heavy line*) versus high (*thin lines*) hair bundle displacements. (Courtesy of Dr. Jonathan Siegel, Northwestern University, Evanston, IL.)

ered to contribute to the motion of the basilar membrane (an active process), rather than just going along for the ride (a passive process). The net result is a localized resonance enhancing the frequency selectivity of vibration at any one point along the basilar membrane. Indeed, it now is clear that sufficiently sharp frequency resolution is present in the vibration of the cochlear partition to account, by and large, for the frequency resolution of the entire auditory system (see Chapter 6). All that fancy bioengineering of the OHC by Mother Nature was not just to make for a very sensitive sensory mechanism, but also to yield a mechanism that can respond selectively to sounds of different frequencies while representing rather precisely the frequency content of complex sounds!

So, why had earlier observations not revealed all this? Well, even the use of modern sophisticated measurement techniques required refinement along the way, particularly with regard to the maintenance of a highly stable preparation and the minimization of contamination introduced by the measurement technique itself. Of course, measurements are only as good as the tools and methods used to obtain them. Even though the mystery of (indeed, the need for) a second filter seems to have been laid to rest, micromechanics is still the hot area of interest. There remain other mysteries to be solved regarding the details of exactly how the OHC motile response interacts with basilar membrane mechanics—the relative contributions of active versus passive processes (not to mention the debate about which processes are active versus passive). Another intriguing issue is the possible regulation of these processes by the CNS (as discussed in Chapter 6).

## C. INTERLUDE 1

A significant amount of signal processing occurs via the mechanics of the cochlea, before any neural encoding. The sound spectrum has, in effect, been translated from amplitude-versus-frequency to amplitude-versus-distance coordinates, with distance corresponding to the place of the traveling wave maximum. Thus, for example, the response of hair cells situated at a specific place along the basilar membrane looks like the response of a bandpass filter (see Chapter 3), given a broad-band signal at the input to the cochlea. The cochlear filter's response characteristics will be examined in Chapter 6, and its impact on auditory behavior will be discussed in Chapter 7. Therein, the response characteristics will reveal the cochlear filter to have a relatively narrow bandwidth with a steep high-frequency slope and a more gradual low-frequency slope. The sharpness of the traveling (mechanical) wave, and thus this filter, is facilitated by the micromechanics processes just described and determines the auditory system's ability to distinguish one frequency of sound from another or to analyze the frequency content of complex sounds.

The total chain of *macromechanical* events leading to the micromechanical events actually involves more than the cochlea, as illustrated in Figure 5.16. Sound impressed on the tympanic membrane sets the ossicular chain into vibration, which, in turn, causes a displacement of the basilar membrane and initiates the propagation of traveling waves along it. It might be expected that, because the sound

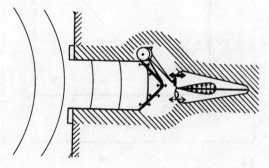

**Figure 5.16.** Highly schematized diagram of the total events leading from the occurrence of sound at the entrance of the ear to the excitation of traveling waves in the cochlea.

energy is passed through other mechanisms before entering the cochlea, the mechanisms will affect the efficiency of energy coupling to the cochlear system. Consequently, the spectrum of the sound arriving at the cochlea is expected to be somewhat tainted. Indeed, the influence of the outer and middle portions of the peripheral mechanism on the spectrum of sound reaching the cochlea is substantial. These parts of the system, in fact, determine what sounds are audible and how well they are heard. They thus require, and deserve, in-depth discussion.

## 5. Function of the Middle Ear

### A. THE AIR-COCHLEA MISMATCH

Recalling the problems of transmitting sound from one medium to another (Chapter 2), the function of the middle ear mechanism is not too difficult to conceive. Indeed, with the acoustic principles of Chapter 2 in hand, one actually can state in 25, or even 10, words or less the primary role of the middle ear: it acts as an ***impedance-matching transformer***. Therefore, it acts to make the input of the cochlea, the oval window, "look" acoustically more like air. This is very important if the sensory receptors within the cochlea are to make efficient use of sound energy.

Because optimal power transfer from one medium or vibratory system to another is attained only when their impedances are matched, it is tempting to conclude that the role of the middle ear mechanism, in more specific terms, is to improve the match between the gaseous medium outside of the cochlea to the fluid medium inside. Thus, the magnitude of the mismatch might be assessed by assuming that the cochlear fluid is contained in a tube that is effectively infinite in length. The input impedance of the cochlea then would be directly determined by the characteristic impedance of the cochlear fluid or, in essence, the impedance of sea water. From this analogy, the input impedance would seem to be independent of frequency or purely resistive.

In Chapter 2 it was learned that only about 0.1% of the sound energy is transmitted from air to water, and 99.9% is reflected. The absence of the middle ear would thus be assumed to cause a loss of transmission of sound energy of 1000:1 or 30 dB (and, therefore, a loss of hearing of 30 dB). However, the accuracy of this prediction relies on: 1) the actual efficiency of the middle ear transformer, 2) the frequency range over which the transformer performs efficiently, 3) the dynamic (intensity) range of the transformer, and 4) the appropriateness of the simple air-water analogy in the first place.

In the detailed analysis, the air-water analogy really does not seem to be appropriate, despite its attractive simplicity and ball-park accuracy of prediction. First, the dimensions of the cochlear fluid medium are decisively finite, because they are small relative to the wavelengths of audible frequencies of sound. The most recent, and to date most direct, estimates of the cochlear input impedance (albeit from experiments on infrahuman species) suggest it to be only about 1/10 of the value computed from the characteristic impedance of water, namely, the characteristic impedance divided by the area of the stapes footplate, approximately 112,000 rayls (MKS). This still reflects a considerable mismatch with the impedance of air, 415 rayls. Also, were the problem facing the middle ear mechanism simply one of making up for an air-to-water mismatch, the medium would comprise the entire head! Most of the tissues of the body have about the same density as water. (Recall that the characteristic impedance is determined by the density of the medium and speed of sound in that medium; see Chapter 2.) The problem is that, were sound (compressional) waves transmitted to the entire head, the acoustic isolation between the two ears would not be nearly as great as it is known to be.

Interestingly, much of the available data do reveal at least one characteristic predicted from the air-water analogy (an example of the classic paradox of the right answer for the wrong reason). In the mid- to high-frequency ranges of hearing, the cochlear input impedance seems to be essentially independent of frequency. However, the measured magnitude of the cochlear input impedance is still an order of magnitude off, but then the cochlea is not an unbounded sea water–like medium! Indeed, the effective input to the cochlea is the pressure gradient across the cochlear partition, so an important component of the cochlear input impedance is the input impedance across the cochlear partition. This impedance depends on the properties of the cochlear partition, or more explicitly, the physical properties of the basilar membrane, and thus is not expected to be either purely resistive or equal merely to the impedance of the cochlear fluids (or essentially the impedance of sea water). The cochlear impedance has been shown to be equal, basically, to the difference between the cochlear input impedance at the oval window and the impedance of the round window, which, in turn, acts to relieve the pressure difference across the partition. Again, the incompressible fluid displaced in the process has to go somewhere. Indeed, both the cochlear input impedance and the input impedance across the partition have been shown to have reactive components that are influential, particularly at low frequencies. Coincidentally, the pressure gradient vanishes toward the lower-frequency limit of hearing.

A more tenable approach to the analysis of the cochlear input impedance that has been suggested in recent years takes into account the fact that the dimensions of the oval window also are smaller than the wavelengths of sounds of practical interest and treats the oval window opening as though it were a piston mounted in an infinite baffle (the head). The input impedance is equated with the radiation impedance of this piston and represents mathematically a problem for which analytical methods are established. Interest-

ingly, the results of such an analysis suggest the air-cochlear mismatch to be worth much more than that predicted by the simple air-water analogy (30 dB), particularly at low frequencies (50 dB). Once more, the cochlear input impedance seems to be reactive, rather than purely resistive. Although this approach itself may not prove necessarily to be the definitive one, it certainly is attractive from the point of view that it is based on more realistic assumptions about the acoustics of the cochlea than are evident in the air-water analogy.

It should be evident at this juncture that there are various problems involved in attempting to assess the air-cochlea mismatch. Overcoming these problems is fundamental to the precise evaluation of the contribution of the middle ear mechanism to the resolution of the mismatch and, more generally, to the comprehension of the contribution of the middle ear to hearing sensitivity. Numerous attempts have been made, via both direct measurements and mathematical analyses, to determine the cochlear input impedance. In any event, the empirical data come from either live infrahuman preparations or human cadavers. Species differences and postmortem effects can be substantial. So, the question arises as to just what is an appropriate analytical approach. The classical approach is described below, but it will be shown later to be limited. At this time, a completely satisfactory analysis and description of the middle ear transformer, and its contribution to hearing, is still lacking, despite the great strides that have been made in research in this area. But, regardless of the remaining uncertainties, one thing will become perfectly clear. Without some intermediary process to improve the match between air and cochlea, hearing sensitivity would not be nearly as good as it is known to be.

## B. THE MIDDLE EAR TRANSFORMER—CLASSICAL THEORY

The classical approach to the analysis of the middle ear transformer treats the

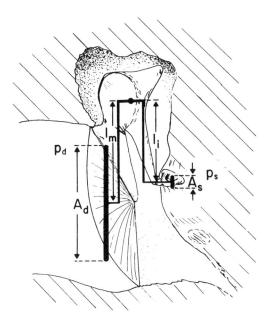

**Figure 5.17.** Components of the middle ear transformer, viewed as a system of two pistons connected by a folded lever. $A$, area; $p$, sound pressure; $l$, length; $d$, eardrum; $m$, manubrium of the malleus; $i$, long crus of the incus; and $s$, stapes footplate. (Schematic drawing based on Zwislocki, J. [1965]. Analysis of some auditory characteristics. In *Handbook of Mathematical Psychology*, vol 3, pp 1–97, edited by R. R. Bush, R. D. Luce, and E. Galanter. John Wiley & Sons, New York.)

eardrum as a rigid piston attached to a lever system formed by the ossicles, as illustrated in Figure 5.17. That the eardrum could act like a solid piston may be appreciated by considering the construction of a conventional loudspeaker. By shaping the material of the speaker diaphragm into a cone, a fairly rigid structure is formed from an otherwise light and pliable substance. Using sufficiently elastic materials around the edge, the cone can then move back and forth like a piston. The elastic fibers of the tympanic membrane (Chapter 4), particularly around its circumference, make this kind of motion possible for the eardrum as well. As illustrated in Figure 5.17, the entire surface of the eardrum, like the speaker cone, does not constitute the piston; rather, there is

an effective area that is smaller than that of the entire membrane that is capable of vibrating as a whole. The effective area is approximately 70% of the anatomical area or approximately 0.594 cm$^2$ in humans. The major component of the middle ear transformer then is the ratio of the *effective* area of the eardrum to the area of the stapes footplate, approximately 0.032 cm$^2$. (The whole stapes footplate is considered rigid.) These numbers reveal that the tympanic membrane has an effective area that is 18.6 times greater than the area of the stapes footplate (although estimates of these figures vary). This means, in turn, that the sound pressure acting on the larger area of the tympanic membrane is funneled down onto the smaller area of the stapes footplate. Because pressure is force per unit area ($p = F/A$), then the same force acts over a smaller area, which causes the pressure to be increased at the stapes. This is because that area now is a smaller number in the denominator of the term $F/A$. In other words, the sound pressure is increased by a factor of 18.6, the areal ratio (0.594/0.032).

Now, the manubrium of the malleus and the long crus of the incus together form a lever (Fig. 5.17). It does not matter that they do not go together in such a manner as to form a straight lever, like the teeter board of a seesaw; it works just the same "folded." Some additional force amplification, then, is expected from the leverage of the ossicular chain. Because the manubrium is approximately 1.3 times longer than the long crus of the incus, the gain attributable to leverage is 1.3. Consequently, a total pressure amplification of $18.6 \times 1.3 = 24.2$ is obtained. Thus, one way in which the middle ear meets the opposition of the cochlea to the airborne sound (because of the higher impedance of the cochlea) is by stepping up the sound pressure. Actually, any impedance transformation is accompanied by a pressure transformation, and if the direction is from low to high impedance, the pressure transformation will be from low to high as well.

It is tempting to assume that the sound pressure gain itself represents the contribution of the middle ear to hearing sensitivity. Plugging the number 24 into the decibel equation for sound pressure level (Eq. 3.7) yields a gain figure of 28 dB. The natural conclusion is that removal of the tympanic membrane and ossicular chain would lead to a 28-dB decrease in hearing sensitivity. That is, in the absence of the middle ear, the sound pressure level would have to be increased by 28 dB for the sound to be just detectable. However, the value of the middle ear is only partly reflected in the sound pressure gain. If no motion results, no energy is transferred to the inner ear. It was learned in Chapter 1 that energy must be conserved. This is the law—the law of physics, that is. A transformer cannot increase energy; it is a passive device, unlike an electronic amplifier, for example (which includes active devices in its design). Recall from Chapter 1 that $Z = F/v$ (derived from Eq. 1.18); a similar equation can be written here:

$$Z = p/v \qquad (5.1)$$

where $Z$ is *specific* impedance, $p$ is sound pressure, and $v$ is velocity. Specific impedance has the same dimensions as characteristic impedance (see Chapter 2). A complete evaluation of the contribution of the middle ear mechanism thus requires that the impedance transformation itself be evaluated, namely, that the *impedance transformation ratio* be determined. The question to be answered is, "Just how good is the impedance match provided by the middle ear?" Once the impedance transformation ratio is established, the proportion of sound energy transmitted through the middle ear can be estimated. Still, a part of the analysis requires the computation of the *pressure transformation ratio*:

$$p_d/p_s = A_s l_i / A_d l_m \qquad (5.2)$$

where $A$ is area, $l$ is length, and the subscripts $d$, $m$, $i$, and $s$ denote the eardrum,

manubrium, incus (long crus), and stapes (footplate), respectively. Alternatively, the pressure transformation ratio is equal to 1/pressure gain, so its value is approximately $1/24 = 0.042$.

Now, the leverage of the ossicular chain also brings about a velocity transformation, because the fulcrum of this lever is at the junction between the manubrium and the incus, and the long crus of the incus is shorter. Consequently, the tip of the shorter arm moves through a smaller distance (arc) than is covered by the tip of the longer arm, per unit time. The velocity transformation ratio is given by the equation.

$$v_d/v_s = l_m/l_i \qquad (5.3)$$

As indicated earlier, its value is 1.3.

The (specific) impedance transformation ratio can now be derived. Combining Eq. 5.1–5.3,

$$\frac{Z_d}{Z_s} = \frac{p_d/p_s}{v_d/v_s}$$

$$= \frac{A_s l_i / A_d l_m}{l_m / l_i} \qquad (5.4)$$

$$= \frac{A_s}{A_d} \frac{l_i^2}{l_m}$$

When the appropriate values are entered into Eq. 5.4, the impedance ratio is found to be approximately 0.032. (Because the pressure and velocity transformation ratios were computed earlier, the impedance transformation ratio could be calculated directly: $0.042/1.3 = 0.032 = 3.2 \times 10^{-2}$. Using an estimate of specific cochlear input impedance in humans, $1.12 \times 10^5$ MKS rayls (based on estimates of the cross-sectional area of the cochlea and the compliance of the basilar membrane at the basal end), the transformed impedance is found to be $3.2 \times 10^{-2} \times 1.12 \times 10^5 = 3.58 \times 10^3$ rayls. In other words, the middle ear serves to step down the input impedance of the cochlea from 112,000 to 3580 rayls, bringing it much closer to the impedance of air (415 rayls). The amount of transmission now can be computed (using Eq. 2.9):

$$X = \frac{4 \times (4.15 \times 10^2) \times (3.58 \times 10^3)}{[(4.15 \times 10^2) + (3.58 \times 10^3)]^2}$$

$$\simeq 0.37$$

Using (in essence) Eq. 3.6, the amount of transmission can be estimated in decibels to be $10 \log 0.37 = -4.3$. Invoking Eq. 2.9 once more and entering the specific cochlear input impedance, the transmission without the middle ear transformer would be estimated to be only 0.015 or $-18.3$ dB. The worth of the middle ear, in decibels, can then be estimated by taking the difference between the energy transfer with the transformer versus without it:

$$-4.3 - (-18.3) = -4.3 + 18.3 = 14 \text{ dB}$$

This value is notably smaller than that which would have been assumed based on the sound pressure gain of the middle ear (28 dB). Had the middle ear mechanism been treated as an acoustic, rather than a mechanical, transformer, slightly more favorable values would have been obtained, a transmission figure of about 0.46. (Such an analysis is a bit more involved, because acoustic impedance is equal to specific impedance divided by the surface area over which the sound wave acts.) The important point is that there is a residual mismatch, at least according to the results of this analysis and the assumptions and estimates on which it is based. Nevertheless, it is clear that the middle ear transformer provides for more sound transmission to the cochlea than would be possible via direct sound transmission to the oval window. The use of this same analysis with data from other animals, such as the guinea pig and the cat, suggests their middle ear mechanisms to be even more efficient.

The moral to this story, and a point that bears repeating, is that the pressure transformation itself does not determine the efficiency of the system. This can be understood by considering what happens when one attempts to push a disabled automobile. Pushing with the hands, pressure is felt against them as force is applied to move the car. If it moves, work is done (by definition) and energy is transferred. However, if the emergency brake is accidentally left on, regardless of how hard one pushes, the car is not moved. Tremendous pressure against the hands is felt, but no work is done in the physical sense. The same is true for the middle ear. Unless the sound pressure gain leads to sufficient motion of the stapes, namely, sufficient velocity, then the pressure amplification will be in vain. It was learned in Chapter 1 that power is equal to force times velocity, or in this case, sound pressure times velocity (that is, $P = pv$). So, the bottom line is that it is not just how much sound energy (totally) is transferred that is important. It is the time rate of energy transfer or the amount of power (in essence, acoustic intensity) reaching the cochlea that is important. This is precisely what is determined by the impedance transformation ratio.

## C. So, What Is the Middle Ear Worth?

The 14-dB value assessed the middle ear in the above analysis seems small. Indeed, this value does not reflect the entire worth of the mechanism, nor would it even if it were more favorable! The worth of the middle ear mechanism, in other words, does not rest entirely on the transformer ratio, and the complete absence of the tympanic membrane and the ossicles, or simply disrupting the ossicular chain, certainly has a more profound effect on hearing, causing hearing losses up to 60 or 70 dB. When the ossicular pathway is effectively broken, there is the additional problem that sound can reach the round window directly, as well as the oval window. This leads to some degree of cancellation of the sound entering the oval window and, consequently, some cancellation of the resulting pressure gradient across the cochlear partition. However, total cancellation does not result at least at all frequencies, because the two windows are not in the same plane. On the contrary, small pressure differences do occur between the two windows, and, although not of significance in the functioning of the normal ear, they may be primarily responsible for the residual hearing of individuals without middle ear mechanisms or disruptions thereof. Nevertheless, the middle ear mechanism is often said to protect the round window from the airborne sounds, and this principle has guided some creative reconstructive surgeries in cases in which the tympanic membrane and most of the ossicular chain have been lost. This condition can lead to losses of hearing on the order of 60 dB over frequencies of relevance for hearing speech. Approximately 40 dB of this loss can be overcome by simply using a graft to act as a barrier between the stapes and the round window, thereby restoring the protection of the round window. Yet, this treatment is considerably less efficient than nature's own. Clearly, the normal middle ear mechanism offers the path of least resistance, or, more accurately, the path of least impedance.

The piston model of the middle ear transformer also is of great heuristic value, namely for purposes of fundamentally explaining concepts such as pressure amplification and impedance transformation in a vibratory system such as the middle ear. It also can lead to predictions and computed values reasonably consistent with clinical observations and empirical facts. For example, the model places relatively little value on the leverage of the ossicular chain, leading one to expect that a disrupted ossicular chain might be effectively repaired without necessarily replacing all its parts. Reconstructive surgery, indeed, can be reasonably successful, even with such an approach as merely connecting the eardrum to the stapes! After all, in birds and reptiles the counterpart of the mammalian ossicular chain is a single bone (the columella). Another example is

the prediction of the differences in efficiencies of middle ear transmission among species. The cat's middle ear provides a pressure amplification of about 37 dB, which, of course, is substantially higher than that of the human (as discussed in the preceding section). The sound pressure at the oval window has been directly measured in this animal, and pressure gains of approximately the same amount have been observed. (In the cat's ear, purportedly by virtue of its greater efficiency compared with humans, essentially the full sound pressure gain of the middle ear transformer is realized at the input of the cochlea.)

However, the assumed mechanism of the impedance transformation in the piston model is not totally consistent with the findings of some of the most modern experiments. Laser holography has been used to study the minute vibrations of the eardrum, permitting a detailed analysis of its entire surface. These observations have revealed that the eardrum rarely, if ever, vibrates as a whole, that is, like a rigid piston (as per the classical analysis). Interestingly, the results of such measurements tend to support an idea originally set forth by Helmholtz over a century ago. Helmholtz believed that the curvature of the tympanic membrane forms the most significant aspect of the middle ear transformer. A curved membrane can provide leverage. This can be appreciated from the analogy of a cable strung between two poles. The weight of the cable causes it to sag, and, theoretically, an infinite amount of force is required to pull it taut and perfectly straight. Conversely, if the cable were stiff, force applied in the middle of the cable could be translated into a considerable force at the ends. The tympanic membrane curves inwardly as it attaches along the manubrium of the malleus, and some rigidity is given to the membrane by virtue of its fibrous middle layers (see Chapter 4). Not only does the eardrum not vibrate as a whole or work as a rigid piston, but at frequencies greater than about

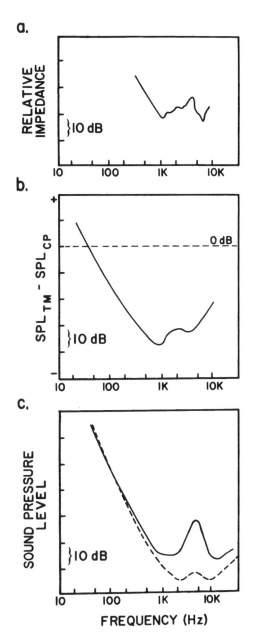

**Figure 5.18.** Comparison in the cat of impedance at the eardrum (**a**), sound pressure gradient across the cochlear partition (**b**), and behavioral thresholds, that is, the minimal audibility curve (**c**). *Dashed line* in **c**, minimum audibility curve, which has not been corrected for the effects of resonance in the ear canal (discussed later in this chapter). (Based on data of Moller, A. R. [1963]. Transfer function of the middle ear. *J. Acoust. Soc. Am.* 35:1526–1534 [**a**]; Nedzelnitsky, V. [1974] Measurement of sound pressure in the cochleae of anesthetized cats. In *Facts and Models in Hearing*, pp 45–53, edited by E. Zwicker and E.

2 kHz it "breaks up." So, all regions of the vibrating membrane do not move together at higher frequencies. In other words, increasingly less area of the tympanic membrane is effectively involved above 2 kHz. Clearly, the details of how the middle ear mechanism does its job are complicated.

## D. MIDDLE EAR RESPONSE CHARACTERISTICS AND OTHER CONSIDERATIONS, OR, HOW WELL DOES IT REALLY WORK?

Earlier discussions of the simple harmonic oscillator (Chapter 1) revealed a vibratory system that is highly efficient at one frequency and extremely inefficient at all others. Although the middle ear mechanism is certainly much more elaborate than the simple harmonic oscillator, it too has a (major) resonant frequency, and it is not equally efficient at all frequencies. Therefore, the values obtained for pressure gain and the like (in The Middle Ear Transformer—Classical Theory above) can be considered valid only near the resonant frequency of the middle ear. In humans, this is around 1.2 kHz. Hearing is expected to be more sensitive in the vicinity of the middle ear resonant frequency and less sensitive at frequencies above and below. Indeed, the response characteristics of the middle ear substantially contribute to the shape of the ***minimum audibility curve (MAC)***; this is the function that relates the threshold of hearing (that is, the sound pressure level [SPL] required for sound to be just detected) to frequency. In other words, this function reflects the sensitivity of hearing as a function of frequency. (The detail of how this function is obtained will be discussed

Terhardt. Springer-Verlag, New York [**b**]; and adaptation of data from Miller et al. [1963] by Dallos, P. [1973]. *The Auditory Periphery: Biophysics and Physiology*. Academic Press, New York [**c**]. In **a** and **b**, the middle ear cavity or bulla was open, contributing to a slightly different slope of the low-frequency portion of these graphs compared with **c**.

in depth in Chapter 7.) The MAC for the cat is shown in Figure 5.18c. By comparing this graph with that describing the sound pressure level required to obtain a constant sound pressure gradient across the cochlear partition (Fig. 5.18b) and also that of the input impedance of the middle ear as a function of frequency (Fig. 5.18a), it becomes evident that the response characteristics of the middle ear are strongly reflected in the MAC. Now, where the MAC (overall) falls along the SPL axis (i.e., the sensitivity of hearing) is determined by the hair cell receptors and the events that happen in the cochlea and beyond. However, where the MAC falls along the frequency axis is determined by the structure and function of both the middle and inner ears. In other words, a horse's cochlea and a bat's middle ear will not work very well together. Also, the low-frequency slope of the MAC seems to increase more sharply than would be expected from the roll-off of the middle ear response characteristics. So, the middle ear transformer clearly does not completely determine the MAC, but the band-pass filtering that is extant in the auditory system, attributable to the limits of the middle ear's response characteristics, is clearly evident. Again, it is the shape of the MAC, not the MAC per se, that is influenced by the middle ear mechanism.

In the detailed analysis, the middle ear is a fairly elaborate system. Each middle ear structure contributes certain amounts of mass, stiffness, and friction that, in turn, ultimately determine the impedance of this vibratory system. The block diagram in Figure 5.19 represents the major components of the middle ear mechanism and the manner in which they seem to be connected within this vibratory system. The reactance of each component, or each block in the diagram, is determined by its mass and stiffness; the manner in which

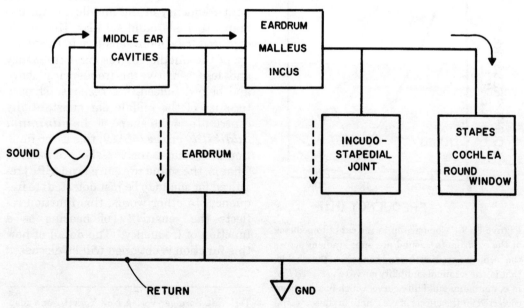

**Figure 5.19.** Block diagram of the middle ear. The *solid arrows* show the primary (and desired) path of motion, whereas the *broken arrows* indicate motion which is lost with respect to the ultimate goal of vibrating the stapes and, consequently, the transfer of energy to the cochlea. As in electronics, a return path is shown and a ground, which simply indicates the side of the system that is at the lowest potential (sound pressure or force, or in terms of acoustics, atmospheric pressure). (Based on a diagram of Zwislocki, J. [1962]. Analysis of the middle-ear function. Part I: Input impedance. *J. Acoust. Soc. Am.* 34:1514–1523.)

they are connected to one another, that is, in series (one after the other) or in parallel branches, governs the frequency response of the system. The *solid arrows* in Figure 5.19 represent the velocity flow or motion through the series elements to the load of the stapes and cochlea. This is the desired pathway. The *broken arrows* indicate shunt pathways, parallel to the stapes and cochlea load, which tend to "sap off" motion, thereby reducing the velocity flow reaching the load. For instance, this occurs at the joints in the ossicular chain. The middle ear seems to be critically damped; that is, the motion of the ossicles follows the driving force (sound) with a minimum of overshoot, so when the sound stops, so does the motion of the ossicles. The damping in the system is attributed largely to the resistance of the cochlear load.

Any change in one of the components of the middle ear mechanism can lead to a change in its impedance and, subsequently, the efficiency of energy transfer and the frequency response of the system. Pathology of the middle ear, again, can cause such changes. Consider otosclerosis, for example. This disease causes fixation of the stapes footplate in the oval window. This causes stiffening of the ossicular chain and a transmission loss that generally increases with decreasing frequency below the resonant frequency of the middle ear. However, impairments of sound conduction involving the middle ear more often create flat losses, that is, roughly equal losses across frequency. A commonly experienced temporary change in hearing sensitivity, which is also caused by changes in middle ear impedance, is associated with sudden changes in atmospheric pressure. An example is the pressure sensations experienced with rapid changes in elevation, as when riding in fast elevators or in airplanes. In such instances, variations in air pressure outside the middle ear cavity are not equalized inside. As described in Chapter 4, it is the role of the auditory (eustachian) tube to equalize this pressure, but it opens and closes only with swallowing or other maneuvers that activate the proper musculature of the nasopharynx. From time to time, there may be a substantial buildup of pressure in the middle ear cavity, particularly when there is a fairly rapid change in the atmospheric pressure (for instance, during an ascent in an airplane). A deadening effect on the sound (signaling decreased sound transmission and, consequently, decreased hearing sensitivity) is experienced in this event. A popping sound occurs when the tube finally opens, because of the rapid escape of air from the middle ear. Sound is again heard loud and clear. Before the pressure buildup is relieved, the acoustic compliance of the middle ear is reduced, because of the stretching of the eardrum as it is pushed outward by the higher middle ear air pressure. The compliance of the middle ear cavity is itself also decreased because of the relatively higher air pressure within it.

If the auditory tube were not to function for a prolonged period of time (e.g., as sometimes occurs as a sequela of the common cold), the membranous lining of the middle ear would absorb the oxygen from the air inside, causing a decreased pressure in the middle ear and ultimately the secretion of fluid by the lining. This leads to an even more substantial loss of transmission through the middle ear (up to 30 dB or more, particularly if the fluid becomes infected and other complications ensue). Although it does not have a direct acoustic role, the normal functioning of the auditory tube clearly is essential to the proper functioning of the middle ear mechanism. Returning to the main point, diseases of the middle ear usually can be detected by selectively testing the conduction of sound energy through the middle ear (see Chapter 7) or by measuring the input impedance of the middle ear (i.e., effectively at the tympanic membrane).

A useful way of checking for negative or positive pressure in the middle ear and, more generally, assessing the mobility of the tympanic membrane and ossicular chain is through the use of **tympanometry**. This is an application of the measurement of the input impedance or, as implemented practically, input admittance of the ear. Rather than just measuring the static admittance, the middle ear system is manipulated via the application of positive (above ambient) and negative (below ambient) pressures to the ear canal. The essence of the method is illustrated in Figure 5.20*a*. The most basic tympanometric test uses a relatively low-frequency sound (226 Hz) delivered through one of three tubes in an earplug that has been sealed tightly in the ear canal. Some sound energy is reflected from the tympanic membrane, even in the normal ear, as discussed above. This adds to the net sound pressure in the ear canal, which is detected by a microphone and circuitry somewhat like that of the sound level meter. As applied air pressure is increased or decreased by an air pump, the eardrum is pushed in or pulled out, respectively, placing it under tension and causing it to be much stiffer than usual. This results in increased sound reflection, caused by less transmission of sound energy through the middle ear. This indicates decreased admittance and, in effect, decreased mobility of the system.

Sweeping across a range of applied pressures, a graph of admittance versus pressure is traced by the tympanometer; this is called the *tympanogram* (Fig. 5.20*b*). The middle ear, if functioning normally, should have a maximal admittance at ambient air pressure (0 decapascals [dPa] along the pressure axis) and minimal admittance at the extremes of the applied pressure range (+200 and −400 dPa or so). Therefore, the normal tympanogram appears as an inverted *V*. Changes in admittance attributable to malfunction of the middle ear will displace and/or modify the height or shape of the tympanogram (Fig. 5.20*b*). Such changes may reflect the presence of negative or

positive pressure in the middle ear cavity and/or decreased or increased loading of the eardrum and/or the ossicular chain, respectively, as typically occur in middle ear infections, dislocations and fixations of the ossicular chain, etc. Consequently, tympanometry is sensitive to middle ear disease. Tympanometry is one component of the immittance test battery, which is discussed in the following section.

## E. THE ACOUSTIC REFLEX

The auditory system itself has the ability to alter the impedance (or admittance) of the middle ear to some extent and, thereby, alter the transmission of sound through the middle ear. This is made possible by the musculature of the middle ear, primarily the stapedius muscle. The stapedius muscle reacts reflexively to sound. This response of the auditory system is called the **acoustic** or **stapedius reflex**. The magnitude of the response increases with increasing intensity of the stimulus, although it ultimately saturates at very high levels of sound (around 120-dB SPL). The reflex is bilateral; a sound stimulus delivered via an earphone to one ear will elicit the reflex in both ears. The reflex can be monitored by observing the change in the input impedance of the middle ear, as illustrated in Figure 5.21. Its threshold is defined as the lowest sound level (typically referenced to the average, normal, hearing threshold at the test frequency) at which a change in impedance or admittance can be detected. In practical and clinical applications, this phenomenon may be detected by a significant deflection on the meter of the measuring instrument. From the tracings shown in Figure 5.21, the threshold of the reflex response is seen to be approximately 82 dB. This is typical for normal hearing subjects; in terms of SPL, the threshold is usually approximately 85 dB re $2 \times 10^{-5}$ Pa. However, it is possible to demonstrate reflexes at much lower levels than this. First, the sensitivity of the acoustic reflex can be substantially enhanced by the oc-

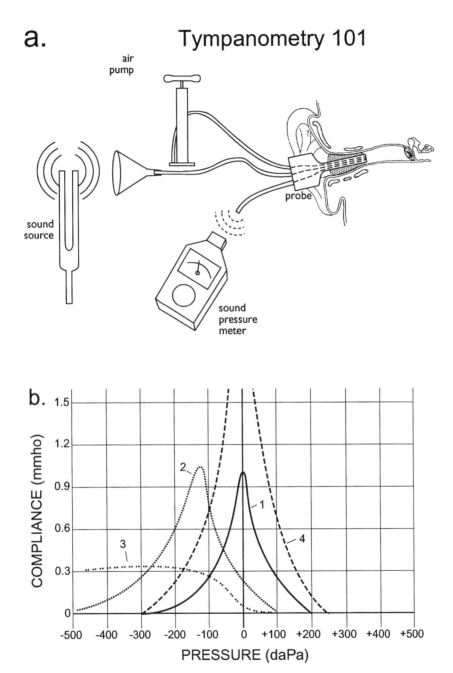

**Figure 5.20.   a.** Concept of tympanometry. **b.** Characteristic normal tympanogram (*1*) and some common abnormal variants, indicating negative middle ear pressure (*2*), negative pressure plus probable fluid (*3*), and hypermobility caused by probable ossicular dislocation (*4*).

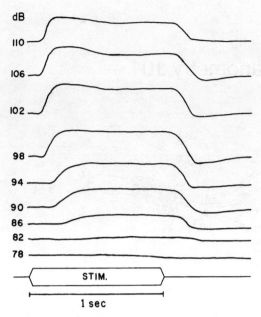

**Figure 5.21.** Impedance changes at the input of the middle ear (viz. at the eardrum) resulting from activation of the acoustic reflex. Upward deflections indicate increased impedance. The sound level is referenced to normal hearing. The impedance was measured at 220 Hz, whereas the eliciting stimulus was a 1-kHz tone burst of 1-sec duration. (Note: the bulk of the delay between the stimulus onset and the beginning of the response is caused by the inherent sluggishness of the measuring system used in this type of measurement.)

currence of a preceding sound. Second, detection of the response can be substantially improved by using digital signal processing via a computer (using a technique called *signal averaging*); reports from studies using such methods suggest the presence of reflexes, although small in magnitude, down to levels perhaps at the limits of hearing.

Presumably, the change in impedance is caused mostly by an alteration in the stiffness of the ossicular chain. The contraction of the middle ear muscles pull on the chain, and the muscles themselves are stiffened when the muscle fibers contract (i.e., shorten). The response of the middle ear itself seems to be stiffness dominated at frequencies below the resonant fre-

quency. Consequently, the activation of the reflex brings about very little, if any, change in impedance at frequencies greater than approximately 1.2 kHz. Higher-frequency stimuli are effective in eliciting the reflex, but attenuation of sound is practically nil. Therefore, the reflex causes substantial decreases in the transmission of low-frequency sounds through the middle ear. This transmission loss may be as much as 20 to 30 dB, although in humans 5 to 10 dB is more typically observed.

The role of the acoustic reflex is often described in terms of protection of the cochlea. Clearly, in the noisy technological world of today, some protection against high-level noises will be afforded by the reflex, because the intensity of the noise entering the cochlea is effectively attenuated by the middle ear muscles.[2] However, the protection of the acoustic reflex is limited, because, again, the transmission of sound is affected only at frequencies less than about 1.2 kHz. Higher-frequency sounds generally have been viewed as potentially more hazardous to hearing, and yet it is in this range of frequencies that the reflex offers little or no attenuation. Another problem with the protection theory is that the reflex is not instantaneous; rather, a certain minimal time is required for it to be activated (10 msec or more to develop full contractile force, depending on the intensity of the sound stimulus). The acoustic reflex thus can afford little protection from impulsive sounds, such as gunshots, unless the reflex is primed by stimulation with longer-lasting background sounds.

The protection theory also has its problems from an evolutionary perspective. The development of a protective reflex it-

[2] An additional mechanism seems to be activated at very high levels of sound. The mode of vibration of the stapes footplate changes from essentially an in-out motion to a rocking motion, which reduces its volume displacement. Consequently, the intensity of sound at the input of the cochlea is reduced relative to that which would be realized via the normal mode of vibration.

self would require the proper stimulus. Before the emergence of the human, the world was presumably free of hazardous noises, other than perhaps thunder or an occasional volcanic explosion. Noise pollution was hardly a concern of Mother Nature. Alternatively, a regulatory role of the acoustic reflex can be suggested. The commonly cited analogy is the action of the pupil of the eye.

Like the pupillary reflex, the acoustic reflex affords a means of attenuating the stimulus at the input of the system, thereby reducing the energy absorbed by the sensory receptors. The influence of the pupil, however, seems to be (comparatively) much more substantial, and it reduces transmission of light energy at all frequencies. The specific mechanisms involved in the two different reflexes are fundamentally different as well. So, the pupillary reflex is really not a very good analog of the acoustic reflex. The influence of the middle ear muscles actually does not rest entirely on the activation of the reflex arc, because even their normal tonus seems to affect the response characteristics of the middle ear mechanism. This influence is subtle but significant, in that it results in smoothing of the frequency response of the middle ear mechanism. Otherwise, it would have sharp dips and peaks at various frequencies, because of resonances and antiresonances. Interestingly, the muscles are also activated before and during vocalization. Consequently, the intensity of one's own voice reaching the cochlea is attenuated.

Finally, it should be noted that the acoustic reflex is not entirely controlled by events in the periphery. It can be modified by the organism's state of attention to the sound stimulus, and it is mediated by a reflex arc or circuit involving lower centers of the brain. (This matter will be taken up again in Chapter 6, in which the subject of feedback-control mechanisms of the auditory system is discussed.) Whatever the original purpose of the middle ear muscles with regard to evolutionary development, it seems that, in humans, they serve several functions. These functions are really complementary, even though their theoretical bases may somewhat conflict (protection versus other theories). It also is likely that the contribution to hearing of the middle ear muscles has yet to be fully appreciated. For instance, little attention has been paid to the possible influence of these muscles on binaural (two-eared) hearing, which might arise by virtue of fine interaural differences in the sound spectra arriving at the cochleae because of slight differences in contractions or the tonus of the muscles on the two sides of the head.

## 6. Role of the Outer Ear

### A. EAR CANAL RESONANCE

Sound energy destined for the cochlea must pass through yet another system—the outer ear. Up to this point, the acoustical contribution of the outer ear has been essentially ignored. However, in a detailed comparison between the MAC and the response characteristics of the middle ear, differences are evident that can be attributed, in part, to the contribution of the outer ear. Reexamining Figure 5.18c, a clear difference is seen between the MAC per se (*dashed line graph*) and the MAC corrected to remove the contribution (primarily) of the ear canal (*solid line graph*), wherein the latter reflects less sensitivity. Sensitivity of hearing thus is improved by the presence of the external meatus, particularly at frequencies greater than about 1 kHz. These data are from the cat, but a similar contribution is made by the ear canal in the human. However, as will be seen later in this section, this is only the beginning of the story.

Acoustically, the external meatus resembles a pipe with one end open (laterally) and the other end closed (medially, namely, by the tympanic membrane), as

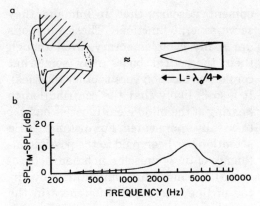

**Figure 5.22.**  **a.** Representation of the external auditory meatus as a tube with one end closed and the resulting standing wave (peak-to-peak sound pressures shown). **b.** Actual canal resonance observed in human subjects. (Based on Wiener, F. M., and Ross, D. A. [1946]. The pressure distribution in the auditory canal in a progressive sound field. *J. Acoust. Soc. Am.* 18:401–408.) Plotted along the ordinate is the decibel difference between the SPL at the eardrum (*TM*) and that in the sound field at the entrance of the canal (*F*).

illustrated by Figure 5.22*a*. Therefore, standing waves form at odd-integer multiples of the frequency, which has a wavelength four times the length of the ear canal. In humans, the length of the external canal is approximately 2.5 cm or 0.025 m. Using Eq. 2.13, the fundamental mode of this pipe can be found:

$$f_o = c/4L = 343/0.025 \times 4 = 3430 \text{ Hz}$$

$$\approx 3.4 \text{ kHz}$$

At the modes, a pressure node occurs at the entrance of the canal with an antinode at the tympanic membrane. Thus, there is sound pressure amplification at the closed end of the pipe. More fundamentally, the ear canal acts as another impedance-matching transformer. The transformation required is from the relatively low impedance of air to the input impedance of the middle ear, which, from preceding analyses, seems to be substantially higher. Again, this is attributable to the residual air-cochlea mismatch at the input of the middle ear transformer (the ear-

drum). By virtue of the nature of the ear canal transformer, it also is expected to be efficient only over limited frequency ranges, namely, at or near the modes. Examination of the actual pressure transformation observed in the human external meatus (Fig. 5.22*b*) bears out these predictions. The upper-frequency limit of the measurements presented in Figure 5.22*b* permits observation of only the resonant peak at the first mode (around 3.4 kHz). Measurements made at higher frequencies reveal a second peak anywhere from 8 to 12 kHz (not shown in Fig. 5.22*b*); the calculated second mode is $3 \times 3.4 = 10.2$ kHz. The exact frequencies of the resonance peaks and amount of gain from ear canal resonance derive from the facts that the external meatus is not really a straight hard-walled tube (it has slight bends) and is lined with absorptive material (skin). Skin seems to provide a substantial amount of damping, thereby broadening the resonant peaks (see Fig. 5.22*b*) and limiting gain. Nevertheless, the ear canal provides some 12- to 15-dB gain near the first mode (somewhat less at the second), but below 1 kHz, the contribution of ear canal resonance is negligible.

In recent years, considerable attention has been given to the contribution of ear canal resonance to the overall performance of hearing aids and to direct or probe microphone assessment of the sound generated by the device in situ. This requires much the same measurements as those that produced the data plotted in Figure 5.18, including a determination of SPL deep in the ear canal, near the tympanic membrane. Modern probe microphones and electronic instrumentation have made the process safe and efficient and thus highly conducive to clinical application. Using so-called real-ear analysis systems, it indeed is possible to replicate the results presented in Figure 5.22 by simply carrying out the test protocol without a hearing aid (i.e., an open ear canal). However, using the particular methods that are now popular for this application of real-ear sound calibration and measurement, a resonant peak typically will be seen in the vicinity of 2700 Hz, not 3400 Hz as stated above. The frequency region of SPL gain also will seem broader, perhaps with a secondary peak in the 4- to 5-kHz region, and the overall gain may be found to be 12 to 25 dB (see Fig. 5.25, curve *B*, below). This is not a discrepancy of results but, rather, merely a reflection of differences in the reference SPL measurement. In Figure 5.22, the object of the measurement was to quantify specifically the ear canal gain, so the reference measurement was carried out at the entrance to the meatus. Current practice favors a reference to the sound field in the absence of the subject, or sampled above the auricle. The effect, then, is a more complete sampling of acoustic effects of the outer ear, which includes the ear canal, the auricle, and even the head and upper torso (depending on details of the method used). The latter anatomical components contribute acoustically what might be called *baffle effects*.

## B. HEAD BAFFLE AND RELATED ACOUSTIC EFFECTS

Even if it were located on the surface of the head, the SPL appearing at the eardrum would not necessarily equal the SPL measured in the sound field in the absence of the head. In effect, sound gets to the eardrum through a hole in a wall. The hole is the entrance to the external auditory meatus, whereas the combination of the auricle and head forms the wall or *baffle*, in acoustical terms. When the wavelength of the sound is long compared with the dimensions of the head, the wavefront is diffracted (Chapter 2), so the sound waves just bend around the head. For sounds with relatively long wavelengths, then, the head has little effect on the SPL at the eardrum, regardless of which way the head is turned. (Head position does affect how long it takes for sound to travel there, but this matter will be taken up in discussions of sound localization in Chapters 6

and 7.) An indication of the frequencies at which diffraction can be expected to occur is obtained simply by solving the equation $\lambda = c/f$ (i.e., Eq. 2.5), given that $\lambda$ (wavelength) = 0.18 m, the approximate diameter of the average adult head. Because $\lambda = c/f$, then $f = c/\lambda$, and:

$$f = 343/0.18 \approx 1906 \text{ Hz} \approx 2 \text{ kHz}$$

Therefore, for the human, no diffraction is anticipated above 2 kHz. A test of this prediction can be made by comparing the SPL measured in a sound field using a small microphone alone versus the SPL measured with the microphone mounted in a wooden sphere, or spherical baffle, about the size of the head. This is admittedly an oversimplified representation of the human ear and head, but it roughly simulates the situation of one ear cocked toward a sound source. As shown by the graph in Figure 5.23, the diffraction above 2 kHz is practically nil, as suggested by the greater SPL recorded with the baffled microphone. This occurs because of a sound pressure buildup on the surface of the sphere. Most of the sound energy striking the baffle is reflected back into the sound field and interacts with the incident sound waves, apparently resulting in a net

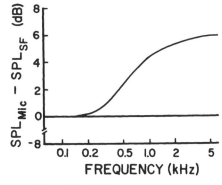

**Figure 5.23.** The difference between the SPL in the sound field (*SF*) and that monitored via a microphone in a spherical baffle (*Mic*) about the size of a human head. The microphone is aimed in the direction of the sound source. (Based on Kinsler, L. E., and Frey, A. R. [1962]. *Fundamentals of Acoustics*, pp 310–312. John Wiley & Sons, New York.)

constructive interference. Below 2 kHz, diffraction becomes increasingly more significant with decreasing frequency, as total diffraction is approached (around 150 Hz). So little or no sound pressure buildup occurs at low frequencies. For real human heads, total diffraction seems to occur below approximately 500 Hz. Stated alternatively, the head baffle effect is practically nil below approximately 500 Hz.

The real ear-head situation is considerably more complex. First, the auricle itself can have significant effects on the SPL appearing at the eardrum, above and beyond the head baffle effects. Also, skin is acoustically an absorbent material, as implied above. Additionally, when one ear is cocked toward the sound source (the near ear), the other (far) ear is obviously on the other side of the head. In the high-frequency range, in which there will be little or no diffraction, the head then casts a sound shadow on the far ear. The influence of the head-auricle baffle can be seen in the data shown in Figure 5.24.

It is evident the SPL appearing at the tympanic membrane is dependent on both azimuth of the sound source (angular displacement from midline in the horizontal plane through the head) and the frequency of the sound. Looking across frequency at 90° azimuth, the SPL difference between the eardrum (i.e., of the near ear) and the sound field is seen to approach or exceed the difference created by a simple spherical baffle. This is evident for frequencies of 1 kHz and greater. Likewise, at the far ear (namely at −90°), the SPL at the tympanic membrane is reduced, because of the head shadow. When the sound source approaches the midline in front of or behind the head (0° or 180°, respectively), these effects progressively diminish. Interestingly, with the sound directly behind the head, the SPL at the eardrum is actually decreased, especially around 5 kHz and greater. This is attributable to the sound shadow cast by the auricles.

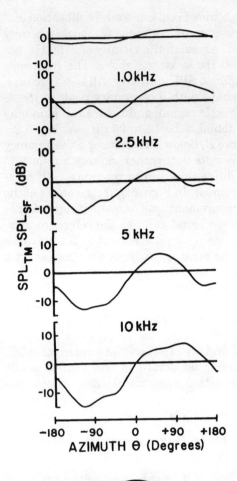

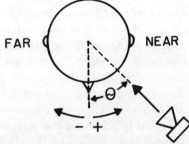

**Figure 5.24.** Influence of the head-auricle baffle observed in human subjects. The differences between the sound pressure level at the eardrum (*TM*) and that in the sound field (*SF*) are plotted as a function of azimuth for different frequencies, as indicated. *Inset*, Measurement procedure as though the sound source were moved about the head: positive (+) azimuths indicate movement toward the near ear and negative (−) away from the near ear (or toward the far ear; see text). (Based on Shaw [1974], based on a synthesis of data from various studies.)

## C. So, What Is the Outer Ear Worth?

In lower animals the auricle or pinna generally is more influential than it is in humans. It is often larger (proportionally), and it is usually quite mobile. The human outer ear apparently has been simplified during the course of evolution, but it is still contributory to auditory function. Indeed, the acoustic effects of the head and auricle combined with the resonance of the external canal can lead to as much as a 15- to 20-dB sound pressure gain at the eardrum in the mid to high frequencies. The outer ear and the dense pseudospheroid on and in which it is mounted thus serve to promote more efficient sound transmission to the inner ear and to extend sensitive hearing into the upper frequency range, where it otherwise would diminish, because of the high-frequency roll-off in the response characteristics of the middle ear transformer (specifically above the primary resonant frequency, ap-

proximately 1.2 kHz). The acoustical contributions of the ear canal, auricle, and head collectively are illustrated in Figure 5.25.

Fortunately for humans, who are so dependent on communication via speech, the frequency range over which hearing sensitivity is enhanced by the acoustics of the outer ear and head corresponds to that in which the energy in the upper-vowel formants and the consonants (the real information-bearing parts of speech) is concentrated. The outer ear is also of importance in directional hearing. Admittedly, this is primarily a binaural (two-eared) hearing function that is dependent on the head baffle effect. Still, the auricle baffles are themselves important for distinguishing sounds in front versus in back and in discriminating changes in elevation of the sound source. (Again, a more detailed discussion of this topic will be given in Chapters 6 and 7.) However, a completely nonacoustic role also is performed by the outer

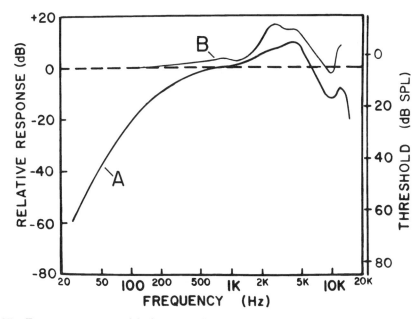

**Figure 5.25.** Frequency response of the human auditory system, derived by inverting the minimum audibility curve (*A*, adapted from Robinson and Dadson [1956]) and contribution of the combined head-baffle and ear-canal resonance effects (*B*, adapted from Shaw [1974]). (Adapted from Durrant [1978], from Durrant, J. D. [1982]. Fundamentals of sound generation. In *Bases of Auditory Brain Stem Evoked Responses*, pp 15–49, edited by E. J. Moore. Grune & Stratton, New York.)

ear, that is (as stressed in Chapter 4), it is protective. The slightly S-shaped contour of the external canal, the hairs in the canal, the secretion of cerumen, and the location of the middle and inner ears deep in the skull all serve to protect the more delicate parts of the system. These factors minimize the likelihood of damage to the middle and inner ears from adverse environmental conditions or contact with foreign objects.

## D. INTERLUDE 2

It should be clear by now that what was called the *coupler* in the first part of this chapter, namely, the mechanism for conveying energy to the receptor cell, is elaborate in the auditory system. It requires a considerable amount of hardware external to the receptor cell itself, as well as processes that culminate in the performance of a basic spectrum analysis (via the frequency-to-place transformation). The principles underlying this stage of the stimulus-encoding process encompass three fairly autonomous areas of physics: acoustics, mechanics, and hydrodynamics (fluid mechanics).

In summary, there are several events in the periphery that lead to the excitation of the hair cells. The sound reaching the eardrum undergoes a transformation by virtue of the acoustics of the outer ear. This altered sound is transformed into mechanical motion (vibration), and at the same time, there is a transformation from the low impedance of air to the high input impedance of the cochlea. Associated with this impedance transformation is sound pressure amplification and, because of the motion of the stapes, the development of an alternating pressure gradient across the cochlear partition. This leads to the propagation of a wave of displacement up the basilar membrane, which is the event long awaited by the hair cells. It is, of course, the displacement of the basilar membrane that brings about the effective stimulus of these receptor cells—the shearing displacement of the stereocilia.

It is now possible to look at signs of having successfully coupled energy to the auditory receptor cell, the first indications of forward signal flow in the system. Both electrical and acoustical signs or signals are generated in the cochlea.

# 7. Signs of Activation of the Auditory Periphery

## A. COCHLEAR ACOUSTIC EMISSIONS

There is an old saying, "What goes up, must come down." Could it be that, at least in part, what goes into the ear must come out? Well, perhaps not literally, but there is reason to expect that a certain amount of sound energy going into the ear should be reflected back into the medium. One possibility arises from the residual air-cochlea mismatch, which causes sound to be reflected from the eardrum. Indeed, it is the comparison of incident and reflected waves that make impedance measurements possible in the ear canals of awake, cooperative, and relatively comfortable subjects. This technique also serves to demonstrate the presence of the acoustic reflex. But, what if further down the line, at some stage of the cochlear hydromechanical system or even at the micromechanical level, some energy from the motion of the basilar membrane displacement could be coupled back to the cochlear fluids? Could such an event lead to the production of sounds that ultimately could radiate back into the ear canal like an echo?

At first glance, the prospects seem remote. The cochlea represents a rather high-impedance source. It is small physically; it obviously is not engineered to generate large amounts of acoustic power. The situation is analogous to using an insert earphone connected to a transistor radio as the acoustic power source of music for a dance in a large ballroom. This is not to say that acoustic emissions from the ear are unprecedented or hitherto unknown. Tumors of the middle ear and stenoses (constrictions) of large blood vessels of the head and neck can create sounds, called *bruits* (French for *noises*), that are audible to another individual. For this reason, this phenomenon is called *objective* **tinnitus**. Tinnitus is the medical term for head and ear noises, and objective implies observability by someone other than the patient. Bruits, as such, do not arise from the cochlea, and, until recently, tinnitus of cochlear origin was classified strictly as subjective (implying audibility only to the individual experiencing it). It thus was inconceivable that an objective tinnitus could arise from the cochlea.

Bekesy actually demonstrated some time ago that, indeed, some sound must be emitted from the cochlea back into the external meatus. On the presentation of sounds to the ear, more distortion is observed in the ear canal than is attributable to nonlinearities of the sound source. However, it is only relatively recently that **cochlear echoes** or, more precisely, **otoa-** **coustic emissions (OAEs)**, have been demonstrated and studied extensively. Using miniature transducers for sound generation and measurement in the ear canal, together with computer signal-processing techniques, it is now possible for researchers and clinicians alike to investigate OAEs (Fig. 5.26), and considerable interest in this phenomenon has developed. That the OAEs really do come from the interior of the cochlea is suggested by several factors: the substantial latency or time lag that characterizes this acoustic response (4 to 20 msec or more after stimulation with an acoustic click), the fact that the OAEs are vulnerable to adverse metabolic conditions, and the absence of OAEs in cases of partial or complete hearing loss. Additional evidence that the OAEs are not simple reflections is the fact that they do not grow in proportion to the input, characteristic of a nonlinearity (as discussed in Chapter 3). There are doubtless reflections from the eardrum, as sug-

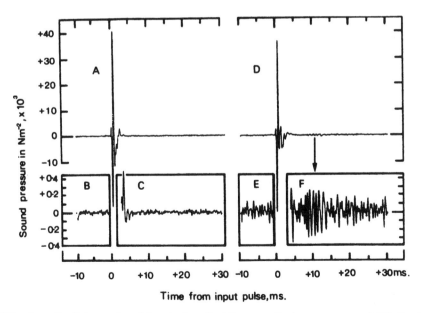

**Figure 5.26.** Acoustic click monitored in a test cavity (*A*) versus the human ear canal (*D*). *Insets (B, C, E, and F)*, Highly amplified views of what is recorded just before and after the click. Only background noise is evident in the test cavity, whereas an echo—the cochlear acoustic emission—is seen in the ear canal (*F*). (From Kemp, D. T. [1978]. Stimulated acoustic emissions from within the human auditory system. *J. Acoust. Soc. Am.* 64:1386–1391.)

gested by the discussion of tympanometry earlier, but these echoes have very short latencies and are difficult to distinguish from the initial barrage of sound seen at the beginning of the tracings in Figure 5.26. Although the use of a transient signal, like the click, facilitates the observation of the cochlear echo, it also can be elicited by brief tone bursts and by continuous sounds. Distortion products in the OAE, which again demonstrate nonlinear growth, also can be recorded and account for the increased distortion in ear canals observed by Bekesy. A particularly strong emission is demonstrable using two tones ($f_1$ and $f_2$), thus producing intermodulation distortion, namely, at a frequency of $2f_1 - f_2$. This is known as a *cubic distortion product*. Also, many adults with normal hearing and most newborns produce measurable spontaneous OAEs, that is, OAEs in the absence of external stimulation. Spontaneous OAEs may appear at one to five or more frequencies, typically in the midrange of hearing.

OAEs are readily produced by a wide range of frequencies of stimulation, although they are difficult to measure reliably below 1000 Hz because of noise. The OAE can reach SPLs of 20 dB or more. Although transient OAEs are not demonstrable in all mammals, such as gerbils, these animals do produce distortion product OAEs. So, the OAE phenomenon is pervasive among mammals. OAEs provide clear signs of reaction of the hearing organ to sound and activation of micromechanical processes now thought to be critical to the optimal sensitivity and frequency tuning of the system.

The exact source of OAEs continues to be debated. The OHCs are strongly implicated and are widely accepted as the generators of OAEs of all types. Current debate centers on the details of the underlying processes; are they direct manifestations of OHC motility (OHCs literally vibrating) or reflections of energy in the traveling wave, encouraged perhaps by the micromechanical contribution of the OHCs? Actually, if the OHCs in fact serve to produce a positive feedback in the transduction process of the hearing organ, then the occurrence of spontaneous OAEs is not at all surprising. Positive-feedback circuits tend to be unstable and oscillatory. Interest in OAEs thus is more than a matter of curiosity. A comprehensive understanding of their origin should reveal much about cochlear mechanics and the cochlear transduction process. They also allow the hearing scientist the opportunity to see something of the mechanical response of the cochlea using a noninvasive technique. Finally, OAEs are sensitive to cochlear disease, so clinical applications are evolving.

## B. COCHLEAR ELECTROPHYSIOLOGY

The hair cells, as noted earlier, are excitable cells; their resting membrane potentials are depolarized or hyperpolarized by the shearing displacements of the stereocilia. Stimulating hair cells thus produces stimulus-related potentials. However, the resting or non–stimulus-related potentials also are very important to the workings of these excitable cells. In addition to the hair cell's own resting membrane potential, there is an unusual, extracellular, resting potential. The resting potentials are fundamental to the production of the forward signal flow through the system and the most essential event for hearing—excitation of the auditory sensory neuron.

### Resting Potentials of the Cochlea

Using the appropriate electrophysiological techniques, it is possible to record a variety of potentials in and around the organ of Corti. Some of these potentials, as just suggested, require no stimulation; they are present in the absence of sound. These are the *resting potentials*. A microelectrode (formed from a very fine glass pipette) penetrating a cell of the organ of Corti will register a negative voltage, typically in the range of $-35$ to $-90$ millivolts (mV). This potential, of course, is the resting membrane potential (see Section 1); its presence is fully expected if the cell penetrated by the electrode is viable. For years, it seemed impossible to record this potential in individual cells of the mammalian organ of Corti, particularly hair cells. Penetration of the organ typically produced a negative potential of the expected magnitude, but, paradoxically, only electrodes with relatively large tips seemed to record stable (long-lasting) potentials! What actually was being recorded was an injury potential[3], probably generated by numerous cells, but at the cost of their demise. Only during the last couple of decades have the actual resting potentials of viable IHCs and OHCs been recorded in the mammalian hearing organ, wherein the cell is literally impaled by the electrode and is later verified histologically. However, there is another resting potential whose existence has been known for nearly a half-century. It is relatively easy to record (compared with intracellular resting potentials) and is observed within scala media—the ***endocochlear***, or ***endolymphatic, potential (EP)***. For instance, the EP can be recorded by inserting a micropipette electrode and penetrating the stria vascularis through a small hole drilled in the bony labyrinthine wall.

The first intriguing facet of the EP is that it is clearly an extracellular potential. The second interesting fact is that it is relatively large, typically 80 to 100 mV. The third and most intriguing thing about it is that the EP is a positive voltage. These features make the EP unusual in the body. In the inner ear it exists only within the cochlear duct, even though the semicircular ducts, utricle, and saccule all contain endolymph (Chapter 4). This is because the EP is produced by the stria vascularis.

The obvious question about the EP is, "What is it doing there?" Well, assume, for the sake of discussion, that the hair-cell resting potential is $-80$ mV, and the EP is 80 mV. Then, looking at a given hair cell, there is a total gradient of 160 mV (80 $- [-80] = 80 + 80 = 160$) acting across the hair-bearing surface of the hair cell, as illustrated by Figure 5.22. Thus, current through the hair cell membrane is subject to twice the driving force as that provided by the resting potential of the hair cell alone. Consequently, the EP enhances the excitability of the hair cells, namely, by amplifying the receptor potential(s) of the hair cell. This is the essence of a model that has enjoyed considerable popularity since it was first suggested by Hallowell Davis approximately 40 years ago. Admittedly, the generation of the EP could be entirely coincidental to the production of endolymph, suggesting a chicken-or-egg paradox; the exchange of ions generally leads to the production of a voltage gradient. In this case, $K^+$ must constantly be pumped into scala media and $Na^+$ removed. Evidence is mounting, however, for the notion that the EP is a reflection of an equally extraordinary occurrence of a positive membrane resting potential of cells at the margin of the stria, facing the endolymphatic fluid space. This condition, nevertheless, seems to be maintained by the same sort of metabolically driven ionic pump that is responsible for the more typical negative resting potentials. The mechanisms are beyond the scope of discussion here, but the point is that current thinking has shifted the role of the stria to EP production.

That the generation of the EP is an active metabolically driven process is well proven. The electrical potential that would arise merely because of the differences in ionic concentrations between perilymph and endolymph, known as the *equilibrium potential*, would be negative were the EP generated purely by ionic diffusion. A negative EP, interestingly, is observable, but only under such adverse con-

---

[3] The injury potential is commonly observed at the crushed end of a nerve; physiologists took advantage of this phenomenon during the earlier part of this century, before the development of microelectrodes. Indeed, using the crushed-nerve preparation, these scientists gained considerable insight into the workings of neurons.

ditions as prolonged anoxia of the cochlea, as occurs, for example, in a "recently departed" ear. On the other hand, the normal (positive) EP requires a healthy system and is generated by aerobic (oxygen-dependent) processes. Finally, that the EP is generated by the stria, and not the organ of Corti, is a fact well demonstrated by specially bred rodents who fail to develop a hearing organ but do develop essentially normal EPs.

Cochlear Microphonic

Davis's mechanoelectrical model of the hair cell transduction process, mentioned above, has served to guide much research in the area of cochlear electrophysiology. The schematic drawing of Figure 5.27 is a simplified representation of this model. The general notion is that the voltage gra-

dient across the hair-bearing surface of the hair cell forces a steady "leakage" current through the cell membrane. Mechanical deformation of the hairs alters the resistance of the membrane. Thus, the alternating pressure gradient across the cochlear partition (created by sound stimulation) is transformed by the hair cells into alternating current that, across the resistance of the cochlear fluids, appears as an alternating-current (AC) voltage. This particular potential is called the **cochlear microphonic (CM)** or **cochlear potential**. Whereas the EP is a resting potential, the CM is clearly a stimulus-related potential. What is particularly intriguing about the CM is that, by virtue of the way in which it is transduced, it seems to mimic the sound stimulus.

In the late 1920s Ernest Glen Wever

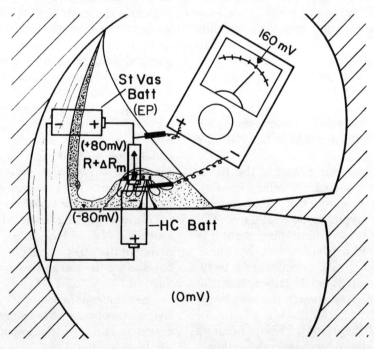

**Figure 5.27.**  Symbolic representation of the components of the system by which the cochlear receptor potentials may be generated (in the most general terms) and the primary circuitry of a unit cross-section of the cochlea. The component denoted $R + \Delta R_m$ is the lumped resistance in the circuit plus the small variable membrane resistance ($R_m$). Battery sources are seen in the stria vascularis (*St Vas Batt*) and in the hair cells (*HC Batt*). The potential in scala media is the EP, whereas the perilymphatic spaces are essentially at zero potential. (Based on Davis, H. [1965]. A model for transducer action in the cochlea. *Cold Springs Harbor Symp. Quant. Biol.* 30:181–189.)

and Charles Bray first demonstrated that sounds, even complex sounds such as speech, are transduced into electrical signals by the cochlea. These signals, in turn, can be amplified and reproduced like the (AC) voltage from a microphone. Originally called the ***Wever-Bray effect***, the CM was observed while recording from a wire on the auditory nerve. It was later found that the CM also can be picked up from a wire in contact with the round window membrane. Wever and Bray really had hoped to observe the activity of the auditory nerve, but it was soon learned that the CM, regardless of where it is recorded, emanates from the hair cell receptors. The oscillograph in Figure 5.28*a* is an example of a CM recording from the

a.

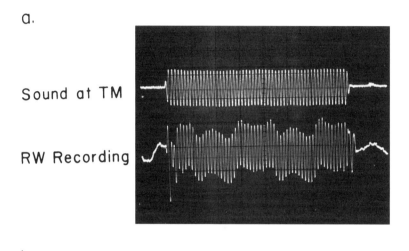

b.

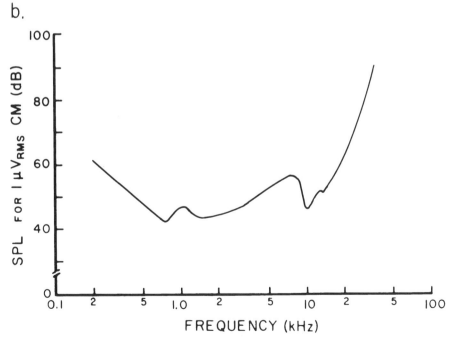

**Figure 5.28.** Exemplary oscillographic tracing of the cochlear microphonic (**a**) and the typical sensitivity of a round-window recording of this potential in the guinea pig (**b**).

round window of a guinea pig in response to a tone burst. Except for some background noise, the waveform of this electrical signal does resemble that of the sound stimulus.

An early aspiration of scientists for the use of the CM was to provide an objective measure of hearing sensitivity (in other words, eliminating the subjectiveness of perceptual responses and the need for a voluntary response by the subject in general). For instance, the SPL needed to obtain a criterion magnitude of response (say, 1 $\mu$V) might be determined as a function of frequency. The results could then be plotted as shown in Figure 5.28b; this graph is called an *isopotential* or *pseudo-threshold curve*. The term *pseudo* is used here because, even though the derivation of this graph somewhat resembles the manner in which the MAC is determined, the CM has no real threshold. As the sound is decreased, the CM just becomes too small to discern from the background noise. As the stimulus level is increased, the recorded CM simply grows in direct proportion to the SPL. This is demonstrated by another graph called the *input-output function*, shown in Figure 5.29. For each 10-dB increase in SPL, the CM increases by about three times (or 10 dB). However, the linearity of this function is maintained only up to a certain SPL, above which the input-output function exhibits a fairly rapid saturation. Once the maximum output is attained, the function then tapers off or bends over; then, less microphonic output is observed than at lower levels! The range of linearity and the maximum output voltage observed depends on the combination of recording technique, site of recording, and the frequency of the sound. CM voltages typically encountered in experiments with animals range from fractions of microvolts to several thousand microvolts (i.e., several millivolts). Incidentally, the CM can be recorded from humans under clinical test situations using nonsurgical techniques. The voltages are small, because of the re-

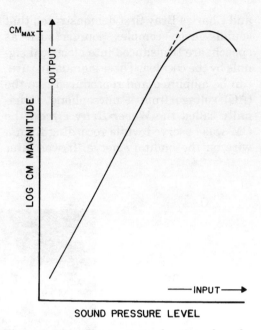

**Figure 5.29.** Input-output function for the cochlear microphonic (based on data from the guinea pig). Regardless of the actual magnitudes observed, a maximum CM output is observed ($CM_{MAX}$) beyond which the output decreases with increasing sound pressure. *Dashed line*, Extrapolation from the linear part of the function at lower stimulus levels to indicate the beginning of the bend-over.

moteness of the recording site from the cochlear fluid spaces, and signal averaging (via computer digital processing) is required for practical measurements.

Examining the graphs of Figures 5.28 and 5.29, it can be seen how, in fact, the ear could be used literally as a microphone with good fidelity! This depends on the species used, but recording from the round window of the guinea pig, the microphonic is roughly equally sensitive over a range of 300 to 5000 Hz. This exceeds the frequency response of many telephones. The hearing organ microphone also has a very good dynamic range, as noted above. The voltages involved are admittedly small but still compare favorably with some types of microphones (e.g., the condenser microphone). With some preamplification, all that is needed is a power amplifier and a speaker to make the signal audible (or an oscilloscope to make it visible). It is also noteworthy that the shape of the graph in Figure 5.28, somewhat resembles the minimum audibility curve shown previously in Figure 5.18c, despite the species difference. In fact, when compared in the same species, the 1-$\mu$V pseudothreshold curve (round-window recording) and the MAC look very much alike. It is tempting to conclude from such observations that, in fact, the CM does provide an objective measure of hearing. Unfortunately, correlation alone does not establish causal relationships. What the strong correlation between the pseudothreshold curve and the MAC does reflect is their mutual dependence on the response characteristics of the middle (and outer) ear. Because the round window is on the basal end of the cochlea, an electrode at this site "sees" electrical activity elicited largely on the trailing edges of traveling wave envelopes for all but the highest frequencies of stimulation (greater than 12 kHz in the guinea pig). However, the middle ear acts like a bandpass filter and thereby dominates the frequency response manifested by the pseudothreshold curve.

This explains why the CM seems to mimic the sound stimulus; it actually mimics the displacement of the basilar membrane. Specifically, the recording electrode sees a weighted average of basilar membrane motion within its pickup region. If located at the round window, activity generated primarily in the basal coil is registered. Also, it can be shown that the displacement of the basilar membrane is directly dependent on the stapes velocity, rather than stapes displacement. When this factor is taken into account, and when techniques are used that permit selectively recording from different turns inside the cochlea, the traveling-wave phenomenon and the associated tonotopic transformation are clearly manifested in the microphonic data, as shown in Figure 5.30. Here, stapes displacement was held constant for sound stimuli of different frequencies, as Bekesy did in his experi-

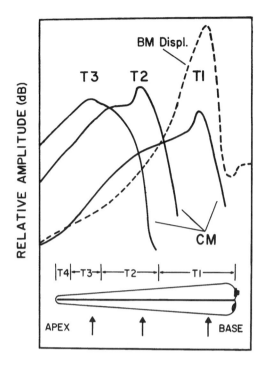

**LOG FREQUENCY (Hz)**

**Figure 5.30.** Relative amplitude of the CM recorded in different coils or turns (*T1, T2,* and *T3*) of the guinea pig cochlea (based on data of Dallos [1975]). For comparison, the displacement pattern of the basilar membrane (*BM Displ.*) is shown, as would be observed at about the same location along the basilar membrane as the T1 recording of the CM (first turn). (Based on data of Wilson and Johnstone [1972].) In both cases the data are plotted as though the displacement of the stapes, rather than sound pressure, had been kept constant. This is the same way that von Békésy obtained his traveling-wave data. The approximate location of the CM recording electrodes in each turn is indicated by *arrows* in the *inset.* (Based on Dallos, P. [1975]. Electrical correlates of mechanical events in the cochlea. *Audiology* 14:408–418.

ments, and the magnitudes of the CM was measured from recordings in different turns of the cochlea and plotted as a function of frequency. The results reveal different optimal frequencies of stimulation that decrease as the apex is approached (as expected from the tonotopic transformation). The individual functions resemble the traveling-wave envelope or, more directly, the function relating the displacement of the basilar membrane at one point versus frequency of stimulation. However, the CM functions are not as sharp. The reason is that recordings made from the fluid spaces of the cochlea are inevitably the result of an averaging of the output of numerous hair cells, causing the functions to be smoothed. The selectivity with which recordings can be made in the different cochlear turns also is limited by some cross-talk between turns.

For the kinds of measurement represented by both the CM pseudothreshold curve and the graphs in Figure 5.30, it is most desirable to work with relatively low-level stimuli to remain within the linear part of the CM input-output function. However, the high end of the CM's dynamic range is of interest, as well. The bend-over in the input-output function (Fig. 5.29) is associated with levels of sound that are potentially hazardous for the organ of Corti. It is thought to be a manifestation of sound overloading the cochlea. As the limits of the cochlear system are approached, the microphonic output becomes increasingly distorted. Energy in the stimulus, which is normally transduced into CM at the fundamental, is diverted by increasing amounts to its harmonics. This occurs between the beginning of the bend-over region and the SPL at which the maximum CM output occurs. However, the transduction system ultimately becomes inefficient, so the function bends completely over as the output decreases with increasing stimulus input. It really is not surprising that the CM output ultimately reaches a limit. All systems, physical and biophysical, have their limits. If anything, it is surprising that the CM has such a wide dynamic range, often in excess of 100 dB. The bend-over, nevertheless, reflects levels of sound that, if maintained, may place the hearing organ in danger of permanent damage.

## Summating Potential

The recorded activity illustrated in Figure 5.28a contains other stimulus-related

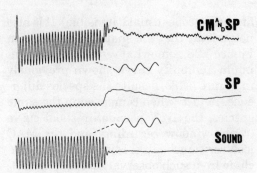

**Figure 5.31.** Tracings from recordings of the CM and SP along with the output of the monitoring microphone (*SOUND*). *Insets*, Details of CM and sound tracings via an expanded time base. (From Durrant, J. D. [1981]. Auditory physiology and an auditory physiologist's view of tinnitus. *J. Laryngol. Otol. Suppl.* 4:21–28.)

potentials in addition to the cochlear microphonic. By appropriately recording and processing the electrical potentials, it is possible to isolate selectively these other potentials. In Figure 5.31 a tone burst–elicited response, which obviously contains microphonic, is shown. However, the CM is not symmetrical at the baseline. It seems to be riding on a negative pulse. Indeed, when the CM is stripped away, a steplike, direct-current (DC), voltage is seen with a duration that closely follows the stimulus on time. This unidirectional potential is called the ***summating potential (SP)***.[4] The SP can be either positive (upward shift) or negative (downward shift), as in Figure 5.31, depending on the frequency and intensity of the sound and the site and technique of recording.

[4] It should be noted that the term *summating potential* is a misnomer and should not be taken literally. Specifically, the SP, for the most part, does not seem to be the result of spatial or temporal summation of graded potentials, such as that which occurs at synapses. Nevertheless, summating potential has become firmly established in the hearing literature as the name for this potential. Actually, *cochlear microphonic* is also a bit of a misnomer, because this potential is not really a microphonic. The term *microphonic* traditionally has been used to denote an effect in electrical instruments, particularly vacuum-tube audio amplifiers, wherein a mechanical vibration (such as tapping on the chassis) is picked up directly because of vibration of the elements in one or more of the tubes.

The SP, like the CM, is (largely) a receptor potential. Although it does not follow the stimulus waveform or mimic the sound in the same manner as the CM, its waveform tends to follow (essentially) the envelope of the stimulus. In this regard, it too is an electrical analog of the stimulus. Data similar to that shown in Figure 5.30 for the CM also can be obtained for the SP, using the same basic (intracochlear) recording techniques. When this is done, it is found that the SP also strongly reflects the mechanical events of the cochlea during sound stimulation. The general picture (for any given site of recording) is summarized by Figure 5.32, wherein the SP − tends to be associated with the apical or leading slope of the traveling wave and the SP + with the basal or trailing slope. The frequency at which the polarity transition occurs (given stimuli of moderate intensities) is associated with the peak of the traveling-wave pattern. Therefore, this transition occurs at lower and lower frequencies as the site of recording is moved toward the apex. (Note: the makeup of the SP is more complicated than portrayed here; only the major components are considered, specifically those that are caused primarily by current flow

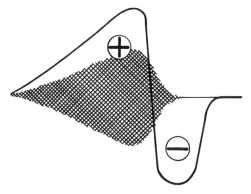

**Figure 5.32.** Schematic representation of the spatial pattern of the SP versus the traveling wave (*cross-hatched area*). (Based on drawing by Dallos, P. [1971]. SPs of the cochlea. In *Physiology of the Auditory System*, pp 57–67, edited by M. B. Sachs. National Educational Consultants, Baltimore.)

through the organ of Corti in the vicinity of the recording electrodes.)

For some time now the SP has been viewed as a distortion product of the hair cell transduction process. The basis for this point of view is simple and straightforward. If a vibratory or AC-like signal is input to a system, but a DC pulse is obtained at the output, this is a form of distortion. This is also an example of what is called *rectification* (in electronics). The question is, "At what stage(s) might such rectification occur?" The most obvious possibility is that the basilar membrane simply can move more easily in one direction than the other. The other possibility, but not mutually exclusive with the first, is that the rectification is inherent to the hair cell transduction process, presumably at the level of the variable membrane resistance in the Davis model (see Fig. 5.27). However, long-standing debates have surrounded the issues of how the SP is generated, how the SP, CM, and harmonic distortion in the CM all interrelate, and whether the SP and/or CM are themselves essential products of the transduction process, which leads to the excitation of the auditory sensory neuron. Before really getting into this issue, because the discussion has been focused on potentials recorded extracellularly, there is one other stimulus-related potential that appears in recordings from in and around the cochlea—the response of the auditory nerve.

Whole-Nerve Action Potential

Although not easily seen in the *inset* oscillograph of Figure 5.28, there is another electrical response that is identifiable, appearing as a transient near the onset of the stimulus (in contrast to the CM and SP, which have durations that are essentially the same as that of the stimulus). Unlike the CM and SP, the origin of this potential has never been clouded in controversy, because it is well known to be the response of the VIIIth cranial nerve. Although it arises from the nerve trunk, rather than from within the organ of Corti, the electrical pathways of the temporal bone are such that there is usually good pickup of the action potential (AP) at any site that permits favorable recordings of the cochlear receptor potentials. (The one exception is scala media that is insulated fairly well from the nerve.) Thus, the AP can be recorded from within the cochlea, on the round window, and even as far away as the ear canal, ear lobe, or mastoid process. This response, even when recorded using a wire lying directly on the VIIIth nerve, comprises the neural impulses of multiple nerve cells. Therefore, this potential constitutes a compound AP, often referred to as the ***whole-nerve AP***. To see the AP clearly, it is necessary to suppress the CM (another recording trick) and expand the time base, as shown in Figure 5.33.

The transient nature of the AP and its association with the onset (and, some-times, offset) of the sound stimulus can be explained as follows. Before the sound is turned on, the neurons are relatively rested. Most auditory neurons at this level of the system are never totally inactive but discharge randomly at modest rates. With the abrupt switching on of the sound, many fibers are activated together or discharge synchronously with the onset of the stimulus. However, during the next few milliseconds, the individual fibers settle down to their more-normal average rates of discharge, and the compound response becomes too small to observe. A broad-band stimulus, such as the acoustic click (see Chapter 3), evokes an AP that reflects mostly neural activity associated with the basalward (high-frequency) region of the cochlea (Fig. 5.34$a$). Because high-frequency traveling waves have the highest speeds of propagation, they reach their destinations first. Consequently, they are the first to excite the auditory neurons

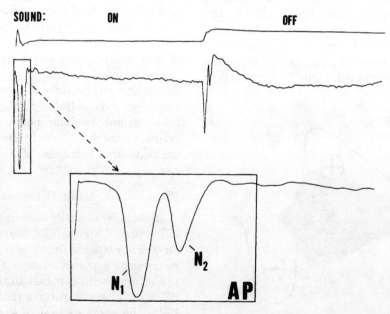

**Figure 5.33.** Recording of the whole-nerve AP. *Inset,* Time-base expanded to illustrate major component waves of the AP ($N_1$ and $N_2$). The *top trace* is actually the SP$-$, used here to indicate exactly when the stimulus has been turned on and off at the level of the hair cell transducer (thus eliminating inherent time delays caused by propagation of sound down the ear canal and of the traveling wave in the cochlea). (From Durrant, J. D. [1981]. Auditory physiology and an auditory physiologist's view of tinnitus. *J. Laryngol. Otol. Suppl.* 4: 21–28.)

a.

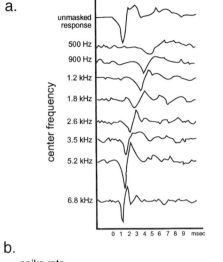

b.

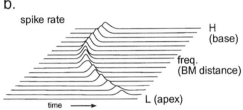

**Figure 5.34.** **a.** Contributions of different bands of activity to the (unfiltered) click-evoked AP, obtained by partially masking (i.e., suppressing) the response with high-pass noise, sequentially lowering the filter cut-off, and subtracting one masked response from the other. These data were obtained in a human subject using the transtympanic recording technique (needle electrode through the eardrum, resting on the promontory). (Based on Eggermont, J. J. [1976]. Analysis of compound action potential responses to tone bursts in the human and guinea pig cochlea. *J. Acoust. Soc. Am.* 60:1132–1139.) **b.** Panorama of activity across the auditory nerve trunk in response to a click. The tracings are based on single-unit recordings (see Chapter 6) in the cat. (Based on Kiang, N. Y.-S. [1975]. Stimulus representation in the discharge patterns of auditory neurons. In *The Nervous System: Human Communication and Its Disorders*, vol 3, pp 81–96, edited by E. L. Eagles. Raven Press, New York.)

(Fig. 5.34*b*) and to provide inherently the best synchronization of the individual spike APs. The more neurons active at the same time, the larger and better defined the compound AP. In contrast, the contribution of apicalward fibers also tends to be self-canceling because of the progressive

time delay associated with the propagation of the traveling wave up the cochlea (Fig. 5.34*b*). This creates phase opposition among nerve fibers activated at different places along the lower-frequency regions of the hearing organ. It is important to bear in mind that these regions, in fact, are being activated by this stimulus. Using appropriate techniques, frequency-specific information, including the low frequencies, can be obtained from the AP. This issue is discussed further in the next chapter. At this juncture, the most important aspect of the AP is that it represents the desired end product of the first stage of sensory processing in audition, that is, the activation of the auditory sensory neurons. The AP does not directly reflect the neural code of the stimulus being transmitted to the central system, but because it is a compound potential, the AP does increase in magnitude with increasing stimulus intensity, reflecting the recruitment of increasing numbers of neurons into activation.

## So, What Are the Auditory Receptor and Generator Potentials?

That the CM and SP (at least its major component[s]) are receptor potentials has become a well-established fact, but considerable controversy has existed concerning whether they singly or together constitute the receptor potential. In other words, are the CM and/or SP electrical event(s) directly responsible for initiating the process by which the sensory neuron is ultimately excited? Great advances have been made during the past two decades of research because of the ability to record from inside individual mammalian auditory hair cells to obtain the unit receptor potential. Recordings from inside mammalian hair cells are technically demanding feats. Highly specialized and precise instruments and considerable skill and patience on the part of the scientist are needed to hang on to a mere handful of hair cells long enough to get reasonably complete data. The extremely fine electrodes required for such recordings do not make the sampling of CM favorable at high frequencies, and, initially, successful recordings were made only in inner hair cells in the base of the cochlea. More recently, single hair cell recordings have been successfully accomplished in the upper cochlear turns in OHCs, as well as IHCs, and such recordings demonstrate AC potentials with a DC offset (Fig. 5.35; see also Fig. 5.15). Therefore, both CM- and SP-like potentials have been recorded from individual cells in the mammalian hearing organ, as had also been observed previously in other hair cells of the acousticolateralis system.

Because there is no a priori basis for assuming otherwise, an electrode impaled in an individual hair cell is presumed to record a unitary receptor potential—call it the RP. However, the RP from mammalian hair cells, particularly the DC component, is relatively large (compared with gross microphonics and SPs), reaching 20 mV or so in magnitude at high levels of stimulation. Interestingly, the DC component recorded from OHCs exhibits a polarity reversal at relatively low frequencies of stimulation, as does the SP. Without

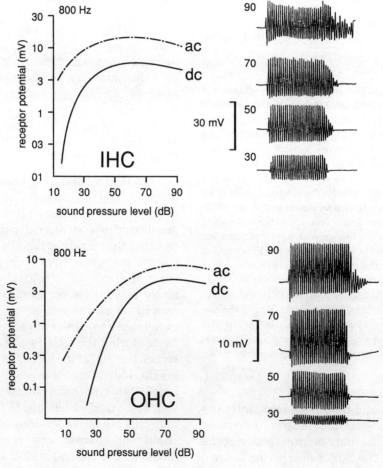

**Figure 5.35.** Recordings from single hair cells from IHCs and OHCs. Measurements from both AC and DC RPs are indicated. (Modified from Dallos, P. [1985]. Response characteristics of mammalian cochlear hair cells. *J. Neurosci.* 5:1591–1608.)

getting into details, there are, indeed, various other favorable comparisons between both RP components and the CM and SP. Still, some caution must be exercised in attempting to equate the grossly recorded CM and SP with the AC and DC components of the RP. There are some matters that require further deliberation concerning how the RP might be conducted to the extracellular fluid spaces and how the individual hair cells or their RPs might interact. In this regard, it is interesting that the RP (both DC and AC components) recorded from OHCs is about one third of the magnitude of that of IHC, although the RPs from both types of cells have the same basic sensitivity. In contrast, earlier estimates based on the gross CM (recorded extracellularly) suggested that the CM output of IHCs to be roughly 20 dB less than the output of OHCs. Of course, the OHCs have a three-to-one advantage in number, but this can account for only a part of the difference in output. It also is clear that the Davis model, as originally put forth, is too simplistic to account completely for the complicated electrophysiological phenomena observed in the cochlea.

The pursuit of a generator potential, at least in the mammalian inner ear, has been less successful than the search for the RP. This term was used in the beginning of this chapter to denote potentials that arise in the sensory neuron and directly trigger the generation of APs. This is a role, incidentally, originally attributed to the CM. Demonstration of such potentials, however, poses a formidable task. If, as was suggested by Figure 5.2, the receptor and generator potentials have very similar characteristics, they obviously would be difficult to separate, particularly in the extracellular recording. Indeed, there is some evidence that generator potentials contribute to the gross SP and can be observed only under very restrictive conditions, namely recording on the trailing and basal-ward slope of the traveling wave at low SPLs, using a recording technique to cancel the local DC RPs (which produce SP+; see Fig. 5.32). Under other conditions, this potential, which is negative in polarity and small (only 10 $\mu$V or so at most), is overshadowed by much larger SPs of hair cell origin. So, although cochlear electrophysiology may provide a glimpse of the generator potentials, it is fleeting.

In conclusion, details aside with respect to how the grossly recorded CM and SP are constituted from the AC and DC unit potentials, the CM and SP afford convenient means for monitoring the mechanical events of the cochlea by virtue of their dependence on the displacement patterns of the cochlear partition. They seem to be direct products of the hair cell transduction process, further defining their value to the hearing scientist in determining the status of the hair cells. Indeed, it now is practical to record routinely the CM and SP, as well as the AP, in humans via noninvasive methods, even in the clinical setting, thereby obtaining electrophysiological indicators of the presence or absence of disease in the inner ear. Cochlear electrophysiology thus has contributed and continues to contribute to better understanding of how the normal cochlea functions and how its function is influenced by adverse conditions, such as disease, toxic chemicals, anoxia, and noxious sound stimulation. It is safe to say that cochlear electrophysiology will remain of keen interest to the hearing scientist for some time to come.

## BIBLIOGRAPHY

Allen, J. B. (1980). Cochlear micromechanics—a physical model of transduction. *J. Acoust. Soc. Am.* 68:1660–1670.

Allen, J. B., and Neely, S. T. (1992). Micromechanical models of the cochlea. *Phys. Today* 45(7):40–47.

Békésy, G. v. (1960). *Experiments in Hearing*, translated and edited by E. G. Wever. McGraw-Hill, New York.

Bracho, H., and Budelli, R. (1978). The generation of resting membrane potentials in an inner ear hair cell system. *J. Physiol.* 281:445–465.

Brownell, W. E. (1983). Observations on a motile response in isolated outer hair cells. In *Neural Mechanisms of Hearing*, pp 5–10, edited by W. Webster and X. Aitkin. Monash University Press, Clayton, Australia.

Brownell, W. E., Bader, C. R., Bertrand, D., and deRibaupierre, Y. (1985). Evoked mechanical responses of isolated cochlear outer hair cells. *Science* 227: 194–196.

Brownell, W. E., and Kachar, B. (1986). Outer hair cell motility: a possible electro-kinetic mechanism. In *Lecture Notes in Biomathematics: Peripheral Auditory Mechanisms*, vol 64, pp 369–375, edited by J. B. Allen, J. L. Hall, A. Hubbard, S. T. Neely, and A. Tubis. Springer-Verlag, Berlin.

Brundin, L., Flock, A., Khanna, S. M., and Ulfendahl, M. (1991). Frequency-specific position shift in the guinea pig organ of corti. *Neurosci. Lett.* 128: 77–80.

Dallos, P. (1971). Summating potentials of the cochlea. In *Physiology of the Auditory System*, pp 57–67, edited by M. B. Sachs. National Educational Consultants, Baltimore.

Dallos, P. (1973). *The Auditory Periphery: Biophysics and Physiology*. Academic Press, Inc., New York.

Dallos, P. (1975). Electrical correlates of mechanical events in the cochlea. *Audiology* 14:408–418.

Dallos, P. (1981). Cochlear physiology. *Annu. Rev. Psychol.* 32:153–190.

Dallos, P. (1984). Peripheral mechanisms of hearing. In Handbook of Physiology—The Nervous System III, pp 595–637, edited by S. R. Geiger. Williams & Wilkins, Baltimore.

Dallos, P. (1985). Response characteristics of mammalian cochlear hair cells. *J. Neurosci.* 5: 1591–1608.

Dallos, P. (1988). Cochlear neurobiology: revolutionary developments. *ASHA* 30(6):50–56.

Dallos, P. (1992). The active cochlea. *J. Neurosci.* 12(12):4575–4585.

Dallos, P., and Cheatham, M. A. (1976). Production of cochlear potentials by inner and outer hair cells. *J. Acoust. Soc. Am.* 60:510–512.

Dallos, P., and Durrant, J. D. (1972). On the derivative relationship between stapes movement and cochlear microphonic. *J. Acoust. Soc. Am.* 52: 1263–1265.

Dallos, P., Cheatham, M. A., and Ferraro, J. (1974). Cochlear mechanics, nonlinearities, and cochlear potentials. *J. Acoust. Soc. Am.* 55:597–605.

Dallos, P., Evans, B. N., and Hallworth, R. (1991). Nature of the motor element in electrokinetic shape changes of cochlear outer hair cells. *Nature* 350:155–157.

Dallos, P., Santos-Sacchi, J., and Flock, A. (1982). Intracellular recordings from cochlear outer hair cells. *Science* 218:582–584.

Davis, H. (1965). A model for transducer action in the cochlea. *Cold Spring Harbor Symp. Quant. Biol.* 30:181–189.

Davis, H., and Walsh, T. E. (1950). The limits of improvement of hearing following the fenestration operation. *Laryngoscope* 60:273–295.

De Boer, E. (1981). Short waves in three-dimensional cochlea models: solution for a "block" model. *Hearing Res.* 4:53–77.

De Boer, E. (1982). Correspondence principle in cochlear mechanics. *J. Acoust. Soc. Am.* 71: 1496–1501.

Durrant, J. D. (1978). Anatomic and physiologic correlates of the effects of noise on hearing. In *Noise and Audiology*, pp 109–141, edited by D. M. Lipscomb. University Park Press, Baltimore.

Durrant, J. D. (1979). Comments on the effects of overstimulation on microphonic sensitivity. *J. Acoust. Soc. Am.* 66:597–598.

Durrant, J. D. (1981). Auditory physiology and an auditory physiologist's view of tinnitus. *J. Laryngol. Otol. [Suppl.]* 4:21–28.

Durrant, J. D., and Gans. D. (1975). Biasing of the summating potentials. *Acta Otolaryngol.* 80: 13–18.

Duvall, A. J., Flock, A., and Wersall, J. (1966). The ultrastructure of the sensory hairs and associated organelles of the cochlear inner hair cell with reference to directional sensitivity. *J. Cell Biol.* 29: 497–505.

Eldredge, D. H. (1974). Inner ear—cochlear mechanics and cochlear potentials. In *Handbook of Sensory Physiology, Auditory System: Anatomy, Physiology (Ear)*, vol V/1, pp 549–584, edited by W. D. Keidel and W. D. Neff. Springer-Verlag, Berlin.

Eggermont, J. J. (1976). Analysis of compound action potential responses to tone bursts in the human and guinea pig cochlea. *J. Acoust. Soc. Am.* 60: 1132–1139.

Eggermont, J. J. (1976). Electrocochleography. In *Handbook of Sensory Physiology, Auditory System: Clinical and Special Topics*, vol V/3, pp 625–705, edited by W. D. Keidel and W. D. Neff. Springer-Verlag, Berlin.

Feldman, A. S., and Wilber, L. A., eds. (1976). *Acoustic Impedance & Admittance—The Measurement of Middle Ear Function*. Williams & Wilkins, Baltimore.

Ferrary, E., Bernard, C., Julien, N., Sterkers, O., and Amiel, C. (1993). Is the endolymphatic K secretion electrogenic? *Acta. Otolaryngol.* 113:335–337.

Flock, A. (1965). Transducing mechanisms in the lateral line canal organ receptors. *Cold Spring Harbor Symp. Quant. Biol.* 30:133–144.

Flock, A. (1977). Physiological properties of sensory hairs in the ear. In *Psychophysics and Physiology of Hearing*, pp 1–11, edited by E. F. Evans and J. P. Wilson. Academic Press, London.

Flock, A., Jorgensen, M., and Russell, I. (1973). The physiology of individual hair cells and their synapses. In *Basic Mechanisms in Hearing*, pp 273–302, edited by A. R. Moller. Academic Press, New York.

Flock, A., Cheung, H. C., Flock, B., and Utter, G.

(1981). Three sets of actin filaments in sensory cells of the inner ear. Identification and functional orientation determined by gel electrophoresis, immunofluorescence and electron microscopy. *J. Neurocytol.* 10:133–147.

Geisler, C. D. (1991). A cochlear model using feedback from motile outer hair cells. *Hear. Res.* 54: 105–117.

Geisler, C. D. (1993). A model of stereociliary tip-link stretches. *Hear. Res.* 65:79–82.

Geisler, C. D., Mountain, D. C., and Hubbard, A. E. (1980). Sound-induced resistance changes in the inner ear. *J. Acoust. Soc. Am.* 67:1729–1735.

Grummer, A. W., Johnstone, B. M., and Armstrong, N. J. (1981). Direct measurement of basilar membrane stiffness in the guinea pig. *J. Acoust. Soc. Am.* 70:1298–1309.

Grundfest. H. (1971). The general electrophysiology of input membrane in electrogenic excitable cells. In *Handbook of Sensory Physiology, Principles of Receptor Physiology*, vol 1, pp 135–165, edited by W. R. Lowenstein. Springer-Verlag, Berlin.

Hall, J. L. (1980). Cochlear models: two-tone suppression and the second filter. *J. Acoust. Soc. Am.* 67:1722–1728.

Holmes, M. H. (1980). An analysis of a low-frequency model of the cochlea. *J. Acoust. Soc. Am.* 68: 482–488.

Honrubia, V., Strelioff, D., and Sitko, S. T. (1976). Physiological basis of cochlear transduction and sensitivity. *Ann. Otol.* 85:697–710.

Howard, J., Roberts, W. M., and Hudspeth, A. J. (1988). Mechanoelectrical transduction by hair cells. In *Annual Review of Biophysics and Biophysical Chemistry*, vol 17, pp 99–124, edited by D. M. Engelman, C. R. Cantor, and T. D. Pollard. Annual Reviews Inc., Palo Alto, CA.

Hudspeth, A. J. (1986). The ionic channels of a vertebrate hair cell. *Hear. Res.* 22:21–27.

Hudspeth. A. J. (1989). Mechanoelectrical transduction by hair cells of the bullfrog's sacculus. *Prog. Brain Res.* 80:129–135.

Hudspeth, A. J., and Corey, D. P. (1977). Sensitivity, polarity, and conductance change in the response of vertebrate hair cells to controlled mechanical stimuli. *Proc. Natl. Acad. Sci. USA* 74:2407–2411.

Hung, I., and Dallos, P. J. (1972). Study of the acoustic reflex in human beings. *J. Acoust. Soc. Am.* 52: 1168–1180.

Huxley, A. F. (1969). Is resonance possible in the cochlea after all? *Nature* 221:935–940.

Kemp, D. T. (1978). Stimulated acoustic emissions from within the human auditory system. *J. Acoust. Soc. Am.* 64:1386–1391.

Kemp, D. T. (1982). Cochlear echoes: implications for noise-induced hearing loss. In *New Perspectives on Noise-Induced Hearing Loss*, pp 189–207, edited by R. P. Hamernik, D. Henderson, and R. Salvi. Raven Press, New York.

Kemp, D. T. (1988). Developments in cochlear mechanics and techniques for noninvasive evaluation. *Adv. Audiol.* 5:27-45.

Khanna, S. M., and Leonard, D. G. B. (1982). Basilar membrane tuning in the cat cochlea. *Science* 215: 305–306.

Killion, M. C., and Dallos, P. (1979). Impedance matching by the combined effects of the outer and middle ear. *J. Acoust. Soc. Am.* 66:599–602.

Kiang, N. Y.-S. (1975). Stimulus representation in the discharge patterns of auditory neurons. In *The Nervous System—Vol 3: Human Communication and Its Disorders*, pp. 81–96, edited by E. L. Eagles. Raven Press, New York

Kirikae, I. (1973). Physiology of the middle ear including eustachian tube. In *Otolaryngology, Basic Sciences and Related Disciplines*, 2nd ed, vol 1, pp. 199–215. edited by M. M. Paparella and D. A. Shumrick. W. B. Saunders Co., Philadelphia.

Kohlloffel, L. U. E. (1977). On the connection membrana corti-organ of Corti. In *Inner Ear Biology*, pp 15–24, edited by M. Portmann and J.-M. Aran. INSERN, Paris.

Kringlebotn, M. (1988). Network model for the human middle ear. *Scand. Audiol.* 17:75–85.

Kuhn, G. F. (1979). The pressure transformation from a diffuse sound field to the external ear and to the body and head surface. *J. Acoust. Soc. Am.* 65:991–1000.

Lawrence, M. (1965). Dynamic range of the cochlear transducer. *Cold Spring Harbor Symp. Quant. Biol.* 30:159–167.

Lawrence, M. (1965). Middle ear muscle influence on binaural hearing. *Arch. Otolaryngol.* 82:478–482.

Lawrence, M., and Burgio, P. A. (1980). Attachment of the tectorial membrane revealed by scanning electron microscope. *Ann. Otol.* 89:325–330.

Leng, G. (1980). The Davis theory: a review and implications of recent electrophysiological evidence. *Hearing Res.* 3:17–25.

LePage, E. L. (1987). Frequency-dependent self-induced bias of the basilar membrane and its potential for controlling sensitivity and tuning in the mammalian cochlea. *J. Acoust. Soc. Am.* 82: 139–154.

Lim, D. J. (1980). Cochlear anatomy related to cochlear micromechanics. A review. *J. Acoust. Soc. Am.* 67:1686–1695.

Lonsbury-Martin, B. L., Harris, F. P., Hawkins, M. D., et al. (1990). Distortion product emissions in humans I. Basic properties in normally hearing subjects. *Ann. Otol. Rhinol. Laryngol. [Suppl.]* 147: 3–14.

Lynch, T. J., Nedzelnitsky, V., and Peake, W. T. (1982). Input impedance of the cochlea in cat. *J. Acoust. Soc. Am.* 72:108–130.

Mehrgardt, S., and Mellert, V. (1977). Transformation characteristics of the external human ear. *J. Acoust. Soc. Am.* 61:1567–1576.

Mellon. D. (1968). *The Physiology of the Sense Organs*. W. H. Freeman, San Francisco.

Moller, A. R. (1963). Transfer function of the middle ear. *J. Acoust. Soc. Am.* 35:1526–1534.

Moller, A. R. (1972). The middle ear. In *Foundations of Modern Auditory Theory*, vol 2, pp 135–194, edited by J. V. Tobias. Academic Press, New York.

Naftalin, L. (1965). Some new proposals regarding acoustic transmission and transduction. *Cold Spring Harbor Symp. Quant. Biol.* 30:169–180.

Naftalin, L. (1977). The peripheral hearing mechanism: new biophysical concepts for transduction of the acoustic signal to an electrochemical event. *Physiol. Chem. Phys.* 9:337–382.

Nedzelnitsky, V. (1974). Measurement of sound pressure in the cochleae of anesthetized cats. In *Facts and Models in Hearing*, pp 45–53, edited by E. Zwicker and E. Terhardt. Springer-Verlag, New York.

Nedzelnitsky, V. (1980). Sound pressures in the basal turn of the cat cochlea. *J. Acoust. Soc. Am.* 68:1676–1689.

Neely, S. T., and Kim. D. O. (1986). A model for active elements in cochlear biomechanics. *J. Acoust. Soc. Am.* 79:1472–1480.

Nuttall, A. L., Brown, C. M., Masta, R. I., and Lawrence, M. (1981). Inner hair cell responses to the velocity of basilar membrane motion in the guinea pig. *Brain Res.* 211:171–174.

Offner, F. F., Dallos, P., and Cheatham, M. A. (1987). Positive endocochlear potential: mechanism of production by marginal cells of stria vascularis. *Hear. Res.* 29:117–124.

Peake, W. T., and Rosowski, J. J. (1991). Impedance matching, optimum velocity, and ideal middle ears. *Hear. Res.* 53:1-6.

Peake, W. T., Rosowski, J. J., and Lynch, T. J. III (1992). Middle-ear transmission: acoustic versus ossicular coupling in cat and human. *Hear. Res.* 57:245–268.

Pickles, J. O., Comis, S. D., and Osborne, M. P. (1984). Cross-links between stereocilia in the guinea pig organ of corti, and their possible relation to sensory transduction. *Hear. Res.* 15: 103–112.

Pickles, J. O., and Corey, D. P. (1992). Mechanoelectrical transduction by hair cells. *Trends Neurosci.* 15(7):254–259.

Rhode, W. S. (1973). An investigation of post-mortem cochlear mechanics using the Mossbauer effect. In *Basic Mechanisms in Hearing*, pp 39–63, edited by A. R. Moller. Academic Press, New York.

Rhode, W. S. (1978). Some observations on cochlear mechanics. *J. Acoust. Soc. Am.* 64:158–176.

Rhode, W. S. (1980). Cochlear partition vibration—recent views. *J. Acoust. Soc. Am.* 67: 1696–1703.

Rhys Evans, P. H., Comis, S. D., Osborne, M. P., Pickles, J. O., and Jeffries, D. J. R. (1985). Cross-links between stereocilia in the human organ of corti. *J. Laryngol. Otol.* 99:11–19.

Roberts, W. M., Howard, J., and Hudspeth, A. J.

(1988). Hair cells: transduction, tuning, and transmission in the inner ear. In *Annual Review of Cell Biology*, vol 4, pp 63–92, edited by G. E. Palade, B. M. Alberts, and J. A. Spudich. Annual Reviews Inc., Palo Alto, CA.

Robinson, D. W., and Dadson, R. S. (1956). A re-determination of the equal loudness relations for pure tones. *Br. J. Appl. Phys.* 7:166–181.

Rosowski, J. J. (1991). The effects of external- and middle-ear filtering on auditory threshold and noise-induced hearing loss. *J. Acoust. Soc. Am.* 90(1):124–135.

Ruggero, M. A. (1992). Responses to sound of the basilar membrane of the mammalian cochlea. *Curr. Op. Neurobiol.* 2:449–456.

Russell, I. J., and Cody, A. R. (1986). Transduction in cochlear hair cells. In *Lecture Notes in Biomathematics: Peripheral Auditory Mechanisms*, vol 64, pp 349–360, edited by J. B. Allen, J. L. Hall, A. Hubbard, S. T. Neely, and A. Tubis. Springer-Verlag, Berlin.

Russell, I. J., and Sellick, P. M. (1977). Tuning properties of cochlear hair cells. *Nature* 267:858–860.

Russell, I. J., and Sellick, P. M. (1978). Intracellular studies of hair cells in the mammalian cochlea. *J. Physiol.* 284:261–290.

Ryan, A. and Dallos, P. (1984). Physiology of the cochlea. In *Hearing Disorders*, 2nd ed, pp 253–266, edited by J. L. Northern. Little, Brown & Co., Boston.

Santos-Sacchi, J. (1989). Asymmetry in voltage-dependent movements of isolated outer hair cells from the organ of corti. *J. Neurosci.* 9(8): 2954–2962.

Santos-Sacchi, J. (1988). Cochlear physiology. In *Physiology of the Ear*, pp 271-293, edited by A. F. Jahn and J. Santos-Sacchi. Raven Press, New York.

Schmiedt, R. A., and Adams, J. C. (1981). Stimulated acoustic emissions in the ear canal of the gerbil. *Hear. Res.* 5:295–305.

Schubert, E. D. (1978). History of research in hearing. In *Handbook of Perception: Hearing*, vol IV, pp. 41–80. edited by E. C. Carterette and M. P. Friedman. Academic Press, New York.

Sellick, P. M., Patuzzi, R., and Johnstone, B. M. (1982). Measurement of basilar membrane motion in the guinea pig using the Mossbauer technique. *J. Acoust. Soc. Am.* 72:131–141.

Shaw, E. A. G. (1974). The external ear. In *Handbook of Sensory Physiology. Auditory System: Anatomy, Physiology (Ear)*, vol V/1, pp 455–490, edited by W. D. Keidel and W. D. Neff. Springer-Verlag, Berlin.

Spoendlin, H. (1966). Ultrastructure of the vestibular sense organ. In *The Vestibular System and Its Diseases*, pp 39–68, edited by R. J. Wolfson. University of Pennsylvania Press, Philadelphia.

Sprague, B. H., Wiley, T. L., Block, M. G. (1981). Dynamics of acoustic reflex growth. *Audiology* 20: 15–40.

Taber, L. A., and Steele, C. R. (1981). Cochlear model

including three-dimensional fluid and four modes of partition flexibility. *J. Acoust. Soc. Am.* 70: 426–436.

Tasaki, I., and Spyropoulos, C. S. (1959). Stria vascularis as source of endocochlear potential. *J. Neurophysiol.* 22:149–155.

Tilney, L. G., Derosier, D. J., and Mulroy, M. J. (1980). The organization of actin filaments in the stereocilia of cochlear hair cells. *J. Cell Biol.* 86: 244–259.

Tonndorf, J. (1958). The hydrodynamic origin of aural harmonics in the cochlea. *Ann. Otol. Rhinol. Laryngol.* 67:754–774.

Tonndorf, J. (1960). Shearing motion in scala media of cochlear models. J. Acoust. Soc. Am. 32:238–244.

Tonndorf, J. (1975). Davis—1961 revisted: signal transmission in the cochlear hair cell-nerve junction. *Arch Otolaryngol.* 101:528–535.

Tonndorf, J., and Khanna, S. M. (1970). The role of the tympanic membrane in middle ear transmission. *Ann. Otolaryngol.* 79:743–753.

Voldrich, L., and Ulehlova, L. (1982). The role of the spiral ligament in cochlear mechanics. *Acta Otolaryngol.* 93:169–173.

Wever, E. G., and Lawrence, M. (1954). *Physiological Acoustics.* Princeton University Press, Princeton.

Wiener, F. M., and Ross, D. A. (1946). The pressure distribution in the auditory canal in a progressive sound field. *J. Acoust. Soc. Am.* 18:401–408.

Wilson, J. P., and Johnstone, J. R. (1972). Capacitive probe measures of basilar membrane vibration. In *Hearing Theory,* pp 172–181. Institution for Perception Research, Eindhoven.

Yates, G. K., and Johnstone, B. M. (1976). Localized cochlear microphonics recorded from the spiral lamina. *J. Acoust. Soc. Am.* 59:476–479.

Zenner, H. P., Gitter, A. H., Rudert, M., and Ernst, A. (1992). Stiffness, compliance, elasticity and force generation of outer hair cells. *Acta. Otolaryngol.* 112:248–253.

Zito, F., and Roberto, M. (1980). The acoustic reflex pattern studied by averaging technique. *Audiology* 19:395–403.

Zwislocki, J. (1962). Analysis of the middle-ear function. Part I. Input impedance. *J. Acoust. Soc. Am.* 34:1514–1523.

Zwislocki, J. (1965). Analysis of some auditory characteristics. In *Handbook of Mathematical Psychology,* vol 3, pp 1–97, edited by R. R. Bush, R. D. Luce, and E. Galanter. John Wiley & Sons, New York.

Zwislocki, J. (1975). The role of the external and middle ear in sound transmission. In *The Nervous System: Human Communication and Its Disorders,* vol 3, pp 45–55, edited by E. L. Eagles. Raven Press, New York.

Zwislocki, J. (1980). Five decades of research on cochlear mechanics. *J. Acoust. Soc. Am.* 67: 1679–1685).

Zwislocki, J. (1981). Middle ear, cochlea, and Tonndorf. *Am. J. Otolaryngol.* 2:240–250.

## CHAPTER 6

# NEUROPHYSIOLOGY OF THE

# AUDITORY SYSTEM

The innervation of the organ of Corti was described briefly in Chapter 4. At that juncture, and later in Chapter 5, the neurons of the auditory system were referred to without any detailed discussion of their structure and function. It is, of course, by means of neurons that sensory information is transmitted to and relayed within the central nervous system (CNS). A requisite for fully appreciating the design of the auditory system, and basically understanding how it functions, is knowledge of the pathways formed by neurons leading from the auditory periphery, through the brain stem, to cortical areas of the brain. This is not to say that auditory information is processed only at the level of the cortex, the highest level of the CNS. Once encoded by the peripheral auditory system and transmitted to the CNS, some degree of information processing of the acoustic stimulus will occur at each level within the central auditory system. Consequently, the various way stations at the different levels of the system, including subcortical levels (namely, the brain stem), are of importance in and of themselves. This chapter is devoted to the neurophysiology of sensory processing in the auditory nervous system and, thus, the underlying pathways and mechanisms involved in this task.

## 1. Structure and Function of Neurons

### A. THE NEURON

The most fundamental unit, that is, the building block, of the nervous system is the nerve cell or **neuron**. The generalized neuron is illustrated in Figure 6.1a. In reality, neurons come in many varieties, but, as illustrated by Figure 6.1, there are common basic features among them: a **soma** or *cell body*, which contains the cell nucleus; one or more processes, known as **dendrites**, which effectively increase the surface area of the soma and serve as an input device; and a fiber-like structure, called the **axon**, which typically is long and cylindrical in shape, may vary in length from a few millimeters to more than a meter, and serves as an output device. Therefore, dendrites and axons typically differ greatly in structure and invariably serve different functions. The dendrites and cell bodies receive input from receptor cells or other neurons, whereas axons convey signals away from their cells' somas, toward other cells (nerve, receptor, or motor, depending on the neural pathway involved). Axons branch into many finger-like projections called *teleodendria* or *endbrushes* with

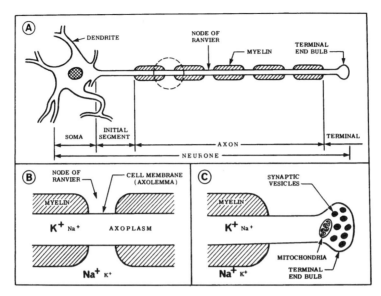

**Figure 6.1.**   Structure of the general neuron. (From Freeman, A. R. [1975]. Properties of excitable tissues. In *Basic Physiology for the Health Sciences*, edited by E. E. Selkurt. Little, Brown & Co., Boston.)

endings called **terminal endbulbs** or **boutons**. It is in the terminal boutons of neurons of interest here that subcellular mechanisms are found that produce and control the release of a chemical transmitter substance, a major component of the mechanism by which neurons communicate with each other and with other types of cells.

In mammalian nervous systems, connections between neurons or between a receptor or motor (muscle) cell and a nerve cell are achieved through **synapses**. Among nerve cells, synapses may occur between the axon of one neuron and the dendrite (*axodendritic*), soma (*axosomatic*), or axon (*axoaxonic*) of the other. Functionally, the synapse may be either *excitatory* (leading to excitation) or *inhibitory* (leading to inhibition or suppression) of the other neuron. For the time being, the discussion will focus on excitatory synapses between a receptor cell and a neuron or of the axodendritic or axosomatic types between neurons. Such synapses represent neural wiring designed for the forward flow of information, that

is, transmission of neural signals in an afferent pathway from the periphery to the CNS, from lower to upper brain stem, etc.

The synapse comprises a minute space, the *synaptic cleft*, between cells and the specialized areas near the cell membranes on either side of the cleft. On the input side of the synapse, in the sensory-cell or terminal boutons of the axon of a neuron, are *presynaptic* regions, wherein numerous minute sacs—*synaptic vesicles*—are found. These are the above-mentioned subcellular structures that contain and release the chemical transmitter substance (Figs. 6.1c and 6.2). On the output side of the synapse, the other side of the synaptic cleft, are specialized areas of the dendrites or somas of the next neuron—the *postsynaptic* membrane. These areas are sensitive to the transmitter substance and react by causing a localized graded depolarization of the cell membrane. *Graded* means that the amount of depolarization is proportional to the amount of stimulation—the number of packets of transmitter substance released into the synaptic

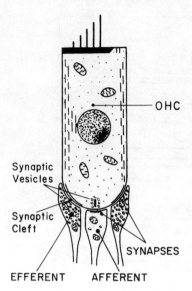

Figure 6.2. Schematic drawing of synapses between afferent and efferent nerve endings and an OHC. (Based on a drawing by Lim, D. J., and Melnick, W. [1971]. Acoustic damage of the cochlea. *Arch. Otolaryngol.* 94:294–305.)

cleft. The synapse is a unidirectional mechanism, serving (in effect) to transmit signals in only one direction. However, there may be more than one synapse between cells, and more than one neuron may terminate on a given cell. The summed action of local graded depolarizations of the postsynaptic membrane is the basis of what was defined as the **generator potential** in Chapter 5 and determines what happens next (as described below). Meanwhile, the chemical transmitter is recycled and ultimately restored in the synaptic vesicles, although prolonged and excessive activity of a cell can cause a temporary depletion of the store of transmitter substance. Removal of the transmitter substance from the cleft allows the postsynaptic cell membrane to recover its normal resting membrane potential.

Figure 6.2 illustrates synapses specifically between a hair cell in the auditory system and nerve endings of both **affer-** **ent** and **efferent neurons**. *Afferent* neurons, again, carry information toward the CNS. *Efferent* neurons carry information to the periphery or away from the CNS. Within a given system (for example, the peripheral auditory system), the transmitter substance contained in the synaptic vesicles of the afferent cell differs from that of the efferent cell (in this example, the transmitter substance contained in the synaptic vesicles of the hair cells versus that of the efferent nerve endings in Fig. 6.2). Various afferent and efferent transmitter substances have been identified, and a given substance may serve different roles in different parts of the body. The afferent transmitter released by hair cells still is not known with certainty, but glutamate or a similar substance is the strongest candidate. The efferent transmitter seems to be acetylcholine, a substance (along with epinephrine or adrenalin) found extensively throughout the body.

## B. THE ACTION POTENTIAL

The neuron, like all living cells, is charged, so a voltage is stored in the cell—the *resting (membrane) potential*—as discussed in the previous chapter. Because the nerve cell has the property of irritability, it can be discharged and then recharged again. However, the course of events in the discharge of the axonal membrane gives rise to an electrical potential that differs remarkably from either a generator or a receptor potential, or graded potentials in general. A cursory treatment of the membrane biophysics accounting for the unique discharge of the neuron's axon will be given below. For now, it is sufficient to know only that the basis of this activity is the selective conductance of ions across the cell membrane, altering the distribution of the ions from the resting state. The distribution of ions is what determined the resting membrane potential in the first place. What is of interest here is the electrical event of depolarization itself; its time course is portrayed in

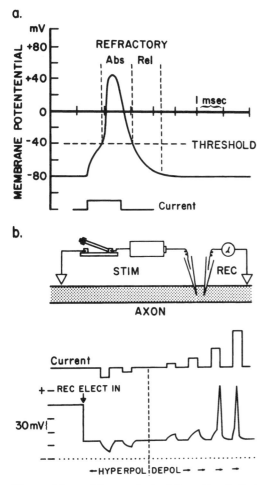

**Figure 6.3.** **a.** Time analysis of the action (spike) potential. The occurrence of the electrical current stimulus is indicated. **b.** Illustration of the basic experimental setup for exciting and recording APs from inside the axon of an isolated nerve cell (in this case, from the squid) and the effects of hyperpolarizing and depolarizing currents on the membrane potential. When a sufficient depolarizing current is applied, the AP is elicited; however, larger currents do not evoke larger spikes. (Modified from Katz, B. [1966]. *Nerve, Muscle, and Synapse*. McGraw-Hill, New York.)

Figure 6.3. The graph in Figure 6.3*a* is nothing more than the time analysis of what was referred to in Chapter 5 as a neural impulse or *spike*, or, more properly, the *(spike) action potential (AP)*. This is an all-or-nothing event in that there must either be a full-blown discharge or, if

the stimulation is too weak (namely, below *threshold*), the membrane potential simply returns to its resting value, as illustrated in Figure 6.3*b*. Note that it is possible to hyperpolarize (increase) the membrane resting potential, making it more difficult to initiate a spike discharge.

The time course of the AP is very fast and largely invariant (about 1 msec). This puts a limit on the rate at which the nerve cell can discharge. During the major phase of the spike, known as the absolute *refractory period*, the cell absolutely cannot discharge again, regardless of the amount of stimulation. On the other hand, the membrane potential need not return completely to the resting level before it can again be depolarized or fired. It, however, can be excited before the complete restoration of the resting potential during the relative refractory period, although a greater than normal amount of stimulation is necessary to fire the neuron. Given that the nerve cell is not excitable during the absolute refractory period, it is this parameter that determines the maximum *spike rate* (frequency of APs) at which the neuron can be triggered: 1/absolute refractory period (just as frequency equals the reciprocal of period). This rate is approximately 1000/sec, although in the auditory system rates exceeding 200/sec are rarely observed.

Once the AP is initiated in the initial segment, it propagates itself down the axon, away from the soma, by successive depolarization of sections of membrane. There is a limit to how fast spikes can be propagated, and this depends, in part, on the diameter of the axon. The larger the diameter, the faster the *conduction velocity*. The conduction velocity also depends on whether the axon is myelinated. All nerve cells actually are sheathed by other cells. Within the CNS, glial cells (for example, oligodendroglia and astrocytes) serve this purpose, whereas neurons of peripheral nerves are covered by Schwann cells. For many sensory and motor neurons the cell forming the sheath produces a substance called ***myelin*** by wrapping it-self around the axon in layers. As shown in Figure 6.1, the myelin sheath is not continuous along the axon's length. There are gaps at the junctions between adjacent Schwann cells, called ***nodes of Ranvier***. Because myelin is an insulator, electrically speaking, full-blown depolarizations of the axonal membrane can occur only at the nodes of Ranvier. The result is that spike APs are forced to jump from one node to the next (Fig. 6.1, *a* and *b*), virtually leap-frogging the patches of myelin sheath. This mode of propagation is known as *saltatory* conduction, the virtue of which is that it greatly speeds up conduction. Myelinated neurons, as a class, are characterized by the fastest conduction velocities; therefore, the fibers of these cells conduct information to the brain with the least delays. Still, compared with the rate at which electricity is conducted in wires (at the speed of light, approximately $3 \times 10^8$ m/sec), the conduction velocities in neurons are rather slow (1–100 m/sec). Synapses introduce additional time delays, approximately 0.5 to 1 msec. So, the total travel time of neural information over a given pathway, say, from the periphery to the cortex, depends on the diameter of the nerve fibers involved, the length of the axons, whether they are myelinated, and the number of neurons in the chain forming the pathway (and, consequently, the number of synaptic delays). Although the delays involved may seem small, given units of milliseconds, they are significant. For example 1 to 2 msec are required for the neural discharges initiated in the cochlea to arrive at the lowest level of the central auditory pathways (in the brain stem) and perhaps 10 or more milliseconds before the "message" from the cochlea reaches its destination at the highest level (the cortex). Then, even more time is required for the brain to orchestrate the organism's response to stimulation. As reflected in measurements of reaction time, this may take hundreds of milliseconds.

## C. Some (but—Don't Sweat—Not Much) Membrane Biophysics

Although it is beyond the scope of this text to provide a detailed treatment of the biophysical principles underlying the initiation and propagation of APs, a brief description of the more basic concepts is worthwhile, simply to take some of the mystery out of the phenomenon.

Nerve cells, like other living cells, contain fluid: *intracellular fluid*, which is effectively separated from the fluid bathing the cells—*extracellular* or *interstitial fluid*—namely, by the cell membrane. The cell membrane consists of layers of protein and lipids. Small pores, or *ion channels*, in the membrane, however, are large enough to permit free movement of some ions but not others. Inside the cell, there is initially a high concentration of positive ions or *cations*—potassium ($K^+$)—and organic negative ions or *anions*. Because of their size, the organic anions are incapable of passing through any of the ion channels in the cell membrane. The cell membrane, on the one hand, is penetrable by, or *permeable* to, $K^+$ and is "leaky" or somewhat permeable to another cation, sodium ($Na^+$). Outside the cell, there is a high concentration of sodium, as well as chloride ($Cl^-$) ions, an anion. Given two solutions of different concentrations of an ion, separated by an impermeable barrier, a force is developed, the *concentration gradient*. Consequently, $K^+$ tends to diffuse out of the cell, that is, down its concentration gradient, leaving the organic anions behind. The ion movement or ionic current flow, like physical electrical current, creates an electrical potential, the *voltage gradient*. The flow of $K^+$ down its concentration gradient creates a negative potential inside the cell, called the *potassium diffusion potential*. At the same time, again, $Na^+$ is leaking into the cell, that is, moving down its concentration gradient. The word *leak* is used purposefully here to indicate that $Na^+$ is not entirely free to move across the cell membrane. Nevertheless, because the leakage of Na⁺ leaves Cl⁻ behind, this tends to make the inside of the cell positive; this is the *sodium diffusion potential*. However, because the cell membrane passes K⁺ much more freely than Na⁺, the potassium diffusion potential dominates the polarization of the cell membrane, so the inside of the cell is negative. Therefore, a balance is achieved among the concentration and voltage gradients; the result is that the intracellular fluid has a net electrical potential of approximately $-70$ mV relative to the extracellular fluid. This is the **resting membrane potential**. To maintain this potential, the Na⁺ leakage must be kept in check; that is, a pump is needed to maintain the proper concentration gradients by exchanging Na⁺ ions that diffused into the cell for K⁺ ions that had diffused out of the cell. The sodium-potassium pump is driven by an active or metabolic process, that is, an energy-consuming process requiring oxygen.

The resting membrane potential represents the most stable state of the nerve cell. However, the establishment and maintenance of the resting membrane potential, and thus the appropriate concentrations of Na⁺ and K⁺ in the inside versus outside of the axon (Fig. 6.4a), are fundamental to the excitability (indeed, viability) of the nerve cell. Yet, the conditions just described pertain solely to the resting potential. It is the unique properties of the axonal membrane, specifically the ability to change dynamically the relative permeability of the Na⁺ and K⁺ channels, that permit the nerve cell to generate and conduct APs. Returning to Figure 6.3, when there is sufficient depolarization (because of effective coupling of the stimulus to the neuron), the cell membrane of the axon, unlike that of the dendrite, completely discharges and subsequently builds up a momentary positive membrane potential of some 40 mV. This is why the spike potential is shown crossing the zero axis in Figure 6.3a. The rapid discharge and subsequent polarity reversal

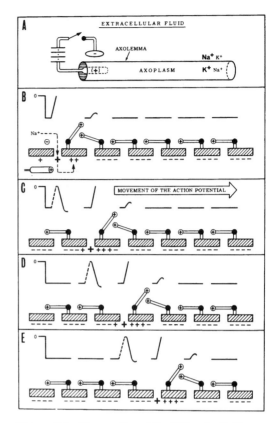

**Figure 6.4.** Propagation of the AP (see text). (From Freeman, A. R. [1975]. Properties of excitable tissues. In *Basic Physiology for the Health Sciences*, edited by E. E. Selkurt. Little, Brown & Co., Boston.)

of the membrane potential, making up the initial phase of the AP, comes about because of changes in the membrane resistance to Na⁺ and K⁺ and the resulting movement of these ions across the cell membrane over time. Na⁺ moves into the cell, and K⁺ moves out. The return of the membrane potential to its resting level is initiated by a sharp decrease in the ability of the Na⁺ ions to cross the membrane. Until the nerve cell is excited again, the movement of Na⁺ ions into the cell is severely limited. As elaborate as this process is, it requires no more than a couple of milliseconds to complete, from initiation of the spike to full recovery of the resting membrane potential.

It should be noted that, as implied earlier, the entire axonal membrane does not discharge all at once. This point is fundamental to understanding the process by which the AP is actually conducted by the axon. This process may be viewed as a sequence of opening and closing gates along the axon, as illustrated in Figure 6.4, *b–e*. In the region of the axonal membrane in which the discharge is initiated, the inside of the cell becomes positively charged, as just described. This creates a current flow down the axon, because of passive ionic current spread, that in turn leads to the depolarization of the next segment of membrane and the triggering of another AP. As this chain of events moves along the axon, away from the point at which the excitation was initiated (and, thus, away from the cell body), the potential across the preceding segments of the axonal membrane returns to the resting state. Thus, a wave of discharge moves down the axon. The fact that this wave arises because of sequential discharges along the axon, rather than via the production of a single AP and a passive depolarization of the entire axonal membrane, helps explain why the propagation of the AP is facilitated by myelinization. Although passive conduction, like electrical current flow in wires, occurs almost instantaneously, a single AP can be carried only small distances because of the great decrement that occurs in its amplitude with distance. So, after one AP occurs, it is not far down the axon before the resting membrane potential is recovered and another AP can be excited. Although the AP is completed in about 1 msec, its completion is still time consuming. Given that as many discharges will occur over the length of the axon as possible, propagation of APs along an unmyelinated axon is inherently slow. In the case of the myelinated axon, the discharges, again, are forced to occur only at certain minimal distances, namely, as defined by the nodes of Ranvier. The spread of depolarization from one part of the axon membrane to the next requires passive conduction between the nodes of Ranvier.

Passive conduction occurs at the speed of light, so the farther apart the nodes, the faster the propagation. The difference in conduction velocities in the two situations is analogous to the difference in speeds with which one can walk by taking short (heel-to-toe) versus long strides. In the case of myelinated neurons, the stride of the AP is set by the distances between the nodes of Ranvier, and this stride is invariably longer than it would be in the case of the unmyelinated axon.

Finally, when the spike potential reaches the terminal endbulb(s), the depolarization causes the synaptic vesicles to release neurotransmitter into the synaptic cleft. This chemical substance, as discussed earlier, depolarizes the postsynaptic membrane (called the *excitatory postsynaptic membrane potential* [EPSP]), causing an increased inflow of $Na^+$. If there is a sufficient amount of transmitter substance released, and, consequently, sufficient depolarization, then APs again will be excited. In this manner excitation is passed along from one neuron to the next. However, this is only true if the transmitter substance itself is excitatory, namely, as a result of an excitatory neuron acting on the postsynaptic membrane. The same basic events could be inhibitory if the transmitter substance causes a hyperpolarization of the postsynaptic membrane (increased or *inhibitory postsynaptic membrane potential* [IPSP]). In reality, both excitatory and inhibitory neurons often act on the same cell. Whether that nerve cell is subsequently excited will depend on which is dominant. In other words, will the excitatory transmitter still cause sufficient depolarization against an increased membrane potential (relative to the resting value) to trigger an AP?

## D. TYPES OF NEURONS

The nerve cell portrayed in Figure 6.1 is actually one of three general types of neurons. It is called a *multipolar cell*, as reflected by its many dendritic processes. This particular rendition of a multipolar cell is perhaps more characteristic of peripheral motor neurons than of sensory neurons or nerve cells in the CNS. Indeed, the neurons within the CNS are often elaborate, and, at first glance, it can be difficult to figure out what exactly is the axon. There also are monopolar cells that have only an axon leaving the cell body. Nerve fibers of other neurons terminate directly on the cell bodies of monopolar cells, because there are no dendrites. In the auditory periphery, the neurons of the eighth nerve are predominantly of still another type, **bipolar** cells (Fig. 6.5). Bipolar or type I neurons seem to have two axons, but such terms as axon and dendrite become somewhat vague in this case. Perhaps the term *initial segment* is more meaningful as a demarcation of the beginning of the functional axon, that is, the point at which a full-blown AP is first initiated. In the auditory periphery, this is probably at the point at which the fibers first leave the habenula perforata—the small openings in the osseous spiral lamina through which the fibers pass on their way to innervate the hair cells. In the auditory periphery, the vast majority of the

neurons are myelinated bipolar neurons, and it is at the habenula that the myelin sheath of each fiber begins. This is thought to be the place at which the AP first arises.

There also is a population of *pseudomonopolar* neurons, called **type II neurons**, whose cell bodies are off to the side of what looks like a continuous axon. Type II neurons are smaller than type I, and their axons may be myelinated or unmyelinated. Whereas inner hair cells (IHCs) are thought to be exclusively innervated by type I neurons, outer hair cells (OHCs) seem to be innervated by type II, but these cells are in the minority, and a small minority at that! Recall from Chapter 4 that the vast majority of all afferent neurons (regardless of type) innervate IHCs; indeed, each IHC is connected to more than 10 neurons. Ten percent or less of the afferents innervate the OHCs, despite the numerical superiority of the outers. Consequently, the type II neurons have numerous branches, or *collaterals*, such that each neuron connects to 10 or more OHCs. Each OHC also tends to be connected to multiple neurons. So, there is a considera-

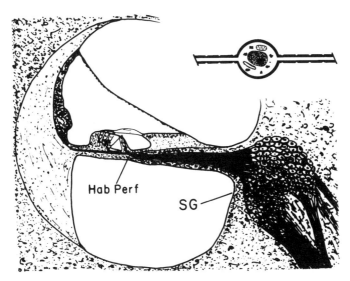

**Figure 6.5.** Neurons in the auditory periphery, the collection of whose cell bodies form the spiral ganglia. *SG*, Spiral ganglion; *Hab Perf*, habenula perforata. *Inset*, Schematic representation of structure of the typical bipolar neuron of the auditory system. (Based in part on drawings and photomicrographs of Spoendlin [1971].)

ble dichotomy in the innervation of IHCs versus OHCs (see Fig. 4.24), and there are words to describe this. The innervation pattern of the IHCs is *divergent*; one receptor cell (IHC) is attached to many neurons. In contrast, the innervation of the OHCs is *convergent*; one neuron communicates with numerous receptor cells (OHCs).

As shown in Figure 6.5, the cell bodies of the neurons innervating the organ of Corti are contained in the **spiral ganglion** (Fig. 6.5). Whereas collections of cell bodies in the periphery are called *ganglia* (ganglion, singular), they are called **nuclei** (nucleus, singular) in the CNS. In the central auditory system, the characteristic nerve cell is of the multipolar type, rather than bipolar. The cell bodies of these multipolar nerve cells and their dendrites are collected in various nuclei at the different levels of the CNS. Their axons provide the connecting pathways between these neural relay or way stations and thus form the central auditory pathways—the next topic of discussion. However, first it will be necessary to get the lay of the land before trying to learn some of the detailed pathways through it.

## 2. Gross Anatomy of the CNS: An Overview (or, You Don't Have to be a Brain Surgeon to Know a Little Neuroanatomy)

The anatomy of the CNS involves two main parts: the **spinal cord** and the **brain**. The cochlea does not communicate directly with the spinal cord, so the processing of auditory information by the CNS is carried out entirely in the brain. The brain, or *encephalon*, traditionally is divided into three major parts: the *cerebrum*, the *cerebellum*, and the *brain stem*, as illustrated in Figure 6.6a. A more detailed breakdown of the organization of

**TABLE 6.1.**
**Organization of the Encephalon (Brain)**

| |
|---|
| I. Prosencephalon (forebrain) |
|   a. Telencephalon: cerebral hemispheres |
|   b. Diencephalon: thalamus, hypothalamus, etc. |
| II. Mesencephalon (midbrain)[a]: cerebral peduncles, colliculi |
| III. Rhombencephalon (hindbrain) |
|   a. Metencephalon: pons,[a] cerebellum |
|   b. Myelencephalon: medulla oblongata[a] |

[a] Structures of the brain stem.

the brain is summarized in Table 6.1, in which the names of the major divisions—*prosencephalon, mesencephalon,* and *rhombencephalon*vare indicated with their common English names—*forebrain, midbrain,* and *hindbrain,* respectively (in parentheses). The major anatomical constituents of each level of the brain also are listed. The most conspicuous part of the brain is the cerebrum. In those science fiction movies, in which the quintessential mad scientist has jars of brains strewn about, one is typically viewing cerebri. The outermost layer of the cerebrum, the major portion of the *telencephalon* (which means "end brain"), is the *cortex* where incoming sensory information ultimately is received. Located in the **diencephalon** is the *thalamus,* a major relay station for all sensory information, particularly the parts of the thalamus known as the *geniculate bodies.* Some very important constituents of the mesencephalon are the *colliculi,* a collection of nuclei concerned with vision and audition. The *pons,* part of the metencephalon or hindbrain, is the downward continuation of the midbrain and is formed by the neural tracts communicating with the cerebellum, the major center for the coordination of locomotion. The lowest part of the brain and, specifically, of the brain stem, is the *medulla oblongata* (or simply medulla), which, in turn, continues downward to form the *medulla spinalis* or spinal cord. It is at the level of the junction of the medulla and pons that the VIIIth cranial

a.

b.

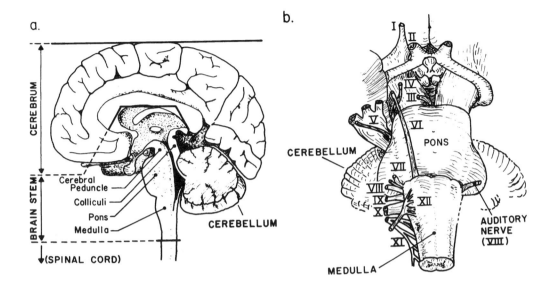

c.

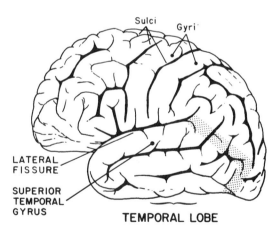

**Figure 6.6.   a.** Parts of the brain as seen from a midsaggital view. (Based on a drawing by Netter, F. H. [1962]. *Nervous System*, Vol I. CIBA Pharmaceutical Co., New York.) **b.** Ventral view of the brain stem. (Modified from Chusid, J. G., and McDonald, J. J. [1960]. *Correlative Neuroanatomy and Functional Neurology.* Lange Medical Publications, Los Altos.) The cranial nerves are indicated by *roman numerals*; however, only the auditory nerve (*VIII*) is shown on the right side of the drawing for simplicity. **c.** Lateral view of the cerebrum. (Modified from Chusid and McDonald, as above.) Again, for simplicity, many of the landmarks on the cortical surface have not been labeled. The *dotted band* roughly demarks the posterior boundary of the temporal lobe.

nerve, part of the peripheral nervous system, enters the CNS (Fig. 6.6*b*). In other words, it is at this level that information borne by neurons arising in the cochlea is first received by the CNS. This is where the central auditory pathways begin, namely, at the nuclei in which the fibers of the acoustic nerve terminate. Thus, the auditory nuclei and pathways are found above the medulla, namely, within the pons and at higher levels in the brain.

The auditory pathways terminate in the cerebral cortices. As shown in Figure 6.6*c*, the cortex is enfolded, as if it had been stuffed into a container that was much too small for it. The result is that the surface of the cerebrum is marked with convolutions formed by crevasses known as *fissures* or *sulci* (sulcus, singular) and ridges known as *gyri* (gyrus, singular). There are several major sulci that divide the cerebrum into lobes. The ***temporal lobe*** is the one of importance here, and it is almost completely separated from the rest of the cerebrum by the *lateral* or *sylvian fissure*. In humans, the ***primary auditory cortex*** actually occupies only a small area of the superior surface of the superior temporal or *Heschel's gyrus* and is mostly obscured from view in Figure 6.6*c*. Adjacent areas of the cortex also serve auditory functions, albeit less directly. These are the *secondary* and *association auditory areas*, located in regions of the cortex surrounding the primary auditory cortex. However, the primary area will be the main focus of attention here.

Throughout the discussion of the central auditory pathways to follow, the occasion will arise to use the terms *ascending* and *descending* in relation to the auditory pathways. Ascending or afferent pathways are those nerve tracts conveying information toward the cortex from the periphery or lower centers of the CNS. Descending or efferent pathways serve to convey information to these lower centers or the periphery from the cortex or higher centers. As might be expected, afferent fibers innervating the hair cells of the organ

of Corti form the first level of the ascending auditory pathway, the *first-order* or *primary* neurons. The ordering of neurons is done in a sequential manner from the first neuron in any given pathway to the last. Thus, the first-order neuron of the auditory system originates in the cochlea (referred to as the sensory neuron in Chapter 5). It enters the brain stem to terminate on *second-order* or *secondary* neurons, and on the numerical ordering goes. Neurons of the descending pathways also could be ordered numerically, but this is not commonly done. The efferent neurons innervating the hair cells of the organ of Corti form the last segment of the descending auditory pathway. They are the most well-known portion of the descending system, projecting from cell bodies in the superior olivary complex (SOC, as discussed in more detail below).

Although the concepts of ascending and descending pathways are useful, it is important to recognize from the start that the organization of the brain is not limited to chains of neurons with information merely being transmitted up or down them. First, the flow of information can be more or less sideways or even backward. There may be *collateral* branches from one neuron or intermediary neurons (relative to the primary pathway) that may carry information, say, from one side of the brain to the other, or may feed back on neurons at a lower level in an ascending pathway. Nevertheless, major pathways are identifiable and provide the bases for practically mapping the CNS. With this primer in neuroanatomy, it is now possible to describe the central auditory pathways in some detail.

## 3. The Central Auditory Pathways

The auditory pathways are illustrated semischematically in Figure 6.7. The emphasis here is on *semischematic*, rather than the complement of this term, *semi-*

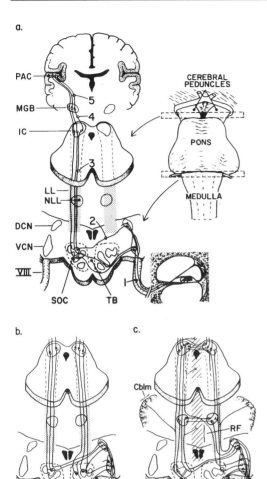

**Figure 6.7.** Ascending auditory pathways. **a.** The major crossed pathway. The *numbers* indicate the order of the nerve fibers at the different levels of the system. *Inset*, Location of the brain stem sections shown (marked by *dashed lines*). These slices are shown as though they were viewed slightly from above, much as one might pull out a drawer on a desk and peer into it to examine its contents. The cerebrum is shown in a frontal section. **b** and **c.** Alternative pathways in the brain stem portion of the central auditory system. The neuronal interconnections are highly diagrammatic and merely indicate general pathways; many collaterals have been eliminated for simplicity. *TB*, Trapezoid body; *VIII*, auditory nerve; *VCN*, ventral cochlear nuclei; *NLL*, nucleus of the lateral lemniscus; *LL*, lateral lemniscus; *IC*, inferior colliculus; *MGB*, medial geniculate body; *PAC*, primary auditory cortex; *Cblm*, cortex of the cerebellum (primarily in the vermis, located on

*anatomical*, because these drawings are not intended to portray the actual point-to-point "wiring" in the central auditory system. They merely show the major routes available for the transfer of information along the ascending pathways. One particularly gross oversimplification made in these drawings is the representation of the neurons along the pathway. Not only are the terminations more complex than shown, there is tremendous heterogeneity of cell types and nerve endings throughout the system, even within single nuclei. Such morphological heterogeneity is generally associated with variations in the functional characteristics of the nerve cells, such that the transfer of information along a given pathway entails more than simply passing it along, as in a relay race. Indeed, the incoming neural code is transformed in various ways as a result of these complexities in the wiring of the system.

On entering the brain stem at the pons-medulla junction, the first-order neurons terminate on the cell bodies of second-order neurons in the **cochlear nuclei** (Fig. 6.7*a*). Neuroanatomical studies have identified numerous nuclei in this complex, but only three seem to be of primary importance in audition: the *anteroventral* and *posteroventral cochlear nuclei* (AVCN and PVCN, respectively) and the dorsal cochlear nucleus (DCN). Each first-order neuron *bifurcates*, that is, it divides into two branches. One branch terminates on second-order nerve cells located in the anteroventral cochlear nuclei and the other on neurons in the posteroventral cochlear nuclei or the DCN. From here, the ascending pathway traditionally is described as crossing the midline of the brain stem to the *SOC* on the opposite or contralateral side. That is, the majority of sec-

the posterior aspect of the cerebellum); *RF*, reticular formation. (Based partly on drawings of Netter, F. H. [1962]. *Nervous System*, Vol I. CIBA Pharmaceutical Co., New York., but represents a synthesis of data from various studies and anatomical treatises.)

ond-order neurons within the cochlear nuclei give off axons that cross over or *decussate* via the *trapezoid body* and the *dorsal stria* to terminate on third-order neurons whose cell bodies are located in the opposite superior olive. As in the case of the cochlear nuclei, the SOC comprises various nuclei, but only two or three are known to be of major importance for hearing. The majority of fibers originating from the cochlear nuclei terminate in the medial olive in humans but in the lateral nucleus (or S segment) in animals such as cats and rodents. Similarly, the superior olivary nuclei assume diverse relative sizes in different species (the medial olive being the largest in the human). The cochlear nuclei and SOC are located, respectively, in the upper medulla and lower pons within the hindbrain.

Third-order neurons in the superior olive give off axons that course centrally through the *lateral lemniscus*, a well-defined tract of neurons, to terminate at the midbrain level in the *inferior colliculus* (primarily in the central nucleus). From here, the fourth-order neurons ascend to one of several nuclei of the thalamus, the *medial geniculate body* (largely the ventral division). Axons of fifth-order neurons then terminate on cell bodies in the temporal lobe. As noted earlier, the main area within which these terminal cell bodies are found is the primary auditory cortex located on the superior surface of the superior temporal gyrus (Fig. 6.7a).

Although the pathway just described is the major, if not the primary, one, it is by no means the only ascending auditory pathway. There are alternative routes within the brain stem, both contralateral and *ipsilateral* (same side), that are substantial. A major ipsilateral pathway develops from second-order neurons in the cochlear nuclei. Many fibers within the cochlear nuclei give rise to axons that may terminate on cell bodies in the SOC on the same side, as shown in Figure 6.7b. The actual connections may be complex, involving interconnections between neurons within the DCN and collaterals from axons that otherwise cross over to the other side. Crossed or uncrossed, fibers arising from the cochlear nuclei need not terminate in the superior olive but, instead, may go directly to the inferior colliculus (Fig. 6.7b). These fibers ascend through the lateral lemniscus, as described previously, but other possibilities exist. Not all fibers ascending in this tract go directly to the inferior colliculus; rather, some fibers or collaterals thereof may terminate in the nuclei of the lateral lemnisci (Fig. 6.7c). Fibers also can cross over to the opposite side at this level, although a more substantial decussation occurs at the level of the inferior colliculus (Fig. 6.7c). Consequently, second-, third-, and possibly even fourth-order neurons originating from either side of the system can terminate at the level of the inferior colliculus. Similarly, the inferior colliculus is not always a point of termination. Some ascending fibers also bypass the inferior colliculus (on either side) to terminate directly in the medial geniculate. Whatever the case, all ascending fibers seem to have synapses with neurons in the medial geniculate nucleus, the last stop along the ascending pathway before connection is made with the cortex.

Ascending auditory fibers also may give off collaterals to areas of the brain other than those that are constituents of the central auditory system per se. For instance, auditory neurons in the brain stem give off collaterals that go to the cerebellum (Fig. 6.7c). Because the cerebellum is involved intimately in the control of locomotion, this connection undoubtedly facilitates reflexive movements signaled by acoustic stimuli, thereby avoiding the more time-consuming pathways to the cortex and from the cortex back to cerebellum. Direct input to the cerebellum certainly would, for example, facilitate the expedient removal of oneself from the path of a heard, but unseen, oncoming vehicle. Collaterals also are given off to terminate in a highly diffuse neural structure known as the ***reticular formation*** (Fig. 6.7c). It is through the reticular formation that an indirect route of communication is provided between various parts of the brain. The reticular formation receives information from all sensory systems, and it is implicated strongly in the control of the level of consciousness or arousal. For this reason it is known alternatively as the *reticular activating system*.

There also is a corticocochlear efferent system or descending pathway that more or less parallels the ascending pathway(s) just described; efferent fibers have been found running from the primary auditory cortex to the inferior colliculi (largely bypassing the thalamus) and projecting to centers below and to the periphery. Both ipsilateral and crossed pathways seem to exist. However, the best-known descending pathways, as alluded to above, are formed by the ***olivocochlear bundles*** (OCBs). These efferent fibers course from the SOC through the internal auditory meatus to innervate the IHCs and OHCs of the organ of Corti. Interestingly, the auditory efferent fibers are found in the vestibular nerve (or vestibular part of the eighth cranial nerve), diverting distally to enter the cochlea. It is curious that the end organ should receive efferent innervation directly from the olives, rather than from the cochlear nuclei, particularly in light of the fact that there are descending fibers projecting from the SOC to the cochlear nucleus.

There are crossed and uncrossed fibers in the OCBs, constituting two distinct systems: the *medial* and *lateral* OCBs. The fibers in the medial OCBs project from areas in the vicinity of the medial superior olives (preolivary group), are relatively large diameter and myelinated, and innervate the OHCs. It is in the medial OCB system that both crossed and uncrossed fibers are found. The fibers of the lateral OCBs originate from areas near the lateral superior olive, are exclusively uncrossed, are small in diameter and unmy-

elinated, and tend to terminate on afferent nerve endings on IHCs (that is, via axoaxonic synapses). This interesting dichotomy of pattern of innervation and the function of the OCBs will be discussed further in Cortical Auditory Information Processing, in this chapter. Here, again, the special characteristics of the OHC, specifically its dual personality, will be found potentially to play a pivotal role in the functioning of the system. Meanwhile, it should be evident, merely from the wiring of the auditory pathways, that the brain not only receives information from the auditory periphery, but also can exercise some control over the peripheral system.

Finally, it is notable that the two temporal lobes can communicate via fibers of the *commissure*, the tract of fibers connecting (via the corpus callosum) the two halves of the cerebrum. Thus, there are points all along the central auditory pathways that allow for possible interaction between the two sides of the system. In other words, it is difficult to envision the right side of the auditory CNS doing something without the left side knowing about it.

## SUMMARY AND OVERVIEW OF THE HUMAN CENTRAL AUDITORY PATHWAYS

The description of the auditory pathways given in the preceding paragraphs reflects a composite of characteristics across most mammalian species, particularly cat, monkey, and human, defining essentially the generic central auditory pathways. As in other areas, studies in animals have permitted methods of inquiry not practical in humans or with human brain specimens. Nevertheless, methods have developed, particularly during the past couple of decades, that permit the scientist and clinician alike to peer into the living human and, thereby, directly observe structure and/or manifestations of function. An example of the latter are methods of monitoring and displaying measures of *cerebral blood flow* that can reveal regions of high metabolic activity, corresponding presumably to regions of high neural activity (that is, populations of neurons burning up lots of energy). Perhaps the most dramatic advances, however, have occurred in the area of imaging. Evolving from the radiological (x-ray) methods that at one time permitted only a crude view of organs and required a good eye for their interpretation, modern imaging techniques, such as magnetic resonance imaging, provide amazingly detailed pictures of the living brain (as shown in Fig. 6.10 below). Such methods permit the examiner, in effect, to view slices of the living specimen, much as one would do via traditional anatomical and histological studies of specimens harvested from cadavers.

At the same time, the detailed wiring of the human central auditory pathways has become much better understood and is summarized, in part and highly schematically, in Figure 6.8. Namely, this diagram characterizes components of the ascending pathways that might contribute well-synchronized reactions of relatively large populations of neurons in the system to the onset of sound. This is the basis for the compound electrical potentials that

are recordable from the brain stem (discussed in the next section) and perhaps is more representative of tracts and nuclei involved with the forward signal throughput in the system than of the detailed subpathways supporting binaural (two-eared) and other brain stem–level processing (discussed later in this chapter). The majority pathway, as diagrammed in Figure 6.8, seems to be crossed but tends to bypass the SOC; only the less-populous uncrossed and an even less-populated crossed pathway incorporate the SOC as a way station. Another remarkable feature is the complexity of the nuclei of the lateral lemnisci. On each side are several nuclei, of which the dorsal nucleus seems to be most influential in human auditory function. Finally, the inferior colliculi seem to be mandatory synapses for all ascending fibers in the lateral lemnisci. The inferior colliculi thus receive terminations of second-, third-, and perhaps even fourth-order neurons. Otherwise, the wiring diagram is pretty much as portrayed above, demonstrating the auditory system to have robust representation of each ear on both sides of the brain and opportunities for cross-over of information at multiple levels of the system.

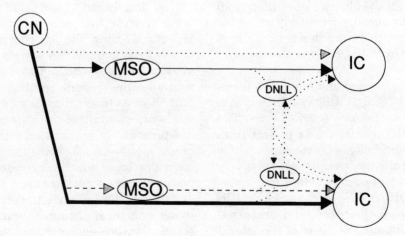

**Figure 6.8.** Schematic diagram of the lower human auditory pathways. *CN*, Cochlear nuclei; *MSO*, medial superior olive; *DNLL*, dorsal nucleus of the lateral lemniscus; *IC*, inferior colliculus. (Based on drawings of Moore [1987].)

## 4. Neuroanatomical and Neurophysiological Methods in Auditory Research

As a preamble to the discussion of information processing in the central auditory system in the section to follow, it will be worthwhile to describe some of the methods, particularly electrophysiological techniques, used to study the auditory system and to discuss some of the difficulties in determining how sensory information is processed in the CNS. A great amount of what is known about the CNS is based on data obtained by anatomical techniques to map out pathways, as just described for the auditory system. Function thus is deduced from the neural wiring of the system. The most rudimentary method available (other than gross dissection) is to cut the brain into slices, stain the tissue, and try to follow the apparent neural tracts. Only the major structures and tracts generally are evident, although with the proper choice of stain, considerable morphological detail of the nerve cells can be revealed. Another method, which is particularly well suited for following pathways per se, is to create lesions in the pathways. After an appropriate waiting period to allow degeneration of the nerve fibers involved (and the appropriate preparation of the tissue), the debris of degeneration can be followed from section to section.

A very useful method for tracing the course of individual neurons is to use an enzyme, horseradish peroxidase, which can be taken up by a neuron and transported through its axon and dendrites. When the tissue is appropriately processed, the nerve cell and all its processes can be seen clearly via microscopy. Nevertheless, given the morphological complexity of most cells in the CNS and the multiplicity of interconnections between them, the mapping of all possible central pathways remains a formidable task.

Electrophysiological techniques also have been used extensively, wherein either electrical potentials are recorded simultaneously from a large number of neurons—*compound potentials*—or discharges are recorded from single neurons—*single-unit potentials*. An example of the former is the whole-nerve AP, discussed in Chapter 5. Electrodes placed in the brain stem or on the surface of the cortex also can be used to monitor stimulus-related compound potentials at various sites along a given pathway. These potentials are likely to arise as much from (if not more so) from electrical activity of the dendrites as from axons, thus reflecting the contribution of dendritic field potentials as well as spike APs. Indeed, compound potentials reflecting stimulus-related events arising everywhere from the VIIIth nerve to the cortex can be recorded from the surface of the head; these are called **evoked potentials** (Fig. 6.9). Because underlying electrical potentials are so small at the scalp, computer processing of the recording is necessary to reduce the background noise (physical and physiological), including the ongoing brain wave (namely, as observed in electroencephalography).

Compound APs and evoked brain stem or cortical potentials are useful indices of the overall response of the system, or even parts of the system, as demonstrated by the unusual case illustrated in Figure 6.10. Yet, the evoked potentials do not provide much detailed information, and not all origins of the auditory evoked potentials are known with certainty. However, recent advances in evoked potential measurement and analysis are providing impressive amounts of information and insights into the probable loci of the generators. Some of these innovations derive from sophisticated displays of many channels of recordings across the scalp (sometimes called *brain mapping*) or mathematical modeling to predict the location and/or orientations in the head of probable generators. Another innovation is the measurement of the weak, but fi-

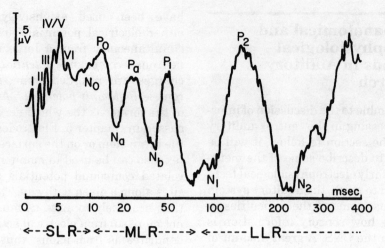

**Figure 6.9.** Components of the auditory-evoked response recorded with scalp electrodes from a human subject and elicited by an acoustic click. Commonly used time windows of analysis are indicated for the short- (*SLR*), middle- (*MLR*), and long-latency responses (*LLR*). The first wave (*I*) of the SLR corresponds to the whole-nerve AP, inverted by the recording amplifier; wave *II* is attributed also to activity of the eighth nerve; waves *III* through *VII* arise from generators along the brain stem auditory pathway. MLR components arise from the upper brain stem and primary auditory cortex. LLR waves come from both auditory and nonauditory cortical areas. (From ASHA [1988]. *The Short Latency Auditory Evoked Potentials: A Tutorial Paper by the Audiologic Evaluation Working Group on Auditory Evoked Potential Measurements.* American Speech-Language-Hearing Association, Rockville, MD.)

nite, magnetic fields generated around active neurons. The method is inherently limited to the study of cortical activity, because the tissue generating the magnetic field must be close to the sensors of the recording instrument. However, the recorded activity seems to be much more focal and localized than corresponding electrical responses.

In contrast to the gross, evoked potential, recording is the recording of discharges of individual neurons, known as *single-unit recording*. The advent of single-unit recording in all areas of the auditory system has provided an especially powerful research tool. The use of single-unit data will be the subject of discussion for the remainder of this section, but some of the difficulties with this technique and limitations of the resulting data should be recognized at the outset.

The most obvious problem with single-unit recording is getting an electrode into the desired place in a viable preparation and then knowing or documenting the

electrode location. Electrode placements in the CNS often are made blindly, wherein the experimenter relies on a *stereotactic* apparatus, a device that holds the animal's head and positions the electrode, and anatomical maps to obtain the desired coordinates. Still, individual variability is appreciable. Fortunately, various histological techniques have been developed that provide reasonably reliable information concerning where, indeed, the electrode penetrated, including the labeling of individual cells.

Next, there is the seemingly insurmountable difficulty (at least in vertebrates) of following the activity along a continuous chain of neurons within a given pathway. Simply picking up the activity from one of tens of thousands of neurons may not be too informative. It is like trying to figure out how a computer works by connecting an oscilloscope to one wire in the maze of electrical circuits therein and observing the signals transmitted through that single wire. To learn much

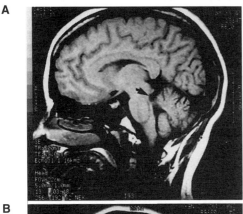

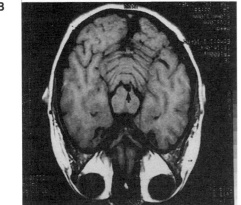

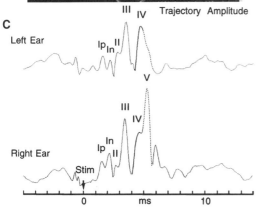

**Figure 6.10.** Unusual case of missing right inferior colliculus (injury secondary to radiation surgery treatment of an arteriovenous malformation nearby). The lesion shown in the magnetic resonance images (**a** and **b**) resulted in essentially total elimination of wave V of the auditory brain stem response (**c**) with stimulation of the left ear, because of the dominance of cross-over pathways. Note: The evoked-potential measurement was derived from three-dimensional analyses (three channels of recorded data), yielding a sort of omnidirectional

about the function of the entire system from a single element requires that some manipulation be made of the event to which this element does or does not react and/or to apply some form of analysis to the signals recorded from that element. This, in fact, is the nature of most single-unit experiments.

Single-unit recording involves the use of electrodes with extremely fine tips, *microelectrodes*, to observe a nerve fiber's discharge pattern and, ultimately, to measure its sensitivity. (Note: what often is recorded is the unit *extracellular* potential, because it is difficult to impale auditory neurons without damage. The fineness of the electrode tip still permits the observation of a single neuron's activity by virtue of proximity.) The applied stimuli generally are kept simple, for example, tone bursts, to make them easily quantifiable. Unfortunately, such stimuli are rarely characteristic of stimuli in the environment, so in recent years there has been a trend toward the use of more complex stimuli, including speech.

By far, the simplest method of analysis of neural activity is the ***spike rate*** or ***rate level function***. The spike rate is measured and plotted as a function of stimulus intensity. This function was discussed previously (illustrated in Fig. 5.1) and is useful for studying the encoding of intensity. However, many auditory neurons are spontaneously active. Therefore, the information yielded by the spike rate function is limited to conditions under which the stimulus is intense enough to elicit a significantly increased rate of discharge over the ongoing rate. Details of the pattern of discharge necessitate a more sophisticated analysis.

view of the response—estimates of the true magnitudes of each significant wave component, independent of generator orientation. (Adapted from Durrant, J. D., Martin, W. H., Hirsch, B., and Schwegler, J. [1994]. 3CLT ABR analyses in a human subject with unilateral extirpation of the inferior colliculus. *Hear. Res.* 72:99–107).

Generally speaking, the analysis of the temporal pattern of discharge requires the derivation of some form of histogram. In the most basic analysis, the intervals between successive spikes ($g_m$ in Fig. 6.11$a$) can be measured and counted, for example, the number of 1-msec intervals, 2- msec intervals, etc. In this example, the time scale is divided into bins of 1 msec. The graph of the number of interspike intervals in each bin covering the period of observation (say, 250 msec) is an *interval histogram*. (Practically speaking, such an analysis requires the aid of computer

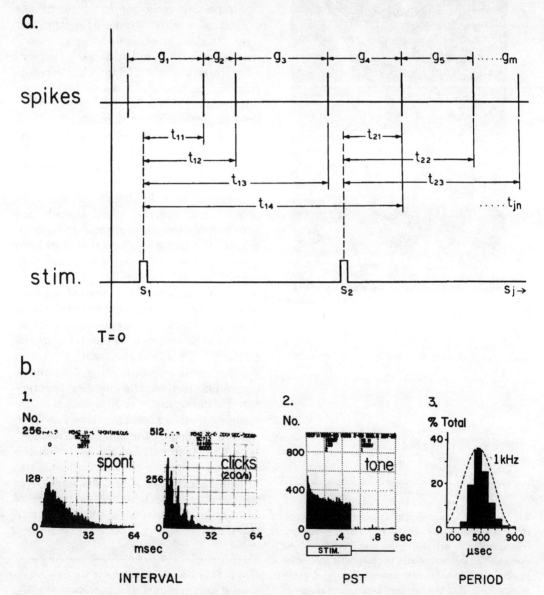

**Figure 6.11.**   **a.** Time intervals required to obtain histograms in **b** (see text). **b.** Interval (spontaneous, or nonstimulus, and stimulus conditions), PST, and period histograms. (Adaptation of drawings and data from Pfieffer and Molnar, Pfieffer and Kiang [1965], and Rose et al. [1967]; Pfieffer, R. R., and Molnar, C. E. [1976]. Computer processing of auditory electrophysiological data. In *Handbook of Auditory and Vestibular Research Methods*, edited by C. A. Smith and J. A. Vernon. Charles C. Thomas, Springfield, IL.)

processing, and there are limits to how small an interval can be resolved, that is, how small the bin can be.) The interval histogram can be informative for both stimulus and nonstimulus conditions, because it reveals patterns of discharges that may characterize a given neuron, even for spontaneous discharges (see Fig. 6.11*b1*).

Neither the interval histogram nor the rate function reveals the relationship between the discharge pattern and the onset and offset of the stimulus and the fine details of neuron's response to the stimulus. Such stimulus-response interactions are reflected, however, in the ***post–stimulus time (PST)*** histogram. In this form of analysis, the intervals between the stimulus onset and the occurrence of each spike are counted ($t_{jn}$ in Fig. 6.11*a*). An example of what a PST histogram might look like for a primary auditory neuron stimulated by a tone burst is shown in Figure 6.11*b2*. Furthermore, if the period of observation is limited to just one cycle of the stimulus, what is obtained is specifically the ***period*** histogram (Fig. 6.11*b3*). In either case, numerous presentations of the stimulus and repeated sampling of the discharges generally are required to obtain sufficient data to reveal the characteristic discharge pattern of a given neuron. Other forms of analysis are possible, but they are essentially variations of these more basic types. Also, measurements of various kinds can be made on the histogram itself or the apparent pattern it represents, such as a quantitative evaluation of the degree of synchrony of discharge, spectrum analysis, etc.

Single-unit recording also has been of keen interest in the search for knowledge of how the auditory system is able to discriminate between sounds of different frequencies. One approach is to latch onto a fiber and see how its spike rate varies as a function of frequency for a given level of the stimulus. The resulting graph of the data is called an *isolevel function* (Fig. 6.12*a*). Alternatively, a search can be made for the level of stimulus that causes a given increase in average spike rate above the spontaneous rate; this level is determined at various frequencies. The graph of the threshold level versus frequency (Fig. 6.12*b*) constitutes an *isorate function*, but it is widely known as the ***tuning curve***. The typical tuning curve reveals a point of maximum sensitivity (minimal threshold level); the frequency at which this occurs is called the ***characteristic frequency (CF)***. Liberally interpreted, the neuron seems to be tuned to one frequency. As in the case of the histograms, more elaborate measurements and analyses can be made that yield variations of isolevel or isorate functions, for instance, measuring the tuning curve in the presence versus the absence of a second interfering tone.

These, then, are the basic neurophysiological methods that have been used widely to study how the auditory system works. They are sometimes powerful and often sophisticated techniques, but they too are have their limitations. First, the hearing scientist is obliged to assess function on the basis of observations of phenomena that are *presumed*, rather than actually known, to be relevant to information processing in the CNS. The scientist has his or her way of analyzing the discharges recorded, and the brain has its way. The scientist is generally limited to looking, in effect, at one channel of input to the brain, or to some nucleus within the brain stem, whereas the brain presumably can look at any or all inputs. It also is most likely that the CNS's methods of analyses are more efficient than those of the scientist. Obtaining a PST histogram, for instance, is relatively time consuming. The CNS's efficiency is enhanced by virtue of spatial (across neurons) and temporal (across time) summation of activity. Next, it is important to bear in mind that the vast majority of available data has been obtained in infrahumans. These animals often are anesthetized, which may further

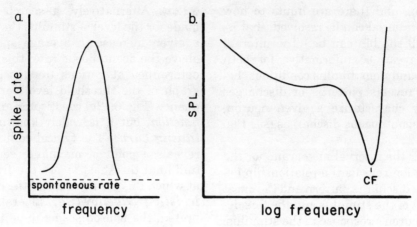

**Figure 6.12.** Schematic isolevel (**a**) versus isorate (**b**) functions from a hypothetical single-unit recording (see text).

limit the applicability of the experimental data to the explanation of the function of a particular neural structure in the conscious human. Nevertheless, an ever-growing amount of data is being accumulated, including those from unanesthetized animals, and a more complete picture of information processing in the central auditory system (and the CNS in general) is developing. After all, the researcher must work with what is available. It is within this context that the data concerning auditory information processing will be considered.

## 5. Frequency Encoding

### A. TUNING AND THE SINGLE NEURON

The two most obvious parameters of the sound stimulus that must be encoded in the central auditory system are frequency and intensity. From the general principles of sensory physiology discussed in Chapter 5, it should be evident that the first-order neurons will be very important in this process. Fundamentally, the intensity of the stimulus should be translated simply into a certain rate of discharge in the neurons stimulated. (Alas, intensity encoding over the entire dynamic range of hearing is not that simple, as will be de-

scribed below, but spike rate still will be found to be at the heart of intensity encoding.) But what of frequency? Neurons are not, in and of themselves, frequency selective in their excitability. Admittedly, there is an upper limit of frequency response imposed by the absolute refractory period, making a simple translation of frequency to spike rate or timing inadequate to account for the total hearing capability of humans and other animals. Although a temporal encoding of frequency actually does have its place in audition (see below), there is nothing obvious in the structure of the neuron to make it selective to one frequency of stimulation over another. Yet, the single-unit tuning function (Fig. 6.12*b*) clearly demonstrates optimal sensitivity for only one frequency of stimulation. The most efficient operation of a primary auditory neuron (and many higher-order neurons) is limited to a narrow range of frequencies. This point is further demonstrated by the tuning function data of Figure 6.13. These graphs are based on data from recordings from three different neurons in the auditory nerve of the cat. Note the widely different characteristic frequencies.

So, individual primary auditory neurons can have remarkably different characteristic frequencies. This is by no

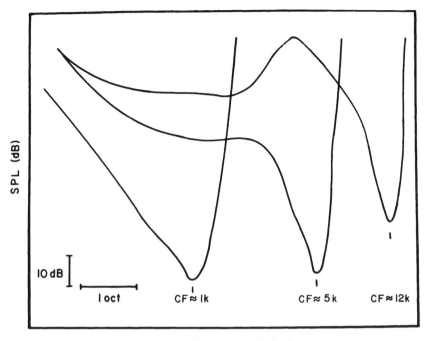

SPL (dB)

10 dB

1 oct

CF ≈ 1k

CF ≈ 5 k

CF ≈ 12k

**LOG FREQUENCY (Hz)**

**Figure 6.13.**  Tuning functions illustrating the frequency response of primary auditory neurons (in this case, from cat). (Based on data of Kiang and Moxon [1974], as presented by Zwicker [1974].)

means, however, a haphazard occurrence. A little digression will help explain just what is happening here. From the anatomy of the cochlea it is known that the nerve fibers leave the cochlea in a orderly fashion, and the fibers then twist around themselves, like the fibers of a rope, to form the nerve trunk in the internal auditory meatus. This means that what makes the primary auditory neuron frequency selective in its response is where it comes from within the cochlea, not some inherent tuning attributable to properties of the neuron itself. Thus, its frequency-specific sensitivity exists by virtue of the anatomy of the cochlea, that is, the IHC to which it is attached and the IHC's location along the basilar membrane. It was already learned (Chapter 5) that a given place along the basilar membrane vibrates in a frequency-specific manner because of the cochlear macromechanics and in a highly frequency-selective manner—demonstrating resonance-like phenomenon—be-

cause of the micromechanics of the organ of Corti.

Perhaps the real beauty of the traveling-wave phenomenon is not only the reciprocity that exists between frequency and place (the frequency-to-place transformation), but also how pervasive the influence of the associated macromechanical and micromechanical events of the cochlea is on the turning of first- and higher-order auditory neurons. For example, if one mentally plots the functions in Figure 6.13 upside down, the mental image would resemble the functions illustrated in Figure 5.30; these functions reflect the displacement of the basilar membrane or amplitude of cochlear microphonic (receptor potential) recorded at one place as a function of frequency. The shapes of these functions were attributed, in Chapter 5, to the wave mechanics of the cochlea. Intuition thus dictates that it should be possible to compare the shape of the single-unit tuning function to that of the traveling-wave envelope (Figs. 5.11 and 5.12), and that the nuances of the former should be dictated by the characteristics of latter. However, some *special considerations must be made* in attempting to make such a direct comparison and to do so honestly. First, in Bekesy's classic experiments, frequency was held constant, and displacement was measured at different distances along the cochlear partition. This problem has been eliminated in more recent experiments, wherein the displacement of the basilar membrane is observed at one point and frequency is varied (as in Fig. 5.30 and in Fig. 6.14 below).

Second, for optimal comparisons, the motion of the basilar membrane must be observed at very low sound levels that typify the sensitivity of primary auditory neurons near their characteristic frequencies. Only during the past decade or so has

this been possible (or nearly so). Previously, the traveling wave or mechanical data were obtained by observing the amplitude of basilar membrane displacement for a constant stimulus level, typically well above threshold levels for the normal organ of Corti. Recall that, in contrast, the neural tuning curves are isorate functions; the stimulus level is the manipulated parameter. To obtain, in effect, a mechanical tuning function, the function describing basilar membrane displacement versus frequency must be inverted (the inverse of the little mental-plotting exercise above). The danger in this approach is the presence of nonlinearities in the system (particularly amplitude distortion) that are now known to exist and to be substantial. Nevertheless, a favorable comparison between the mechanical and neural data can be made, as shown in Fig-

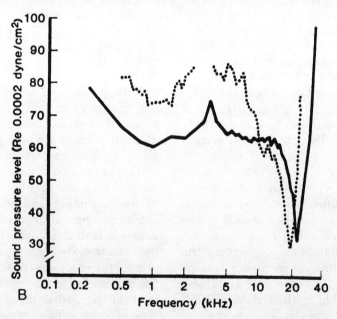

**Figure 6.14.** Comparison of tuning functions for the response of the basilar membrane versus a first-order neuron. *Solid line*, Plot of the SPL required for $3 \times 10^{-8}$ cm basilar membrane displacement at the point of observation in the base of the cat cochlea. A laser-optical method of measurement was used; the stimuli were pure tones. *Dashed line*, Single-unit tuning function (obtained in a different animal and in another laboratory by M. C. Liberman); the data shown are from a unit whose CF is near that at which the minimum of the mechanical tuning function occurs. Although some differences are evident, the mechanical and neural tuning functions seem similar overall. (From Khana, S. M., and Leonard, D. G. [1982]. Basilar membrane tuning in the cat cochlea. *Science* 215:305–306.)

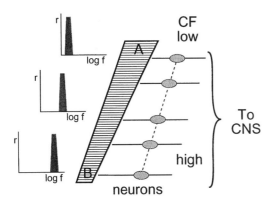

**Figure 6.15.** Scheme of encoding of frequency by place, representing the process as though the primary auditory neurons were connected to a bank of bandpass filters. Basilar membrane (*B*, base; *A*, apex); *r*, response; *f*, frequency.

ure 6.14. Such data suggest that not only is the CF of the primary auditory neuron a matter of the wiring of the cochlea and its *tonotopic* transformation, but also that the sharpness of tuning and the shape of the neuron's response area are dependent entirely on events along the basilar membrane.

The impressively close agreement between the neural and mechanical data evidenced in Figure 6.14 represents a relatively recent turn of events in the physiological acoustics literature. As discussed briefly in Chapter 5, Bekesy's mechanical data failed to predict the sharpness of tuning suggested by the neural data. More modern experimental techniques and work in live preparations led to much more favorable comparisons, but, for some time, there still remained some discrepancy between mechanical and neural tuning. This divergence led to the suggestion that there must be some additional filtering mechanism. That is, viewing the basilar membrane as a series of bandpass filters with each connected to a single neuron (Fig. 6.15), there was assumed to be a stage of filtering between the basilar membrane and the primary auditory neuron—a second filter. The locus of this second filter was uncertain,

but until intracellular recordings were mastered in mammalian hair cells, the bulk of the evidence favored some process beyond the level of the hair cell. However, the theoretical site of this apparent filter moved peripherally, namely, as more facts concerning the detailed response characteristics of the hair cells came to light. In current theory, based again on the reports of mechanical data manifesting equally sharp tuning as that seen in the neural data, the need for a second filter has vanished.

Although much has been learned by using single tones to map out response areas for individual auditory neurons, such as tuning curves, the introduction of more complex sounds naturally create more complex behaviors of the neurons. This can be demonstrated by using two-tone complexes. Within certain frequency limits, the sensitivity of a unit stimulated at its CF can be reduced in the presence of a second tone of a different frequency. This suppressive effect occurs on the "skirts" of the tuning curve (see Fig. 6.16) and is known as **two-tone suppression**. Although this phenomenon is somewhat comparable to edge effects observed in vision, because of lateral inhibition, the

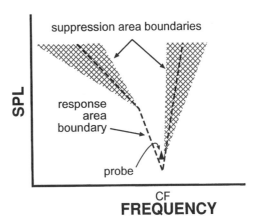

**Figure 6.16.** Idealized representation of suppression areas of the response of a primary auditory neuron stimulated at its CF that are encountered on presentation of a second tone (the suppressor). (Based on Sachs and Kiang [1968].)

term *suppression* is preferred to distinguish this effect from neural inhibition involving inhibitory synapses.[1] Nevertheless, the similarity of effects are compelling. Lateral inhibition serves to sharpen transitions from light to dark, that is, to enhance contrast. In the two-tone suppression, as the suppressing tone is moved from below CF, to near CF, and then above CF (but within the suppression areas), the discharge rate at CF is decreased, increased, and then decreased, respectively, compared with the rate observed with the CF tone presented alone. The mechanism of two-tone suppression is still not completely understood but seems to be attributable to the nonlinearities inherent in the motion of the basilar membrane. In fact, a related effect, *two-tone interference*, is observable in the cochlear electrical potentials, as is intermodulation distortion, which also is manifested heartily in the otoacoustic emissions. In short, just as the tuning functions of the primary auditory neurons intimately reflect the cochlear macromechanics and micromechanics, so too do the response characteristics of these fibers to complex stimuli. Therefore, not only is there a robust mechanism for selectively encoding the frequency components of complex sounds but also an inherent mechanism of enhancing contrast, thereby further facilitating the processing of complex stimuli.

Before delving more deeply into the processing of complex stimuli, however, it is necessary to consider the evidence for preservation of the place code in the central pathways. As obvious as the mechanism may be, it need not be an essential mechanism of central processing. Again, the peripheral place-encoding process could be simply a byproduct of practical considerations in the design of the cochlea,

addressing the problem of how to have a mechanical system that responds efficiently to a range of frequencies of 10 or more octaves.

## B. PLACE CODE

Recapping the place-encoding process, neurons innervating different regions of the cochlea respond optimally to frequencies of stimulation according to the frequency-to-place transformation performed on the basilar membrane. The question is, "Is this transformation really relevant to the encoding and processing of frequency centrally and, ultimately, to frequency discrimination and pitch perception?" Critical to the proof that, indeed, place is relevant is the demonstration that the tonotopical layout of the cochlea is reflected throughout the organization of the central auditory system. Again, the first-order neurons originate from discrete sites along the basilar membrane and depart the cochlea in an orderly fashion. Therefore, the spatial organization or topography of nuclei along the central auditory pathways is expected to reflect this innervation pattern. In other words, the nuclei are expected to be organized *tonotopically*. The test of tonotopicity is whether along any axis of penetration a recording electrode encounters fibers that vary systematically in their characteristic frequencies as the electrode is advanced. Given a tonotopically organized nucleus, CFs should progress, for instance, from low to high (or vice versa) along some axis. It is as if a tonal map of the cochlea were projected onto the nucleus, as illustrated schematically in Figure 6.17.

Much attention in hearing research has been devoted to the demonstration of tonotopical organization, or the lack of it, within the various nuclei of the auditory pathways. It now seems that the major nuclei at all levels of the auditory system are tonotopically organized. However, the tonotopical organization rarely is as simple as the scheme suggested by Figure 6.17. Real nuclei are not particularly symmetri-

---

[1] In the peripheral visual system there are intermediary neurons that make lateral inhibition possible. No such neural wiring exists in the peripheral auditory system. Indeed, the term *two-tone inhibition* is certainly a misnomer, if the term *inhibition* is reserved strictly for phenomena involving neural interactions or actions of neurons on receptor cells.

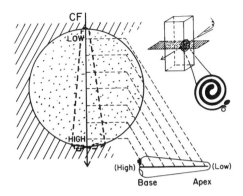

**Figure 6.17.** Diagrammatic illustration of tonotopical organization. A tonal map of the cochlea is projected onto this hypothetical auditory nucleus by virtue of the orderly connection between it and the hair cells along the basilar membrane (*inset*). Thus, an electrode traversing the path indicated by the *arrow* records activity from neurons, the CFs of which vary systematically varies from low to high.

cal in either their physical shape or their tonotopical organization, so the map of the cochlea may be altered appreciably from one level to the next. Nuclei also are three dimensional, not two dimensional as in the drawing in Figure 6.17. Nevertheless, it seems that, in fact, the (primary) basis of frequency encoding in the auditory CNS, and, ultimately, frequency discrimination and pitch perception, lies in the initial place code established in the periphery and the maintenance of this code at the higher levels of the system. Although place theory has had its ups and downs over the years, and various aspects of the frequency-encoding process still require explanation, a place code for frequency is strongly supported by the research literature.

## C. TEMPORAL CODE

Although place is the primary encoding paradigm for frequency, it is not the only one used. In fact, although the place theory of frequency encoding (and pitch perception, ultimately) has enjoyed unprecedented support in recent years, it has not always been the favored theory. Popularity has drifted back and forth between

some form of a place theory, beginning with Helmholtz in the latter part of the 19th century, and some form of a *frequency theory*, beginning with William Rutherford's *telephone* theory from about the same period. Rutherford took exception to Helmholtz's notion that the fibers of the basilar membrane are tuned, like the strings of a harp. Helmholtz thought that this feature of the basilar membrane's structure might provide for some form of spectrum analysis, namely, by virtue of sympathetic vibration of the strings. Drawing from anatomical considerations, suggesting that the fibers of the basilar membrane are not really free to vibrate independently, Rutherford postulated that the basilar membrane acts more like a diaphragm. He reasoned that all hair cells thus should be stimulated by sounds of all frequencies. He thought that the frequency of vibration of the basilar membrane must be preserved in the frequency of discharge of the auditory neurons, rather than the place of excitation. However, in the early part of the present century, physiologists demonstrated that all neurons are limited in terms of how rapidly they can fire, because of their refractory periods. This fundamental fact made Rutherford's theory untenable, because frequencies approaching the upper limits of hearing, at least for humans and many other species, could not be encoded in the temporal patterns of discharge. For example, assuming a maximal rate of 2000 spikes/sec (given an absolute refractory period of approximately 0.5 msec), the upper-frequency cutoff for hearing would be merely 2000 Hz, about 1/10 of the upper-frequency limit of hearing in humans (approximately 20 kHz). Other species (guinea pigs, bats, and cats, to name just a few) have even higher upper-frequency limits of hearing!

However, this discovery proved to be only a minor setback, and a modification of the telephone theory regained some degree of acceptance. It was postulated that, even though one nerve cell might be incapable of carrying high-frequency informa-

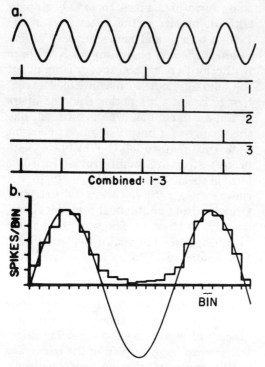

**Figure 6.18.** Temporal code of frequency information. **a.** Illustration of the volley principle. Tracings *1* through *3* represent neural discharges from three different nerve fibers in response to the pure tone represented above. (Based on Wever, E. G. [1949]. *Theory of Hearing.* Dover Publications, New York.) **b.** Periodicity in the pattern of neural discharges manifest in a histogram of the spikes occurring in each time bin over the period observed. For clarity of illustration, one and one-half cycles are shown. (Based on Brugge et al. [1969].)

tion, a group of neurons could. Figure 6.18*a* illustrates how a relatively high frequency might be encoded by just three neurons. This scheme is analogous to having different ranks of soldiers fire at different times, in volleys, so that a continuous barrage of firing is maintained, even though some time must be allotted to each rank for reloading. Although a temporal code based on the volley principle, that is, a *volley theory*, is more tenable than a "straight" frequency theory, current knowledge of the discharge patterns of auditory neurons suggests that the discharge of individual neurons is not keyed

precisely to one instant in time during any given cycle of the stimulus waveform. Rather, a more statistical picture must be invoked. This is reflected in the period histogram, as illustrated in Figure 6.18*b* (as well as Fig. 6.11*b3* above). Discharges occur predominantly within alternating half-cycle intervals. (The remaining half-cycles are most likely inhibitory, as discussed in Chapter 5.) In other words, the probability of discharge is greatest at one instant during the excitatory phase; at other times, discharge becomes increasingly less likely. If the waveform is sinusoidal, the probability function also will have a sinusoidal shape (that is, for one half-cycle) as illustrated in Figure 6.18*b*. Thus, it is not necessary for each neuron's discharges to be periodic. What is important is that the overall temporal pattern of discharges of a neuron or group of neurons be *phase-locked*, thereby reflecting synchronization of their discharges to the stimulus waveform.

Whether the central auditory system can or does use this timing information, it is there for frequencies perhaps as high as 7000 Hz and often can be demonstrated in the interval histogram, as illustrated by the data in Figure 6.19. Even at frequencies remote from the CF of the neuron, the intervals between spikes occur at periods equal to $1/F$. There is evidence that, indeed, this timing information can be used to encode frequency. If a pure-tone stimulus is varied in amplitude such that the fluctuations in amplitude are themselves sinusoidal (an example of amplitude modulation), neurons in the CNS can be observed to follow these amplitude fluctuations, as shown in Figure 6.20. Because the tone being modulated is much higher in frequency than the modulation rate, the periodicity in the pattern of the neuronal discharges is a function of the periodicity in the amplitude fluctuations, rather than in the period of the pure tone or carrier being modulated, even though the carrier may be nearer to or at the neuron's CF. Such a stimulus elicits the perception of a pitch corresponding to the frequency of amplitude modulation. This phenomenon is called *periodicity pitch* and will be discussed more thoroughly in the next chapter. The important point here is that there really is no sound energy present at the frequency of modulation or frequency corresponding to the perceived frequency or pitch component (namely, the periodicity pitch). Consequently, there is no traveling wave in the cochlea corresponding to the modulation frequency. This precludes a place cue, so the modulation observed in the neuron's discharge pattern, and ultimately the pitch percept, must depend on the detection of the periodicity or temporal

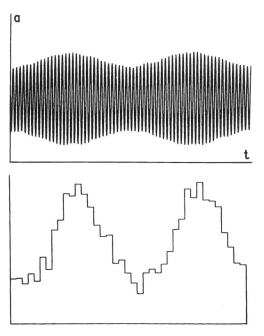

**Figure 6.20.** Pattern of neural discharges synchronized with the variations in the amplitude (amplitude modulation) of a tonal stimulus. (From Moller, A. R. [1973]. Coding of amplitude modulated sounds in the cochlear nucleus of the rat. In *Basic Mechanisms in Hearing*, edited by A. R. Moller. Academic Press, New York.)

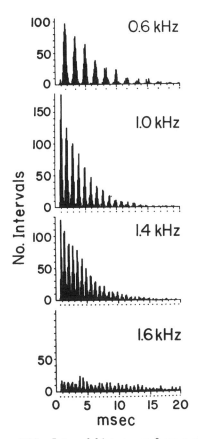

**Figure 6.19.** Interval histograms from a single-unit recording in a monkey. The stimuli were 1-sec tone bursts of the indicated frequencies. (Adapted from Rose, J. E., Brugge, J. F., Anderson, D. J., and Hind, J. E. [1967]. Phase-locked response to low-frequency tones in single auditory nerve fibers of the squirrel monkey. *J. Neurophysiol.* 30:769–793.

structure of the envelope of the stimulus. However, a point made earlier is worth echoing here. In reality, it is doubtful that the brain analyzes the discharges of single fibers to obtain period histograms. This is much too time consuming. However, if the activity of several fibers is analyzed collectively, then the synchrony of discharges could be detected expediently.

In the final analysis, the encoding of frequency seems to be the result of a combination of place and temporal encoding, as suggested more than four decades ago by Wever in his ***place-volley theory***. Based on available information at the time (late 1940s), Wever believed that the place mechanism was inadequate for distinguishing between tones of frequencies below 400 Hz and that, even with volleying, temporal encoding was limited to 2000 Hz and below. So, temporal and place

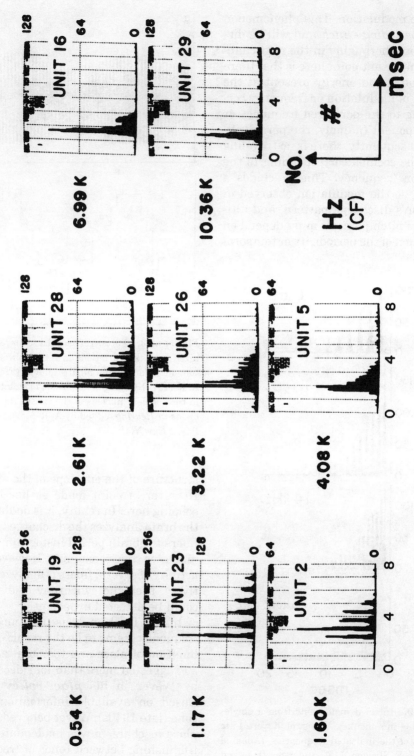

**Figure 6.21.** PST histograms from single-unit recordings in the cat. Each unit's CF is indicated. The stimuli were acoustic clicks. (Adapted from Kiang, N. Y.-S. [1965]. *Discharge Patterns of Single Fibers in the Cat's Auditory Nerve*. MIT Press, Cambridge.)

codes were assumed to dominate in respective low- and high-frequency regions where they were most suited. However, the results of modern measurements of basilar membrane displacement have revealed much sharper mechanical tuning than seen originally by Bekesy and suggest the availability of a reasonably precise place code below 400 Hz. Modern experiments also have revealed periodicities in discharge patterns of neurons to at least 6000 Hz, and this frequency limit was imposed by technical problems (such as noise) rather than physiological factors, indeed! Of course, the CNS might have the same kind of limitations as the experimenter in this regard. Nevertheless, the most comprehensive theory of frequency encoding must include both place- and temporal-encoding mechanisms, operating more in a parallel fashion than separately. Both cues clearly can be shown to exist in the neurophysiological record. This is particularly well demonstrated by scanning across the output of an array of fibers (in actuality, recording from one fiber, then the next, etc.) while stimulating with an acoustic click. As was illustrated previously (see Fig. 5.34b), this stimulus naturally stimulates a wide array of neurons, by virtue of its broad spectrum. Which neurons are activated (or which show increased amounts of activity) will provide place information. Still, as demonstrated by the PST histograms in Figure 6.21, there are obvious periodicities in the discharge patterns as well. It is also worth pointing out here that the discharges from fibers with low CFs have peaks that occur noticeably later than those with higher CFs. This, again (as revealed in Chapter 5 and illustrated in Fig. 5.34), is attributable to the time required for the traveling wave to propagate up the cochlea.

# 6. Intensity Encoding

## A. ELEMENTS OF THE INTENSITY CODE

The most fundamental parameter of a stimulus that must be encoded by any sensory system is its intensity. In the case of audition, the intensity of the sound stimulus is the primary factor that determines its perceived loudness, but intensity encoding is also important in other aspects of auditory information processing (such as in binaural hearing, discussed in Subcortical Binaural Information Processing, below). The first stage of intensity encoding was discussed briefly in Chapter 5; the (average) rate of the neural discharges varies in proportion to the stimulus intensity. The graph in Figure 6.22a illustrates the spike rate-versus-sound level function that is typically observed in recordings from single (primary) auditory neurons at the CF. It is notable that the dynamic range of most primary auditory neurons is limited; the maximal spike rate is reached at merely 20 to 30 dB greater than the level at which a just-noticeable increase in the spontaneous rate is observed. In some cases, a decrement in spike rate may occur with further increases in sound pressure level (SPL). Yet, the dynamic range of hearing in humans and other mammals is on the order of 140 dB!

The discrepancy between the dynamic range of the entire auditory system and that of single-unit responses poses a dilemma as to just how intensity is encoded. It suggests that the encoding of intensity must involve more than just the spike rate of any individual neuron stimulated at its CF. Rather than invoking another mechanism in the encoding of intensity at the periphery (analogous to the temporal code for frequency), one strategy the central auditory system might adopt for decoding intensity is to "listen" off frequency, that is off CF. Although a single unit's response is rather selective, it is by no means discrete. A fiber exhibiting a particular CF can be stimulated by higher- and, even more readily, by lower-frequency tones, if they are sufficiently intense. This fact is clearly evident in tuning curves (isorate functions) discussed previously (see Fig. 6.13), but an even more compelling demonstration is provided by *isolevel* func-

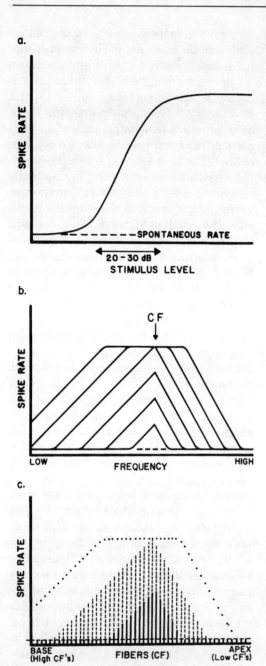

tions. When isolevel functions (that is, graphs of spike rate versus frequency with stimulus SPL held constant) are determined for different stimulus levels, the results appear as shown schematically in Figure 6.22*b*. (Real data from individual neurons typically show great variability in the actual configurations of the graphs.)

The isolevel functions also reveal the effects of saturation of the individual neuron. However, if one fiber can be stimulated by tones of frequencies other than its CF, it follows that a given tone will excite an array of neural fibers, reflecting the traveling-wave pattern in the cochlea (Fig. 6.22*c*). Then, even at levels of the stimulus at which a given unit's response saturates (no longer increases with increasing stimulus), the total discharges per unit time—the *density of discharges*—will increase as more fibers are "recruited" into activity above their spontaneous rates. Those already activated also will respond more vigorously, at least to their saturation rates.

This scheme of intensity encoding is doubtlessly an oversimplification, and there is reason to question whether the central auditory system listens as far off the CF as suggested by this model. The actual fibers activated by a given stimulus must be determined by the cochlear mechanics, but there are other factors in-

**Figure 6.22.** Schema of intensity encoding in the primary auditory neurons. **a.** Typical graph of spike rate as a function of intensity for a first-order neuron monitored at the CF. (Based on data from the cat from Kiang [1968].) **b.** Hypothetical isolevel (or isointensity) functions for an individual auditory neuron; each plot, from the frequency axis up, reflects the spike rate as a function of frequency for increasing intensities of the sound stimulus (such as 5-dB intervals). The maximal response is seen at the CF, except

at the higher levels of the stimulus, at which it saturates, as expected from **a. c.** Histogram type of plot of the spike rate of an array of fibers. (Modified from Whitfield, I. C. [1956]. Electrophysiology of the central auditory pathway. *Br. Med. Bull.* 12:105–109.) The activity of these fibers is shown at only a few levels (namely 10-dB intervals). The *dotted line* demarks the upper limits of the histogram at saturating levels of the stimulus for fibers, the CFs of which approximate that frequency that gives rise to the peak of the traveling wave in the cochlea. (Note that a simple one-to-one relationship was assumed between the response characteristics of the single neuron and the equally simplified displacement pattern of the basilar membrane. Thus, for purposes of illustration, **b** and **c** are hypothetical.)

volved. First, neurons may exhibit wider dynamic ranges when stimulated off the CF. Second, not all neurons of the same CF are equally sensitive. Third, not all auditory neurons have the same spontaneous rates of discharge. Some have unusually low spontaneous rates (compared with the majority). Coincidentally, these cells have nonsaturating functions wherein the spike rate increases in proportion to sound level over a range of at least 80 dB. Fibers with high spontaneous rates tend to be most sensitive but have the saturating characteristic noted above. In between are neurons with moderate spontaneous rates and a sloping or more gradually saturating spike rate function. The implication is that a group of fibers can have a wider dynamic range than any individual neuron within the group. Fourth, the synchrony of discharge also may be important for intensity encoding, especially in the case of low-frequency fibers. Because auditory neurons generally do exhibit spontaneous activity, the detection of sound by the auditory system is not a matter of simply turning a neuron on (like turning on a light). For detection to occur, there must be a significant change in a neuron's ongoing activity. This change could be an increase in the average spike rate, as already suggested. Alternatively, the significant change might be in the organization of the ongoing activity; the discharges become more frequent at certain times rather than occurring completely randomly. Thus, the appearance of periodicities in the response patterns of neurons (Fig. 6.21), reflecting the synchronization of discharges with the stimulus waveform, could provide an additional cue for intensity. In fact, it has been observed that some fibers will exhibit phase locking to sinusoidal stimulation at levels as much as 10 to 20 dB below that which first causes a significant increase in spike rate per se. Finally, it is a well-known property of neural discharges that there is less time between the occurrence of the stimulus and the first signs of neural response,

yielding decreased *latency* as the intensity of the stimulus increases.

## B. CONTRIBUTION OF FIBERS INNERVATING OHCs VERSUS IHCs—ANOTHER INTENSITY CUE?

Intensity encoding also may depend on the individual contributions of the two types of hair cells in the cochlea and, consequently, activity of the neurons innervating them. Specifically, a long-held notion is that the OHCs serve hearing only at or near levels of the sound stimulus that are just detectable. The reasons for this contention are severalfold. First, the OHC evolved later than the IHC and seems to be more highly developed or structurally more sophisticated than the IHC. Second, the OHCs are located over the portion of the basilar membrane that undergoes the greatest displacement. Finally, there is the dichotomy of innervation of the OCHs versus IHCs noted earlier, wherein the IHCs command the vast majority of neurons in the acoustic nerve. Yet, the convergent innervation pattern of the OHCs would favor summation of excitation, a well-known mechanism in sensory physiology for the facilitation of sensitivity.

In experimentally deafened animals with differing degrees of impairment, for example, from overexposure to sound or treatment with an ototoxic drug, the OHCs typically are found to be the first to go. The total absence of OHCs, but with (apparent) preservation of IHCs, results in a dramatic decrease in the cochlear microphonics and summating potentials. Via electrophysiological or behavioral methods of assessment, the associated loss of hearing sensitivity is found to be on the order of 40 dB. In contrast, on the other end of the dynamic range, clinical observations and tests in persons with similar hearing losses demonstrate essentially normal loudness perception at high levels of stimulation! This phenomenon is called loudness *recruitment*, reflecting the once-held belief that individuals with (cochlear) hearing loss were gaining something, despite their loss of sensitivity. Other manifestations of the recruitment effect may be found. For example, APs, other evoked potentials, and acoustic reflexes usually are found to be essentially normal at high levels of stimulation, if the hearing loss is not too severe. The recruitment effect is explained on the assumption that the complete loss of OHCs would lead to only a small loss in the nerve fiber population (10% or less) and would be unnoticed when the rest were vigorously activated. Then there is the observation of the characteristic input-output function for the whole-nerve AP (Fig. 6.23). The

change in slope of this function in the mid-intensity range suggests some transition in the intensity-encoding process.

The tempting conclusion from these observations (indeed, one that dominated theories of intensity encoding for many years) is that they reflect a transition from activity predominantly of neurons innervating OHCs at low levels to that of neurons innervating IHCs at high levels of stimulation. However, it is now clear that the contributions of neurons innervating OHCs versus IHCs cannot be distinguished in the intensity domain. Many single-unit recordings have been made from primary auditory neurons

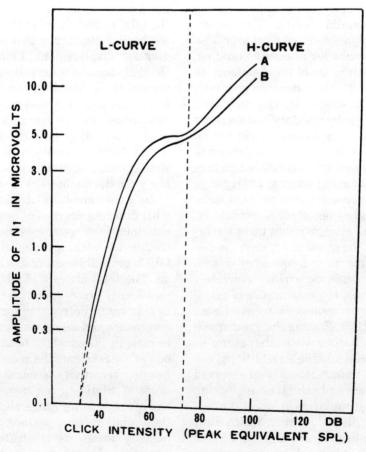

**Figure 6.23.** Input-output functions of the whole-nerve AP ($N_1$ component) recorded from the promontory of human subjects (*A* and *B*). The low- (*L*) and high-level (*H*) segments of the functions are demarked. (Adapted from Yoshie, N., and Ohashi, T. [1969]. Clinical use of cochlear nerve action potential responses in man for differential diagnosis of hearing losses. *Acta Otolaryngol. Suppl.* 252:71–87.)

whose thresholds at CF were found to fall very close to the minimum audibility curve at that frequency. By virtue of the majority rule of the IHCs over the population of neurons in the acoustic nerve and the smallness of fibers arising from OHCs, it is likely that these recordings have been almost exclusively from neurons arising from IHCs. In fact, with few exceptions, when recorded fibers have been labeled (by injecting them with horseradish peroxidase via the recording micropipette), they were traced to IHCs.

What about such phenomena as the transition in the input-output function of the whole-nerve AP, once held as compelling evidence of differential intensity encoding by neurons innervating outer and IHCs? Well, in the final analysis, such phenomena do not require two separate neuron pools to be explained. A very similar function can be generated by a model that is based on the assumption of only one type of neuron but takes into account the nature of the single-unit tuning function. The transition occurs because, once the stimulus intensity is high enough to exceed the low-frequency thresholds of the neurons innervating the IHCs, the numbers of neurons activated change dramatically, again by virtue of the spread of excitation along the basilar membrane, as discussed above. Therefore, the input-output function that had begun to saturate somewhat at moderate intensities takes an upswing in the high-intensity range. What is clearly involved here is the difference in frequency selectivity of the individual neurons operated at frequencies near the tips, that is, near their CFs, versus at frequencies falling on the low-frequency slopes of the tuning functions. Even the idea that responses mediated by IHCs ought to be more sharply tuned than those dependent on OHC function has been laid to rest by recent intracellular recordings from the hair cells themselves, in which tuning curves for the IHC and OHC receptor potentials have been found to closely resemble one another.

The current theoretical climate thus favors the notion that the two hair cell populations interact in such a manner that they actually work together rather than independently. Over the history of hearing science, analogous to theories of frequency encoding, the site of interaction of the two types of hair cells has moved peripherally (just like the allusive second filter). As discussed in Chapter 5, the underlying mechanism of the interaction now seems to be the facilitation of IHC responsivity, and, consequently, the activity of the neurons innervating them, via cochlear micromechanical processes. In this regard, of course, the motile response of the OHCs has commanded much attention. Indeed, the OHCs have been suggested to act as hearing aids for the IHCs; their gain is presumed to be on the order of 40 dB, namely on the order of magnitude of losses of auditory sensitivity observed when OHCs are systematically destroyed while leaving seemingly intact IHCs (as described earlier). This is why, for example, the manifestation of such losses in the single-unit tuning function is one involving attenuation or loss limited largely to the tip region, rather than an overall upward shift of the function. It is the OHCs and associated micromechanics to which the gain and selectivity of the tip region are now attributed (as discussed above; see also Chapter 5, Section 4).

## C. OTHER CONSIDERATIONS AND LOOKING CENTRALLY

It is important to point out that the separate treatment of frequency and intensity is somewhat artificial. It should be evident that the two encoding processes are intertwined. The same limited dynamic range of (most) primary auditory neurons that makes the explanation of intensity encoding difficult also imposes difficulties for frequency encoding, particularly with regard to the validity of the place code. At moderate to high intensities of stimulation, at which most of the neurons are at saturation, there must be an effective broadening of the mechanical events in the cochlea, as reflected in the neurons' discharge patterns. This suggests another instance in which temporal cues might help. Here, as well as in the area of extending the dynamic range, the degree of synchrony may be of value. However, the range of stimulus intensities over which the degree of synchrony grows and over which average spike rate increases overlaps somewhat, and synchrony may decrease at high levels of stimulation. This all adds up to the need for further processing of the signals carried by the primary auditory neurons from the cochlea to the CNS. In lieu of any other tricks that might be possible in the periphery (as of yet unknown), one is compelled to look centrally for such additional processing. Although many central auditory neurons have similar response characteristics to first-order neurons, they are not all primary like. In general, it seems likely that a great amount of additional processing of incoming information is required for the organism to arrive at its final perception of the sound stimulus. An impressive amount of this processing seems to occur within the brain stem auditory system.

# 7. Central Auditory Processing: Initial Stages

## A. THE PROBLEM OF PROCESSING COMPLEX STIMULI

Before jumping right into a discussion of central auditory processing, and to better appreciate the need for further processing of information encoded by the peripheral system, it will be useful to give a little more consideration to the quality of information transferred to the central auditory system and the problems presented to the system in analyzing complex sound stimuli. It was established earlier that the primary auditory neurons strongly reflect the mechanical events of the cochlea. This can be demonstrated in the "neurophysiological record" obtained from multiple sin-

gle-unit recordings. This point is further illustrated in Figure 6.24, in which it is demonstrated that the vibration pattern of the basilar membrane elicited by a tone can be reconstructed from period histograms obtained from an array of neurons (namely, using amplitude and phase coordinates at the instant in time at which the pattern is frozen). However, complex stimuli naturally involve more than one spectral component, so the central auditory system does not see, in effect, a single traveling wave pattern but, rather, a commensurately complex wave pattern. A feel for what the central auditory system faces in the analysis of speech is provided by Figure 6.25. This figure is perhaps best understood by way of analogy to the animated cartoon (or, for the history buff, the method of animation that was used in the nickelodeon). Each tracing could be placed on a separate card and the cards stacked in order. Flipping the cards rapidly in sequence, the motion of the basilar membrane could then be seen in response to the word *information*. Although the prominent spectral features are evident in Figure 6.25 (note the pattern within the time frame of the phoneme [I]), individual peaks of traveling waves are not easily detected. The difficulty of the task of recognizing spectral features is appreciated even more when it is considered that the reader has the benefit of leisure scrutiny of this one segment of speech frozen in time. Think about how fast the central processor must work to decipher free-running speech! Now, if things seem complicated regarding the mechanical events elicited by speech, the neurophysiological record will be just as complicated. Indeed, the picture is likely to be muddied somewhat by the spread of excitation and saturation discussed earlier regarding intensity encoding. This point is demonstrated by recordings from an array of neurons responding to a sustained phoneme, as shown in Figure 6.26. Although the spectral features are fairly well preserved in the function of spike rates versus fre-

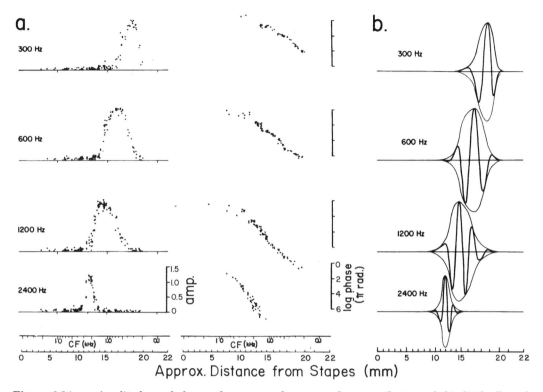

**Figure 6.24.** **a.** Amplitudes and phases of responses of an array of neurons (but recorded individually and sequentially) in response to tones of the frequencies indicated, presented at 20-dB SPL. The values were obtained via Fourier transform of the period histograms from each single-unit recording. **b.** Traveling-wave patterns derived from data in **a** (after averaging or smoothing). (Adapted from Pfeiffer, R. R., and Kim, D. O. [1975]. Cochlear nerve fiber responses: distribution along the cochlear partition. *J. Acoust. Soc. Am.* 58: 867–869.)

quency at low levels of stimulation, they are smeared considerably at moderate to high levels (Fig. 6.26*b*).

An additional complication of the encoding process will be the inherent nonlinearities of the cochlear macromechanics and micromechanics. It was suggested earlier that such nonlinearities seem to provide an advantage in processing of complex sounds by effectively enhancing frequency selectivity in the response of the primary neurons, as exemplified by two-tone suppression. On the other hand, these same nonlinearities generate harmonic and intermodulation distortion. A great amount of research has been directed specifically toward the difference tones of $f_2 - f_1$ and $2f_1 - f_2$ (where $f$ is the frequency of one of the primaries and the

subscripts *1* and *2* designate the lower- and higher-frequency components, respectively). These distortion products are unusually prominent, and considerable argument has raged over the issue of whether these distortion products are propagated as tones of equal frequency or simply are products of the electromechanical transduction process of the hair cells. The latter process presumably does not give rise to traveling waves corresponding to the distortion products. Without engaging in this debate at this juncture (cochlear distortion will be considered further in Chapter 7), it will be noted simply that the presence of these distortion components can contribute to the neurophysiological record. Although the amplitude of the distortion products usually will be

distance from oval window in mm

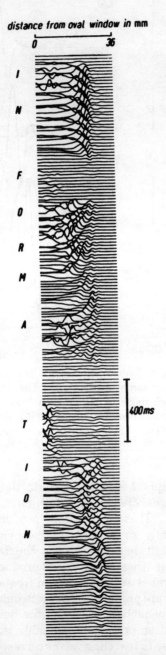

**Figure 6.25.** Model representation of basilar membrane movement in response to the word *information* (see text). (Adapted from David [1972] in Keidel, W. E. (1980). Neurophysiological requirements for implanted cochlear prostheses. *Audiology* 19:105–127.)

lower than that of the primaries, their presence may become more evident at levels of stimulation at which fibers responding to the primaries are becoming saturated. It is interesting to note that when the contribution of nerve fibers responding to distortion products falling between major vowel formants, in effect, are suppressed, the primary spectral features of the vowel sounds, as shown in Figure 6.26c, are preserved across intensity. Whether the central auditory system carries out the kinds of computations required to obtain the data in Figure 6.26c is not known, but at least the basis for the necessary suppression is clearly demonstrated by the two-tone suppression phenomenon. It is well established that speech discrimination ability is fairly constant across a wide range of intensities. So, what is under scrutiny is not whether the CNS gets the information it needs from the periphery and has mechanisms by which speech stimuli can be deciphered, but just how it does it.

One other aspect of the character of the neural signal transmitted from the periphery to the central auditory system should be mentioned, namely, the dependence of the neural discharge on the duration of the stimulus. This is reflected in the PST histogram shown in Figure 6.11b2. The onset of the stimulus gives rise to a vigorous barrage of discharges, but the spike rate decays rapidly toward an asymptotic value that may be only about half the rate at stimulus onset. This behavior, known as **adaptation**, is further illustrated in Figure 6.27. Adaptation is a common characteristic of the response of primary auditory neurons (if not neurons in general) to sustained stimulation. On the one hand, it reveals that, indeed, the auditory system provides both phasic and tonic responses. The onset of the stimulus represents a rapidly changing event, to which the neurons respond vigorously (phasic component). However, although there is a reduction in discharge rate thereafter, there is sustained discharge throughout the duration of the stimulus,

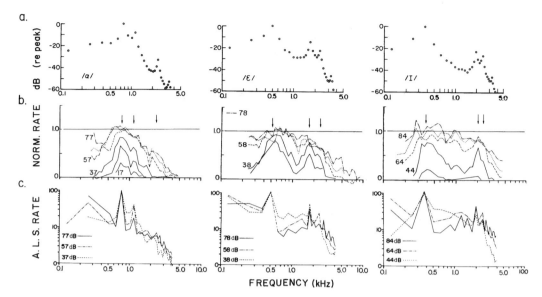

**Figure 6.26.** **a.** Amplitude spectra of the phonemes [a], [ɛ], and [I] as measured in front of the eardrum of a cat (each recorded on separate dates in different animals). **b.** Plots of spike rates at characteristics frequencies of numerous single units in response to the indicated phonemes presented at SPLs indicated. The spike rates have been normalized essentially to the saturated rate of each fiber recorded. Data have been smoothed. *Arrows* indicate formant frequencies. (**a** and **b** adapted from Sachs, M. B., and Young, E. D. [1979]. Encoding of steady-state vowels in the auditory nerve: representation in terms of discharge rate. *J. Acoust. Soc. Am.* 66:470–479.) **c.** Response profiles as in **b**, except spike rate is quantified in terms of the averaged localized synchronized rate (see text). (From Young, E. D., and Sachs, M. B. [1979]. Representation of steady-state vowels in the temporal aspects of the discharge patterns of populations of auditory-nerve fibers. *J. Acoust. Soc. Am.* 66:1381–1403.)

signaling its continued presence and providing information concerning its intensity (tonic component). Furthermore, this behavior is relevant to how responses to both simultaneous and nonsimultaneous sounds interact. The latter is illustrated in Figure 6.27. Thus, the neural code for time-varying complex sound stimuli, such as speech, will be subject to the adaptive properties of the neurons.

Clearly there are various idiosyncracies of the neural code established in the periphery and reflected in the pattern of response of the primary auditory neuron. The first-order neurons exhibit the following:

1. Specific frequency response areas;
2. Synchronization to the period of the stimulus waveform;
3. Spike rates in proportion to stimulus intensity (but);

4. Saturation at high intensities of stimulation;
5. Manifestations of cochlear nonlinearities; and
6. Adaptation with a fairly characteristic time course.

In looking centrally, the extent to which these characteristics are modified may be taken as a sign of further processing by the central auditory system. Despite the impressive amount of processing that occurs in the periphery, by virtue of the initial stimulus-encoding processes, it is safe to say that the central auditory system still has its work cut out for it.

## B. BRAIN STEM MECHANISMS OF AUDITORY PROCESSING

It is not possible within the confines of this text to discuss all mechanisms that might be involved in central auditory pro-

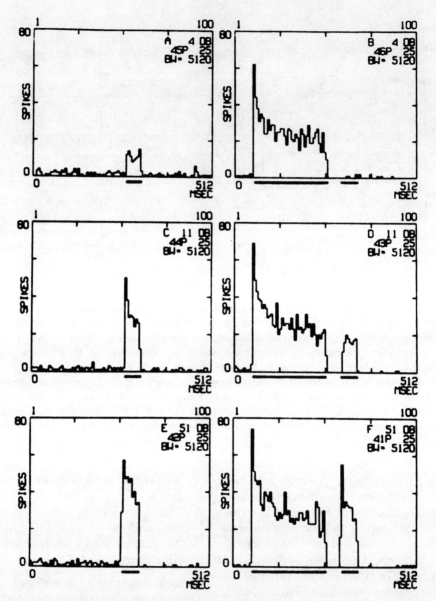

**Figure 6.27.** *Left,* PST histograms from single-unit recording (primary neuron, gerbil). Responses are to a brief tone burst (42 msec) presented at SPLs indicated in the *upper right* corner of each graph. *Right,* PST histograms as on left, but with 204-msec, 25-dB adapting tone. *Horizontal bars* below each graph indicate occurrence of the stimuli. (From Smith, R. L. [1977]. Short-term adaptation in single auditory nerve fibers: some poststimulatory effects. *J. Neurophysiol.* 40:1098–1112.)

cessing in the brain stem, and a comprehensive discussion still would be highly theoretical. Nevertheless, it is possible to detail certain neuroanatomical and neurophysiological aspects of the brain stem auditory system that are known and that point to possible mechanisms of auditory processing. It will be worthwhile to take note of these features, if only as the handwriting on the wall, because they do suggest that incoming auditory information is further processed at this level, or perhaps reencoded, before going to the cortex. One might ask, "Why not just relay the information encoded in the periphery directly to the cortex and get on with the important task of cognitive processing?" Well, although the cortex is certainly the desired destination for auditory information, subcortical processing can greatly enhance the efficiency of the brain's operation. This situation is akin to the operation of a digital computer. There is a considerable advantage to accomplishing routine stages of analyses at more peripheral branches of the system (in this case, the brain stem), thereby leaving the central processing unit and the core memory (the cortex) free for higher-level processing. Also, the initial stages of the analyses may require high-speed processing, such as sampling periodicities in the incoming signal. This is best left to the lower levels of the system, at which there are inherently minimal delays in data transmission attributable to synaptic and propagation delays.

Evidence of brain stem–level auditory processing is suggested, first, by the multiplicity of the auditory pathways. Although the cochlear nuclei and SOC are perhaps the most outstanding examples, there are multiple nuclei or subnuclei at every level of the brain stem system. In other words, within each nuclear complex there are groups of neurons that are more or less autonomous. The result is that there are multiple representations of the cochlea at all levels of the central auditory system. Not all maps of the cochlea necessarily reflect the same degree of tonotopical organization, nor are they all necessarily important for frequency encoding. This multiple representation suggests a means by which different aspects of auditory information can be processed simultaneously while taking advantage of the "preconditioning" of the incoming information from the periphery that, in turn, is afforded by the frequency-to-place transformation in the cochlea. That there are complexes of nuclei and/or distinct subnuclear groups is evidenced by the morphological

heterogeneity of the auditory neurons, as illustrated in Figure 6.28a. Even at the level of the cochlear nuclei there are at least a half-dozen different types of neurons. Not only do they look different (morphologically), they react differently to the same sound stimulus. In other words, the different cell types each have a characteristic discharge pattern, as shown in Figure 6.28b. However, it should be pointed out hastily that not all cell types have been demonstrated to produce unique discharge patterns, and the association between discharge pattern and cell type is based largely on inference. The important point is that, whereas most primary fibers exhibit fairly simple patterns of discharge (high rate of discharge at stimulus onset followed by rapid asymptotic adaptation), this is only one of various patterns observed from second- and higher-order neurons. Yet, most cells respond vigorously at the onset of the stimulus, so differences between patterns of discharges from different cell types are most evident after the stimulus onset. These variations include differences in both excitatory and inhibitory response areas from those of primary-like neurons that will affect contrast in the spectral and/or temporal domains in the processing of complex sounds.

There is also ample evidence that neurons in the brain stem auditory system are differentially sensitive to certain types of stimuli or certain features of the stimulus. For instance, there are neurons that are most responsive to stimuli of varying amplitude and/or frequency, and they even may respond selectively to different rates and directions of change in these parameters. The response of a neuron to such complex stimuli—amplitude and frequency modulated—depends on its own response characteristics and those of preceding neurons. If all neurons involved are primary like, the response of a given neuron will depend mainly on the neuron's tuning function and how its passband matches up with the stimulus spectrum. However, there is a trend toward in-

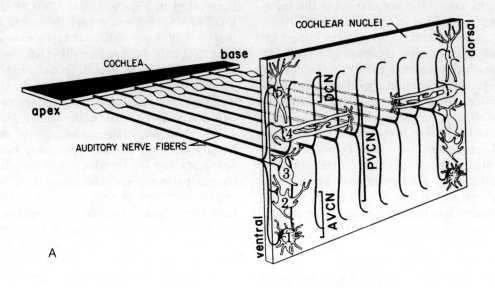

A

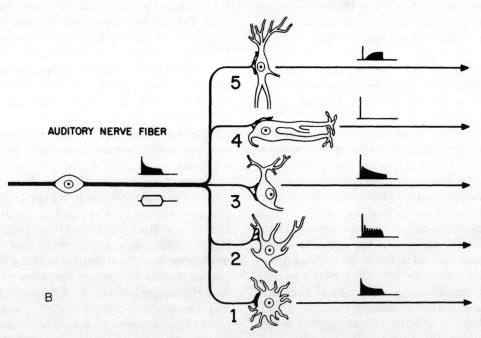

B

**Figure 6.28.** **a.** Highly schematic representation of connections between the peripheral auditory system and the cochlear nuclei. *AVCN*, Anterior ventral cochlear nuclei; *PVCN*, posterior ventral cochlear nuclei. Some of the complexity of the morphology of the second-order neurons is indicated (five different types shown). **b.** Relation between cell types and discharge patterns as reflected in PST histograms. Response types are: *1*, primary-like; *2*, "chopper"; *3*, primary-like with notch; *4*, on; and *5*, "pauser." (From Kiang, N. Y.-S. [1975]. Stimulus representation in the discharge patterns of auditory neurons. In *The Nervous System: Human Communication and Its Disorders*, Vol 3, edited by E. L. Eagles. Raven Press, New York.)

creased specialization of neurons in the upper–brain stem levels. Such specialization permits the detection of specific features of the stimulus and doubtlessly facilitates the processing of complex sounds such as speech.

Even at the lowest level of the brain stem auditory system, again by virtue of the heterogeneity of cell types in the cochlear nuclei, certain features of speech and other complex sounds can be extracted or emphasized by certain second-order neurons. For example, on-type neurons (Fig. 6.28*b*) tend to emphasize peaks of the waveform. Primary-like fibers, presumably, will simply relay the spectral and temporal information borne by the first-order neurons. There is also evidence that some of the cochlear nucleus cells have strong inhibitory sidebands, manifested by the reduction of discharges, even below the spontaneous rate, at frequencies above and (particularly) below the CF. These cells are likely to influence significantly the overall scheme of intensity encoding.

The variability in ordering of the neurons above the level of the cochlear nuclei, another manifestation of the multiplicity of the auditory pathways, is also an impressive feature of the central auditory system. As noted earlier, the inferior colliculus (and, consequently, the medial geniculate) receives inputs from several orders of fibers. The alternative pathways may provide a means by which incoming signals can be compared against themselves or *autocorrelated*. Each synapse in a pathway introduces a time delay, so information borne by second-order neurons reaches the inferior colliculus before that carried by third-order neurons. Fourth-order neurons would introduce further delays. By creating time disparities between signals arriving at the same level, such aspects as the periodicity and redundancy of incoming information could be evaluated. For instance, it would be possible for the central auditory system to determine whether a sound was changing in amplitude over time.

## 8. Subcortical Binaural Information Processing

The fact that not all second-order neurons leaving the cochlear nuclei cross over the midline in the trapezoid body indicates that the SOC and higher nuclei receive information from both ears, and that the superior olives constitute a major center of *binaural*, or two-eared, information processing. The most obvious need for two ears is for the accurate location of sound in space. The two ears receive sound from different listening points, so sounds coming from directions other than directly in front or behind the listener reach the two ears at different times and/or intensities. The time disparity occurs by virtue of a difference in distance between each ear and the sound source, causing a difference in the time required for sound to travel to the near versus the far ear. The intensity disparity occurs by virtue of enhancement of the sound pressure at the near ear and the sound shadow cast on the far ear because of the head baffle effect. As discussed in Chapter 5, this occurs at frequencies greater than approximately 2 kHz, at which sound diffraction around the head is minimal. Therefore, the cues for the location of sounds in space via binaural processing, that is, *binaural localization*, are spectral. Because the intensity disparity is frequency dependent, the spectrum of the sound is different at the two ears. Also, for periodic signals, interaural time disparities yield interaural phase differences. Because a more lengthy discussion of binaural phenomena is given in the following chapter, it will suffice here to consider only neurophysiological mechanisms for binaural information processing and the ability of the auditory CNS to adequately encode these cues.

Given the extensive bilateral representation of input to the CNS from each ear, it is not difficult to visualize some process of *cross-correlation*, a statistical process by which two signals are compared. It already should be evident that the temporal pattern or synchrony of neural discharges contains information about the sound acting on the auditory system. The system thus may be expected, at least to some extent, to evaluate time disparities between the discharge patterns in the contralateral and ipsilateral pathways. Indeed, single neurons at the level of the superior olive and above have been found to demonstrate changes in spike rate as a function of the time delay between pure tones presented at the two ears, as illustrated in Figure 6.29. The most notable feature of these data is the occurrence of maximal spike rates at certain time delays—their *characteristic delays*. In other words, the spike rate of each neuron reaches a maxi-

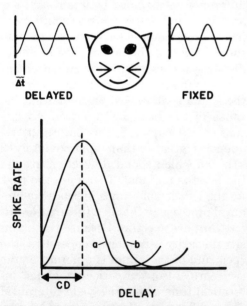

**Figure 6.29.** Illustration of encoding of time differences by auditory neurons at levels of SOC and above. The spike rate is a periodic function of the delay ($\Delta t$) and reaches a peak at the characteristic delay (*CD*) that is independent of frequency. Curves **a** and **b** are for two different frequencies of the stimulating tone. (Based on data from recordings from single neurons in the cat at the level of the inferior colliculus by Rose et al. [1966]).

mum at a certain disparity between the time of arrival of the sound at the two ears. For a given neuron, the characteristic delay is independent of frequency.

Whether the central auditory system uses the characteristic delay, per se, is debatable. Some compelling evidence suggests that it is not essential. For instance, characteristic delays can be demonstrated in the kangaroo rat that are larger than the interaural time disparities that could exist in nature, considering the small size of the animal's head. Nevertheless, data of the type illustrated in Figure 6.29 are worthy of attention, because they clearly demonstrate the faithful encoding of interaural time disparities in the neural activity of the auditory brain stem pathways. Furthermore, amazingly small time differences have been observed, namely, characteristic delays less than 100 $\mu$sec. This is remarkable because two or more synaptic delays may be involved in the transmission of the neural signal to the brain stem centers involved. Again, each delay is worth about 0.5 to 1 msec (500–1000 $\mu$sec)!

It seems likely that intensity differences and time disparities are processed by virtue of the different groups of neurons that are specialized to handle binaural information. Without going into great detail, there would seem to be several groups and/or subgroups of neurons that can be characterized by the manner in which they respond to stimulation of the contralateral ear, the ipsilateral ear, or both ears. Two major types of cells are those that have been identified as the *excitatory-excitatory* and *excitatory-inhibitory* types. With the excitatory-excitatory type, stimulation from either ear can be excitatory. They do not seem to be very sensitive to interaural intensity disparities, as long as the average intensity between ears remains constant. On the other hand, the excitatory-inhibitory type neurons are excited by stimulation from one ear and inhibited by stimulation of the other. In general, there are neurons that may be excited by monaural stimulation, whereas others may be excited only by input from both sides. Other groups may be excited by contralateral inputs but inhibited by ipsilateral stimulation or vice versa. At higher levels of the system, the binaural interactions are expected to be further modified. Indeed, at the level of the inferior colliculus, the majority of neurons in the rat, for example, demonstrate suppressive effects of binaural stimulation, whereas the remainder either exhibit binaural summation or a complex or mixed response pattern. However, how the brain stem actually maps the sound space is not entirely understood, but the resulting patterns of excitation and inhibition seem to underlie the encoding of binaural information.

It was noted in Section 2 above that there are various nuclei in the SOC, but the lateral and medial superior olives are the most outstanding. They also differ somewhat in the response type typically associated with neurons from the two nuclei. It seems that the lateral superior olive is dedicated primarily to the detection of interaural intensity disparities, limited mainly to high frequencies. The medial superior olive, on the other hand, seems to be mainly involved in the detection of low-frequency interaural time disparities. At least this is the picture that has evolved from experiments on lower mammals such as the cat, so it remains to be seen just how generalizable these notions are to humans. In general, the lateral superior olive is the most prominent nucleus within the complex in the brain stem of animals such as the cat, whereas the medial superior olive is the most prominent in the human brain stem.

It is worth noting that, although binaural processing depends on bilateral input, each "hemifield" of auditory space is represented on the contralateral side of the brain stem, as evidenced by the fact that unilateral lesions above the superior olives cause primarily contralateral deficits in auditory function. Again, just how auditory space is represented internally remains controversial, and theories have come and gone, as in the case of theories of pitch perception. Coincidentally, one of the contenders is a place theory in which neurons are thought to be tuned spatially. Selective responses to interaural intensity and time disparities have been demonstrated, but the degree of selectivity has not always been observed to be adequate to account for auditory localization ability demonstrated behaviorally. However, a resurgence of support for the place theory of sound localization has occurred in recent years. A suggestion from work in the owl for a possible mechanism, namely, to detect interaural time disparities, is the difference in lengths of axonal branches of an ascending neuron from each ear, converging on common groups of cells but in complementary order. This creates different delays in excitation between the two sides, causing a shift in the locus of optimal excitation according to whether stimulation leads at the right or left and degree of disparity, hence, a place code.

Although the superior olive is the first level at which decussation of auditory neurons occurs (namely, fibers crossing over via the trapezoid body and dorsal stria), it is not the only level at which binaural information is processed. Actually, it is only one of the initial stages, because cross-overs occur at higher levels, as noted earlier. The higher brain stem nuclei receive binaural input directly, as well as that which is relayed via the superior olive. Lower centers also may be involved, albeit indirectly. There is increasing evidence that the cochlear nuclei play some role in binaural processing by virtue of descending pathway connections with the SOC and/or by virtue of inherent properties of DCN neurons that may help suppress echoes that could obscure sound localization (namely, by means of temporal masking). The DCN also has been implicated in the localization of sounds at different elevations, demonstrating great sensitivity to spectral features, on which this type of localization depends (see Chapter 7). Clearly, the central auditory system not only receives information separately from the two hearing organs, but it extensively compares and integrates the information from the two sides of the system. It is doubtful that this sensitive and elaborate system is intended purely for sound localization. Various auditory phenomena involve binaural information processing and seem to share some common features with sound localization (Chapter 7). It can be speculated, for instance, that the cross-correlation of information transmitted on the two sides of the brain stem system is an essential process for other forms of auditory information processing, such as selective auditory attention. To optimize attention to a relevant signal coming predominantly from one side, irrelevant information coming from the other side could then be deemphasized, such as when someone is trying to listen to a caller on the telephone while someone else is yelling, "Get off the phone!"

## 9. Central Control of the Peripheral System

### A. THE EFFERENT SYSTEM

It was stated earlier that, along with the various ascending pathways, there are essentially (although not perfectly) parallel descending pathways. Only the lowest portions of these pathways are very well known both anatomically and physiologically. For this reason, the influence of the efferent system will be described within the context of subcortical information processing and, thus, will be considered before discussing cortical processing of auditory information.

As noted earlier, in effect, the terminal parts of the descending pathways are those formed by the medial and lateral *OCBs*. As their names imply (and as discussed earlier), the OCBs comprise fibers originating in the superior olive and terminating in the organ of Corti. As illus-

trated in Figure 6.30, the medial fibers (crossed and uncrossed) terminate directly on the OHCs and, thereby, influence activity in the first-order neurons only indirectly. This is an example of *presynaptic inhibition*. Generally speaking, this form of inhibition is said to occur when the activity of one neuron is suppressed by virtue of some event before the synapse between it and the previous unit (in this case, a receptor cell). The lateral OCBs (uncrossed fibers) directly influence activity of afferent neurons terminating on the IHCs. This is because their endings tend to terminate on the dendritic terminals of first-order (afferent) neurons, rather than on the hair cells (Fig. 6.30). This type of innervation is expected to effect *postsynaptic* inhibition.

That olivocochlear fibers can act directly on the periphery has been clearly demonstrated experimentally. Electrical stimulation of efferent fibers in the OCBs via electrodes placed in the floor of the fourth ventricle (one of the cavities of the brain) leads to changes in the cochlear potentials and suppression of the whole-nerve APs (Fig. 6.30) and responses of individual primary neurons. The OCB fibers have been found to be spontaneously active in awake animals, although efferents also have been found that do not discharge spontaneously. OCB fibers also have been shown to respond to sound stimuli; indeed, research in this area has revealed afferent-like tuning properties in efferents.

What is unclear, however, is the extent to which the OCBs influence the periphery under normal means of activation (that is, as opposed to the tetanic electrical shock used experimentally) and the role of OCBs in the first place. Although definitive evidence is still scarce, it long has been held that the olivocochlear fibers somehow must control the sensitivity of the end organ or perhaps even the frequency selectivity of the peripheral system. The seeming paradox, however, is that there are very few efferent fibers (on the order of 500 in the cat) compared with the number

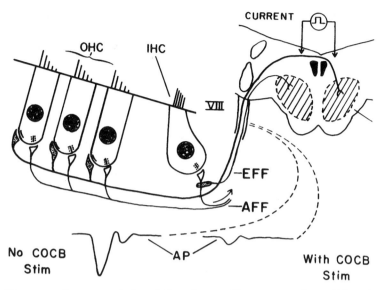

**Figure 6.30.** Diagrammatic representation of the primary efferent connections of fibers in the OCBs and the effects of applying stimulating current to the crossed bundle (*COCB Stim*) on the whole-nerve AP elicited by sound. The highly ramified terminal endings of efferent neurons typically spread in both directions in the cochlea to innervate many more hair cells than shown here. *VIII*, Auditory nerve; *EFF*, efferent fibers; *AFF*, afferent fibers. (Based on drawings of Klinke, R., and Galley, N. [1974] and Galambos, R. [1958].)

of afferent fibers (approximately 50,000). This is a ratio of 100:1 (afferents to efferents). Here, too, is a case of divergent innervation; each efferent fiber terminates on many hair cells by virtue of the great ramification of nerve endings (some 40,000 terminal end bulbs in total, that is, nearly 100 times as many endings as efferent neurons). At first glance, this innervation pattern would not seem to lend itself to providing very fine control. Also, the majority of efferent endings terminate on OHCs, so the situation is not one that would seem to allow the efferent system to substantially influence the activity of the primary afferents directly. Yet, as noted earlier, the whole-nerve AP can be suppressed by OCB stimulation. How is this possible?

Well, the most likely mechanism lies, again, in the greater contribution of the OHCs to the mechanics of the organ of Corti, not as receptor cells. If the OHCs effectively give the IHCs some 40 dB greater sensitivity, and if the single-unit tuning functions of the primary neurons

are much sharper with an intact organ (meaning viable OHCs), then the efferents can be expected to affect overall sensitivity and frequency selectivity. Indeed, such effects of efferent activation have been observed—with direct electrical stimulation of the OCBs. As such, the effects are robust and seemingly definitive. However, much less robust and definitive are the effects of natural activation, for example, changes in the response of one ear while simultaneously stimulating the other ear. Furthermore, such effects demonstrated in animals, until recently, were much less accessible in humans. Then came *otoacoustic emission* (OAE) measurement, a convenient instrument to sample OHC response specifically, applicable in humans and infrahumans alike. The otoacoustic emissions excited in one ear have been shown to be slightly depressed when a noise is presented to the opposite ear. The reduction in OAEs is typically worth only a few decibels or less (depending on how it is measured) but can be argued to represent a more substantial effect on the throughput of signals in the auditory system than merely represented by the measured contralateral suppression effect. Not surprisingly, this effect has been embroiled in controversy, because the effects of acoustic-cross-over and/or acoustic-reflex activation must be carefully avoided (see below). The jury is still out on the issue of significant effects of contralateral input on frequency selectivity. Therefore, although there is no lack of demonstrations of effects of OCB activation, there remains considerable uncertainty as to exactly what and how much effects the efferents have on the auditory input.

So far, reports on the effects of deactivating the OCB have been conflicting, but this may be because of species and/or methodological differences across studies. In monkeys, transection of the medial (crossed) OCB has been observed to cause a marked decrease in frequency resolution, whereas the effects of this kind of lesion have been found to be practically nil in the cat or affecting only spontaneous discharge rates of primary neurons. In general (for example, see Fig. 6.30), the effects of OCB stimulation diminish with increasing level of sound stimulation. Last, the natural mode of excitation of OCB neurons, again, does not lead to as well-synchronized activity as direct electrical stimulation, and, thus, less dramatic effects of OCB activation, further detracting from the (presumed) role of the efferent system under normal circumstances. Various issues thus remain to be resolved. This area, however, is expected to be one of continued active research, fervent debate, and even clinical interest for some time to come.

## B. THE ACOUSTIC REFLEX

The *acoustic reflex* was discussed in Chapter 5 with respect to its acoustic role and, so, will be discussed only briefly here. It was suggested that, in effect, the role of the reflex can be viewed in a similar light as that of the efferent pathways. The

acoustic reflex potentially affords the central auditory system another means of controlling its input at the periphery. The wiring diagram of the reflex is shown schematically in Figure 6.31. The reflex is mediated via the SOC. This explains why the reflex is bilateral; that is, a sound in one ear can cause a simultaneous reflex in both ears. Of course, other centers in the brain stem are required to execute the reflex, especially the motor nuclei of the facial (VIIth cranial) nerve. Although apparently not a significant component of the acoustic or stapedial reflex, per se, middle ear reflexes also can be mediated by the tensor tympani. This reflex arc involves the trigeminal (Vth cranial) nerve and nonauditory inputs. For instance, the tactile sensation caused by a puff of air in the eye is effective in eliciting a middle ear reflex via activation of tensor tympani.

Ultimately, the acoustic reflex is subject to influence from auditory centers above the superior olive via descending pathways from the cortex. It can be demonstrated that the magnitude of the auditory reflex is altered by the listener's state of attention (such as the performance of a task to direct the listener's attention rather than merely allowing his or her mind to wander). The involvement of rather high levels of the auditory system certainly is implied. However, as discussed in Chapter 5, the influence of the reflex seems limited, at least as judged by the amount of sound attenuation attributable to the reflex and the limitation of this attenuation to frequencies less than 1 kHz.

## C. FEEDBACK

Both the OCB system and the acoustic reflex constitute what engineers call *feedback* mechanisms. The idea of feedback is that a certain amount of throughput or output signal is fed back to the input and influences the system's response. The OCBs and the acoustic reflex seem to provide primarily negative feedback and thus have subtractive effects, subsequently re-

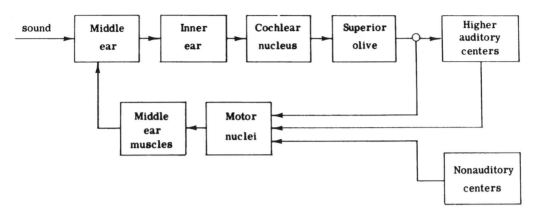

**Figure 6.31.** Block diagram of the middle ear reflex arc, representing it as a feedback mechanism. (From Dallos, P. [1973]. *The Auditory Periphery: Biophysics and Physiology.* Academic Press, New York.)

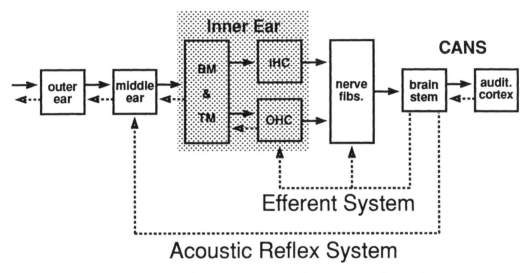

**Figure 6.32.** Diagrammatic representation of signal (or feed-forward) and feedback pathways of the auditory system. *BM*, Basilar membrane; *TM*, tectorial membrane; *nerve fibs.*, nerve fibers; *CANS*, central auditory nervous system. (Adapted from Dallos [1988].)

ducing the effective input to the auditory nerve. A sort of loop circuit is envisioned (Fig. 6.32); the term *feedback loop* is often applied to the connecting pathways involved. Doubtless other feedback loops exist in the auditory pathways between or even within nuclei. However, feedback need not always be negative or inhibitory but may be positive or facility. In the peripheral system, the interaction of the OHCs with the IHCs is viewed as providing a positive feedback. Even the OCBs,

generally viewed as a source of negative feedback in the auditory system, are thought by some researchers to provide effectively a positive feedback by influencing the operating point of the basilar membrane motion via net shifts in displacement, namely, by influencing the motile response of the OHCs. Centrally, there are various prospects for positive-feedback loops. Fibers descending to the cochlear nuclei have been observed to have facility effects on neurons of the ascending system at this level, because stimulation of these efferent fibers brings about increased excitation in the afferents. Such mechanisms will have some influence on information processing, although the extent of the influence will remain in question until the complete descending system is known in detail. Similarly, without detailed knowledge of the descending connections and their function, the ability of the cortex to control both its own inputs and the events at the lower levels of the central and peripheral systems cannot be realistically evaluated.

## 10.　Cortical Auditory Information Processing

### A.　ORGANIZATION OF THE PRIMARY AUDITORY CORTEX—IS THERE A PLACE FOR PLACE AT THE TOP?

Because of the interest commanded by the place code (for frequency) in the theory of pitch perception, a major issue that has pervaded the hearing literature is whether the auditory cortex, especially the primary auditory cortex, is tonotopically organized. That is, across the surface of the cortex, can an axis be found along which the CFs of the nerve cells vary systematically as a function of location? Actually, the existence of some form of tonotopical organization has not been disputed so much as the degree to which it exists. More than four decades ago, C. N. Woolsey and E. M. Walzl conducted experiments that seemed to demonstrate strict tonotopical organization of the primary auditory cortex. Perhaps a more accurate statement is that they demonstrated *cochleotopic* organization of the cortex, because what they actually did was to electrically stimulate primary auditory neurons along the extent of the hearing organ and record near-field–evoked (electrical) potentials in the cortex. However, later experiments using sound stimuli to excite the auditory neurons provided less-convincing evidence of strict tonotopicity.

The degree of tonotopical organization attributed by researchers to the auditory cortex waxed and waned over the ensuing years. In recent years, support has grown steadily for the existence of definite tonotopical organization of the primary auditory cortex, based on single-unit recordings. A critical factor not fully appreciated by earlier researchers was the need for extremely careful placement of the electrode and subsequent verification of its location. What makes this matter particularly demanding for the investigator is that the enfoldings of the cortex are so variable between individual subjects that familiar landmarks on the cortical surface cannot entirely be trusted to help locate even the primary auditory cortex, much less the cochlear map on its surface. The general layout and orientation of this map in the human brain, nevertheless, seems to follow that which was first observed in the monkey by Walzl, as shown in Figure 6.33. High-frequency stimulation, activating the base of the cochlea, ultimately leads to excitation of neurons located in the more medial and relatively posterior portion of the primary area, deep in the lateral fissure. Low-frequency information from the apex of the cochlea is handled by neurons located anterolaterally. However, as in the case of the brain stem nuclei, multiple maps also appear on the auditory cortex, and these maps can be fairly complicated in detail.

Some degree of tonotopicity is expected at the cortical level, if for no other reason than as a reflection of the organization of the lower auditory centers and the pathways leading from them. The more debatable issue is whether tonotopical organization of the cortex is truly essential. In other words, is tonotopicity a necessary component of the process(es) by which pitch is perceived? With tonotopical organization, presumably only a small group of neurons are optimally sensitive to a certain frequency. If so, stimulation of a certain group of cortical neurons should lead to the perception of a corresponding pitch

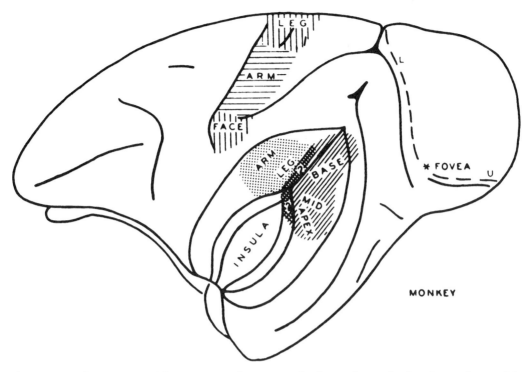

**Figure 6.33.**  Organization of the primary auditory cortex in the monkey, reflecting the tonal map of the cochlea that is projected onto the cortical surface. This drawing illustrates a view of the superior plane of the temporal lobe. To obtain this view, some of the brain would have to be cut away from the lateral fissure, and the temporal lobe deflected slightly downward. (From Walzl, E. M. [1947]. Representation of the cochlea in the cerebral cortex. *Laryngoscope* 57:778–787.)

according to their location. This line of development leads then to the question of whether place of excitation in the cortex is itself the cue for pitch perception. Although this is an issue that is likely to be debated for some time to come, it is not difficult to conceive how tonotopical organization might serve a more general purpose. Each group of cells, tuned to a given frequency, is expected to handle auditory information other than that which is relevant to pitch per se. Such an organization would afford a simplistic method of information transfer to the cortex, much like the pigeonhole method used in handling mail.

From this perspective, a group of neurons rather than a single neuron is visualized as the functional unit for auditory information processing in the cortex,

consistent with the fact that the cortex has depth as well as breadth. The cortex is composed of six layers of cells wherein each layer is characterized by a prevalent type of cell that is structurally different from those in the other layers. In the earlier part of this century, Rafael Lorente de No demonstrated the presence of circuitous connections between cells in different layers. These connections suggest the possibility that there is vertical or ***columnar*** organization of the nerve cells, as well as the *laminar* organization or layering just mentioned. In fact, both motor and sensory areas of the cortex have been shown to be organized functionally along the lines of columns that extend radially through the depths of the cortical layers. In the case of the sensory cortex, nerve cells lying within a column respond optimally to the same basic aspect of the stimulus. Some evidence for columnar organization has been demonstrated in the primary auditory cortex, although it would seem to be less distinct than that of motor, somatosensory, and visual cortices. Perhaps as expected by now, the most clear-cut parameter along which this organization has been observed is the CF of the nerve cells. Those neurons sharply selective to one frequency of stimulation tend to have the same, or nearly the same, CF if they lie within the same column, as illustrated schematically in Figure 6.34.

Evidence also has mounted suggesting the characteristics of the neurons' responses to binaural stimulation to be another parameter of cortical organization. Cutting across the isofrequency contours of the primary auditory cortex are bands of neurons that, for the most part, are of either the excitatory-excitatory or excitatory-inhibitory types, thereby defining summation and suppression columns, respectively. Analogous to tonotopical organization, this scheme also may merely reflect subcortical organization. The medial geniculate body of the thalamus and lower nuclei are also characterized by laminar organization, wherein neurons lying in isofrequency laminae or sheets are typi-

cally either excitatory-excitatory or excitatory-inhibitory cells. These laminae seem to project to the different binaural bands in the cortex.

There are still many matters to be settled concerning columnar organization of the auditory cortex, so the significance of this organizational scheme cannot be appreciated fully. There is need for much more information to determine what stimulus parameters, other than CF, govern the formation of columns or, for that matter, any other functionally autonomous grouping of neurons. The nerve cells of the auditory cortex seem to reflect increased specialization, thus following the trends set at lower levels of the system. Nerve cells at the upper levels of the system thus become increasingly more selective in their response to novel stimuli or certain features of the stimulus. Until the advent of recordings in awake animals, it seemed that, in fact, many cells at the cortical level are largely unresponsive to simple stimuli, such as sustained pure tones. However, the on-response pattern, described in reference to brain stem auditory neurons, now seems to be the most common pattern in the discharge of cortical neurons responding to tones (or relatively long-lasting tone bursts, for example, 200 msec). Therefore, cortical auditory neurons tend to have phasic response characteristics.

One very important difference between cortical auditory neurons and those at the brain stem level is seen in the representation of intensity at the cortical level. First, and in general, the dynamic range of the fibers is broad, in many cases exceeding 50 dB. However, there is disagreement on this point in the literature; this, in turn, may be attributable to species differences and/or the level of arousal of the animal (namely, anesthetized versus awake). In the discussion here, emphasis is placed on findings from relatively recent observations in awake performing monkeys that, in turn, would seem to be most generalizable to the alert human. Second, a sub-

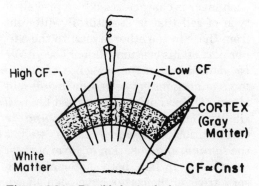

**Figure 6.34.** Possible basis of columnar organization in the auditory cortex. The neurons in each column have a CF that varies across the surface, according to the tonotopical organization but is essentially constant (*Cnst*) within the column at different depths.

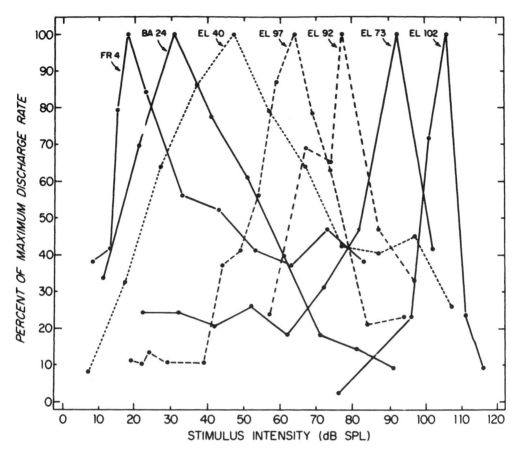

**Figure 6.35.** Spike rate functions (in which spike rate is normalized to maximum discharge rate) from single-unit recordings from cortical neurons of awake performing monkeys (reaction time task). Stimuli were 200-msec tone bursts. (From Pfingst, B. E., and O'Connor, T. A. [1981]. Characteristics of neurons in auditory cortex of monkeys performing a simple auditory task. *J. Neurophysiol.* 45:16–34.)

stantial population of cortical fibers exhibits nonmonotonic spike rate functions, which have peaks at one stimulus intensity, as illustrated in Figure 6.35. In other words, these units tend to be tuned to a particular intensity. Neurons characterized by nonmonotonic functions are found at lower levels (even at the level of the cochlear nucleus, namely, in the DCN), but it is their prevalence in the cortex that is so impressive. In some cases the functions are rather complex.

In addition to the primary cortex, as mentioned earlier, there are secondary and association areas that serve auditory functions, although not exclusively. They are distinguished from the primary cortex by the fact that neurons in the ascending auditory pathway do not project directly to these areas. Neurons in the association areas, in particular, are excitable via other sensory modalities, such as visual and somatosensory stimulation. Most of the neurons are responsive to sound but exhibit very broad frequency-tuning functions, although some sharply tuned cells can be found. The prevalence of broadly tuned neurons in these areas seems consistent with the presumed integrative role of association cortices; in other words, they reflect a considerable amount of convergence of inputs from other cells at cortical or subcortical levels, that is, from nonspecific projections to the cortex.

## B. Do You Really Need Your Cortex To Hear?

This may seem like a really dumb question, but, given the extent to which auditory information is processed at subcortical levels, one is inclined to query whether the auditory cortex is necessary for hearing at all! Certainly, it is not unreasonable to question which aspects of auditory function absolutely require cortical-level processing. Some insight into the answers to these questions has been provided from some now-classic experiments by Dewey Neff in which animals (cats) were trained to perform certain auditory tasks. Subsequently, the auditory cortices were ablated (cut out) bilaterally.[2] After a suitable recovery period, the ability of the animal to perform the task was reevaluated. Although the exact nature of the task is itself an influential factor, it can be stated, in general, that the following kinds of tasks could be performed without the auditory cortices:

1. Response to the onset of a sound;
2. Response to changes in the intensity of a tone;
3. Response to changes in the frequency of a tone; and
4. Response to changes in the location of a sound.

For example, a cat can be trained to go to one side of a box when it hears a tone of slightly changing frequency. After ablation of the auditory cortices, the animal is still capable of responding to these frequency changes and, after some relearning, can perform the task at its preoperative level.

Success with the performance of the tasks outlined above reflects the extent to which the basic sensitivity of the hearing system and the ability of the system to resolve differences are established at the lower levels of the auditory system. The ability to discriminate one frequency of sound from another is most likely determined by the tuning functions of the primary auditory neurons (at least for frequencies above approximately 2 kHz), because increased sharpening in the tuning curves is rarely observed at higher levels of the system. In the case of intensity discrimination, the mechanisms involved are less obvious, and it is not clear yet whether the limits of resolution are essentially set at subcortical levels. Still, intensity differences should be detectable by neurons at subcortical auditory centers, at least for low-level stimuli, by virtue of peripheral intensity encoding alone. The ability to detect interaural intensity and temporal and phase disparities also is well established at the subcortical levels, hence retention of the ability of the auditory-decorticate animal to detect changes in interaural intensity or phase differences and to react to changes in the location of the sound.

Bilateral ablation of the auditory cortices, on the other hand, causes deficits in the performance of the following tasks:

1. Discrimination of tonal pattern;
2. Discrimination of sound duration; and
3. Localization of sounds in space.

For example, an animal trained to respond only to the tonal sequence low-high-low after surgery is unable to distinguish this pattern from the patterns of low-low-high or high-low-low (given that the low- and high-frequency tones themselves are unchanged). Distinguishing changes in duration is a troublesome task, as well, for animals deprived of their auditory cortices. Apparently, one's sense of time is something that requires cortical-level processing. Last, even though considerable binaural processing occurs in the brain stem, bilateral ablation of the auditory cortices causes decreases in the proficiency of per-

---

[2] This typically included all areas receiving projections from the medial geniculate, that is, auditory areas I and II, the posterior ectosylvian gyrus, and the insular-temporal region.

forming localization tasks. The judgmental process of deciding where a sound is located and the subsequent ability to approach the sound source apparently depends on the presence of intact auditory cortices. However, the demonstration of the latter requires that the task be structured so that the animal is required to do more than just turn its head to one side or the other to respond. The most dramatic breakdown in performance, thus, is seen only in those tasks in which the animal must know the origin of the sound and directly approach it. If the animal's approach is not direct, that is, its course of travel to the source is somewhat of a zig-zag pattern, it is very likely that intensity discrimination ability, rather than sound localization, is what is really being observed; the intensity of the sound naturally increases as the sound source is approached. So, the deficit becomes critical when the animal must rely on some kind of internal map of the sound in space.

To some extent, the difficulties in performing the tasks listed above reflect situations in which few new neural units (in terms of numbers activated) are likely to be excited when a change is made from a background or negative stimulus (such as the tonal pattern low-low-high) to a positive stimulus (for example, low-high-low). In general, cortical processing is strongly implicated in the more interpretative and integrative stages of processing. This underlines, once more, the importance of the novelty of the stimulus to the cortex. It seems that the greater the complexity of the sound, and thus the more information borne by it, the greater the extent to which the cortex is likely to be interested and involved in the processing of auditory information. The understanding of speech, for example, not only requires cortical level processing; it also obviously requires processing by an auditory system that is terminated by a highly developed cortex, such as that found in humans. Infrahuman species may be taught to respond appropriately to certain spoken commands,

and some degree of speech processing almost certainly occurs at subcortical levels. Still, it is the linguistic and cognitive aspects of speech that place the ultimate demand on the central auditory system, and one to which the auditory cortex of the human seems to be so well adapted. Humans are not entirely unique in this regard; porpoises and whales offer some competition with respect to the level of sophistication in their methods of communication. Furthermore, monkeys can be taught a rudimentary (human) language.

The processing of speech is likely to involve much more than the primary auditory cortex. Again, there are secondary and association areas that certainly must be involved in this task. Consider for a moment the complexity of cortical function that must be involved in the ability to visualize a picturesque scene while listening to a verbal description of that scene. Such processing transcends even the auditory areas of the cortex. Although it is difficult to draw a distinct line between which aspects of hearing require cortical-level processing and which do not, it certainly is not difficult to appreciate the need for an intact auditory cortex.

## C. One Brain, Two Hemispheres

A final problem worth considering is whether both temporal lobes are necessary. The considerable extent to which both ears are represented by both contralateral and ipsilateral pathways was discussed earlier. There are ascending fibers that decussate at three different levels of the brain stem, plus there are commissural fibers in the cerebrum through which the two lobes of the telencephalon can communicate. The popular belief is that the two hemispheres do not serve exactly the same function. Indeed, there is believed to be *cerebral dominance* for various sensory and motor functions. An expression of cerebral dominance in the overall organization of the brain is *handedness*, although this can be a misleading criterion in the evaluation of dominance.

Nevertheless, Paul Broca demonstrated more than a century ago that lesions of the left hemisphere were responsible for the preponderance of language disorders. There similarly is a certain amount of *earedness* involved in the processing of auditory information; that is, a listener is capable of processing auditory information received via one ear (typically the right) more efficiently than via the other. This is called the *strong ear advantage* (or *right ear advantage*). Despite the bilaterality of the ascending auditory pathways, the contralateral pathways are still predominant, so the right ear is represented more abundantly in the left hemisphere. Of particular importance is the apparent dominance of speech perception (and production) by the left hemisphere. Thus, in a speech-oriented world, an individual with a lesion of the right temporal lobe may get along fairly well in terms of speech understanding, although pragmatic problems may be pronounced. On the other hand, a lesion of the left temporal lobe can cause substantial deficits of speech comprehension and may preclude full recovery of the individual's ability to communicate via speech.

Various forms of neuroanatomical and neurophysiological evidence now exist that are interpreted as supportive of the notion of cerebral dominance, particularly with regard to speech and language. The qualifier *interpreted* is used here, because the bulk of the evidence represents various kinds of demonstrations of asymmetries between the hemispheres or the temporal lobes on the right versus the left side. Structurally, such asymmetries are manifested in differences in surface area of the superior temporal gyri and other cytoarchitectural aspects and differences in the distribution of gray versus white matter. Other manifestations of asymmetries are seen in differences between the hemispheres in terms of cortical-evoked (electric) responses elicited by meaningful stimuli (speech) and differences in cerebral blood flow and metabolism. For the most part, the various asymmetries that have been observed seem to favor the notion of dominance of the left hemisphere for the majority of the population, who are right handed as well. However, not all studies have demonstrated significant asymmetries, and others have produced conflicting evidence. One thus must be careful not assume inferiority of the right hemisphere's level of processing, even if it is not dominant. It would seem that the right hemisphere serves to process complex nonverbal signals, such as music. Furthermore, the plasticity of the brain, as well as individual differences, cannot be underestimated. For example, to the professional musician, music is a language, and in these individuals music may be processed extensively in the left hemisphere.

From an anatomical point of view, the presence of two temporal lobes and the connecting pathways between them would seem to be yet another redundancy in the organization of the central auditory system. The importance of this redundancy may be seen only in the most subtle manner when it comes to processing simple and relatively invariant stimuli in quiet or a relatively simple background (such as continuous white noise). However, as increasing demand is placed on the system, for example, in the processing of novel (spectrally complex and/or time-varying) sounds presented in relatively complex backgrounds, the importance of this redundancy emerges. Although the less-complex sounds and sound environments are found primarily in the laboratory, real-world listening situations generally involve the tasks of encoding, discriminating, perceiving, and understanding of complex sounds in competing backgrounds. Exemplary of what the brain is capable is the "cocktail party effect." This is a classic problem of selective attention that has stimulated decades of research in an effort to answer the question, "How it is possible to have numerous conversations going on and still select one to which to listen?" Brain stem–level binaural processing, as noted earlier, certainly helps make such complex listening tasks feasible. Still, further processing is needed here, because not only can the brain perform such a task, but attention can be directed from one conversation to another! Even unilateral cortical lesions can interfere substantially with one's ability to perform well in such situations or, in general, to handle tasks strongly dependent on binaural integration. Consequently, it takes little speculation to suggest that, indeed, two temporal lobes are better than one.

# BIBLIOGRAPHY

Abeles, M., and Goldstein, M. H., Jr. (1970). Functional architecture in cat primary auditory cortex: columnar organization and organization according to depth. *J. Neurophysiol.* 33:172–187.

Allen, J. B., and Neely, S. T. (1992). Micromechanical models of the cochlea. *Physics Today.* 45(7)40–47.

Benson, D. A., Hienz, R. D., and Goldstein, M. H. (1981). Single-unit activity in the auditory cortex of monkeys actively localizing sound sources: spatial tuning and behavioral dependency. *Brain Res.* 219:249–267.

Brugge, J. F. (1980). Neurophysiology of the central auditory and vestibular systems. In *Otolaryngology: Basic Sciences and Related Disciplines*, vol 1, pp 253–279, edited by M. M. Paparella and D. A. Shumrick. W. B. Saunders Co., Philadelphia.

Brugge, J. F. (1982). Auditory cortical areas in primates. In *Cortical Sensory Organization: Multiple Auditory Areas*, vol 3, pp 1–41, edited by C. N. Woolsey. Humana Press, Clifton, NJ.

Brugge, J. F., and Geisler, C. D. (1978). Auditory mechanisms of the lower brainstem. *Annu. Rev. Neurosci.* 1:363–394.

Brugge, J. F., Anderson, D. J., Hind, J. E., and Rose, J. E. (1979). Time structure of discharges in single auditory nerve fibers of the squirrel monkey in response to complex periodic sounds. *J. Neurophysiol.* 32:386–401.

Brugge, J. F., and Merzenich, M. M. (1973). Responses of neurons in auditory cortex of the macaque monkey to monaural and binaural stimulation. *J. Neurophysiol.* 36:1138–1158.

Buunen, T. J. F., and Rhode, W. S. (1978). Responses of fibers in the cat's auditory nerve to the cubic difference tone. *J. Acoust. Soc. Am.* 64:772–781.

Calford, M. B., and Webster, W. R. (1981). Auditory representation within principal division of cat medial geniculate body: an electrophysiological study. *J. Neurophysiol.* 45:1013–1028.

Canford, J. L. (1979). Auditory cortex lesions and interaural intensity and phase-angle discrimination in cats. *J. Neurophysiol.* 42:1518–1526.

Casseday, J. H., and Covey, E. (1987). Central auditory pathways in directional hearing. In *Directional Hearing*, pp 109–145, edited by W. A. Yost, and G. Gourevitch. Springer-Verlag, New York.

Casseday. J. H., and Neff, W. D. (1975). Auditory localization: role of auditory pathways in brain stem of the cat. *J. Neurophysiol.* 38:842–858.

Chusid, J. G., and McDonald, J. J. (1960). *Correlative Neuroanatomy and Functional Neurology*. Lange Medical Publications, Los Altos.

Cody, A. R., and Johnstone, B. M. (1982). Acoustically evoked activity of single efferent neurons in the guinea pig cochlea. *J. Acoust. Soc. Am.* 72: 280–282.

Comis, S. D. (1973). Detection of signals in noisy backgrounds: a role for centrifugal fibres. *J. Laryngol. Otol.* 87:529–534.

Dallos, P. (1973). *The Auditory Periphery: Biophysics and Physiology*. Academic Press, New York.

Dallos, P., Billone, M. C., Durrant, J. D., Wang, C.-y., and Raynor, S. (1972). Cochlear inner and outer hair cells: functional differences. *Science* 177: 356–358.

Dallos, P. (1988). Cochlear neurobiology: revolutionary developments. *ASHA.* 30:50–56.

deBoer, E. (1975). Synthetic whole-nerve action potentials for the cat. *J. Acoust. Soc. Am.* 58: 1030–1045.

Dickson, J. W., and Gerstein. G. L. (1974) Interactions between neurons in auditory cortex of the cat. *J. Neurophysiol.* 37:1239–1261.

Durrant, J. D., and Shallop, J. K. (1969). Effects of differing states of attention on acoustic reflex activity and temporary threshold shift. *J. Acoust. Soc. Am.* 46:907–913.

Durrant, J. D., and Wolf, K. E. (1991). Auditory evoked potentials: basic aspects. In *Hearing Assessment*, 2nd Ed, pp 321–381, edited by W. F. Rintelmann. Pro-Ed, Austin.

Durrant, J. D., Martin, W. H., Hirsch, B., Schwegler, J. (1994). 3CLT ABR analyses in a human subject with unilateral extirpation of the inferior colliculus. *Hear. Res.* 72:99–107.

Erulkar, S. D. (1972). Comparative aspects of spatial localization of sound. *Physiol. Rev.* 52:238–360.

Erulkar, S. D., Nelson, P. G., and Bryan, J. S. (1968). Experimental and theoretical approaches to neural processing in the central auditory pathway. In *Contributions to Sensory Physiology*, Vol 3, pp 149–189, edited by W. D. Neff. Academic Press, New York.

Evans, E. F. (1970). Narrow "tuning" of cochlear nerve fiber responses in the guinea-pig. *J. Physiol. (Lond.)* 206:14–15.

Evans, E. F. (1978). Place and time coding of frequency in the peripheral auditory system: some physiological pros and cons. *Audiology* 17: 369–420.

Evans, E. F., and Palmer, A. R. (1980). Relationship between the dynamic range of cochlear nerve fibers and their spontaneous activity. *Exp. Brain Res.* 40: 115–118.

Fex, J. (1968). Efferent inhibition in the cochlea by the olivocochlear bundle. In *Hearing Mechanisms in Vertebrates*, pp 169–181, edited by A. V. S. De-Reuck and J. Knight. Little, Brown & Co., Boston.

Fitzpatrick, K. A. and Imig, T. J. (1982). Organization of auditory connections: the primate auditory cortex. In *Cortical Sensory Organization: Multiple Auditory Areas*, Vol 3, pp 1–41, edited by C. N. Woolsey. Humana Press, Clifton, NJ.

Freeman, A. R. (1975). Properties of excitable tissues. In *Basic Physiology for the Health Sciences*, pp 31–53, edited by E. E. Selkurt. Little, Brown & Co., Boston.

Freeman, A. R. (1975). Physiology of intercellular communication, neuronal interaction, and the reflex. In *Basic Physiology for the Health Sciences*, pp 55–88, edited by E. E. Selkurt. Little, Brown & Co., Boston.

Galaburda, A. M., LeMay, M., Kemper, T. L., and Geschwind, N. (1978). Right-left asymmetries in the brain. *Science* 199:852–856.

Galaburda, A., and Sanides, F. (1980). Cytoarchitectonic organization of the human auditory cortex. *J. Comp. Neurol.* 190:597–610.

Galambos, R. (1958). Neural mechanisms in audition. *Laryngoscope* 68:388–401.

Gardner, E. (1968). *Fundamentals of Neurology*. W. B. Saunders Co., Philadelphia.

Geisler, C. D. (1974). Hypothesis on the function of the crossed olivocochlear bundle. *J. Acoust. Soc. Am.* 56:1908–1909.

Geisler, C. D., Rhode, W. S., and Kennedy, D. T. (1974). Responses to tonal stimuli of single auditory fiber and their relationship to basilar membrane motion in the squirrel monkey. *J. Neurophysiol.* 37:1156–1172.

Green, D. M. (1976). *An Introduction to Hearing*. Lawrence Erlbaum Associates, Hillsdale, NJ.

Gulley, R. L., and Reese, T. S. (1977). Freeze-fracture studies on the synapses in the organ of Corti. *J. Comp. Neurol.* 171:517–544.

Harrison, J. M., and Howe, M. E. (1974). Anatomy of the afferent auditory nervous system of mammals. In *Handbook of Sensory Physiology, Anatomy, Physiology (Ear)*, Vol V/1, pp, 183–336, edited by W. D. Keidel and W. D. Neff. Springer-Verlag, Berlin.

Harrison, J. M., and Howe, M. E. (1974). Anatomy of the descending auditory system, (mammalian). In *Handbook of Sensory Physiology, Anatomy, Physiology (Ear)*, Vol V/1, pp 363–388, edited by W. D. Keidel and W. D. Neff. Springer-Verlag, Berlin.

Heffner, H. (1978). Effect of auditory cortex ablation on localization and discrimination of brief sounds. *J. Neurophysiol.* 41:963–976.

Hodgkin, A. L. (1964). *The Conduction of the Nervous Impulse*. Charles C. Thomas, Springfield, IL.

Igarashi, M., Cranford, J. L., Nakai, Y., and Alford, B. R. (1979). Behavioral auditory function after transection of crossed olivo-cochlear bundle in the cat: IV. Study on pure-tone frequency discrimination. *Acta Otolaryngol.* 87:79–83.

Imig, T. J., Reale, R. A., and Brugge, J. F. (1982). The auditory cortex: patterns of corticocortical projections related to physiological maps in the cat. In *Cortical Sensory Organization: Multiple Auditory Areas*, Vol 3, pp 1–41, edited by C. N. Woolsey. Humana Press, Clifton, NJ.

Irvine, D. R. F., and Huebner, H. (1979). Acoustic response characteristics of neurons in nonspecific areas of cat cerebral cortex. *J. Neurophysiol.* 42: 107–122.

Irving, R., and Harrison, J. M. (1967). The superior olivary complex and audition: a comparative study. *J. Comp. Neurol.* 130:77–86.

Irvine, D. R. F., and Phillips, D. P. (1982). Polysensory "association" areas of the cerebral cortex: organization of acoustic input in the cat. In *Cortical Sensory Organization: Multiple Auditory Areas*, Vol 3, pp 1–41, edited by C. N. Woolsey. Humana Press, Clifton, NJ.

Johnson, D. H. (1980). The relationship between spike rate and synchrony in responses of auditory-nerve fibers to single tones. *J. Acoust. Soc. Am.* 68: 1115–1122.

Kaltenbach, J. A., Meleca, R. J., Falzarano, P. R., Myers, S. F., and Simpson, T. H. (1993). Forward masking properties of neurons in the dorsal cochlear nucleus: possible role in the process of echo suppression. *Hear. Res.* 67:35–44.

Katsuki, Y. (1959). Neural mechanism of auditory sensation in cats. In *Sensory Communication*, pp 561–583, edited by W. A. Rosenblith. MIT Press, Cambridge.

Katz, B. (1966). *Nerve, Muscle, and Synapse*. McGraw-Hill, New York.

Keidel, W. D. (1974). Information processing in higher parts of the auditory pathway. In *Facts and Models in Hearing*, pp 216–226. edited by E. Zwicker and E. Terhardt. Springer-Verlag, New York.

Keidel, W. E. (1980). Neurophysiological requirements for implanted cochlear prostheses. *Audiology* 19:105–127.

Kelly, J. P., Glenn, S. L., and Beaver, C. J. (1991). Sound frequency and binaural response properties of single neurons in rat inferior colliculus. *Hear. Res.* 56:273–280.

Kelly, J. P., and Wong, D. (1981). Laminar connections of the cat's auditory cortex. *Brain Res.* 212: 1–15.

Khana, S. M., and Leonard, D. G. (1982). Basilar

membrane tuning in the cat cochlea. *Science* 215: 305–306.

Kiang, N. Y.-S. (1965). *Discharge Patterns of Single Fibers in the Cat's Auditory Nerve.* MIT Press, Cambridge.

Kiang, N. Y.-S. (1975). Stimulus representation in the discharge patterns of auditory neurons. In *The Nervous System: Human Communication and Its Disorders*, Vol 3, pp 81–96, edited by E. L. Eagles. Raven Press, New York.

Kiang, N. Y.-S. (1968). A survey of recent developments in the study of auditory physiology. *Ann. Otol.* 77:656–675.

Kiang, N. Y.-S., and Moxon, E. C. (1974). Tails of tuning curves of auditory-nerve fibers. *J. Acoust. Soc. Am.* 55:620–630.

Kiang, N. Y. S., Rho, J. M., Northrop, C. C., Liberman, M. C., and Ryugo, D. K. (1982). Hair-cell innervation by spiral ganglion cells in adult cats. *Science* 217:175–177.

Kimura, D. (1967). Functional asymmetry of the brain in dichotic listening. *Cortex* 3:163–178.

Kitzes, L. M., Farley, G. R., and Starr, A. (1978). Modulation of auditory cortex unit activity during the performance of a conditioned response. *Exp. Neurol.* 62:678–697.

Klinke, R., and Galley, N. (1974). Efferent innervation of vestibular and auditory receptors. *Physiol. Rev.* 54:316–357.

Knudsen, E. I., and Konishi, M. (1978). A neural map of auditory space in the owl. *Science* 200:795–797.

Konigsmark, B. W. (1973). Neuroanatomy of the auditory system. *Arch. Otolaryngol.* 98:397–413.

Konishi, M., Takahashi, T. T., Wagner, H., Sullivan, W. E., and Carr, C. E. (1988). Neurophysiological and anatomical substrates of sound localization in the owl. In *Auditory Function: Neurobiological Bases of Hearing*, pp 721–745, edited by G. M. Edelman, W. E. Gall, and W. M. Cowan. Wiley, New York.

Kuwada, S., and Yin, T. C. T. (1987). Physiological studies of directional hearing. In *Directional Hearing*, pp 146–176, edited by W. A. Yost and G. Gourevitch. Springer-Verlag, New York.

Liberman, M. C. (1982). Single-neuron labeling in the cat auditory nerve, *Science* 216:1239–1241.

Liberman, M. C. (1988). Physiology of cochlear efferent and afferent neurons: direct comparisons in the same animal. *Hear. Res.* 34:179–192.

Licklider, J. C. R. (1959). Three auditory theories. In *Psychology: A Study of a Science*, Vol 1, pp 41–144, edited by S. Koch. McGraw-Hill, New York.

Lim, D. J., and Melnick, W. (1971). Acoustic damage of the cochlea. *Arch. Otolaryngol.* 94:294–305.

Lorente de No, R. (1949). Cerebral cortex: architecture, intracortical connections, motor projections. In *Physiology of the Nervous System*, 3rd Ed, pp 288–310, edited by J. F. Fulton. Oxford University Press, New York.

Lorente de No, R. (1981). *The Primary Acoustic Nuclei.* Raven Press, New York.

Massopust, L. C., Wolin, L., and Frost, V. (1971). Frequency discrimination thresholds following auditory cortex ablations in the monkey. *J. Aud. Res.* 11:227–233.

Masterson, R. B. (1974). Adaptation for sound localization in the ear and brainstem of mammals. *Fed. Proc.* 33:1904–1910.

Masterson, R. B., Glendenning, K. K., and Nudo, R. J. (1982). Anatomical pathways subserving the contralateral representation of a sound source. In *Localization of Sound: Theory and Applications*, pp 113–125, edited by R. W. Gatehouse. Amphora Press, Groton, CT.

Matsumiya, Y., Tagliasco, V., Lombroso, C. T., and Goodglass, H. (1972). Auditory evoked response: meaningfulness of stimuli and interhemispheric asymmetry. *Science* 175:790–792.

Maximilian, V. A. (1982). Cortical blood flow asymmetries during monaural verbal stimulation. *Brain Lang.* 15:1–11.

McEvoy, L., Hari, R., Imada, T., and Sams, M. (1993). Human auditory cortical mechanisms of sound lateralization: II. Interaural time differences at sound onset. *Hear. Res.* 67:98–109.

Merzenich, M. M., Knight, P. L., and Roth, G. L. (1975). Representation of cochlea within primary auditory cortex in the cat. *J. Neurophysiol.* 38: 231–249.

Merzenich, M. M., Colwell, S. A., and Andersen, R. A. (1982). Auditory forebrain organization: thalamocortical and corticothalamic connections in the cat. In *Cortical Sensory Organization: Multiple Auditory Areas*, Vol 3, pp 1–41, edited by C. N. Woolsey. Humana Press, Clifton, NJ.

Middlebrooks, J. C., Dykes, R. W., and Merzenich, M. M. (1980). Binaural response-specific bands in primary auditory cortex (AI) of the cat: topographical organization orthogonal to isofrequency contours. *Brain Res.* 181:31–48.

Mills, J. H., and Schmiedt, R. A. (1983). Frequency selectivity: physiological and psychophysical tuning curves and suppression. In *Hearing Research and Theory*, Vol 2, pp 233–336, edited by J. V. Tobias and E. D. Schubert. Academic Press, New York.

Moller, A. R. (1972). Coding of sounds in lower levels of the auditory system. *Q. Rev. Biophys.* 5:59–155.

Moller, A. R. (1973). Coding of amplitude modulated sounds in the cochlear nucleus of the rat. In *Basic Mechanisms in Hearing*, pp 593–617, edited by A. R. Moller. Academic Press, New York.

Moller, A. R. (1975). Latency of unit responses in cochlear nucleus determined in two different ways. *J. Neurophysiol.* 38:812–821.

Moller, A. R. (1978). Neurophysiological basis of discrimination of speech sounds. *Audiology* 17:1–9.

Moore, J. K. (1987). The human auditory brain stem

as a generator of auditory evoked potentials. *Hear. Res.* 29:33–43.

Moushegian, G., and Rupert, A. L. (1974). Relations between the psychophysics and neurophysiology of sound localization. *Fed. Proc.* 33:1924–1927.

Moushegian, G., Stillman, R. D., and Rupert, A. L. (1971). Characteristic delays in superior olive and inferior colliculus. In *Physiology of the Auditory System: A Workshop*, pp 245–254, edited by M. B. Sachs. National Educational Consultants, Baltimore.

Musiek, F. E. (1989). Probing brain function with acoustic stimuli. *ASHA.* 31(8):100–106.

Musiek, F. E., and Lamb, L. (1992) Neuroanatomy and neurophysiology of central auditory processing. In *Central Auditory Processing: a Transdisciplinary View*, pp 11–37, edited by J. Katz, N. A. Stecker, and D. Henderson. Mosby Year Book, St. Louis.

Neff, W. D. (1968). Localization and lateralization of sound in space. In *Hearing Mechanisms in Vertebrates*, pp 207–231, edited by A. V. S. DeReuck and J. Knight. Little, Brown & Co., Boston.

Neff, W. D. (1959). Neural mechanisms of auditory discrimination. In *Sensory Communication*, pp 259–278, edited by W. A. Rosenblight. MIT Press, Cambridge.

Netter, F. H. (1962). *Nervous System*, Vol. 1. CIBA Pharmaceutical Co., New York.

Nieuwenhuys, R. (1984). Anatomy of the auditory pathways, with emphasis on the brain stem. *Adv. Otorhinolaryngol.* 34:25–38.

Pfeiffer, R. R. (1966). Classification of response patterns of spike discharges for units in the cochlear nucleus: tone-burst stimulation. *Exp. Brain Res.* 1:220–235.

Pfeiffer, R. R., and Molnar, C. E. (1976). Computer processing of auditory electrophysiological data. In *Handbook of Auditory and Vestibular Research Methods*, pp 280–305, edited by C. A. Smith and J. A. Vernon. Charles C. Thomas, Springfield, IL.

Pfeiffer, R. R., and Kim, D. O. (1975). Cochlear nerve fiber responses: distribution along the cochlear partition. *J. Acoust. Soc. Am.* 58:867–869.

Pfingst, B. E. (1986). Encoding of frequency and level information in the auditory nerve. *Semin. Hear.* 7: 45–63.

Pfingst, B. E., and O'Connor, T. A. (1981). Characteristics of neurons in auditory cortex of monkeys performing a simple auditory task. *J. Neurophysiol.* 45:16–34.

Phillips, D. P. (1988). Introduction to anatomy and physiology of the central nervous system. In *Physiology of the Ear*, pp 407–429, edited by A. F. Jahn and J. Santos-Sacchi. Raven Press, New York.

Phillips, D. P., and Irvine, D. R. F. (1981). Responses of single neurons in physiologically defined primary auditory cortex (AI) of the cat: frequency tuning and responses to intensity. *J. Neurophysiol.* 45: 48–58.

Prosen, C. A., Moody, D. B., Stebbins, W. C., and Hawkins, J. E. (1981). Auditory intensity discrimination after selective loss of cochlear outer hair cells. *Science* 212:1286–1288.

Reale, R. A., and Geisler, C. D. (1980). Auditory-nerve fiber encoding of two-tone approximations to steady-state vowels. *J. Acoust. Sci. Am.* 67: 891–902.

Roland, P. E., Skinhoj, E., and Lassen, N. A. (1981). Focal activations of human cerebral cotex during auditory discrimination. *J. Neurophysiol.* 45: 1139–1151.

Romani, G. L., Williamson, S. J., and Kaufman, L. (1982). Tonotopic organization of the human auditory cortex. *Science* 216:1339–1340.

Rose, J. E., Brugge, J. F., Anderson, D. J., and Hind, J. E. (1967). Phase-locked response to low-frequency tones in single auditory nerve fibers of the squirrel monkey. *J. Neurophysiol.* 30:769–793.

Rose, J. E., Gross, N. B., Geisler, C.D., and Hind, J. E., (1966). Some neural mechanisms in the inferior colliculus of the cat which may be relevant to localization of a sound source. *J. Neurophysiol.* 29: 288–314.

Ruggero, M. A., Robles, L., and Rich, N. C. (1992). Two-tone suppression in the basilar membrane of the cochlea: mechanical basis of auditory-nerve rate suppression. *J. Neurophysiol.* 68:1087–1099.

Ryan, A., and Dallos, P. (1975). Effects of absence of cochlear outer hair cells on behavioral auditory threshold. *Nature* 235:44–46.

Sabo, D. L., Durrant, J. D., Curtin, H., Boston, J. R., and Rood, S. (1992). Correlations of neuro-anatomical measures to brainstem auditory evoked potential latencies. *Ear Hear.* 13:213–222.

Sachs, M. B., and Abbas, P. J. (1974). Rate versus level functions for auditory-nerve fibers in cats: tone-burst stimuli. *J. Acoust. Soc. Am.* 56: 1835–1847.

Sachs, M. B., and Kiang, N. Y.-S. (1968). Two-tone inhibition of auditory-nerve fibers. *J. Acoust. Soc. Am.* 43:1120–1128.

Sachs, M. B., and Young, E. D. (1979). Encoding of steady-state vowels in the auditory nerve: representation in terms of discharge rate. *J. Acoust. Soc. Am.* 66:470–479.

Sams, M., Hamalainen, M., Hari, R., and McEvoy, L. (1993). Human auditory cortical mechanisms of sound lateralization: I. Interaural time differences within sound. *Hear. Res.* 67:89–97.

Sellick, P. M., Patuzzi, R., and Johnstone, B. M. (1982). Measurement of basilar membrane motion in the guinea pig using the Mossbauer technique. *J. Acoust. Soc. Am.* 72:131–141.

Shore, S. E. (1986). Coding of complex sounds in the auditory system. *Semin. Hear.* 7:65–85.

Shucard, D. W., Shucard, J. L., and Thomas, D. G. (1977). Auditory evoked potentials as probes of hemispheric differences in cognitive processing. *Science* 197:1295–1298.

Siegel, J. H. (1992). Spontaneous synaptic potentials from afferent terminals in the guinea pig cochlea. *Hear. Res.* 59:85–92.

Smith, R. L. (1977). Short-term adaptation in single auditory nerve fibers: some poststimulatory effects. *J. Neurophysiol.* 40:1098–1112.

Snider, R. S., and Stowell, A. (1944). Receiving areas of the tactile, auditory, and visual systems in the cerebellum. *J. Neurophysiol.* 7:331–357.

Spoendlin. H. (1966). The organization of the cochlear receptor. *Adv. Otorhinolaryngol.* 13: 1–227.

Spoendlin, H. (1971). Degeneration behaviour of the cochlear nerve. *Arch. Klin. Exp. Ohren. Nasen Kehlkopfheilkd.* 200:275–291.

Spoendlin. H. (1981). Neuroanatomy of the cochlea. In *Audiology and Audiological Medicine*, Vol 1, pp 72–102, edited by H. A. Beagley. Oxford University Press, New York.

Spoendlin, H., and Schrott, A. (1989). Analysis of the human auditory nerve. *Hear. Res.* 43:25–38.

Studdert-Kennedy, M., and Shankweiler, D. (1970). Hemispheric specialization for speech perception. *J. Acoust. Soc. Am.* 48:579–594.

Suga, N. (1971) Feature detection in the cochlear nucleus, inferior colliculus, and auditory cortex. In *Physiology of the Auditory System: A Workshop*, pp 197–206, edited by M. B. Sachs. National Educational Consultants, Baltimore.

Syka, J., Popelar, J., Druga, R., and Vlkova, A. (1988). Descending central auditory pathway—structure and function. In *Auditory Pathway: Structure and Function*, pp 279–292, edited by J. Syka and R. B. Masterson. Plenum Press, New York.

Trahiotis, C., and Elliott, D. N. (1970). Extension of the Neff neural model to situations demanding discrimination among complex stimuli. *J. Acoust. Soc. Am.* 47:1116–1127.

Warr W. B., Guinan J. J. (1979). Efferent innervation of the organ of corti: two separate systems. *Brain Res.* 173:152–155.

Walzl, E. M. (1947). Representation of the cochlea in the cerebral cortex. *Laryngoscope* 57:778–787.

Wever, E. G. (1949). *Theory of Hearing.* Dover Publications, New York.

Whitfield, I. C. (1967). Coding in the auditory nervous system. *Nature* 213:756–760.

Whitfield, I. C. (1967). *The Auditory Pathway.* Williams & Wilkins, Baltimore.

Whitfield, I. C. (1978). The neural code. In *Handbook of Perception: Hearing*, Vol 4, pp 163–186, edited by E. C. Carterette and M. P. Friedman. Academic Press, New York.

Wilson, J. P., and Johnstone, J. R. (1972). Capacitive probe measures of basilar membrane vibration. In *Hearing Theory*, Perception Research, Eindhoven.

Winter, I. M., Robertson, D., and Yates, G. K. (1990). Diversity of characteristic frequency rate-intensity functions in guinea pig auditory nerve fibres. *Hear. Res.* 45:191–202.

Woolsey, C. N. (1971). Tonotopic organization of the auditory cortex. In *Physiology of the Auditory System: A Workshop*, pp 271–282, edited by M. B. Sachs. National Educational Consultants, Baltimore.

Yeni-Komshian, G. H., and Benson, D. A. (1976). Anatomical study of cerebral asymmetry in the temporal lobe of humans, chimpanzees, and rhesus monkeys. *Science* 192:387–389.

Young, E. D., and Sachs, M. B. (1979). Representation of steady-state vowels in the temporal aspects of the discharge patterns of populations of auditory-nerve fibers. *J. Acoust. Soc. Am.* 66: 1381–1403.

Young, E. D., and Spirou, G. A., Rice, J. J., and Voigt, H. F. (1992). Neural organization and responses to complex stimuli in the dorsal cochlear nucleus. In *Processing of Complex Sounds by the Auditory System*, pp 407–413, edited by R. P. Carlyon, C. J. Darwin, and I. J. Russell. Clarendon Press, Oxford.

Zwicker, E. (1974). On a psychoacoustical equivalent of tuning curves. In *Facts and Models in Hearing*, pp 132–141, edited by E. Zwicker and E. Terhardt. Springer-Verlag, New York.

Zwislocki, J. J. (1974). A possible neuro-mechanical sound analysis in the cochlea. *Acustica* 31: 354–359.

## CHAPTER 7

# INTRODUCTION TO PSYCHOACOUSTICS

The physical nature of sound, the stimulus for hearing, was discussed in the first three chapters. At the same time, a technical vocabulary was developed to permit a fairly detailed and technical description of how the auditory system works. The latter task was undertaken in Chapters 4 through 6 and began with a description of the structure of the ear. Finally, the discussion of the mechanisms of hearing was directed toward the manner by which sound is translated into appropriate electrical signals in the auditory periphery and subsequently processed in the central auditory system. The present chapter deals with the end product of the neural processing of auditory information—the sensation and perception of sound. *Psychoacoustics* is a branch of *psychophysics* that deals with the quantification of sensation and the measurement of the psychological correlates of the physical stimulus. Psychoacoustics, thus, is the study of the psychological response to acoustical stimulation.

The field of psychoacoustics represents a substantial area of hearing science, and a thorough treatment of psychoacoustics easily would command several volumes. The purpose here, as the title of the chapter implies, is merely to provide an introduction to the basic principles of psychoacoustics and an overview of the salient psychological attributes of sound. Initially, the auditory response area will be described, namely, the limits of the physical stimulus within which hearing exists. Another important issue is just how small a difference in some aspect of the sound the human ear can detect. This will lead to a discussion of the nature of loudness and pitch sensations elicited by sound and how these sensations relate to physical parameters of the sound. Finally, some of the special auditory phenomena, including binaural hearing, will be described. This will provide a glimpse into some of the most fascinating aspects of hearing and a demonstration of the truly intricate nature of hearing.

## 1. The Concept of Threshold

The field of psychophysics developed during the mid-1800s. A landmark in the historical development of the field was a treatise entitled *Elements of Psychophysics*, which was written in 1860 by Gustav Fechner. Fechner developed several psychophysical methods for the measurement of *thresholds* that have remained in wide use since the appearance of his treatise.

The concept of threshold implies the existence of a discrete point along the physical continuum of the stimulus, such as its intensity, above which the organism always responds to the stimulus and below which it never does. However, it generally has been recognized that such a discrete point is difficult to demonstrate empirically by virtue of the influence of various internal and external events that may not be under the control of the tester. External events might include environmental noise and small but finite fluctuations in the stimulus magnitude attributable to instrumentation or procedural limitations. Internal events could include noise in the nervous system and variations in the experimental subject's state or level of attention over time or even the subject's well-being (especially in clinical applications). Consequently, threshold is likely to vary from moment to moment. The best one can do then is to sample responses repeatedly and treat the data statistically to yield a threshold estimate. Indeed, as the concept has come be used, threshold is a statistic and is typically defined as the value of the stimulus magnitude that, on average, elicits the desired response a specified percentage of the time that the stimulus is presented. This, in particular, is the definition of **absolute threshold**. For example, to find the magnitude of sound that is just detectable, the sound is presented at different levels, and the subject's responses are tabulated. The level at which the sound is heard, say 50% of the number of times that it was presented, may be *defined* as the absolute threshold. Above this magnitude, the subject responds more frequently to the stimulus, whereas below this value, responses are elicited less frequently. Therefore, the threshold is a value that divides the range of the stimulus magnitude into regions of relatively high (above threshold) versus low (below threshold) probabilities of response.

As mentioned above, there are various factors that exist at the time of the threshold measurement and that may not be under the control of the experimenter. These uncontrolled variables can affect the accuracy of threshold measurement substantially. On the other hand, many external and internal factors can be placed under the experimenter's control, or their influence can be reduced, compensated, or at least measured. For example, the modern psychophysicist is not only interested in the subject's responses but also his or her criterion for making a response. In addition to yielding important information for understanding how the presence or absence of the stimulus is judged, this factor has a predictable influence and can be manipulated by the experimenter. The use of sound-treated booths for hearing measurement is an example of how the effects of extraneous variables can be minimized, namely, by reducing unwanted interfering noises. Nevertheless, there has been considerable debate concerning the reliability with which threshold can be specified. Modern psychophysicists have gone as far as to question the validity of the threshold concept altogether. A key factor that may preclude the existence of a "true" threshold, namely, one invariant point along the stimulus continuum, is the internal noise in the nervous system caused by spontaneous random neural discharges. The experimenter cannot control internal noise. There also are other internal factors, such as the day-to-day changes in the subject's emotional state, that typically are not subject to experimenter control. Even how the subject is instructed to respond affects the measured threshold value. Such variables thus produce fluctuations or biases in the subject's response that make it highly unlikely that one and only one value of the stimulus can be found above which the subject always responds and below which there is never a response.

Despite the theoretical arguments surrounding the concept of threshold, the threshold measurement, as previously described, is a valuable psychophysical research and clinical tool. Threshold provides one measure of the capabilities of a sensory system. Experience has shown that, even though there is inherent variability in the threshold measurement (as there is in any measurement, for that matter), reasonably reproducible threshold measurements can be obtained on humans and animals alike. Thus, even within the clinical setting, wherein measurements often must be made using untrained observers and there is little control of the subject's response criterion, thresholds can be determined within certain limits of confidence that are acceptable for practical purposes.

## 2. The Auditory Response Area

Before moving into more complex aspects of audition, it will be useful to map out the physical domain of hearing using the absolute threshold of hearing and related measures as the descriptors. Consider the following scenario. A listener is seated in a sound-isolation chamber, directly in front of and facing a loudspeaker, that is 0° azimuth. The available sound pressure levels (SPLs) at various frequencies of the stimulus have been determined previously via a microphone that was positioned where the listener's head is now located. The listener is simply instructed to listen carefully and to indicate (by pressing a button) when the presence of a sound is just detected. The level of a tone at one frequency is then varied in increasing and decreasing steps until the threshold at that frequency is found (typically, the level of the stimulus at which the subject responds 50% of the time that it is presented). Other frequencies of the test stimulus are then presented to the subject until his or her absolute thresholds are obtained at a sufficient number of frequencies to permit the drawing of a graph similar to the *lower curve* in Figure 7.1. Presuming this listener to have average (normal) hearing, these data reveal the typical sensitivity of the human auditory system and define the ***minimum audibility curve***. At the same time, these data characterize (albeit indirectly) the frequency response of this system. Some details of this curve are worth noting. The maximal sensitivity is observed around 2 to 5 kHz; it is in this range that the least sound pressure—on the order of 20

$\mu$Pa—is required for the average listener to just detect the presence of the sound. The thresholds for these frequencies thus fall around 0 dB SPL re 20 $\mu$Pa (that is, 2 $\times$ $10^{-5}$ N/m$^2$). Within the range of 500 to 5000 Hz, hearing sensitivity typically varies less than 10 dB. This frequency range encompasses the spectral components of speech sounds that are most important for the understanding of speech, which presumably is no mere coincidence. Outside this frequency range, however, hearing becomes increasingly less sensitive, meaning that greater SPLs are necessary to reach absolute threshold.

The fact that hearing sensitivity varies as a function of frequency was demonstrated previously in Chapter 5, using behavioral data from the cat (see Fig. 5.18c). Sound transferred to the cochlea by the outer and middle ear seems as though it has been fed through a bandpass filter. The human threshold data shown in Figure 7.1 are similar to that of the cat, in terms of the overall shape of the minimum audibility curve, although the useful frequencies of hearing differ in the two species. The precise frequency limits of human hearing remain a subject of some debate. On the low-frequency side of the hearing range, responses from human listeners have been obtained at frequencies around 2 Hz, but the SPL required to reach threshold approaches 120 dB! However, test tones suffer in tonality below 100 Hz and fail to elicit any sense of tonal quality below approximately 20 Hz. Such sounds also are frequently described as eliciting a feeling, rather than a purely auditory sensation, doubtlessly because of the high SPLs necessary to reach audibility. Thus, 20 Hz traditionally has been considered the lower-frequency limit of hearing in human.

The upper-frequency limit also has been variably stated, probably because it varies greatly depending on the otological history and age of the listener. Measurements above the fundamental mode of the ear canal (3.4 kHz; see Chapter 5) also are

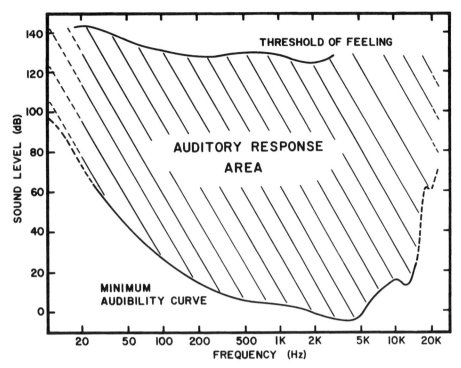

**Figure 7.1.** Auditory response area. The minimum audibility curve is based on data of Robinson and Dadson (1956). The low- and high-frequency portions of the curve (*broken line*) have been extended based on data of Yeowart and Evans (1974) and Corso (1965), respectively. The curve representing the threshold of feeling is based on data of Wegel (1932). Along the frequency axis, the auditory response area is shown to extend from 20 to 20,000 Hz by the *solid cross-hatched lines*, although responses to sounds outside these limits are demonstrable (*broken cross-hatched areas*).

inherently more variable because of sound calibration errors from the formation of standing waves. For adults, sound in the vicinity of 18 kHz requires levels greater than 80 dB SPL for minimum audibility. Above 22 kHz, the SPLs needed again approach thresholds of feeling. So, for practical purposes, 20 to 20,000 Hz traditionally has been considered the range of human hearing. Therefore, these limits represent the boundaries along the frequency axis of the physical domain over which useful hearing exists. In other words, the minimum audibility curve extending between 20 and 20,000 Hz defines the lower boundary of the *auditory response area* (Fig. 7.1).

As alluded to above, if sound is made increasingly intense, it ultimately will elicit a feeling or tactile sensation. De-

pending on the individual's tolerance, this may even be experienced as a tickling sensation, and, in any event, with further increases in the level of sound, a sharp pain will be experienced. These sensations can be elicited at any frequency, and the level of the stimulus at which feeling is first experienced is called the ***threshold of feeling***. As shown in Figure 7.1, the threshold of feeling varies much less across frequency (130–140 dB SPL) than does the absolute threshold of hearing.

The function of threshold of feeling versus frequency thus defines the upper boundary of the auditory response area, because hearing is no longer the sole sensory system activated by the sound stimulus. The tactile sensation elicited by intense sound stimulation is mediated by sensory receptors in the skin lining the eardrum. This is why the threshold of feeling is nearly constant across frequency. The noxious value of a sound on the order of 130 dB SPL also doubtlessly benefits from the intense loudness sensation that is stimulated. (It will be shown later in this chapter that the loudness of intense sounds also varies much less than absolute thresholds as a function of frequency.) Actually, sounds typically are considered uncomfortably loud at much lower levels, namely, around 100 to 110 dB SPL. When the threshold of feeling is reached, an area of response thus is entered wherein hearing no longer can be considered either the primary sensation or a desirable listening condition. Indeed, levels of sound at which tactile sensations are elicited are hazardous to the hearing organ, even for brief durations of exposure. Such SPLs are not considered *physiological* (that is, physiologically appropriate for the sensory system in question). These issues further validate the definition of the upper limit of the auditory response area by the threshold of feeling.[1]

In summary, the auditory response area represents a region in the physical domain of sound that is bounded on one side by the limits of detectability of sound and on the other side by the limits of tolerability of sound. The island also extends over a limited range of frequencies. The exact shape, dimensions, and position of this island along the intensity and frequency axes are unique to the species. Nevertheless, in humans and many other mammals, the limits of hearing are impressive, considering that the length of this island is more than three decades (or more than 10 octaves) along the frequency axis, and its maximum width is nearly 140 dB along the intensity axis (in other words, a range of nearly $10^7$:1 in sound pressure or $10^{14}$:1 in acoustic intensity).

[1] Nevertheless, the upper limit of the auditory response area often is defined as the function of the threshold of pain versus frequency, which hovers around 140 dB SPL.

## 3. Measurement of Minimum Audibility: Considerations

It is important to bear in mind that the minimum audibility curve in Figure 7.1 does not necessarily represent the hearing sensitivity of any given individual. Indeed, the data in Figure 7.1 are representative of the central tendencies of absolute thresholds for a group of subjects, although they were indeed tested under roughly the same conditions as described previously. Individual thresholds for this sample varied by at least 20 dB. The degree to which any given individual's thresholds approximate the minimum audibility curve in Figure 7.1 thus depends on just how closely that individual's hearing sensitivity approaches the mean thresholds of the group tested and the extent to which the appropriate test conditions were approximated. There are, again, various factors that ultimately contribute to the response and, consequently, to any measurement of hearing sensitivity. For example, in attempting to define the typical minimum audibility curve as an index of average normal human sensitivity, the choice of the experimental sample of listeners is itself an important consideration. The most widely accepted data today are those obtained from a group of young adults who had no history of hearing problems and whose otological (or medical ear) exams were unremarkable. Such individuals are old enough to be able to report their sensations accurately, but young enough not to have the type of hearing impairments associated with a lifetime of ototoxic agents, such as noise and certain medications and/or advancing age.

### A. MINIMUM AUDIBLE FIELD VERSUS MINIMUM AUDIBLE PRESSURE

Procedural matters associated with the measurement of hearing sensitivity also are influential. The data shown in Figure 7.1 reflect the minimum audible sound as presented in a sound field via a loudspeaker (ear canals open bilaterally) and define the ***minimum audible field (MAF)*** response of the subjects tested. These data also reflect the binaural sensitivity of hearing (assuming the subjects to have essentially identical hearing in the two ears). The sound source was located at 0° azimuth. (Note: the measurement of absolute threshold with the sound source at other azimuths would not yield the same results, because of the head and pinna baffle effects on the SPL at the eardrum; see Chapter 5.)

A dramatic divergence from the data of Figure 7.1 occurs when the sound stimuli are presented monaurally via earphones, rather than by loudspeakers in a sound field. The minimum audibility curve obtained is shown in Figure 7.2 and is called the ***minimum audible pressure (MAP)*** response (labeled MAPC in Fig. 7.2 for reasons to be discussed below). For comparison, the binaural MAF curve also is shown. An overall difference on the order of 10 dB is seen between the two curves, wherein the MAPC data reflect higher thresholds.

The MAPC data thus reflect less-sensitive hearing than do the MAF data. How can this be? Well, a portion of this difference simply is attributable to head and body diffraction effects. The greater portion of the difference, however, is the result of using earphones. This sometimes is called the "missing 6 dB." Various factors must be considered to account for the MAF-MAPC difference. About 3 dB of the difference is attributable to the binaural advantage inherent to the MAF test conditions (specifically when the listener is facing the sound source). It is as if the acoustic intensity of the stimulus reaching the two ears was added. ($10 \log_{10}2 = 3$ dB.) Additionally, in using earphones, a volume of air is enclosed in the ear canal between the diaphragm of the earphone and the eardrum. This seems to introduce two effects: a slight impedance mismatch and an enhancement of physiological noise in the ear canal because of pulsating blood flow in the tissues. These factors cause a reduction in hearing sensitivity for low-frequency sounds.

There is yet another factor contributing to the mysterious missing 6 dB, one that is purely artifactual. It is introduced by

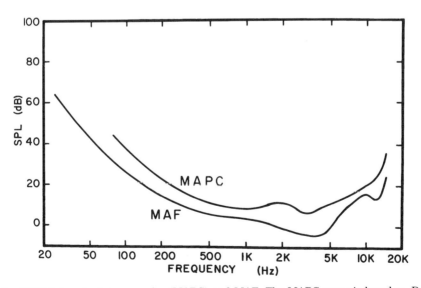

**Figure 7.2.** MAP determined in a coupler (MAPC) and MAF. The MAPC curve is based on Dadson and King's (1952) data; the MAF curve is the same as that shown in Figure 7.1, based on data from Robinson and Dadson (1956), and represents measurement of binaural free-field (0° azimuth) sensitivity.

the manner in which the SPL from the earphone used in the MAPC measurement is calibrated. A 6-cm$^3$ rigid-walled cavity is used to represent the average volume of air between the earphone diaphragm and the tympanic membrane. This cavity only roughly approximates the load impedance of the real ear—and then mostly just its elastic reactance. In any event, the external auditory meatus is not a rigid-walled cavity. MAP, technically, is the just-detectable sound pressure measured in the plane of the tympanic membrane. Such a measurement is demanding, requiring the use of probe microphones (very small microphones or microphones coupled to fine tubes) and careful placement close to the eardrum. The 6-cm$^3$ cavity is understandably a more attractive alternative, especially for routine calibration measurements. However, the true MAP curve lies below the MAPC curve (Fig. 7.2), that is, closer to the MAF curve. The $C$ stands for *coupler*, because the cavity serves to couple (or connect) the measuring microphone to the earphone and to terminate the earphone with an acoustic load intended to approximate that of the ear. The difference between the true MAP curve and the MAPC curve is thus an expression of the inadequacy of the 6 cm$^3$ as an acoustic model of the ear. The less-sensitive estimate of minimum audibility and inaccuracies of coupler calibration aside, the ease of using earphones (compared with sound field stimulation) and the simplicity of coupler measurements (compared with real-ear measurements) makes MAPC measurements very attractive for use in research and clinical applications alike. Indeed, calibration standards from the American National Standards Institute for diagnostic audiometers and other hearing test instruments rely entirely on coupler measurements.

For more critical measurements there is, nevertheless, a better "artificial ear" than the 6-cm$^3$ coupler, namely, the Zwislocki coupler. This coupler precisely simulates the average real-ear impedance and,

thus, nuances of the frequency response of the real ear canal. Furthermore, probe microphone measuring systems have been developed in recent years. Such systems make real-ear measurements practical, even for clinical applications. Indeed, real-ear calibrations are common in measurements of otoacoustic emissions and hearing aid selection and fitting, and they are readily accessible to the psychoacoustician. On the other hand, real-ear measurements are not without their own sources of error (a topic beyond the scope of coverage here). Indeed, there are advantages and disadvantages to all types of measurements of minimum audibility or sound calibration. Each can be validly used to describe hearing sensitivity, but one cannot be substituted for another without appropriate transformations. In any event, the MAPC data and 6-cm$^3$ coupler calibration continue to serve a useful and reliable function in routine audiometric calibration and other hearing measurement applications.

## B. ALTERNATIVE REFERENCES FOR SOUND LEVELS IN HEARING MEASUREMENTS

Under various circumstances, the MAF or MAP and MAPC response may not be stated directly in terms of SPL or intensity level (IL). It is especially valuable in the clinical setting to compare an individual's hearing with estimates of average hearing, such as the mean MAPC data determined in a sample of young adult subjects without significant histories of ear disease. In this application, the task at hand is to determine the deviation of an individual's hearing from what is judged to be normal hearing. A graph or chart of the results thus obtained is called an ***audiogram***, as illustrated in Figure 7.3. The abscissa is used to represent frequency, marked off and labeled according to a standard set of test frequencies. The ordinate is a decibel scale, marked off in units of ***hearing (threshold) level (HL)***. The minimum audibility curve thus is flat-

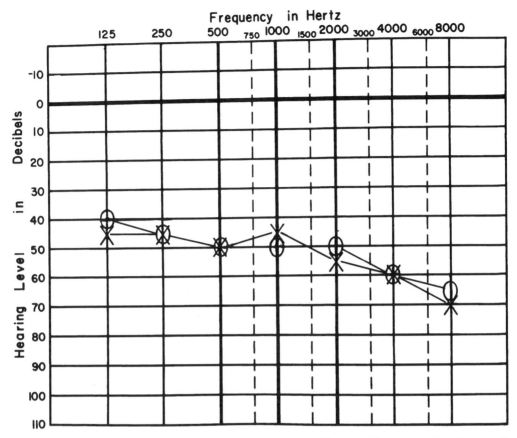

**Figure 7.3.** Audiogram showing a hearing loss for a hypothetical listener. *X*s represent the air-conduction thresholds for the left ear and *O*s for the right ear.

tened so that 0 dB HL represents the reference at all test frequencies. In reality, of course, the reference sound pressure varies from frequency to frequency (namely, according to the MAPC data determined or adopted to characterize average normal hearing), but the interest here, again, is simply how the individual differs from the reference values or the norm. Individuals exhibiting less than normal hearing sensitivity, as illustrated in Figure 7.3, demonstrate thresholds greater than 0 dB HL, and their HLs are plotted below the 0-dB HL line, but in positive values. Absolute thresholds reflecting better-than-average hearing appear above this line, yielding negative-decibel HL values. (This is analogous to the situation in which the measured sound pressure is less than 20 μPa;

such a sound then is described as having a magnitude of −N dB SPL re 20 μPa; see Chapter 3.)

If a person has a hearing loss, further testing, such as speech recognition tests, might be performed. Suppose that an individual's audiogram reflects an overall HL of 50 dB. To test this person's ability to understand speech, regardless of hearing sensitivity, it is necessary to adjust the level of presentation for the decreased sensitivity. Consequently, the speech stimulus would be presented at some number of decibels above this individual's absolute threshold for speech, known as the *speech reception threshold*. To make speech clearly audible, the test materials typically are presented 20 to 40 dB above the speech reception threshold (depending on the nature of the hearing loss). In reporting the results, it would be stated that the word *list* was presented at *N* dB **sensation level (SL)**.

There are thus three decibel measures that are widely used in hearing science. Although they are all fundamentally the same quantity, they differ in their references and intents. The *decibel SPL* is an index of the magnitude of sound referenced to some arbitrary, but generally understood, sound pressure (such as 20 $\mu$Pa). This is a purely physical reference, chosen for convenience. The *decibel HL* is referenced to a physical measurement of sound, but one that reflects statistically the SPL for that particular test stimulus that is just detectable by a person with average hearing sensitivity. Therefore, decibel HL is referenced to normal hearing. The *decibel SL*, finally, is referenced to an individual's absolute threshold, typically determined in decibel HL. All of these applications of decibel notation are widespread in clinical hearing testing and hearing research. Each has its particular virtues in hearing measurement: decibel SPL for absolute specifications of stimulus level, decibel HL for quantifying hearing losses or otherwise using average hearing sensitivity as a standard of comparison, and decibel SL for expressing some aspects of hearing within the individual's own hearing capabilities.[2]

---

[2] The term *SL* has yet another application. Suppose that a new type of earphone were to be developed, and it was desirable to use this device to study hearing, for example, with persons demonstrating a particular medical condition. On the one hand, it might be of interest to present the test stimuli to these subjects at a level referenced to their individual absolute thresholds. The presentation level of the stimulus would be stated properly as *X* dB SL. On the other hand, it might be preferable to present the stimuli at a level referenced to a level more reflective of average normal hearing sensitivity. Without an established standard of reference, it would not be possible to specify an HL. However, a group of normal hearing subjects could be tested to establish their average absolute threshold and this value used for referencing the stimulus presentation level in decibels. This too would constitute an SL. SL thus applies to presentation levels referenced to absolute thresholds of either individual subjects or a specified group of subjects.

## C. ALTERNATIVE MODE OF STIMULATING HEARING

Sound energy actually can reach the inner ear via two routes. All of the data discussed previously were from measurements involving the conventional route, that of **air conduction**, wherein sound travels through air in the outer ear, and its energy is conveyed to the cochlea via vibratory motion of the middle ear. This is the pathway that nature developed to achieve the most efficient hearing. It was noted in Chapter 5, however, that sound waves striking the bones of the skull also can induce vibrations capable of stimulating the inner ear. This secondary or **bone conduction** route is of minor consequence under normal listening conditions for individuals with normally functioning outer and middle ears. Little of the energy in airborne sound is transferred directly to the head because of the substantial impedance mismatch between the dense tissues of the head and the much less dense medium of air. If bone conduction provided the only means by which sound could reach the cochlea, as is the case in some ear diseases, there would be a loss of hearing sensitivity on the order of 40 to 60 dB. In effect, sound is attenuated by this amount (because of the impedance mismatch involved) before reaching the cochlea. Consequently, sound entering via the air conduction route is 40 to 60 dB greater at the cochlea than that entering via bone conduction. It is for this reason that sound-induced bone vibration contributes negligibly to normal hearing.

It is possible, nevertheless, to use a vibratory transducer, or *bone vibrator*, applied directly to the skull to stimulate the ear via bone conduction. This is an important aspect of **diagnostic audiology**—the use of hearing tests to contribute to the diagnosis of a hearing impairment. Differential effects of a given ear disease on air versus bone conduction thresholds can help the clinician distinguish between defects of the outer and/or middle ear versus the inner ear and/or the central auditory pathways. For purposes of this text, the greatest importance of the bone conduction route is that it sets the limit on how discretely one ear can be stimulated via the air conduction route. When sound is presented to one ear via air conduction at more than 40 to 60 dB above the threshold of the opposite ear (if using standard supraaural earphones), the non-test ear will be stimulated. The actual amount of interaural attenuation is frequency dependent, ranging from about 40 dB in the low frequencies to 60 dB or more above 1000 Hz. Although this does not represent a significant problem in testing normal hearing listeners at moderate intensities, the crossover of sound energy from one ear to another can be important when working with high-level stimuli, because the assumption of monaural stimulation is no longer valid. However, when extreme differences in sensitivity between ears exists (as is frequently encountered in clinical hearing testing), this may be even more significant. The result is that, even though the activated earphone is placed, for example, on the right ear, it is the left ear that is actually responding, because of signal crossover. It then becomes necessary to bias the sensitivity of the better ear to preclude its contribution to the subject's response, through the use of an interfering stimulus or masking (a phenomenon that will be discussed later).

## 4. Differential Sensitivity

Thus far, only one kind of threshold has been described—the absolute threshold. There actually are other kinds of thresholds that are of interest. Therefore, terms such as *absolute*, in this context, merely identify the type of measurement involved. A distinction will be made in this section between absolute and differential thresholds.

Any description and discussion of differential sensitivity beg a comparison be-

tween the concepts of *absolute* and *differential* thresholds. An even more fundamental issue is just why the differential threshold is of interest in the first place. After all, the absolute threshold nicely maps out the auditory response area. Differences among species and individuals (including those with and without hearing disorders) are well defined by differences in absolute thresholds, are they not? What else do you need to know?

Insight into the answer to this question and, specifically, the value of the concept of differential threshold is provided by considering yet another question. Are lower absolute thresholds *necessarily* better? Putting aside the reality of the practical limits of improvement of hearing over average normal hearing sensitivity (in other words, ignoring the problems of internal physiological and external ambient noise), the intuitive answer to this question is "yes," and not illogically so. Persons with decreased hearing sensitivity are offered treatments (surgery or hearing aids) in an effort to recover lost sensitivity. Imaginary super heroes, such as Superman, are endowed with so-called superhuman hearing! Yet, at least theoretically, a hearing system with extremely low absolute thresholds would not necessarily be better for various hearing tasks, including the processing of spectrally complex stimuli. For example, there is no obvious benefit of increased hearing sensitivity when tuning a musical instrument; the task at hand is one of differentiating between the pitch produced (such as by plucking the string on a violin) and that produced by a reference (such as the desired note struck on the piano). Similarly, super hearing sensitivity is of no obvious advantage when one is endeavoring to discriminate between words such as *chin* and *shin* (assuming the words are presented at sufficient levels, so that all spectral components are audible in the first place). Here the task is to distinguish between subtle differences in the spectral content of these words. = DIFFERENTIAL

It is interesting that, in clinical examinations of hearing, so much attention is paid to sensitivity. In contrast, examinations of vision concentrate more on acuity, that is, scrutinizing the individual's ability to discriminate among shapes or symbols, rather than measuring the least detectible luminescence. To fully characterize and appreciate auditory capabilities, it thus is necessary to consider the limits for detecting changes in the stimulus, or the *differential sensitivity* of the auditory system. Because intensity and frequency can be varied independently, differential sensitivity for both intensity and frequency is of interest. The auditory system, though, does not exhibit total independence between intensity and frequency in its response. To some extent, this is evidenced in the minimum audibility curve—the absolute thresholds are not constant across frequency. Consequently, the limits of resolution for intensity at different frequencies and the limits of resolution for frequency at different intensities must be examined to obtain a truly complete picture of the differential sensitivity of the auditory system.

## A. THE DIFFERENTIAL THRESHOLD

A few new terms must be defined to provide a vocabulary conducive to the discussion of differential sensitivity. If a listener is asked to respond when a difference between a standard and a variable stimulus is just detected, the differential threshold is being determined. The subject is not being asked to detect the smallest value of the stimulus (that would be a measurement of absolute threshold), but rather the smallest change in the stimulus that is detectable. A commonly used term for this measure is *difference limen (DL)*. *Limen* is the German word for "threshold"; for example, the term *stimulus or reis limen* (RL) is sometimes used for absolute threshold. The DL is generally equated with the concept of the *just-noticeable difference (jnd)* in a given parameter of the stimulus. Actually, there is also such a thing as the just not-noticeable differ-

ence, or *jnnd*, and the differential threshold technically is the average of the two. Nevertheless, these days DL and jnd are used almost interchangeably. As mentioned previously, DLs can be determined in both the intensity $(DL_I)$ and frequency domains $(DL_F)$

The fundamental units of measure of DLs are the same as those used to express the parameter of sound being varied. Therefore, the jnd for intensity can be given in watts per $m^2$, Newtons per $m^2$, micropascals, etc. The jnd for frequency is given in hertz. For example, if 1004 Hz was found to be just noticeably different from 1000 Hz for a given subject, that person's $DL_F$ would be specified as 4 Hz. Stated as such, differential sensitivity is being expressed in absolute terms.

## B. DL, WEBER FRACTION, AND FECHNER

Differential sensitivity actually can be expressed in more than one way. Rather than the "absolute" change in the stimulus that is just noticeable, the differential threshold also can be expressed as the proportional or relative change in the stimulus that is detectable. Historically, a measure of the latter quantity has been of as much interest as the DL per se. This index of relative differential sensitivity is called the *Weber fraction*. The Weber fraction is determined by dividing the DL (for example, $\Delta I$ or $\Delta F$) by the value of the stimulus $(I$ or $F)$ to which the just detectable increment or decrement is added: $\Delta I/I$ or $\Delta F/F$, respectively. What the Weber fraction does then, mathematically speaking, is to normalize the DL to the stimulus value around which the change in the stimulus is made. The change can be an increase or decrease in the value of the standard stimulus.

Assume, for instance, that it is of interest to determine the intensity resolution for a certain sound. Following the DL procedure, as described earlier, a standard stimulus, of a particular intensity $(I)$, is paired with a variable stimulus of slightly different intensity $(I')$ with all other stimulus parameters being held constant. The intensity is then varied over a number of trials until the point is found at which a difference is just discernible. As in the case of the absolute threshold, this point actually will represent a probability of response, for example, the intensity that is judged to be different from the standard approximately 75% of the time, depending on the measurement procedure and the experimenter's criterion for the DL. Therefore, $\Delta I = I' - I$, and, again, the Weber fraction equals $\Delta I / I$. The Weber fraction thus renders differential sensitivity as a ratio or, if multiplied by 100, a percentage. This means that the physical units of measure are lost because of cancellation between the numerator and the denominator, so, like the decibel, the Weber fraction is a dimensionless number.

Differential sensitivity for intensity of sound, indeed, is typically reported in terms of the decibel difference between two sounds that are of just noticeably different SPLs (or ILs). In essence, this yields a logarithmic transformation of the DL, or, more specifically, it is a transformation of the Weber fraction for intensity. Therefore, a jnd that, as a function of intensity, is constant in decibels reflects a constant Weber fraction (that is, a constant percentage change). Recall that equal ratios yield equal intervals on a logarithmic scale (Chapter 3). Consequently, the measurement of the intensity DL in decibels is a measurement of relative differential sensitivity, just as is the Weber fraction itself, and it represents the auditory system's limits of resolution for proportional changes in the stimulus intensity.[3]

Now, the tie-in to the decibel and the long-standing interest in the Weber fraction are not merely matters of historical curiosity or of convenience for the specification of the DL for a given set of stimulus

conditions. Consider, for example, the implication of the following outcome of an investigation of differential sensitivity for stimulus intensity: the absolute DL is observed to vary widely as a function of the value of the standard stimulus, yet the Weber fraction or *relative* DL remains essentially constant, regardless of the SPL of the stimulus. Such an outcome suggests that it is not a certain *arithmetic* difference between stimuli that is detectable by the organism—that is, a constant DL—but, rather, a certain proportional or *geometric* change—that is, a constant relative DL. This outcome, in turn, has far-reaching implications for how the organism's sensory system encodes this parameter of the stimulus and perhaps how the magnitude of sensation or response relates to the magnitude of the stimulus! So thought Fechner, anyway, as expressed by his "law":

$$R = C \log S \qquad (7.1)$$

where $R$ is the magnitude of the response or sensation (such as hearing), $S$ is the magnitude of the stimulus (such as sound), and $C$ is a constant of proportionality. **Fechner's law** was discussed briefly as a part of the background of the decibel (Chapter 3; see Eq. 3.5). Because the decibel expresses stimulus magnitude in log units, Fechner's law predicts a direct proportionality between the perceived stimulus magnitude (loudness) and SPL. Fechner subscribed to **Weber's law**, that

---

[3] Let $L_v$ be the IL of the variable stimulus and $L_s$ be that of the standard. The differential threshold in decibels may be determined, as follows:

$$DL_I = L_v - L_s = 10 \log_{10} I_v / I_o - 10 \log_{10} I_s / I_o$$

where $I_v$ and $I_s$ are the actual acoustic intensities of the two sounds (namely, $v$, the jnd variable stimulus; and $s$, the

standard stimulus), and $I_o$ is the reference intensity. The above expression may be simplified, as follows:

$$DL_I = 10 \log_{10} I_v / I_s \qquad (i)$$

By definition, the differential threshold in actual intensity terms is given by:

$$\Delta I = I_v - I_s = I_s (I_v / I_s - 1)$$

Dividing through by the standard intensity, $I_s$, yields the Weber fraction in the form:

$$\Delta I / I_s = I_v / I_s - 1 \qquad (ii)$$

Thus, if $I_v / I_s$ were constant, as it would be if the relative DL in decibels were constant, then the Weber fraction would be constant. It is also worth noting that, because $\Delta I = I_v - I_s$, $I_v = I_s + \Delta I$. (Note: the latter term also can be derived by solving for $I_v / I_s$ in Eq. ii.) By substituting for $I_v$ in Eq. i above, then:

$$DL_I = 10 \log_{10} (I_s + \Delta I) / I_s.$$

is, $\Delta S/S = k$, where $k$ is a constant. And, if the Weber fraction indeed is constant, then one has only to map the relative DLs over the dynamic range of the stimulus in physical units to scale the dynamic range of sensation. Consequently, if the relative DL for sound intensity were, say, 1 dB, and the dynamic range of hearing is 140 dB, then loudness should be scaled in 140 steps of 1 dB in the sound pressure. To assess whether this is really the way the auditory system works requires, first, scrutiny of findings from actual studies of the DL for intensity to see if they support Weber's law.

## C. INTENSITY DL

Various estimates of human differential sensitivity for intensity have been generated by experimental studies of the auditory system. A major source of differences among the findings of these studies has been the differences in the experimental approaches used. In the classic study of R. R. Riesz in the late 1920s, intensity increments were created by beating two sinusoids. The observer's task thus was actually one of detecting the presence of amplitude modulation; the same basic results can be found by directly amplitude modulating a sinusoidal carrier. Another method involves the addition of a brief intensity increment to a steady tone or noise. In essence, this is a method that was once a popular clinical test of intensity discrimination (known as the short-increment sensitivity index). Still another method uses sequential presentation of a standard and a variable stimuli. The stimulus paradigms for these different methods are illustrated in Figure 7.4. The influence of the experimental approach on measured differential sensitivity was a particular interest of J. D. Harris. He suggested that all intensity discrimination studies could be classified according to three putative factors that he believed to underlie the listener's ability to detect changes in sound intensity: *loudness-modulation, loudness/masking*, and *loudness*

*memory*. Although these terms are perhaps passé, the implication is still compelling—none of these methods yield pure measures of intensity discrimination, and differences among findings obtained using these different paradigms are fully expected.[4]

The data portrayed in Figure 7.5 reflect the general trend of results from relatively recent studies of intensity discrimination. Note that both axes of the graph are scaled in decibels, namely, the relative $DL_I$ is plotted as a function of SL. The first impression yielded by these data is that, overall, the relative $DL_I$ seems to vary little across frequency and is on the order of 0.5 to 1 dB over a wide range of stimulus intensities (given well-trained observers and well-controlled experiments). Translated into a Weber fraction, the approximate 0.5- to 1-dB limit of intensity resolution represents a ratio of about 0.12 to 0.26 (or 12–26%) change relative to the intensity of the standard. In practical terms, it is about as easy to distinguish between two sounds presented at 30 and 31 dB IL as it is to distinguish between sounds presented at 90 and 91 dB IL.

There are, nevertheless, some noteworthy exceptions to this portrayal of the intensity resolution ability of the auditory system. First, when using a loudness modulation method, the relative $DL_I$ does seem to be somewhat frequency dependent, particularly as the frequency limits of hearing are approached. Second, as the absolute threshold is approached, intensity resolution becomes much poorer. In other words, near the limit at which sound is just detectable, a relatively large change

---

[4] The bases for these descriptors were the stimulus paradigm and/or the perceived task at hand. *Loudness modulation* is self-explanatory. *Loudness masking* suggests the probable influence of both the loudness change attributable to the intensity increment or pedestal and the interaction between the steady "carrier" tone and the pedestal (an effect called *temporal masking*, discussed later in this chapter). The concept of loudness memory reflects the fact that in the sequential presentation of two stimuli, the judgment of whether they are different depends on the observer's memory of the preceding stimulus.

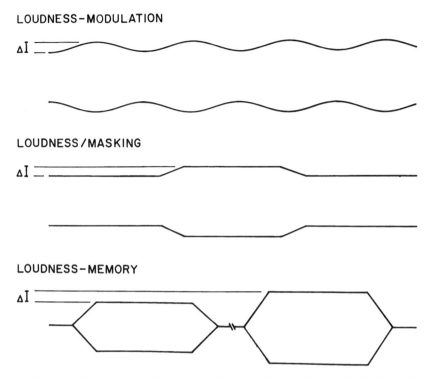

**Figure 7.4.** The three fundamental stimulus paradigms for determining the DL for intensity (see text).

in the stimulus is needed for a change in the stimulus to be detected. Last, it is clear from Figure 7.5 that, although the relative $DL_I$ varies by only a small amount in decibels over a wide range of stimulus intensities, the relative $DL_I$ is *not* constant. This means that, in reality, the relative DL for intensity is somewhat intensity dependent. Therefore, a constant Weber fraction is only *approached*. Consequently, the intensity discrimination data are said to reflect a ***near miss*** to Weber's law.

## D. FREQUENCY DL

The psychophysical methods for the determination of differential sensitivity for frequency are similar to those used in the assessment of differential sensitivity for intensity. Similarly, the methods used somewhat influence the results obtained. A classic study of frequency DL was carried out by E. G. Shower and R. Biddulph using a frequency modulation method, analogous to Riesz' study of the intensity

DL. More recent studies have favored paradigms akin to that labeled in Figure 7.4 as loudness memory, but with the standard and variable stimuli differing in frequency, rather than intensity. Figure 7.6 provides results from one such study of frequency discrimination and serves to illustrate the overall frequency resolution capabilities of the human auditory system. Here the $DL_F$, measured as change in frequency ($\Delta F$) is plotted on a logarithmic scale versus frequency; the frequency axis, in turn, is scaled as a function of the square root of frequency. This seems to yield the most linear graph relating $DL_F$ to the frequency of the standard. The significance of this particular transformation is a matter of theoretical debate, but it clearly demonstrates that neither $DL_F$ nor the Weber fraction for frequency are constant across frequency. This means that frequency resolution changes constantly across the audible frequency range.

It can be stated, in general, that the DL

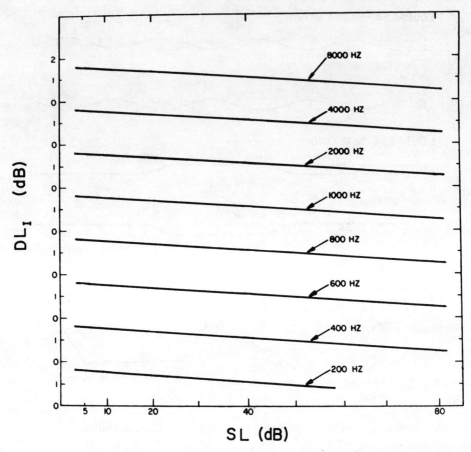

**Figure 7.5.** Relative differential threshold for intensity ($DL_I$ in decibels) as a function of the SL. The parameter for each curve is frequency, as indicated. (Adapted from Jesteadt et al. [1977]).

increases with increasing frequency. For example, at 1000 Hz it takes a 1- to 2-Hz change in frequency for a jnd, whereas at 4000 Hz a 11- to 16-Hz change is required (given trained observers and stimulus presentation at moderate intensities). In relative terms, these DLs yield Weber fractions of 0.001 to 0.002 (or 0.1–0.2%) at 1000 Hz and 0.003 to 0.004 (or 0.3–0.4%) at 4000 Hz. Therefore, over a moderate range of frequencies, trained observers are capable of detecting changes in frequency of a few hertz or under 0.5%.

The data presented in Figure 7.6 were obtained at a level of 40 dB SL. These data do not completely describe the frequency differential sensitivity of the auditory system, because the frequency DL is also in-

tensity dependent. Although the effects of intensity are minor for SLs of 20 dB and above, the differential sensitivity for frequency dramatically decreases (that is, the DL dramatically increases) as the absolute thresholds for the standard stimuli are approached.

## E. Recap: Overall Trends and Implications for Stimulus Perception

The general picture of the resolution capabilities of the auditory system obtained from measurements of intensity and frequency DLs is that the system responds primarily to proportional or relative changes in the stimulus parameter, rather than to absolute differences. The impor-

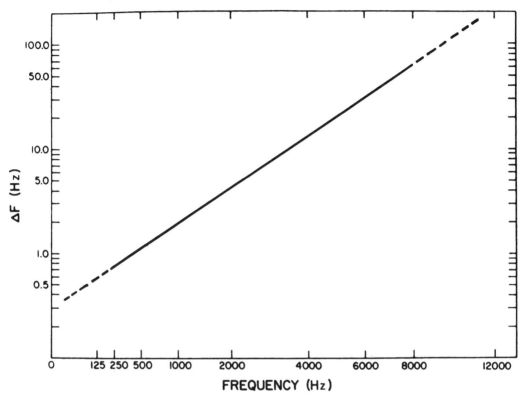

**Figure 7.6.** Differential threshold for frequency ($DL_F$). The function graphed is the best-fit line for data obtained by Wier et al. (1977) at 40 dB SL. Note that, whereas the *ordinate* is logarithmic, the *abscissa* is scaled by the square root of frequency.

tance of measuring differential sensitivity extends beyond the specification of the limits of resolution. The classical psychophysicists viewed the measurement of differential sensitivity as a method of quantifying or scaling sensations. Fechner, again, assumed that indeed the Weber fraction should be constant, and that each time a jnd was added to a stimulus, the sensation should increase by an equal amount. In other words, a change in SPL from 10 to 11 dB would be expected to elicit the same change in magnitude of sensation as a change from 90 to 91 dB! Furthermore, the sensation at 90 dB SPL would be expected to be proportional to the number of jnds between threshold and 90 dB! Although it was shown above that Weber's law does not hold for intensity or frequency, the outcome for intensity is

only a near miss. In any event, the notion that the magnitude scale of sensation merely reflects the accumulative jnds still seems workable. However, the definitive answer to the question of how magnitude of response relates to magnitude of stimulation requires direct measurements of sensations, the subject of the following sections.

## 5. Loudness

The concept of *loudness* is a familiar one, and it is generally expected that the more intense the sound stimulus is, the louder the sound will seem. From this basic relationship between intensity and loudness, it is tempting simply to equate loudness with intensity, but in reality, loudness and intensity concern different aspects of sound. Intensity is a physical quantity—a direct measure of the magnitude of the sound eliciting the sensation of hearing. Loudness is the psychological attribute of sound accorded the quantity of this sensation by the listener. Of practical importance, the measurement of sound intensity is technically much less difficult than the quantification of the psychological attribute of loudness.

## A. Loudness Level

In the earlier part of this century, a system of measurement was devised that provides an index of the relative loudness of sounds of different frequencies. The information provided by such measurements, although of fundamental scientific value, was of particularly keen interest to engineers, because it soon became clear that sounds presented at equal intensities are not necessarily of equal loudness. This might not be too surprising considering the MAF and MAP data, but neither are sounds always of equal loudness when presented at equal SLs! A measure of relative loudness thus was developed and the unit of measurement called the *phon*. The phon is referenced to the level of a pure tone of 1 kHz against which the subjective magnitude (loudness) of all other tones is judged. Consequently, the phon value is arbitrarily equated with the level, in decibels, of the standard for comparison at 1 kHz. In other words, a sound judged to be equally loud to a 1-kHz tone of $n$ dB SPL (re 20 $\mu$Pa) is said to have a *loudness level* of $n$ phons. If, for example, a 250-Hz tone at 50 dB is judged to be as loud as a 1000-Hz tone at 40 dB, the loudness level of the 250-Hz tone is 40 phons. The loudness level of the 1-kHz tone is also 40 phons, by definition.

It is important to emphasize that the term *loudness level* is used here rather than *loudness*. This is because the phon is only an indirect index of the actual magnitude sensation and is still tied directly to

the physical measurement of sound, namely, the intensity of the 1-kHz standard. To reiterate, the *phon* is a measure of *loudness level*. Nevertheless, as noted above, the phon does provide a unit of measure by which sounds of different frequencies can be equated in terms of their subjective magnitude. If a determination is made of the sound pressure (or intensity) levels of different frequency tones that make these tones equally loud to the 1-kHz standard, and if this is done over a wide range of levels of the standard (such as in 20-dB increments), some interesting data emerge, as shown in Figure 7.7. The curves in this graph are called *equal loudness level contours* (also known as Fletcher-Munson curves after the researchers who contributed the major pioneering work in this area). These contours are very revealing with regard to how the auditory system behaves. At lower loudness levels these curves tend to follow the minimum audibility curve. However, at higher levels there is an appreciable flattening of the curves, much as in the case for the threshold of feeling. Consequently, there is some compression in the dynamic range of the auditory system, especially near the lower-frequency limit of hearing. For example, to go from a 20- to a 100-phon loudness level at 2 kHz requires approximately an 80-dB increase in SPL, whereas this same change in loudness level at 100 Hz requires only a 67-dB increase!

The equal loudness level contours readily explain why there is a perceived loss in the fidelity of music reproduced by a stereo system played at low levels. At these levels, the auditory system simply filters out very low and very high frequency sounds. An examination of the 40-phon contour in Figure 7.7 demonstrates this point. Sounds in the frequency range of 300 to 5000 Hz presented at 40 dB SPL are heard with nearly the same loudness level—approximately 40 phons. However, sounds at frequencies outside of this are

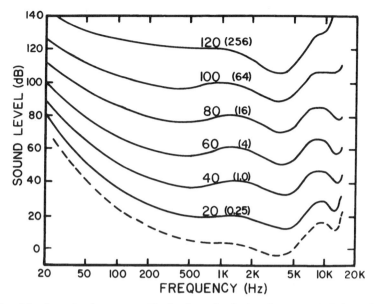

**Figure 7.7.** Equal loudness level contours. The loudness level of each contour is indicated in phons, with estimated loudness in sones indicated in *parentheses* (see text). The *broken curve* represents the MAF response, as shown in Figures 7.1 and 7.2. (Based on Robinson and Dadson [1956]).

softer. For example, a sound of 100 Hz will have a loudness level of only 20 phons. Sounds below 50 Hz will be inaudible (even if the speaker system has a flat enough frequency response to produce the same SPL [40 dB in this example] at such low frequencies). At higher frequencies, the loudness level overall will fall below 40 phons, although the picture is somewhat complicated by the effects of ear canal resonance and head and pinna baffle, accounting for the somewhat wavy quality of the high-frequency end of the contours. The 40-phon contour, incidentally, is of special interest. It is the function after which the dB$_A$ weighting scale is modeled. This is a bandpass filter function that frequently is applied to SPL measurement, especially in surveying noise and assessing its potential risk to hearing. The idea here (in a nutshell) is that sounds of different frequencies are not equally harmful, because of the bandpass filtering of the ear (as reflected by the minimum audibility curve). On the other hand, at the upper extreme of the dynamic range, the con-

tours flatten appreciably. Presumably, "the truth" of risk lies somewhere between these extremes. The 40-phon contour was chosen as a reasonable compromise.

Returning to the high-fidelity listening example, when the stereo is turned up to relatively high levels, all frequencies within the hearing range are heard with roughly the same loudness. A common device used by manufacturers of high-fidelity equipment is the so-called loudness switch, which, when activated, inserts a compensating network to boost the lows and highs. This makes the frequency response characteristics roughly a mirror image of the lower-most phon-level contours. This permits the listener to perceive the full spectrum of musical sounds while listening at relatively low sound levels. However, less-than-scrupulous high-fidelity salespeople and high-fidelity enthusiasts who crave floor-shaking listening experiences have a habit of using the loudness setting to obtain larger-than-life fidelity, especially bass response, and/or to try to compensate for less-than-flat response characteristics of a loudspeaker (especially small, cheap ones).

## B. Loudness and Direct Magnitude Estimation

At about the same time that Fletcher and Munson derived their equal loudness-level contours, S. S. Stevens was involved in extensive experimentation dedicated to what he believed to be a direct determination of scales of sensation. There was no question that a sound presented at 50 phons was louder than one presented at 40 phons. What was in question was, "How much louder is it?" Stevens presented sounds at different levels to trained listeners and had them estimate their magnitudes or, using appropriate instrumentation, produce a numerically prescribed magnitude of sensation. The scales finally adopted represent averages of data from the two types of measurements. For example, he was able to assign values reflecting the average perceived magnitude of sounds of different intensities. The total range of observed loudness was then marked off in equal steps, so that a sound of *n* units of loudness was *n* times as loud as a sound of 1 unit of loudness. Stevens called the unit of loudness the *sone*. Still, a physical point of reference was needed to facilitate a common sense of just how loud a sound of *n* sones is. Again, 1 kHz was chosen as the standard, and the *loudness* of 1 sone was assigned (arbitrarily) to a tone of 1 kHz presented at 40 dB SL. Because, in the sound field test situation, the average normal threshold of hearing is approximately 0 dB SPL (re 20 $\mu$Pa), it is reasonable simply to give the reference

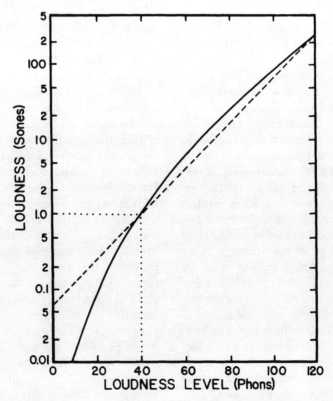

**Figure 7.8.** Relation between loudness and loudness level of a 1-kHz tone. The *broken line* is the graph predicted by Stevens's power law (see text). (Based on Stevens and Davis [1938]).

as 1 kHz at 40 dB SPL. On the average, then, a 1-kHz tone presented at 40 dB SPL will have a perceived loudness of 1 sone. By definition, the loudness level of this tone is 40 phons, so a sound that has a loudness level of 40 phons is said to have a loudness of 1 sone.

The graph in Figure 7.8 illustrates this point and demonstrates the relationship between loudness and the magnitude of the stimulus in loudness levels. Note that this is a log-log plot: log sones versus phons. The phon scale is logarithmic by virtue of its reference to the SPL of the 1-kHz standard of comparison. Indeed, because the graph in Figure 7.8 specifically applies to a 1-kHz stimulus, a given phon value in this case corresponds directly to the same number in decibel SPL. This would not be true at other frequencies, and sone-versus-phon functions obtained at other frequencies would reveal deviations from the graph of Figure 7.8. Such deviations would be particularly dramatic in the low frequencies, at which the range of loudness is more compressed, wherein the graph would be steeper. This peculiarity was evident in the equal loudness-level contours (see Fig. 7.7). Equal loudness contours, per se, have been constructed as well. However, equal loudness contours and equal loudness-level contours have similar configurations, because both reflect the relative loudness between sounds of different frequencies, although the methods by which they are obtained are very different. The latter are determined using a loudness-balancing procedure, whereas the former are derived from magnitude-estimation data obtained at various frequencies. Thus, equal loudness contours can be approximated from equal loudness-level data given the conversion from phons to sones. Such estimates are provided in *parentheses* in Figure 7.7.

The basis of the conversion from phons to sones requires knowledge of the function underlying the loudness scale shown in Figure 7.8. This, in turn, requires an understanding of the relationship between loudness and the magnitude of the stimulus.

## 6. The Power Law

Given that the psychological response, $R$, is a function of the stimulus magnitude, $S$, that is, $R = f(S)$, it is entirely reasonable to ask, "What is the function, $f(S)$?" If loudness were related to intensity in a simple one-to-one fashion, it would be sufficient to measure the intensity of the sound stimulus and merely use the physical unit of measure for loudness as well. This would mean that $f(S) = CS$; the constant $C$ simply would reflect the proportionality between the units of loudness and the units of sound measurement (such as watts per m$^2$), kind of like converting centimeters to inches. However, as discussed in Section 4, a more tenable answer to this question (especially considering the only near miss to Weber's law), is given by Fechner's law. That is, from Eq. 7.1, $f(S) = C \log S$. Loudness thus is expected to grow in proportion to the decibel level of the stimulus, which, of course, is essentially the logarithm of the stimulus magnitude. For example, a sound of 43 dB SPL (or IL) should be twice as loud as a sound of 40 dB, or one of 37 dB would be half as loud as one of 40 dB. The two sounds being compared in each case differ by 3 dB or a 2:1 ratio in intensity (dB = $10 \log_{10} 2 \approx 10 \times 0.3 = 3$ dB). The graph in Figure 7.8 presumably provides a description of the true $f(S)$ and thus a direct test of this prediction. When plotted in log-log coordinates (log sones versus phons, for example), the function approximates a straight line above the 40-phon level. This means that *equal ratios of sensation* correspond to *equal ratios of the physical stimulus.* This is not the outcome expected from Fechner's law, which predicts a straight-line graph on a semilog plot (sones, on a linear scale, versus phons). So, a different equation for $f(S)$ is needed to describe loudness, the sensation $R$ as a function of $S$.[5]

From mathematics it is known that a straight line on a log-log plot represents a power function. (Note: refer to Figure 3.3 in Chapter 3, wherein the function $y = x^2$ is plotted in different coordinates, showing a straight-line graph when log-log coordinates are used.) The slope of the line equals the power of the exponent of the function, so it is on this basis that Stevens formulated his **power law**, which may be written in the form:

$$R = CS^x \qquad (7.2)$$

where $R$ is the magnitude of the response, $C$ is a constant of proportionality (which simply influences the numerical scaling of the response magnitude), $S$ is the magnitude of the stimulus, and $x$ is the power of the function (or, again, the slope of the graph when the function is plotted in log-log coordinates). For the specific case of loudness, based on Stevens' empirical data, this formula can be stated as:

$$L = KI^{0.3} \qquad (7.2a)$$

where $L$ is loudness, $K$ is the constant of proportionality, $I$ is the stimulus intensity, and 0.3 is the slope of function in Figure 7.8 (specifically, the near-linear portion, above 1 sone). (Note: the slope of 0.3 specifically applies to binaurally perceived loudness as a function of acoustic intensity.) For reference purposes, a power function with a slope of 0.3 is shown in Figure 7.8 as a *dashed line*. In practice, SPL is the measure used, rather than

acoustic IL, in which case the exponent is twice as large, because $I$ is proportional to $p^2$. For dB SPL then, because $(p^2)^{0.3} = p^{(2 \times 0.3)} = p^{0.6}$ (see Chapter 1 and Appendix A), the power law may be restated as:

$$L = Kp^{0.6} \qquad (7.2b)$$

Unfortunately, the power law, as expressed in Eq. 7.2, does not reasonably approximate the relationship between loudness and the stimulus intensity near threshold. In the portion of the graph for sound levels below 40 phons, the magnitude of sensation grows much more rapidly than at levels above 40 phons. This apparently reflects the influence of physiological noise in the sensory and nervous systems. Stevens suggested that the effects of this internal noise could be compensated in the power equation by subtracting a small amount of the stimulus, essentially the threshold value, from the total magnitude. Consequently, an equation that better fits the graph in Figure 7.8 is:

$$L = k(p - p_o)^{0.6} \qquad (7.3)$$

where $p_o$ is a small, constant sound pressure. Clearly, at levels well above threshold, $p_o$ becomes insignificant, and Eq. 7.3 approaches Eq. 7.2. Incidentally, the power law does not uniquely apply to hearing. Stevens, like his predecessors (including Weber and Fechner), was endeavoring to establish a scientific law that would be applicable to all sensory modalities. Stevens indeed found his power law to be broadly applicable, although the value of the exponent was found to be specific to the particular sense modality. The exponent thus seems to characterize the individual sensory modality.

It is evident that there is neither a simple proportionality between loudness and intensity (that is, $R$ is unequal to $CS$) nor between loudness and IL or SPL in dB (that is, $R$ is unequal to $C \log S$). Indeed, if Stevens's power law is accepted, loudness would seem to grow even more slowly than might be expected from Fechner's law or

[5] The inability to characterize the loudness scale as the accumulative $DL_I$s, as per Fechner's theory, does not imply no relationship between $DL_I$ and loudness. The issue is just what is the relationship, a topic that continues to receive attention in the research literature. One contender relationship, first put forth by Riesz, is a modification of Fechner's theory, suggesting that the tally of jnds must be scaled to the individual's dynamic range. This yields a "proportional jnd." Experimental findings have yielded mixed support for the proportional jnd concept, although not to the exclusion of other theories. The point is that Fechner's theory is far from being a dead issue, even if not directly tenable and despite more than a century of scientific scrutiny.

a simple logarithmic relationship. Indeed, the power law states that it takes a 10-phon increase in loudness level to achieve a twofold increase in loudness. In general,

$$L = 2^{(LL - 40)/10} \qquad (7.4)$$

where $L$ is loudness in sones, and $LL$ is loudness level in phons.[6] This is the equation that actually was used to obtain the graph represented by the *dashed line* in Figure 7.8. For example, if $LL = 50$ phons,

$$L = 2^{(50 - 40)/10} = 2^{10/10} = 2^1 = 2 \text{ sones}$$

at 1 kHz, where the SPL and phon scales are identical; this means that a 10-dB increase, rather than the 3-dB increase predicted by Fechner's law, is needed to double loudness. It should be emphasized that this relationship is valid only above 40 phons (or 40 dB SPL), hence the correction factor of 40 in Eq. 7.4. This equation also is not valid for the low frequencies at which, again, there is steeper growth in the loudness functions, as noted above.

This reveals how the auditory system manages to handle such a wide range of sound intensities, namely greater than $10^{14}{:}1$ (or $10^7{:}1$ range in sound pressure). The system greatly compresses this range. For instance, at around 1 kHz a 4,000,000-fold (66-dB) increase in intensity is necessary to increase loudness from 1 to 100 sones, a 100-fold loudness change. This compression is the result of the manner in which intensity is encoded in the auditory nervous system (Chapter 6). Presumably, the auditory neurons must be driven to much higher discharge rates and/or more neurons "recruited" into activity above spontaneous discharge rates to encode high stimulus levels compared with the discharge density that is necessary to encode low, near-threshold levels (although other mechanisms may be involved; see Chapter 6). Indeed, a substantial loss of

hearing sensitivity can be incurred without much loss of loudness sensation at high levels of stimulation. This is a phenomenon called *loudness recruitment* and is often observed clinically. Actually, some loudness recruitment occurs in normal listeners, that is, near the frequency limits of hearing. Remember the equal loudness level contours?

## 7. Pitch

*Pitch* is as familiar a psychological attribute of sound as is loudness. For pure tones, low pitches are associated with low-frequency sounds, and sounds of high frequency evoke perceptions of high pitch. Pitch, then, is the attribute by which sounds are ordered along the frequency axis from low to high. Although the basic correspondence of pitch to frequency is obvious and reflects a direct proportionality, the precise relationship between the perceptual and physical quantity is less straightforward. Therefore, it is of interest to determine the pitch-versus-frequency function or ***pitch scale***. As in the case of loudness, it could be assumed that jnds in frequency represent equal distances on the subjective scale of pitch, and a pitch scale could be constructed based on the differential sensitivity data. Here, too, the final test of the validity of such a scale requires the actual measurement of the subjective response—the sensation of pitch. As with loudness, much credit is due Stevens for having undertaken this task. By having subjects divide ranges of frequencies into perceived equal-pitch intervals, he derived a scale of pitch, as shown in Figure 7.9. Note that, following convention, frequency is scaled in logarithmic coordinates, whereas pitch is in linear units—a semilog plot of the pitch scale. Stevens called the unit of pitch the ***mel*** and arbitrarily assigned the mel the value of 1/1000 the pitch of a 1000-Hz tone. In other words, a 1000-Hz tone is said to have a pitch of 1000 mels (Fig. 7.9).

[6] Equation 7.4 is derived from Eq. 7.2a and thus does not include a correction for near-threshold values. Consequently, the conversion from loudness level to loudness is least accurate near threshold.

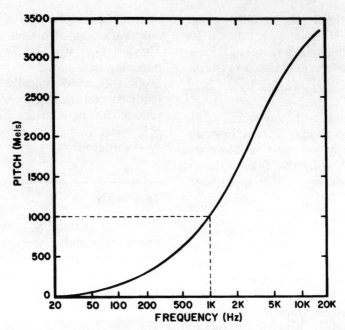

**Figure 7.9.** Relation between pitch and frequency. (Adaptation of the revised pitch scale from Stevens and Volkmann [1940]).

The mel admittedly has not enjoyed any significant popularity of use in hearing science or other areas of acoustics, but the pitch scale, nevertheless, is of heuristic value. As is apparent from Figure 7.9, there indeed does not seem to be a one-to-one relationship between pitch and frequency, or a simple mathematical function relating the two, even for pure tones. Nevertheless, the graph does approximate a straight line in semilog coordinates at frequencies above 1 kHz. In other words, equal intervals in mels on the pitch scale correspond roughly to equal logarithmic intervals in frequency, which in turn represent constant frequency ratios. As was true for the intensity range of the auditory response area, the auditory system also effectively compresses the frequency range. For example, a twofold increase in frequency, say, from 1 to 2 kHz, does not yield a twofold change in pitch. To increase pitch by two times, from 1000 to 2000 mels, requires an approximate threefold change in frequency, namely, from 1 to 3 kHz. Indeed, the entire frequency range of

human hearing, $20,000 - 20 = 19,800$ Hz, is compressed into a pitch range of approximately 3500 mels!

So, the bottom line from the mel experience is that, in the auditory system, frequency is mapped on a somewhat curvy and compressed scale. The next issue is whether frequency is the sole determinant of pitch. The intensity of the stimulus can influence its perceived pitch, although the effect is small. This phenomenon is demonstrated by data from Stevens transformed to yield curves analogous to the equal loudness level contours (loudness level versus frequency). Such curves, shown in Figure 7.10, might be thought of as *equal pitch contours*. These graphs show, in effect, the percentage of change in the indicated frequency of the pure tone that would be required to maintain a constant pitch sensation at all intensities. Shown in parentheses is the approximate pitch of each contour (taken from the pitch scale in Fig. 7.9). Thus, for example, to maintain a constant pitch of 700 mels over a range of 70 dB, the frequency of the stim-

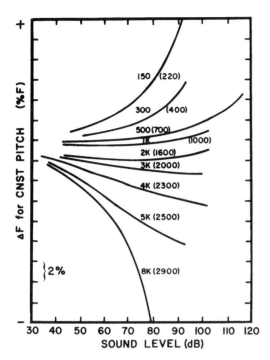

**Figure 7.10.** Equal pitch contours. The parameter of each curve is frequency in hertz (Hz), with the approximate pitch (mels) indicated in *parentheses*. The *ordinate* is segmented in intervals of percentage frequency (%) change (*F*) necessary to maintain a constant (*cnst*) pitch as the level of the sound is varied. (Modified from Stevens [1935]. Note: compared with the original plot of the pitch contours, this graph is upside-down, because Stevens actually measured the apparent frequency shift rather than carrying out a direct pitch balance procedure as the present graph implies.)

ulus eliciting that pitch (500 Hz at low intensities) would have to be varied by as much as 4%. Alternatively stated, the pitch of a 500-Hz tone will decrease by about 4% over a 70-dB range. Interestingly, the direction in which pitch changes with increasing intensity itself depends on frequency. For frequencies above approximately 2 to 3 kHz, increasing intensity causes a (net) increase in pitch, and at frequencies below, decreased pitch.

Only under unusual conditions are such intensity-dependent pitch shifts of sufficient magnitudes to be discriminated (considering the frequency-resolution ca-

pabilities of the auditory system); indeed, these changes tend to go unnoticed. There are several reasons for this. The most important reason is that this phenomenon is most obvious for pure tones, which are not characteristic of sounds in the environment. Furthermore, intensity-dependent shifts that do occur are relatively small; more recent experiments than those of Stevens failed to reveal quite as dramatic effects as suggested by Figure 7.10. Finally, sounds in the environment simply provide little opportunity for one to experience significant pitch shifts. The frequency and intensity of environmental sounds tend to vary dramatically over time, precluding comparisons of sustained tones at high levels to the same tones at low levels. It is fortunate for musicians that intensity-related pitch shifts are not more pronounced and noticeable, because it would be virtually impossible for an orchestra to play in tune unless every instrument produced essentially the same intensities of sound!

## 8. Perception of Complex Sounds

As might be expected, the sensations caused by complex sounds are more intricate than those evoked by pure tones. Naturally, the loudness, pitch, and other perceptual qualities of such sounds will reflect largely the overall physical differences, such as overall SPL or spectral concentration. For instance, if several pure tones are added together, the total energy in the complex sound is greater than that in any one of its components, and loudness is expected to increase accordingly. There are nuances of the perception of complex sounds, however, that are not readily predicted from the spectrum of the stimulus or spectral differences among complex stimuli.

### A. LOUDNESS AND THE CRITICAL BANDWIDTH

As more components are added together to form a complex sound, there is more energy in the total sound, and, again, loudness increases. No surprises here. However, the loudness of complex sounds is dependent on factors other than the number and intensity of the individual components constituting the sound complex. The frequencies of the components also are very important in determining loudness. Consider the case of a two-tone complex and the effects of the frequency spacing of the component tones. Assume that, initially, the pure-tone components are chosen so that, although their frequencies are widely apart, they are perceived to have equal loudness. Consequently, the two tones together will produce a complex tone of twice the loudness of either component alone. If each component has a loudness of 1 sone, together they will have a combined loudness of $1 + 1 = 2$ sones. However, it turns out that complete loudness summation occurs only when the frequency difference exceeds a certain range or band of frequencies. This range is called the **critical bandwidth**.

When the two components fall within the same critical band, the loudness of the complex sound depends merely on the increase in intensity resulting from adding together the individual tones (summation of the energy of the sounds) and the power law relation of loudness to this change in intensity. Continuing with the two-tone example, suppose that each tone is presented simultaneously at 40 dB SPL, but they are separated by less than a critical bandwidth. There will be a twofold increase in intensity, yielding an overall IL of 43 dB or 3 dB higher than the IL of either tone in the complex. For simplicity, assume that these tones are in the vicinity of 1 kHz. Using Eq. 7.4, the expected total loudness of the two sounds in question is:

$$L = 2^{(43 - 40)/10} = 2^{0.3} = 1.23 \text{ sones}$$

which is much less than the 2 sones expected if their loudnesses were completely summating. Now, it was previously revealed, from the power law describing the loudness growth for a single tone, that a

10-phon increase in loudness level (corresponding to a 10-dB increase in IL or SPL) is necessary to cause a twofold increase in loudness. From this perspective, it is not surprising that the loudness of this two-tone complex is substantially less than 2 sones. Consequently, as a rule of thumb, when sounds fall within one critical band, their total loudness is a function of the total loudness level of the complex, which in turn reflects the total SPL (or IL). However, when the components fall in different critical bands, their total loudness approaches the sum of their individual loudnesses. The key word here is *approaches*, because complete loudness summation can be achieved only with very wide separation of the components.

Demonstration of the critical bandwidth phenomenon perhaps is best provided by the classic experiment of E. Zwicker, G. Flottorp, and S. S. Stevens, wherein subjects were presented a four-component complex tone. The subjects were asked to match the loudness of the complex tone with that of a pure tone; the SPL of the matching tone was determined as a function of the "overall spacing" of the tones or bandwidth. Some results from this experiment are shown in Figure 7.11, wherein the level of the matching tone is seen to remain constant for relatively narrow spacing of the components of the complex tone but increases when the spacing exceeds a certain frequency range. These facts reveal that the perceived loudness of the complex tone changes only when the spacing of the components exceeds the critical bandwidth; thereafter, loudness grows in proportion to the spacing of the components.

Figure 7.11 reveals yet another aspect of the critical bandwidth phenomenon: that the critical bandwidth also is dependent on the center frequency of the complex tone. Consequently, there is no single critical bandwidth. If the measurement described in the preceding paragraph is repeated at numerous frequencies, the critical bandwidth is found to vary accord-

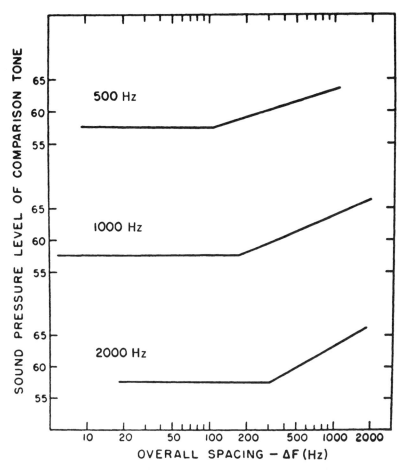

**Figure 7.11.** SPL of comparison tone judged to be equally loud to a four-component complex tone versus the frequency spacing of the components. Graphs are shown for three different center frequencies: 500, 1000, and 2000 Hz. (Adapted from Zwicker et al. [1957].)

ing to the curve in Figure 7.12. Only at frequencies below about 200 Hz is the critical bandwidth nearly constant. Furthermore, Figure 7.12 clearly shows that critical bandwidth is not a fixed proportion of frequency, yet it does grow in relation to frequency. It is noteworthy that the nominal frequency range of hearing, 20 to 20,000 Hz, is spanned roughly by 25 critical bandwidths stacked end-to-end. These bandwidths presumably represent equal intervals of distance along the basilar membrane, estimated in the human to be 1.00 to 1.25 mm.

A sound, naturally, can be made up of many more than four components or even a band of noise. Still, its perceived loudness will depend on the number of critical bands overlapped by its spectrum. On the other hand, as long as the total energy of the sound remains constant, and this energy is contained within a single bandwidth, the loudness of the complex sound will remain constant, regardless of how many components are added together. To reiterate, once the frequency spread of the components exceeds one critical bandwidth, loudness will start increasing according to the number of frequency components being added, even though the magnitudes of the individual components are adjusted to keep the total intensity

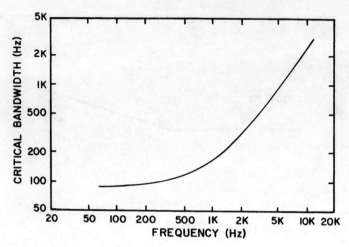

**Figure 7.12.** Critical bandwidth as a function of frequency at the center of the band. (Based on Zwicker et al. [1957]).

constant. As a practical example, consider what happens when a listener is presented with a pure tone versus speech at the same overall SPL. The speech actually sounds louder! This sensation occurs because the energy of speech is spread across numerous critical bandwidths, whereas that of the pure tone clearly is within one critical bandwidth. This effect is useful to the clinical audiologist to uncover cases of nonorganic hearing loss. In such a case, the audiogram obtained initially reflects substantially higher thresholds than ultimately proves to be true. To exaggerate thresholds, the subject must adopt some criterion for response at an HL well above the actual threshold. The decision to respond or not thus becomes a matter of loudness judgment. Because speech sounds louder than pure tones, the subject naturally responds to speech at lower HLs. The threshold for speech, consequently, may be found to be 10 or more dB below that expected threshold from the pure-tone audiogram.

## B. PITCH OF COMPLEX SOUNDS

The pitch of complex sounds is no less intricate than loudness. One phenomenon that has intrigued psychophysicists, acousticians, and musicians alike for many years is **periodicity pitch** (referred to these days, also, as *virtual* or *low pitch*). This phenomenon was mentioned briefly in Chapter 6 in the context of temporal encoding of frequency in the auditory nervous system. There, periodicity in neuronal discharges, following the amplitude fluctuation of an amplitude-modulated tone, was described. This is presumably the neurophysiological correlate of periodicity pitch. Indeed, pitch corresponding to the frequency of amplitude modulation can be detected. There is no physical energy at the frequency corresponding to the perceived pitch, thereby mitigating against involvement of place-based frequency encoding for this perceptual component. Sinusoidal amplitude modulation of a sinusoidal carrier is only one of several ways in which the periodicity pitch phenomenon can be demonstrated. The effect also can be demonstrated using white noise that is periodically turned on and off, wherein the rate of interruption of the noise determines the perceived pitch. Another paradigm is the simultaneous presentation of a group of pure tones, equally spaced in frequency and (usually) of equal intensities. The "fundamental" pitch perceived corresponds, not to the lowest-frequency component, but to the common frequency difference between the individual components. For example, if the frequencies of 1800, 2000, and 2200 Hz are used, the resulting complex sound will be heard with an underlying pitch corresponding to that of a 200-Hz pure tone. In this particular situation, the low pitch is often called the *missing fundamental*, because all components in the sound are integral multiples of the perceived fundamental (1800 = 9 × 200, etc.). In reality, again, no energy is present at that frequency in the complex.

The periodicity pitch phenomenon should not be confused with intermodulation distortion (see Chapter 3). Intermodulation distortion is created by nonlinearities in the micromechanics and macromechanics of the cochlear system and thus reflect place-related mechanisms, rather than temporal decoding at later stages (as discussed below). Amplitude distortion in the ear seems to occur because of the inability of the basilar membrane to follow perfectly the vibrations of the stapes footplate, and there are nonlinearities in the electrical transduction performed by the hair cells. Except for extremely high intensities of sound, incidentally, the motion of the ossicular chain is free of any significant distortion, so all perceptible aural distortion is primarily, if not completely, cochlear in origin. Intermodulation distortion itself has been of particularly keen interest to the hearing scientist, especially the simple difference tone $(f_2 - f_1)$ and the cubic difference tone $(2f_1 - f_2$, where $f_2$ is the higher, and $f_1$ is the lower primary). These distortion products (and higher-order products) are demonstrable in otoacoustic emissions, cochlear microphonics, and neural discharge patterns (see Chapter 5). Listeners can be trained to detect them. The cubic difference tone, $2f_1 - f_2$, is particularly robust, being detectable to as low as about 20 dB SL!

Considerable effort has been devoted to distinguishing between the detection of difference tones and periodicity pitch. A convincing demonstration that periodicity pitch can exist independent of intermodulation distortion is found in the inability of discrete bands of noise centered around the frequency of the fundamental to mask out or obscure the low pitch produced by the multitone paradigm described above. Such noises readily interfere with the detection of corresponding difference tones arising from intermodulation distortion. To reiterate, the low pitch corresponds to a frequency that is not present in the spectrum of the sound and, thus, is not a propagated wave in the cochlea. Consequently, it cannot be masked easily by noise concentrated around the place along the basilar membrane of the frequency that would give rise to the same pitch. Distortion, in contrast, distributes spectral energy to the frequencies of the perceived components, particularly for distortion products arising from hydromechanical nonlinearities. Another compelling demonstration of the autonomy of periodicity pitch is that it can be created via binaural fusion (see below), that is, by splitting the spectrum of the complex tone between the two ears. Presumably the only possible means by which the missing fundamental can be detected is by way of extraction of a corresponding temporal code. In any event, even when a difference in tone does exist at the frequency corresponding to the perceived pitch of the complex tone, timing information can take precedence.

Periodicity pitch, however, cannot account for the pitch of all complex sounds. Especially with complex tones, wherein the lowest component itself is of a relatively low-frequency (around 200 Hz and below), the higher harmonics (such as the fourth and fifth) tend to dominate the pitch percept. As the complex shifts higher in frequency, the dominant harmonic tends to shift down. In general, if the middle harmonics are resolved, they can dominate. Furthermore, especially with regard to sounds consisting of spectral components of unequal amplitudes, the pitch will be determined by a combination of parameters to which more or less bias or *weighting* is given to the envelope, even for relatively simple stimuli such as two-tone complexes. Yet, some of the most recent experiments have yielded results suggesting that, at least for two-tone complexes of unequal-amplitude components, the resultant pitch may reflect weighting of the intensities of the tone, with the pitch percept corresponding to a frequency somewhere between the two components and biased toward the more intense component. Therefore, the number of frequency components, frequency location, frequency spread between them, and (thus) whether the components fall within a single critical band can influence the pitch and its strength. Nevertheless, the periodicity phenomena exemplify the auditory system's ability to encode and use timing information, thus extracting information from the temporal features of the envelope of the waveform. This ability also is very important for another auditory capability—binaural localization—as discussed briefly in previous chapters and further elaborated below.

Random sounds and atonal transients also can elicit sensations of pitch. A high pitch is readily ascribed to consonant sounds of speech such as [s] or a low pitch to the noise of a rocket engine. These sounds have spectra that are rich in components that, in turn, are not harmonically related. And, such sounds cause wide patterns of excitation in the cochlea and/or complicated time patterns of neural discharges in the auditory nerve. Still, the listener is capable of extracting pitch information and easily can discriminate between these sounds.

Factors determining the pitch of noises can be understood to some extent from observing the pitch of some laboratory noises. For instance, the cutoff frequency dominates the pitch of high- or low-pass–filtered white noise. A pitch effect is thus created by the "spectral edge." This effect also occurs with broad-band complex tones with harmonically related components, although periodicities in waveform will contribute pitch cues as well. In any event, edge pitch is not as strong as that associated with, say, a pure tone. In contrast to the edge pitch effect, when white noise is bandpass filtered, its pitch is determined by components somewhere within the band. As might be expected, as the bandwidth of the noise is narrowed, the noise assumes a more tonal quality and evokes a stronger pitch sensation.

## C. Beats and Other Subcritical Bandwidth Phenomena

This subsection may seem like a bit of backtracking, and certainly it is possible to define the phenomena of interest here without ever mentioning the critical-band concept. On the other hand, these phenomena and the frequency bounds within which they occur are more fully appreciated in reference to the critical band, a concept that was necessitated by the observed inability of the auditory system to resolve the spectrum of closely spaced, simultaneously occurring sounds. Now, if the system cannot resolve such sounds, the question becomes, "How does it react to them?" In the foregoing sections it was revealed that the loudness and pitch of such sound complexes will be determined essentially as if they were single tones of energy and frequency equal to a single tone located at the center of their spectra. Yet, there are other psychological attributes of sound that may be considered, namely, qualities of the sound that are affected by the detailed spectral differences among complex sounds, subcritical band or not.

When two tones of very similar, yet different, frequencies are presented simultaneously, the listener will experience an interesting phenomenon known as **beats**. This two-tone complex will not have a steady loudness; rather, the loudness will vary periodically, fading in and out or waxing and waning, namely, at a rate that equals the frequency difference between the two tones. For instance, if one tone is

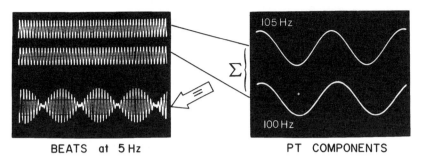

BEATS at 5 Hz                    PT COMPONENTS

**Figure 7.13.** Formation of beats by the addition ($\Sigma$) of two pure tones (*PT*), which differ only slightly in frequency. In the case shown, the pure tones are 100 and 105 Hz, and the beat frequency is thus 105 − 100 = 5 Hz.

100 Hz and the other is 105 Hz, the listener will hear a single tone of intermediate pitch between those of the two components that alternately grows louder and softer five times per second. Actually, these beats are readily evident in the waveform of the sound, as illustrated in Figure 7.13. Because of the frequency inequality, when the 100-Hz tone is added to the 105-Hz tone, there will be some instants in time at which addition occurs between them and other instants at which there is subtraction. The result is that the components add to form a sound of a frequency that is the average of the two but whose amplitude is modulated or varies over time. This amplitude modulation itself is cyclic, with a frequency equal to the difference between the two components. Thus, the greater the difference in frequency, the faster the beats.

However, there are limits to the detection of beats. The lower limit is the rate at which a change in intensity is just noticeable, probably on the order of one beat every 2 min (approximately 0.01 Hz). The upper limit is a bit more complicated. As the frequency difference increases beyond approximately 10 Hz, smooth fluctuations in loudness give way to intermittent or pulsating fluctuations called *flutter* (somewhat analogous to the visual phenomenon of flicker). As the frequency difference increases, around 30 to 40 Hz, flutter gives way to the perception of

*roughness*—a rather unpleasant quality. Ultimately, when the frequency difference is sufficient, the listener is finally able to detect the presence of two tones. In other words a complex tone is perceived, rather than a single tone that merely seems to be rough in quality. The point at which this occurs is frequency dependent but is in the neighborhood of one critical bandwidth (Fig. 7.12; see also the function for the minimal separation of overtones labeled *MFS* in Fig. 7.16). In other words, within one critical bandwidth two simultaneously occurring tones are perceived as beating, fluttering, or roughness of a single tone, depending on frequency separation.

The detection of beats by the auditory system is a reflection of the degree to which there is overlap between the patterns of excitation along the basilar membrane elicited by the two tonal components. In other words, the phenomenon of beats is a manifestation of how imperfect the cochlea is as a spectrum analyzer. When two tones are so close in frequency that they cause the perception of beats, the system cannot separate one tone from the other. Nevertheless, the amplitude fluctuations of the two-tone complex are encoded, and loudness varies accordingly. However, once out of the range of modulation frequencies that the system can faithfully track, the spacing is still inadequate for the resolution of the discrete frequency components of the complex tone, and only qualitative differences (such as flutter or roughness) are perceptible until the components are separated by a critical bandwidth. (Note: the effects described in the forgoing, wherein amplitude modulations predominate, are most characteristic of the situation wherein the two tones are of equal amplitude; unequal amplitudes lead to more complex effects, such as frequency modulation; see Chapter 3.)

## D. QUALITY

As suggested by the preceding subsection, loudness and pitch are not the only psychological attributes of sound. Particularly in the context of the perception of complex sounds, the *quality* of the sound is an important characteristic. Two sounds may be judged as having equivalent loudness and pitch and yet be perceived as being different. Consider the two sounds produced by a vocalist accompanied by a piano. The vocalist has no difficulty matching the pitch and loudness of the complex tone produced by the piano, but there are considerable qualitative differences between the two sounds produced. The most outstanding difference, in this case, is heard in the *timbre* (*tonal color* or *quality*) of the two sounds. Music teachers, for example, constantly encourage the violin student to practice bowing, and students of wind instruments are carefully instructed in how to blow into the instrument. To play the proper note (pitch) is important, but also important is the quality of the tone produced. In general, timbre depends on the frequency components combined, the relative intensities of the components, and their relative phases.

There are also qualities associated with the way different sounds go together. The words *consonance* and *dissonance* are frequently encountered, particularly regarding the musical quality of sounds. In the simplest terms, consonance connotes a pleasing or harmonious sound quality, whereas dissonance is generally considered displeasing. Different tonal components or complex tones combine in such a way as to produce more-or-less pleasing sounds, such as major chords in music. The minor cords are somewhat dissonant. Striking all keys simultaneously on the piano from C to G produces a quite dissonant sound. Of course, what is pleasing or displeasing, and thus consonant or dissonant, in music is also a matter of cultural background, musical heritage, training, and/or taste. Western Europeans and their New World descendants, for example, often find Oriental music to be rather dissonant.

Other qualitative aspects of sound can be cited, such as volume, density, and brightness. Suffice it to say that the qualitative aspects of sound seem to reflect psychological judgments about sound that are generally dependent on the more subtle aspects of sound spectra than on those that determine pitch and loudness.

## 9. Masking

The foregoing discussions on the perception of complex sounds addressed matters concerning how the spectral components of complex sounds combine to form, in essence, a unitary perception of loudness and pitch. However, some maintenance of the individuality of various sounds simultaneously confronting the listener is often important, rather than having these sounds fuse together to form one big sound percept. For example, it is often desirable to distinguish an individual voice from a background of other voices and/or noise in the environment. However, situations often arise in which the sounds in the background are of such a magnitude that they obscure the sound of interest. For instance, two workers talking around a noisy machine may fail to understand much of what each other is saying, because the machinery noise overrides some of the spectral components of their speech.[7] Similarly, it is possible for the presence of one sound to influence the detectability of another sound. This phenomenon is called **masking** and is defined as the process by which the threshold of audibility of one sound is elevated (that is, hearing sensitivity effectively decreases) in the presence of another sound. The sound causing the increased threshold is called the *masker*, whereas the sound being masked is referred to as the *probe* or *test stimulus* (or even *maskee*, although this term borders on technical slang).

The amount of masking can be quantified in terms of the resulting difference between the masked and unmasked thresholds or *threshold shift*. Because sound levels and threshold are specified in decibels, masking also is quantified in decibels. Thus, if a masker causes the threshold for a probe stimulus to be increased from 5 to 55 dB HL, the masker is said to provide 50 dB (55 − 5) of masking. The relationship between the level of the masker and the amount of masking in decibels is linear. If the initial amount of masking was 50 dB, increasing the level of the masker by 20 dB yields a 70-dB threshold shift. (Extending the previous example, the masked threshold would now be 75 dB HL.)

How intense the masker must be to mask the probe effectively depends on the spectra of the two sounds. This can be understood most easily by first considering the effects of one pure tone on another or what is called *tone-on-tone masking*. Figure 7.14a provides an indication of the amounts of masking that can be achieved in normal listeners with three different tones. In this case, the frequency (250, 1000, or 4000 Hz) and level (80 dB SL) of the masker are fixed. The frequency of the probe tone is varied, and at each test frequency the threshold shift is determined. Proper precautions have been taken to ensure that the listener's response is not sig-

nificantly biased by the presence of beats when the masker and probe are close in frequency; the two tones are distinguishable because the probe is interrupted and the masker is continuous. Clearly, the greatest masking effect is observed when the masker and probe have identical frequencies.

At the moderately high levels of maskers used to acquire the data portrayed in Figure 7.14a, there is a discernible upward **spread of masking**. Much more discrete and symmetrical masking patterns are seen when lower levels of the masker are used. However, these data were chosen to demonstrate the important fact that there is a distinct dichotomy between *upward* and *downward* spread of masking. Low-frequency tones can effectively mask high-frequency tones, but it is very difficult, although not impossible, for high tones to mask low tones. (There is such a thing as downward spread of masking, or *remote masking*, but it is observed only in the presence of relatively intense high-frequency sounds.) The reason for this dichotomy can be appreciated by considering data of another form, as shown in Figure 7.14b. In this case, the level of the masking tone that just masks the probe is plotted as a function of masker frequency. In other words, the probe frequency is fixed, whereas the masker frequency is varied, just the opposite of the masking paradigm described above. Plotting the SPL of the stimulus that just masks the probe versus the masker frequency yields the **psychophysical tuning curve**, a function that is strikingly similar to single-unit tuning functions, discussed in the preceding chapter (see Fig. 6.13). The minimums of the curves, or best frequencies, occur at or near the probe frequencies and are analogous to the characteristic frequencies of single-unit tuning functions. The shape of the psychophysical tuning curve thus reflects underlying events in the auditory periphery, primarily the displacement pattern of the basilar membrane. It will be recalled that low-frequency tones excite a wide area along the

---

[7] This is an example of speech *interference*, a suprathreshold phenomenon related to masking.

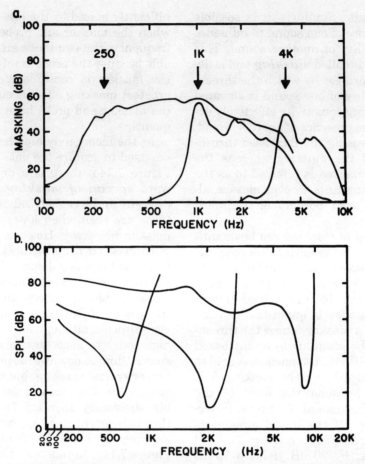

**Figure 7.14.** **a.** Effectiveness of pure tone maskers (frequency as indicated), presented at 80 dB SL. (Based on data of Ehmer [1959].) **b.** SPL of a tonal masker required to cause a criterion amount of masking or threshold shift for three different tones. In contrast to the data in **a**, the probe tone in this instance is fixed in frequency, and the frequency of the masker is varied. The frequencies of the probe tones correspond, essentially, to the characteristic or best frequency of these psychoacoustical tuning curves. The frequency axis is a special nonlinear scale but is roughly logarithmic through the midfrequencies. (Based on data of Zwicker [1974].)

basilar membrane as the traveling wave progresses apically toward the point at which it reaches its maximum and then rapidly diminishes. High-frequency tones, on the other hand, excite a very restricted region of the basilar membrane, because their corresponding peaks of displacement occur nearer the base. There is very little excitation apically to this maximum. It follows that a low frequency, if made sufficiently intense, is capable of masking high frequencies, but the masking effects of high frequencies on lows are limited.

Both clinically and experimentally, it often is more advantageous to use random noise than tones as maskers. Noises are more easily distinguished from tones so that naive (untrained) listeners can attend more readily to the tonal probe stimulus. Also, the potential problem of beats between the masker and probe is obviated when a noise masker is used. The amount of masking obtained with a band of noise depends on its spectrum and its relationship to the probe. Only the energy contained within a certain bandwidth contributes effectively to masking. The width of this band, as might be expected, is related to that of the critical band. In fact, a comparable demonstration to that of the critical band for loudness can be performed with masking. Within the critical band, the bandwidth of the noise does not influence the amount of masking obtained, as long as the spectrum level is proportionally changed to keep the overall level of the masker constant.

However, there is another index that traditionally is viewed as a direct reflection of the limited effective bandwidth of the noise masker, although it itself is taken as an indirect estimate of the critical bandwidth. This is the **critical ratio**. It is determined using a wide-band noise masker, typically white noise. The masked threshold for a particular test tone is determined along with the spectrum level (level per cycle) of the noise masker. The critical ratio is obtained simply by taking the difference, in decibels, between the masked threshold and the level per cycle of the masker. By virtue of the method of measurement and the resulting decibel quantity, this measure generally has been interpreted as the signal-to-noise ratio of the probe tone at the masked threshold. As such, it is assumed that (at the masked threshold) there is equal power in the probe tone and the effective bandwidth of noise that just masks it. Furthermore, considering the basic definition of the decibel, the measure thus obtained has been interpreted as a ratio. This implies, of course, that the measured value is dimensionless (like the decibel, as discussed in Chapter 3). A less-superficial consideration of the quantities involved reveals that, in reality, the dimension of the critical ratio is $T^{-1}$ or, in effect, frequency, and it is relatively simple to calculate a frequency bandwidth from the decibel value.[8] Indeed, even though today the

term *critical ratio*, rather than *critical band*, is applied to this particular measure, it was conceived by Harvey Fletcher as a way of determining critical bandwidths. Fletcher is considered the father of the critical-band concept.

As shown in Figure 7.15, the critical ratio, like the so-called direct estimates of the critical bandwidth (as described above), varies with frequency. It can be seen that the critical bandwidth numerically is about 2.5 times larger than the critical ratio (see Fig. 7.16 below for direct comparison). Given that they should reflect the same underlying mechanisms, in terms of frequency resolution of the auditory system (discussed below), the respective paradigms thus seem to yield different measure estimates. However, although beyond the scope of discussion here, it can be shown that the two measures really are in accord, particularly over the midfrequency range. Otherwise, procedural differences between the two types of measurements reasonably account for differences in estimates (that is,

---

[8] Consider the most basic measures of the two stimuli involved in the critical ratio measurement. The dimensions of the quantity of the probe tone are those of power or energy per unit time: $MLT^{-2}L/T = (MLT^{-2}L)T^{-1}$ (see Chapter 1). The dimensions of the masker noise, on the other hand, are those of energy, deriving from the level-per-cycle measure, which is power per unit bandwith. Bandwith, a frequency measure, has the dimension of time, because $F = T^{-1}$. Therefore, $(MLT^{-2}L)T^{-1}/T^{-1} = MLT^{-2}L$. Because the critical ratio is measured as the decibel difference between the level of the probe tone at threshold and the level per cycle $(L_{pc})$ of the masker, this implies an underlying ratio of the power of the probe to the energy of the masker, yielding the dimension of $[(MLT^{-2}L)T^{-1}]/(MLT^{-2}L) = T^{-1} = F$. The numeric conversion from critical ratios in decibels to hertz may be accomplished, in essence, using Eq. 3.11 (Chapter 3),

$$L_{pc} = OAL - 10\ log_{10}BW$$

but here the object is to find the bandwidth, $BW$, given the overall level $(OAL)$ and $L_{pc}$ of the unknown bandwidth of noise. (Admittedly, this is a bit bizarre, but in math such things are normal.) Rearranging terms:

$$10\ log_{10}BW = OAL - L_{pc}$$

The quantity, $OAL - L_{pc}$ corresponds directly to measurement of the critical ratio (in decibels)—again, threshold of the probe minus the spectrum level. The corresponding bandwith thus can be obtained by solving for $BW$, as follows:

$$10\ log_{10}BW = critical\ ratio\ in\ dB$$

For instance, at 1 kHz the critical ratio is 18 dB (determined empirically). Then:

$$10\ log_{10}\text{BW} = 18$$
$$log_{10}BW = 1.8$$
$$BW = antilog\ 1.8 = 6.3 \times 10^1 = 63\ \text{Hz.}$$

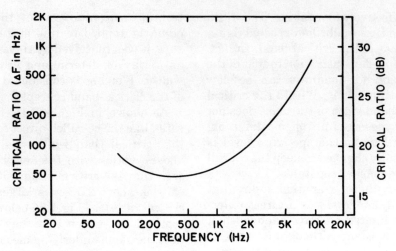

**Figure 7.15.** Critical ratio both in terms of bandwidth (*F*, *left ordinate*) and decibels (*right ordinate*), as a function of frequency at the center of the band. (Based on data of Hawkins and Stevens [1950]).

even after converting from one to the other).

It is of considerable practical value that only a portion of a broadband masker effectively contributes to the masking of a test tone, that is, other than at relatively high levels of masking at which upward spread of masking and/or residual masking occur. Now, although energy falling outside of the critical band of frequencies for a given test tone has negligible masking effects, it nevertheless adds to the loudness (and perhaps annoyance) of the masker! Consequently, in clinical hearing testing, narrow-band maskers are preferred over white noise.

Another point worth mentioning is that, given the data in Figure 7.15 and the bandwidth and overall SPL of a noise, the effective level of masking noise can be derived. A linear relationship between the amount of masking (in decibels) and the effective level is found, as in the case of tonal maskers, but there is a deviation from linearity of this relationship for the lowest masker levels. Specifically, at effective levels below 10 dB, slightly less masking is obtained than is predicted by a simple one-to-one relationship. Under these conditions one is working near the absolute threshold of both the (unmasked)

probe and the masker, so the breakdown in the one-to-one relationship between amount of masking and masker level is not surprising.

Last, there are conditions wherein a masker may be manipulated in a way that leads to a ***release from masking***, so to speak. In other words, one stimulus may mask another by a given amount, and some manipulation(s) of these stimuli can lead to reduced masking. This happens with certain binaural stimulus paradigms, as discussed below. Another paradigm that demonstrates a release from masking is ***comodulation masking***. A stimulus, such as speech, presented with a modulated noise, may undergo as much as 8 dB less masking than under the condition of an unmodulated masker. This effect may have relevance to how listeners manage to cope with complicated listening situations, such as hearing a given talker when many people are speaking or, more generally, distinguishing among multiple sources of complex sounds. There are other masking paradigms that affect listening to complex stimuli and one's ability to recognize changes in a single component, akin to discriminating among similar vowel sounds. There are still other paradigms that may even lead to enhancement of the signal (that is, relative to the unmasked condition). Detailed discussions of such topics are beyond the scope of coverage here. The point to be made, simply, is that the interaction among sounds of more-or-less complex spectra is more intricate than the interaction among simple stimuli or even between a probe tone and a masking noise. Therefore, the masking effects and/or maskability of complex stimuli cannot be entirely predicted from the masking effects and/or maskability of pure tones. The former reflect some of the intricate underlying mechanisms of the stimulus-encoding process, such as cochlear nonlinearities and lateral suppression.

## 10. Frequency-resolving Power of the Auditory System: A Recap and Theoretical Overview

Before proceeding to yet other aspects of audition and capabilities of the auditory system, it will be beneficial to pause for a moment to summarize various phenomena that were discussed in the previous sections, because many relate, in one way or the other, to the *frequency-resolving power* of the system. Specifically, frequency differential sensitivity, pitch, critical ratio, and critical bandwidth are all seemingly related by virtue of the overall similarity in their dependencies on frequency. All presumably reflect, either proportionally or directly, the frequency-resolution capabilities of the auditory system. For simplicity and direct comparison, the data relevant to these phenomena are graphed together in Figure 7.16a. As noted in the legend, the location of the pitch scale on the ordinate is arbitrary, but it has been scaled so that, were it superimposed on the critical-bandwidth curve, 100 mels would correspond roughly to one critical bandwidth. Having thus constructed a composite graph of these data, it is possible to make some direct

comparisons among them. Absolute differences aside for the moment, there are some impressive qualitative similarities. First, these curves best approximate one another in terms of slope and frequency range of linearity (over log frequency) above about 2000 Hz. The reason for this similarity is most likely their mutual strength of dependence on the place mechanism for frequency encoding. A plot of place of maximal basilar membrane displacement versus frequency would compare favorably with these curves and has been shown to correspond reasonably well to the pitch scale. One millimeter along the basilar membrane corresponds to approximately 100 mels or one critical band. Second, it is equally impressive that all curves break somewhere below 2000 Hz. It is, of course, in the lower frequencies that temporal encoding of frequency can be performed efficiently and thus can contribute substantially to frequency analysis performed by the auditory system (see Chapter 6). Indeed, until relatively recently, the temporal code seemed entirely essential because of assumed inadequacies of the place mechanism to fully account for the auditory system's frequency-discrimination ability, that is, judging from Bekesy's traveling-wave measurements. It then was assumed that the place and time mechanisms must be responsible for encoding essentially separate ranges of frequencies, with the temporal code dominating low-frequency discrimination and pitch perception.

No less impressive in Figure 7.16a are the differences among the graphs, particularly with regard to the frequency at which each curve breaks and the slope and configuration of the low-frequency segment of each graph. It is tempting to suggest that these disparities reflect the differences in the degree to which each phenomenon depends on the temporal code for frequency. However, such an explanation creates difficulties, because the high-frequency segments of the graphs are not identical either (although similar in slope). In the

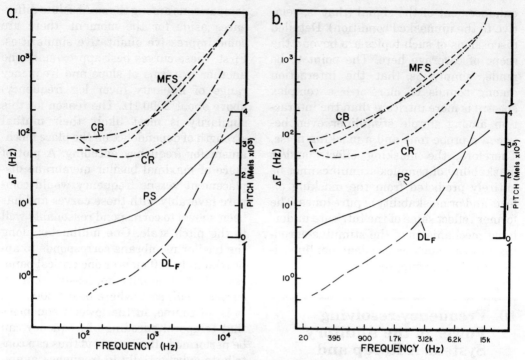

**Figure 7.16.** **a.** Composite of data previously shown for the frequency DL (*DL_F*), pitch scale (*PS*), critical ratio (*CR*), and critical bandwidth (*CB*), along with a graph of the minimal frequency separation (*MFS*) between overtones required for them to be recognized as individual components of the complex tone. The pitch scale has been positioned arbitrarily along the ordinate between the *DL_F* and *CR* curves and scaled so that 100 mels and one critical bandwidth represent roughly the same interval in log frequency. (*MFS* curve after Plomp and Mimpen [1968]). **b.** Same data as in **a**, except plotted against a frequency axis scaled in equal critical bandwidth intervals (using data of Zwicker et al. [1957]).

final analysis, these disparities are likely to reflect, at least in part, experimental variability between the different data and/or inherent differences in the nature of the tasks involved in these measurements. Also, as will be discussed further momentarily, the concept that perhaps most requires tempering is the either-or involvement of time and place codes.

Faced with the different data presented in Figure 7.16*a*, it is tempting to ask which truly represents the auditory system's ability to perform spectrum analyses of complex sounds. By definition, differential frequency sensitivity should reflect the system's limits of frequency resolution; consequently, the DL_F data might be taken as the desired index. Yet, it must be questioned whether the frequency DL is

the most realistic index of the frequency-resolving power of the auditory system. The differential threshold data reflect the system's ability to distinguish between discrete tones that, in the case of a pitch memory task, are not presented simultaneously. In listening to environmental sounds, in which complex spectra are involved, many different frequency components exist simultaneously. Admittedly, in the pitch modulation paradigm the listener is dealing with a complex tone, but in this case the listener's task involves more than frequency discrimination alone. It is the modulation, per se, that is detected—the "wavering" in the frequency, analogous to beats in the amplitude domain. The individual spectral components (the carrier frequency and side tones) are themselves not resolved. Therefore, although the measurement of differential sensitivity is informative, it is not a measure that involves conditions representative of usual listening situations.

A more reasonable index of the resolving power of the auditory system is one that directly concerns the analysis of sounds with complex spectra. The index that immediately comes to mind is the critical bandwidth. The critical bandwidth exists by virtue of the limits of the ability of the auditory system to respond discretely to simultaneously occurring sounds of different frequency. Sound energy seems to be averaged over the range of frequencies encompassed by the critical bandwidth and even beyond, although to a lesser extent. Many of the masking effects discussed earlier, for example, are expressions of the limited ability of the auditory system to resolve the spectral components of complex sounds. The validity of the critical bandwidth as the true index of the resolving power of the auditory system is supported by consideration of other forms of data that depend on frequency analysis of complex sounds. The curve marked *MFS* in Figure 7.16a provides such a case; this is a graph demonstrating minimal frequency separation between successive overtones in a complex tone that must exist for the components to be perceived individually. The similarity of this curve to the critical-bandwidth function is evident.

Now, the idea of the critical bandwidth as an index of frequency resolution suggests that the auditory system acts like a series of cascaded bandpass filters. Sound familiar? Because the involvement of cochlear mechanics is strongly implicated, critical bandwidths might be thought of as reflections of how the frequency range of hearing is mapped from one end of the basilar membrane to the other. An additional test of the critical band as a unifying concept, then, is to plot the data in Figure 7.16a against a frequency axis scaled in equal critical bandwidths, as shown in

Figure 7.16b. It is evident, in so doing, that none of the functions, including the critical bandwidth itself, is completely linearized by this transformation. For example, each critical-bandwidth interval does not lead to a fixed ratio change in the critical bandwidth or in the frequency DL. Additionally, the considerable difference in configurations of these two graphs suggests no simple relationship between the two (such as the $DL_F$ equaling a fixed proportion of the critical bandwidth). Interestingly, graphed this way, the pitch scale nevertheless seems more linear than when plotted against a log frequency scale, as does the MFS function.

A final issue is, "What sets the limits of the resolving power in the auditory system?" Much evidence suggests that it is primarily the manner in which the auditory system encodes frequency, that is, the mechanical events in the cochlea. Still, there is strong evidence to suggest that timing information also is important in encoding frequency, for example, the periodicity pitch phenomenon. Although the limits of resolution are probably established in the periphery, the role of the central auditory system should not be underrated in the actual extraction of pitch, especially for complex sounds. Several theories suggest the existence of a central pitch "extractor." Perhaps the most compelling evidence supporting such theories is that the periodicity pitch phenomenon can be created by splitting up the components of the stimulus between the two ears, thus avoiding any possible interaction of the signals outside of the central auditory system. The output of the cochlea is viewed as a transformation of the sound spectrum into patterns of neural activity in a series of channels established by the filter bank effectively created by the cochlear mechanical system and the neural wiring of the cochlea. Through successive stages of analysis, analogous to computing mathematical transformations, pitch is identified from these patterns. This is in contrast to more rudimentary notions of pitch perception that suggest the central auditory system simply identifies a neural channel or place of maximal activity, or that it directly performs a period histogram of neuronal discharges. The difficulties encountered in formulating a comprehensive theory of pitch perception can be appreciated from the fact that sounds of greatly different time histories and spectra still can be perceived as having the same pitch, as illustrated by the vocalist and piano example used previously. Clearly, much still must be learned about the detailed mechanism(s) of pitch perception.

## 11. Temporal Aspects of Hearing

### A. Temporal Summation

It is evident from the periodicity pitch phenomenon that temporal cues are important in auditory information processing. The auditory system exhibits still other time-dependent phenomena. One particularly important temporal factor is the duration of the stimulus and its influence on different aspects of auditory sensation. An outstanding example of this is the dependence of absolute threshold, or sensitivity, on stimulus duration. Within certain limits, the threshold level of sound decreases with increasing duration, as illustrated in Figure 7.17. This indicates that the auditory system, in effect, integrates (summates) the power of the stimulus over time, suggesting that it is the total energy in the sound that determines threshold. Recall from Chapter 1 that power is the rate at which work is done, and energy is the capacity to do work. Integrating power over time yields the amount of energy used. Consequently, the phenomenon whereby absolute threshold varies as a function of stimulus duration is called ***threshold power integration***. The stimulus power, however, is not summated forever. For most pure tones, by 200 msec the integration process is essentially

complete, and further increases in duration result in little improvement in threshold. The relation between threshold in decibels and the logarithm of duration is essentially linear, as illustrated in Figure 7.17, although this is an idealized representation of the overall trends of results from actual measurements. Real data, in fact, do not always reflect such perfect power integration. This is especially true at very low frequencies. Graphs based on actual data also are asymptotic, rather than demonstrating a sharp break at a certain duration, illustrating the old axiom—there are no corners in nature. Nevertheless, Figure 7.17 illustrates what is generally expected and underscores the assumption that for practical purposes (such as clinical testing), as long as the stimulus duration is greater than or equal to 200 msec (for pure tones), duration-dependent variations in hearing sensitivity are negligible. Indeed, there is such a thing as too long a stimulus! Such stimuli, as discussed below, cause *adaptation*. Conversely, when pure tones are presented for less than 200 msec, the measured threshold will depend directly on the stimulus duration. (Note: the exact limit of threshold power integration depends somewhat on stimulus bandwidth and thus, for example, is not the same for tones versus noise.)

Loudness also can be shown to increase with increasing duration and grows in a manner similar to the increased sensitivity with duration. However, the amount of time required to achieve full loudness integration decreases with increasing intensity of the stimulus. Even at relatively low SLs (approximately 30 dB), integration seems to be complete within a time period of 10 msec or less (in other words, at least an order of magnitude less time than is required for complete threshold power integration). It should be noted that caution must be taken in attempting to track the function of loudness or threshold versus duration down to very brief durations, because spectral splattering can be-

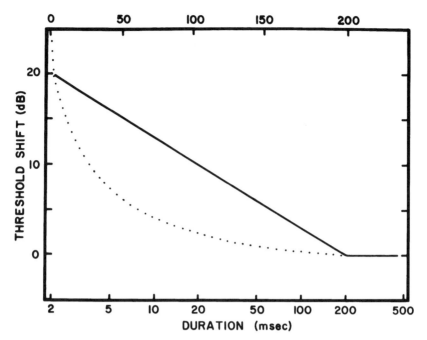

**Figure 7.17.** Absolute threshold in decibels as a function of the log duration of the tonal stimulus (*bottom*). The *dotted curve* shows the same graph replotted in semilogarithmic coordinates—decibels versus duration in linear units (*top*). (Idealized power integration function, assuming complete integration at 200 msec, but based in part on data of Campbell and Counter [1969]).

come a significant artifact and influence the perception or detection of the stimulus. On the other hand, as long as the effective bandwidth of the stimulus is less than one critical bandwidth, the data presumably should not be adversely contaminated, despite the inevitable qualitative differences among the stimuli of different durations.

Speaking of spectral splatter, it is because of this factor that it also is difficult to judge the pitch of very brief duration sounds (such as transients) and to discriminate between transients of different frequencies. Thus, pitch also is influenced by duration. For example, as the duration of a tone burst is increased, the pitch percept changes from that of a fairly nondescript click to a click with some pitch, progressing ultimately to perception of tonality. A definite sense of tonality requires durations in excess of 10 to 25 msec (at moderate levels of stimulation), with

the exact duration being dependent on frequency.

## B. TEMPORAL MASKING

Another time-dependent phenomenon is *temporal masking*. Temporal masking refers to the masking effects between sounds that are not presented simultaneously. As illustrated in Figure 7.18, temporal masking can occur whether the masker is presented before or after the probe stimulus; the amount of masking depends on the relative intensities of the two sounds, their frequencies or spectral content, and the time interval between them. All other things being equal, masking decreases dramatically and systematically as the interval between the masker and probe stimulus increases. When the probe follows the masker (forward masking), essentially no masking occurs beyond a certain interval. Interestingly, this interval is approximately 200 msec, regardless of

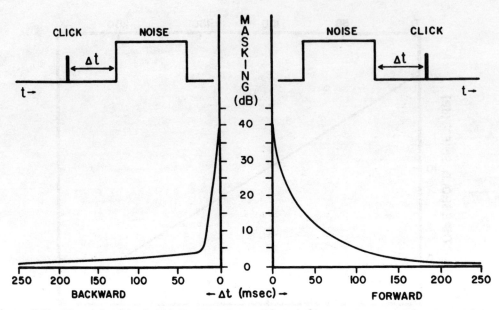

**Figure 7.18.** Forward and backward masking effects of a noise masker (white noise, 500 msec duration) on an acoustic click (approximately 0.4 msec duration). The masker and probe stimuli are separated by the time interval $\Delta t$. (Based on data of Wilson and Carhart [1971].)

the intensity of the masker! (Reminiscent of the minimal interval for full-threshold power integration, is it not?) However, when the probe stimulus precedes the masker (backward masking), the amount of masking decreases much more dramatically with increasing duration of the interstimulus interval, namely, the masking effects are greatly reduced or negligible for intervals of more than 25 msec.

The two temporal masking functions clearly are not identical, suggesting different underlying mechanisms. These mechanisms are not known, but the prevalent notion is that temporal masking reflects differences in the latencies of neural impulses encoding the more-intense masker versus those mediating the less-intense probe. Presumably, the impulses representing the masker reach the central nervous system in advance of those representing the probe. Therefore, even though these stimuli are separated in time, the masker can still "jam" the probe.

Temporal masking has commanded a great amount of attention in the literature

in conjunction with other measures of auditory function, most notably the psychophysical tuning curve. It has been shown that the sharpness of tuning reflected by this function is consistently greater when a forward masking paradigm is used rather than simultaneous masking. This also is true for tuning functions determined by electrophysiological methods (see Chapter 6). The difference between measures obtained using temporal versus simultaneous masking are believed to reflect the involvement of what is known as *lateral suppression*. The term *lateral* comes from the place concept; that is, the masker not only acts at a specific place according to the tonotopic transformation but also on either side of this place or laterally. The phenomenon of lateral suppression, demonstrable in several psychoacoustical phenomena, seems to be related to the two-tone suppression evidenced in single-unit tuning functions and thought to arise from nonlinearities of cochlear mechanics (see Chapters 5 and 6). Under simultaneous masking, the lateral suppression mechanism is defeated. Exactly how this happens is beyond the scope of discussion here, but in simple terms, each stimulus (masker and probe) causes lateral suppression and essentially cancels the suppression caused by the other, when they occur simultaneously. Lateral suppression, incidentally, is somewhat akin to lateral inhibition in vision, which, in turn, is responsible for enhancing changes in contrast (for example, the edges of dark letters printed on a light background). However, because there are no interneurons in the neural wiring of the hearing organ, the term *inhibition* is not used. (This term has a specific physiological meaning and neuroanatomical implications.) Therefore, the more neutral term *suppression* is used.

Returning to the main point, temporal masking thus provides a means of assessing various aspects of auditory function. Other factors that are of interest are critical bandwidths obtained with temporal versus simultaneous masking and differences between forward and backward masking under various paradigms that might reveal the extent to which one or both forms of temporal masking are dependent on central versus peripheral mechanisms. By the way, temporal interactions do not always produce reduced sensitivity. Under favorable conditions, the threshold for one sound actually can be improved by the occurrence of a preceding sound stimulus! This phenomenon is called **sensitization**. More pervasive, nevertheless, are occurrences of *desensitization*, sometimes lasting beyond the 200-msec limit (roughly) of forward masking. This is the subject of the following subsection.

## C. ADAPTATION AND FATIGUE

*Adaptation* and *fatigue* are two other time-dependent phenomena of interest. In Chapter 6 some discussion was given to the fact that the discharge patterns of most auditory neurons demonstrate adaptation, that is, a perstimulatory (during stimulation) decrease in discharge rate. Adaptation can be demonstrated, to some extent, in responses measured via psychoacoustical methods. *Threshold adaptation*, for example, refers to an increase in threshold that results from sustained stimulation but that generally is reversed by momentarily removing the adapting stimulus. For example, the intensity of a tone at threshold may have to be increased by as much as 20 dB (although the observed change is typically 5 dB or less) for the sensation of hearing to be sustained for 1 min. At the end of this time, if the test stimulus is interrupted briefly, threshold returns to its initial value. If a series of reasonably short tone bursts (such as 200 msec) is presented rather than a sustained tone, no adaptation occurs (depending on the level of the adapting stimulus and the interstimulus interval).

Adaptation is a normal process. Functionally, it seems to be the adjustment of the nervous system to an unchanging stimulus. A long-standing debate, however, is whether loudness adapts. There have been numerous studies wherein the investigators presumed to measure *loudness adaptation*, yielding results suggesting substantial reductions in loudness with sustained stimulation. It seems, however, that this adaptation is actually induced by the experimental protocol, which, in turn, involves interaural comparisons. The observed effects are real enough, but they apparently have more to do with binaural lateralization (discussed below) than actual loudness adaptation. True loudness adaptation can and has been studied, namely, using a magnitude-estimation protocol. The results suggest that, for sounds above 30 dB SL, little or no adaptation of loudness occurs. In other words, there is significant loudness adaptation only near threshold, consistent with the fact that the threshold of a stimulus is (again) adaptive. Even this adaptation all but disappears if the stimulus is not steady state (for instance, if it is amplitude modulated). Lack of adaptation to loud sounds is really an advantage, at least in one sense. As will discussed below, prolonged exposure to intense sounds has untoward effects on the auditory system. However, these sounds often are avoided because they are perceived as uncomfortable or annoying. Were the auditory system to adapt to such sounds, there would be less tendency to avoid them, thereby circumventing a natural protective mechanism for the auditory system.

Of course, some people learn to tolerate loud sounds and may not be annoyed by sounds that even approach the threshold of feeling or pain, hence their ability to withstand the high SPLs typical of rock'n'-roll concerts. Although such concert goers certainly flirt with permanent damage to their hearing organs (and the performers are at even greater risk!), the auditory system does show an adaptability of sorts to such overexposures to sound. That is, under certain conditions a prolonged and/or intense stimulus may cause the sensory receptors (and to some extent the neurons of the central pathways) to become less responsive for a protracted period after the cessation of the offending stimulus. This presumably is attributable to the depletion of metabolites or other materials physiologically necessary for maintaining the auditory system's sensitivity to sound. In other words, the system becomes fatigued.

*Auditory fatigue* is demonstrated most readily by observing the transient changes in absolute threshold after a sufficiently intense and/or prolonged sound exposure. Experimentally, this is done as follows. First, the threshold for a test stimulus is determined. Then, a fatiguing sound exposure is given. Threshold for the test stimulus is reestablished after the cessation of this exposure. If the exposure indeed is sufficient to cause fatigue, the postexposure threshold will be elevated. In time, though, threshold gradually recovers to the preexposure level. Herein lie the silver lining and the reason why this phenomenon may be viewed as a type of adaptive mechanism. The ear can actually recover from being overworked and fatigued! However, recovery in not instantaneous; it is a time-consuming process, requiring minutes to hours—or even days. The amount of recovery time required and the exact time course of recovery intimately depend on the parameters of the exposure and test stimuli. For moderate exposures, nevertheless, the recovery functions are predictable (Fig. 7.19).

This reversible loss of hearing sensitivity is called *temporary threshold shift* (TTS) and is the most frequently used index of auditory fatigue. Although this is a laboratory or clinical measure, auditory fatigue is something that most readers are likely to be able to appreciate. Auditory fatigue is often experienced after using home power tools (power saw, belt sander, power lawn mower, etc.) or after listening to any excessively loud music for extended durations. On termination of the exposure, a deadening sensation is experienced, often accompanied by a ringing in the ears. The latter effect is known as *tinnitus*. However, after a period of relative quiet, these sensations typically subside.

Auditory fatigue thus is a phenomenon signaling that the auditory system can handle some overexposure to sound, but it also must be taken as a clear sign of the auditory system's intolerance of excessive sound exposures. Excessive exposure can involve either very intense sounds presented for only brief periods or less-intense sounds presented for extended time periods. In other words, the exposure has dimensions of time and intensity; both the intensity and duration of the exposure stimulus are important. The effective exposure also may be continuous or episodic, and sounds of a variety of intensities, spectral content, and temporal patterns may contribute to the effective exposure. Furthermore, with continued or repeated exposure to noxious sounds without sufficient recovery time from a prior exposure, the hearing loss may become permanent. Some sounds can be immediately permanently damaging if sufficiently intense,

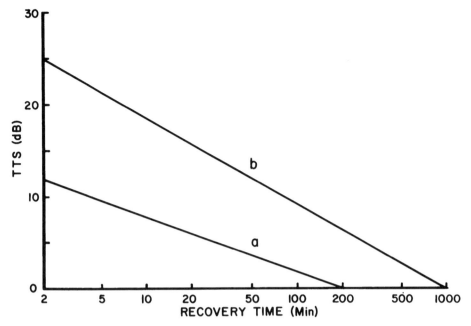

**Figure 7.19.** Temporary threshold shift (*TTS*) after noise exposure. In this case, the exposure stimulus was a 2.4- to 4.8-kHz band of noise presented at levels of 85 dB (**a**) and 90 dB SPL re $2 \times 10^{-5}$ Pa (**b**) for approximately 2 hours. Threshold was measured at 4 kHz at different instants during recovery. (Based on data of Ward et al. [1959].)

that is, even if only of brief duration! In recognition of the detrimental effects of noise overexposure on hearing, governments have enacted legislation limiting the level and duration of noise to which a worker can be exposed; in the United States, for example, for continuous exposure during a typical 8-hour work day, the level may not exceed 85 dBA SPL.[9]

### D. Temporal Acuity

Finally, another extremely important temporal aspect of hearing is the ability of the auditory system to make time discriminations. The ability of the auditory system to distinguish differences in durations of sounds, time intervals between sounds,

and temporal order of sounds is essential to the auditory processing of speech and music. Thus, to fully appreciate the capabilities of the auditory system, the ***temporal acuity*** of the system ultimately must be considered. Although a detailed consideration of temporal acuity is not possible within the confines of this text, various kinds of experiments have revealed that listeners are capable of resolving events within 1 to 2 msec, such as distinguishing the order of occurrence of two clicks that differ only in intensity. Much smaller time intervals may be resolved if other cues are available, specifically, differences in spectra of two sounds. But then, pure temporal acuity is no longer involved. Perhaps one of the most impressive demonstrations of the temporal discrimination ability of the auditory system is seen in the binaural localization of low-frequency sounds. This leads to a discussion of binaural hearing.

[9] The SPL in dbA indicates measurement of SPL using the A weighting scale. This weighting factor is a bandpass filter function approximating the inverse of the 40-phon equal-loudness contour. The intent is for the measure to reflect the filtering of the peripheral auditory system, but not to the degree as manifested by the minimum audibility curves.

## 12. Binaural Hearing

Many of the measurements carried out in hearing laboratories and clinics involve **monaural** or one-eared hearing. As a matter of fact, the majority of information presented previously in this chapter is based on experiments involving monaural listening paradigms. This is a major over-simplification of the real-life listening conditions that, more often than not, involve **binaural** processing of auditory information. There are many facets of binaural hearing that could be discussed, beginning with the binaural advantage that can be demonstrated for most of the auditory abilities discussed in the foregoing sections. For example, the DLs for both frequency and intensity are smaller (that is, differential sensitivity is enhanced) when measured using binaural, rather than monaural, stimulation. The binaural absolute threshold is better than the monaural absolute threshold when the test stimulus is presented via earphones. The binaural advantage is worth about 3 dB. A given stimulus also sounds louder when presented binaurally, rather than monaurally. The loudness function, it turns out, applies equally to monaural and binaural stimulation, but the constant of proportionality ($k$) in Eq. 7.3 differs between the two modes of stimulation, namely, by about 2:1, reflecting essentially perfect summation of loudness across the two ears. For example, a tone presented monaurally and eliciting a perceived magnitude of 8 sones would be perceived to be twice as loud, namely, 16 sones.

The improvement in hearing sensitivity and increased loudness via binaural stimulation are considered examples of the general phenomenon of **binaural summation**.[10] Another is the formation of

[10] It can be argued rather convincingly (although the actual argument and the supporting experimental evidence is beyond the scope here) that the binaural improvement in threshold is a special case of what is called the *binaural masking level difference*, discussed later in this section. The basic premise is that the absolute threshold is a masked threshold, even in "quiet"; some noise is always present,

beats via binaural stimulation. In this case, the physical stimuli are themselves not interacting or beating; rather, **binaural beats** are the result of neural interaction in the central auditory system between discharges excited by a tone of one frequency presented in one ear and those excited by a tone of slightly different frequency in the opposite ear. As noted earlier, the periodicity pitch phenomenon can be evoked in a similar fashion.

### A. TIME-VERSUS-INTENSITY CUES FOR LOCALIZATION

Although the binaural summation phenomena are intriguing, they generally have been considered to represent minor binaural advantages compared with the importance of two ears in the location of sounds in space—**binaural localization**. The acoustical and physiological bases of binaural localization already have been discussed in the previous two chapters and need only be summarized here. Spectral disparities resulting from differences in the intensity and/or arrival time of sound at the two ears arise from diffraction and baffle effects of the head. The general scheme of events is summarized in Figure 7.20. Low-frequency sounds with wavelengths greater than the dimensions of the head essentially wrap around the head because of diffraction. Consequently, there is little if any intensity difference between ears. However, time is required for the sound wave to travel around the head. If the two ears are not located at equal distances from the sound source, then a time disparity arises between the sound appearing at the two ears. The maximal time differential occurs when one ear is pointing directly toward the sound source (90° azimuth with respect to the midline). An estimate of the maximal time disparity can be computed. As illustrated in Figure 7.21, the total dis-

whether internally or externally. Indeed, there seems to be sufficient interaural disparities to provide, as observed, a 3-dB binaural advantage or release from masking.

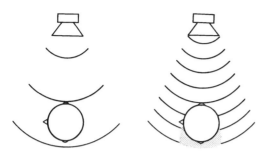

**Figure 7.20.** Simplified representation of the acoustical effects of the head on sound waves with wavelengths greater than the head diameter (*left*), wherein diffraction occurs, and sound waves with shorter wavelengths (*right*), wherein the head casts a shadow.

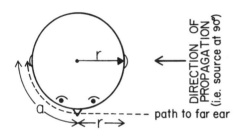

**Figure 7.21.** Geometry of the path of sound around the head: *r*, radius of head; *a*, arc between the nose and the far ear.

tance of travel of the sound wave from the near ear to the far ear will involve two components. One component (*r*) is "line-of-sight" travel over a distance equal to the radius of the head, approximately 0.09 m. The rest of the path (*a*) is curved; that is, the sound must travel around the far side of the head, over a distance equal to one quarter the circumference of the head: 1/4 × 2$\pi$*r* = 0.25 × 2 × 3.14 × 0.09 ≈ 0.14 m. The total distance (*d*) then is *r* + *a* = 0.09 + 0.14 = 0.23 m. Assuming the speed of sound (*c*) to be 343 m/sec, the maximal time disparity is computed as follows:

$$\Delta t = d/c = 0.23/343 \approx 6.71$$
$$\times 10^{-4} \approx 0.67 \text{ msec}$$

where $\Delta t$ is the time disparity.[11] Of course,

for other azimuths the time disparities are less than 0.67 msec.

It is important to bear in mind that time disparities introduce phase differences in ongoing sounds at the two ears. It is interesting in this regard that the estimated 0.67-msec upper limit for (natural) time disparities corresponds to the period of 1.5 kHz (*T* = 1/*f* = 1/1500 ≈ 0.00067 sec = 0.67 msec). At higher frequencies, interaural phase disparities become ambiguous, that is, greater than 360°. In addition, 1.5 kHz is about the highest frequency at which any significant diffraction of sound around the head occurs (see Chapter 5).

Of course, the ability of the auditory system to faithfully encode the time history of the sound, and thus to faithfully encode interaural time disparities, diminishes with increasing frequency. Consequently, it is necessary for the auditory system to rely on another cue for localizing high-frequency sounds. This cue is intensity. When there is no diffraction, the head acts as a baffle (or barrier) in which the ear is mounted. The head casts a sound shadow on the far ear (Fig. 7.20) and, at those same frequencies, reflects sound back into the sound field in front of the near ear to provide a boost in sound pressure. Consequently, at high frequencies an intensity disparity arises between the two ears (namely, SPL lower at the far ear and higher at the near ear; see Chapter 5).

The notion that binaural sound localization and lateralization are dependent on time and intensity disparities at low and high frequencies, respectively, is the principal tenant of what is called the *duplex theory*, attributed to the acoustician Lord Rayleigh. The duplex theory accounts well for the sound localization of simple sounds, such as pure tones, and it provides reasonable bases for understanding and/or predicting a variety of effects observed in binaural listening. For example, a well-known problem reported in hearing clinics is that listeners with substantial unilateral high-frequency hearing loss have

[11] The general equation for the distance traveled by sound across the head as a function of azimuth, $\Theta$, is given by the equation: $d = r\Theta + r \sin\Theta$.

increased difficulty understanding a speaker located on the side of the bad ear. This is an example of adverse effects of the head shadow; in this case, important high-frequency spectral components of the speech are attenuated at the good (far) ear.

This is not to suggest that time disparities play absolutely no role in the binaural localization of high-frequency sounds. Furthermore, the duplex theory seems not to account as well for the localization of complex sounds as it does for simple sounds. The localization of complex sounds, of course, is more germane to sound-localization behavior in the environment. The localization of complex sounds depends more on temporal cues, even for sounds of predominantly high-frequency sound energy. This is because temporal cues are available at high frequencies by virtue of interaural delays in the amplitude envelopes of these sounds. This is somewhat analogous to the periodicity pitch phenomenon, at least for the example of amplitude-modulated high-frequency carriers. Consequently, modulation rate is an influential factor. Of course, for transients, the onset of the stimulus can provide the basis for localization. However, for ongoing complex sounds, the underlying analysis process is further complicated by the multiplicity of channels of input from the two ears, namely, across frequency, by virtue of the cochlear filters (represented by the critical bands). Presumably, some sort of integration across these channels must take place for precise localization of the sound source. Thus there are details about binaural localization that remain to be revealed through further research.

## B. BINAURAL SOUND LOCALIZATION ABILITY

In the spirit of earlier discussions of various auditory phenomena and associated abilities, it is of interest to obtain some impression of just how precise human binaural localization is. However,

the many factors influencing binaural localization make it difficult to decide which single index, if any, is most appropriate. Various factors have been studied, such as the minimal detectable interaural time, phase, or intensity differences. The results from studies of these parameters present a complex picture that precludes the formulation of a simple statement of the limits of binaural localization. Perhaps the most direct index of binaural localization, in sensitivity terms, is the *minimum audible angle*. This is a measure of the ability of a listener to determine whether two successive sounds originated from the same direction. Here, too, the data are complicated, but a minimum audible angle on the order of 2° is typical for the condition wherein the position of the sound source is close to the midline axis (0° azimuth). At other azimuths, spatial resolution ability greatly diminishes; that is, the minimum audible angle increases in a frequency-dependent manner. Interestingly, the minimum audible angle becomes indeterminately large in the vicinity of 1500 Hz as the sound sources approach the 90° azimuth. Thus, directional hearing is most precise for all frequencies when the listener is essentially facing the sound source.

## C. BINAURAL LATERALIZATION

When sounds arise from two sources, the auditory system is capable of fusing them effectively into one auditory image originating from one apparent source. This is another manifestation of binaural summation; the specific phenomenon here is known as *binaural fusion*. The effect is commonly experienced in *stereophonic* listening, whether in the sound field (using two or more speakers) or under earphones, given channelized inputs wherein the sound was sampled from two or more microphones. Therefore, the panorama of sound, from a source such as an orchestra, is sampled in the original recording and recreated on reproduction via the stereo high-fidelity system. Using loudspeakers, there is considerable overlap of the sound fields created by the two loudspeakers, whereas, using earphones, the sound from each source is presented discretely to each ear (within certain limits, dependent on the type of earphone and the sound spectrum). Yet with earphones, binaural fusion is readily achieved that is independent of any sort of acoustic mixing of the sound output from the two channels, as occurs in the sound field using loudspeakers. However, differences between the sounds presented to the two ears affect the extent to which they can be fused into a single auditory image and/or the apparent location of the fused sound. For them to be fused, only small frequency differences between the two sounds can be tolerated. If the two sounds are the same in frequency, but there exists an intensity disparity, the two sounds will fuse into a sound image located somewhere within the head, namely toward the side of the greater intensity. If there exists a time or phase disparity, fusion again can occur, with the image located within the head toward the side at which the sound is leading in time or phase. For example, if the sound in the right ear is leading in time or phase or is greater in intensity, compared with the sound presented to the left, the sound image will seem to be in the right side of the head (Fig. 7.22). In other words, the sound is said to be *lateralized* to the right. This effect is called **binaural lateralization**, to distinguish it from binaural localization of sounds in space (that is, outside the head).

The same basic rules apply to binaural lateralization as to binaural localization. For low frequencies, time or phase disparities are important; for high frequencies, intensity disparity determines the side to which the fused sound is lateralized. A particular advantage of earphone presentation in the study or testing of binaural hearing is that it permits the introduction of intensity differences between the ears at any frequency. Consequently, a time-intensity tradeoff can be demonstrated.

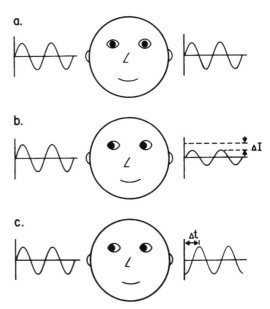

**Figure 7.22.** Illustration of the binaural lateralization of the sound image obtained when the same-frequency tone is presented via earphones: **a**, at the same intensity and time and phase; **b**, at different intensities (*I*); and **c**, at different times or phases (*Δt*) to the two ears.

For instance, the lateralization of the sound image toward the side of a time lead can be offset by increasing the intensity of the sound in the ear on the opposite side. The tradeoff is not always complete, though, in that the juxtaposition of certain time and intensity disparities fails to produce a well-focused fused sound image. This and other observations (for example, the notable increase in the minimum audible angle around 1.5 kHz) are thought to reflect underlying differences between mechanisms involved in processing interaural time and intensity disparities.

The similarities between binaural lateralization and localization are evident, but the differences in the imagery of sounds in sound field versus earphone presentation have been suggested as evidence of a fundamental difference between them. In sound field situations, the sound is usually perceived as coming from somewhere outside the head, whereas the typical impression with earphones is that the sound is inside the head, as noted above. Indeed, the latter effect is a common complaint of high-fidelity enthusiasts about earphone listening; these listeners apparently think that the sensation of having the sound of a full orchestra within their heads is unrealistic and/or distracting. However, there is evidence that localization and lateralization really are not different. Rather, the intracranial lateralization of sound under earphones is suggested to be a unique property of these transducer devices. The details are beyond the scope of interest here, but sound field presentation using loudspeakers can be manipulated to create intracranial sound images characteristic of earphone listening. Similarly, it is possible to use earphones to create an apparent extracranial sound image. In other words, it is possible to simulate sound field listening under earphones. The differences in the two modes of presentation actually seem to reflect the subtle influence of the head and auricle (and possibly the upper torso) on the spectra of sounds reaching the two ears in the sound field situation. These spectral cues, which are discussed further in Monaural and Vertical Localization, are largely eliminated under common earphone-listening conditions.

## D. OTHER FACTORS IN SOUND LOCALIZATION

The substantial separation of the two ears in humans provides for excellent sound localization ability over a broad frequency range, and human sound localization ability seems to be the most acute of all animals. This seemingly peerless localization ability does not seem to be caused by acoustic factors alone (for example, the effect of head size), yet all the factors underlying the human's ability have not been identified with certainty. In general, there are other factors contributing to sound localization, especially when natural behavior is considered. It is important to bear in mind, for example, that in the real-life situation, the head is free to move.

In some lower animals, the pinnae are mobile as well. Directional hearing presumably benefits from such flexibility. The listener is able to sample and compare sounds from different sectors in space or to make comparisons between the same sound as detected with the head or auricles in different positions. In humans, though, head movement does not seem to be a critical factor in sound localization. However, *visual cues and learning*, that is, the listener's knowledge of the sound field, can be important. Precise sound localization thus may depend at times on the integration of auditory and nonauditory information. This is most likely to be the case in reverberant sound fields, wherein, effectively, both ears are receiving multiple time-delayed versions of a given sound. Nevertheless, using acoustic information alone, the auditory system has an amazing ability to precisely locate sounds in such complicated situations, because of a special effect that is the subject of the next subsection.

## E. PRECEDENCE EFFECT

The reverberant sound field effectively creates multiple sources for the same sound, namely because of the incident and (multiple) reflected waves. Consequently, reverberation can degrade binaural localization performance substantially. The binaural listener, nevertheless, generally can localize a sound source in a reverberant sound field. This is because there generally are differences in the time of arrival and/or intensity of the incident and reflected waves such that the incident waves arrive first and/or are the most intense. The earliest or strongest sound takes precedence, thereby effecting "echo suppression" in the analysis of sound location. The ability to locate sounds in reverberant fields thus is attributable to the ***precedence effect***. The precedence effect clearly has direct relevance to real-life listening situations.

The precedence effect also plays an important role in *stereophonic* listening.

Again, the stereophonic effect occurs when the full panorama of the original sounds, such as created by an orchestra, can be reconstructed mentally from as few as two channels of recording. When listening through the two speakers of a stereophonic high-fidelity system located about 45° azimuth to each side of the listener, it is possible to hear the instruments coming from apparent locations corresponding to their actual positions in the orchestra, for example (conventionally), violins from the left, bass violins from the right, winds from the middle, etc. In reality, the sounds of all instruments will radiate from both speakers, and both incident and reflected sounds also will be presented because of reverberation in the recording studio or concert hall. To complicate matters further, the room in which the stereo is situated most likely will be reverberant as well. Despite these variables, the listener has a fairly strong sense of the relative positions of the various instruments of the orchestra. This is because of the fact that the precedence-setting acoustic cues are sampled by the two channels of recording and are reproduced by the playback system, although a proportionally scaled-down sound stage is (re)created.

## F. MONAURAL AND VERTICAL LOCALIZATION

It would be misleading to discuss only binaural localization and, by this omission, leave the impression that directional hearing is possible only by way of two-eared input to the auditory system and binaural processing. First, the origin of a sound can be located through the use of just one ear, that is, by *monaural localization*. Admittedly, binaural localization is several times more precise, but the ability to localize sound monaurally at all is a fortunate circumstance for individuals with unilateral hearing impairments! In the monaural localization of sound, head mobility is important and, although there are no practical temporal cues, intensity cues are available by virtue of the head

baffle effect. As the head is turned toward and then away from the direction of the sound source, the intensity of the sound reaching the functional ear will be louder and softer, accordingly. So, the judgment of sound location must rely on intensity discrimination.

It also is a gross oversimplification of sound localization to consider only those situations in which sounds differ in location in the horizontal plane. In real life, sounds may come from points of different elevation, but they usually can be localized with little difficulty. This is known as *vertical localization*. To study experimentally the ability of the listener to locate sounds of different elevations, specifically without the influence of binaural cues arising from differences in azimuth (that is, *horizontal localization* cues), the sound source must be centered between the two ears so that it lies in the median (midsagittal) plane of the head. The results of such experiments have revealed the cues for vertical localization. Interestingly, there are some underlying relationships between monaural and vertical localization, especially with regard to the importance of the auricle and pinna. In both cases, an intact auricle is essential. It would seem that the auditory system is capable of responding to the fine temporal or spectral cues introduced by sound reflection from the convoluted surface of the auricle. However, the contribution of the auricle is limited to fairly high frequencies (greater than 4 kHz) by virtue of its small size, that is, relative to the wavelengths of low-frequency sounds. In other words, for listeners to accurately judge the elevation of the sound source, the spectrum of the sound must contain energy at frequencies above 4 kHz.

Now, although it is useful to consider these different kinds of localization (binaural, monaural, and vertical) individually, it should not be assumed that they operate independently. The fact is that localization of sound is generally *not* adequate when based solely on binaural in-

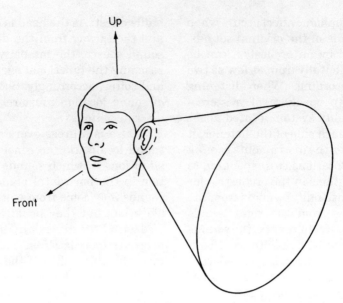

**Figure 7.23.** Cone of confusion. All sound sources located anywhere on the surface of the cone produce identical interaural time disparities. (Based on Mills [1972]; from Moore, B. C. J. [1982]. *An Introduction to the Psychology of Hearing*, 2nd Ed. Academic Press, London.)

tensity or time disparities. There actually are many locations of a sound source that can yield the same interaural disparities, as illustrated in Figure 7.23. This is known as the *cone of confusion*. Clearly, to differentiate between sounds from directions above or below the level of the external auditory meatus, or in front versus in back of the listener, some cues other than interaural time and/or intensity disparities must be used, and presumably these are provided by the auricle. Thus, binaural localization ability is enhanced by spectral cues or, in effect, a monaural localization mechanism. The confusion of the cone of confusion thus seems to be reduced by the spectral nuances caused by the auricle, as illustrated in Figure 7.24. This figure illustrates how slight changes in the elevation of the sound source can cause sharp changes in the SPL at the eardrum, which, in turn, will color the spectra of complex (high-frequency) sounds. Similar effects, by the way, seem to be introduced by sound reflections off the torso for the longer-wavelength sounds, below 2

kHz. Exactly how the auditory system uses this information is not clearly understood. Here too, nonauditory factors, such as learning, are expected to play a role.

## G. BINAURAL RELEASE FROM MASKING

Before concluding this discussion on binaural hearing, a special phenomenon is worth describing briefly to demonstrate the truly exquisite nature of binaural information processing. This phenomenon not only demonstrates the advantage of binaural over monaural (*monotic*) hearing, but also the advantage of **dichotic** (different sounds in the two ears) over **diotic** listening (identical sounds in the two ears). First, consider the situation in which a tonal probe stimulus is presented simultaneously with a white-noise masker to one ear (monotic condition); the level of the probe tone is adjusted such that the noise just masks it. If the masking noise, and only the masking noise, now is presented to the other ear, the tone becomes audible again. In other words, the

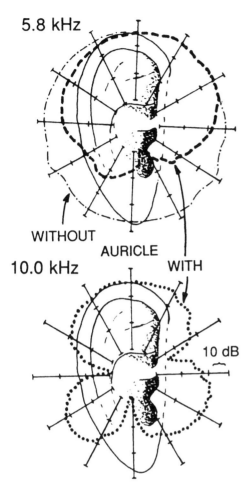

**5.8 kHz**

**WITHOUT AURICLE**

**10.0 kHz**

**WITH**

10 dB

**Figure 7.24.** Vertical directivity of the ear simulated by a microphone in a manikin head with adult-male-like auricle (*KEMAR*). The contours represent the relative microphone output levels as a sound source is rotated about the head. *Dashed lines*, Contours obtained at 5.8 kHz with (*heavy line*) and without (*thin line*) an auricle. Under the latter condition, the auricle was replaced with a flat plate. *Dotted line*, 10 kHz, with auricle. (Adapted from Kuhn, G. F. [1987].)

probe tone is unmasked; there is a *release from masking* under this dichotic condition—noise in one ear, noise plus tone in the other.

What would happen if both the noise and tone were presented to both ears? This condition constitutes a diotic condition, to be designated here as $S_0N_0$, and the tone would be masked once more. However, a

release from masking can be demonstrated with both the probe and masker presented binaurally, namely, via a paradigm that constitutes a dichotic condition, although more subtle than the paradigm described above. Consider the situation, for example, wherein the tonal probe stimuli are presented dichotically, specifically 180° ($\pi$ radians) out of phase at the two ears, while the noise is presented diotically, that is, in phase. This condition may be designated $S_\pi N_0$, and under this condition the probe tone, once more, is audible. A release from masking (although somewhat less) also is realized under the $S_0N_\pi$ condition, that is, with the signal in phase and the noise 180° out of phase at the two ears. Consequently, to mask the probe tone under the dichotic conditions ($S_\pi N_0$ or $S_0N_\pi$), the level of the noise masker must be increased, relative to that under the diotic ($S_0N_0$) or monotic ($S_mN_m$) conditions, to yield the same amount of masking as under the diotic or in-phase condition ($S_0N_0$) or, for that matter, as under the monotic condition ($S_mN_m$). The decibel difference between the masked thresholds under the $S_0N_0$ or $S_mN_m$) versus the $S_{II}N_0$ or $S_0N_\pi$ conditions is the ***masking level difference (MLD)***.

The MLD is dependent on several factors, especially the frequency of the test signal. Large MLDs (large being 10–15 dB) occur only at frequencies below 1000 Hz. Above 1 kHz, only a few decibels of MLD may be achieved. Thus, the MLD resulting from the introduction of phase differences between the sounds at the two ears is essentially restricted to low frequencies. This should not be surprising, because the MLD is clearly dependent on temporal cues and is subject to the same limitations in temporal encoding as is binaural localization.

Although the demonstration of the MLD, per se, is a laboratory phenomenon produced by using earphones, some form of this phenomenon is likely to be involved in real-life listening situations. The various sounds in the field often will have different points of origin and will be affected differentially by the interaural spectral differences introduced by the head (for example, phase disparities). The binaural release from masking can be demonstrated for temporal as well as simultaneous masking. However, the dichotic conditions that bring about substantial MLDs may not be optimal for other auditory processes. For example, the critical bandwidth for monotic or diotic stimulation is smaller than for dichotic stimulation. So, the realization of the binaural release from masking, presumably of value in auditory information processing, is not without some cost.

The potential practical importance of MLDs is suggested by the observation that the detectability and intelligibility (understandability) of speech in a background of noise are superior when binaural listening is used compared with monaural listening and, more importantly, when the speech or noise is received out of phase (dichotic listening) versus in phase by the two ears (diotic listening). It thus takes little speculation to suggest that the superiority of binaural hearing goes beyond the improvement of sensitivity and other binaural summation effects or even the more sophisticated process of binaural sound localization. Binaural information processing is important in other situations, such as when a listener must attend to one signal in a background of competing sounds. Consider the scenario wherein someone is trying to listen to something on the television while others are talking in the same room, a noisy truck is driving by, and the neighbor next door is mowing the lawn. Distracting? Yes. Demanding listening? Certainly. Yet, if the competing sounds are not so overwhelming as to totally mask the sound from the television, the situation is workable. Herein lies the greatest importance of two ears to a listener: to facilitate the hearing of a relevant sound submerged in a plethora of unwanted, competing sounds. It truly is a two-eared world out there!

## BIBLIOGRAPHY[12]

Anantharaman, J. A., Krishnamurthy, A. K., and Feth, L. L. (1993). Intensity-weighted average of instantaneous frequency as a model for frequency discrimination. *J. Acoust. Soc. Am.* 94:723–729.

Berger, E. H. (1981). Re-examination of the low-frequency (50-1000 Hz) normal threshold of hearing in free and diffuse sound fields. *J. Acoust. Soc. Am.* 70:1635–1645.

Bilger, R. C. (1976). A revised critical-band hypothesis. In *Hearing and Davis: Essays Honoring Hallowell Davis*, pp 191–198, edited by S. K. Hirsh, D. H. Eldredge, I. J. Hirsh, and S. R. Silverman. Washington University Press, St. Louis.

Butler, R. A. and Helwig, C. C. (1983). The spatial attributes of stimulus frequency in the median sagittal plane and their role in sound localization. *Am. J. Otolaryngol.* 4:165–173.

Butler, R. A., and Musicant, A. D. (1993). Binaural localization: influence of stimulus frequency and the linkage to covert peak areas. *Hear. Res.* 67:220–229.

Butler, R. A., Humanski, R. A., et al. (1990). Binaural and monaural localization of sound in two-dimensional space. *Perception* 19:241–256.

Burns, E. M. (1972). Pure-tone pitch anomalies. I. Pitch-intensity effects and diplacusis in normal ears. *J. Acoust. Soc. Am.* 72:1394–1402.

Campbell, R. A., and Counter, S. A. (1969). Temporal integration and periodicity pitch. *J. Acoust. Soc. Am.* 45:691–693.

Cherry, C. (1959). Two ears—but one world. In *Sensory Communication*, pp 99–117, edited by W. A. Rosenblith. MIT Press, Cambridge.

Corso, J. F. (1965). Cited in Corso, J. F. (1967). *The Experimental Psychology of Sensory Behavior*, p 280. Holt, Rinehart, and Winston, New York.

Dadson, R. S., and King, J. H. (1952). A determination of the normal threshold of hearing and its relation to the standardization of audiometers. *J. Laryngol. Otol.* 66:366–378.

Diercks, K. F., and Jeffress, L. A. (1962). Interaural phase and the absolute threshold for tone. *J. Acoust. Soc. Am.* 34:981–984.*

Divenyi, P. L. (1979). Is pitch a learned attribute of sounds? Two points in support of Terhardt's pitch theory. *J. Acoust. Soc. Am.* 66:1210–1213.

Doughty, J. M., and Garner, W. R. (1947). Pitch characteristics of short tones. I. Two kinds of pitch threshold. *J. Exp. Psychol.* 37:351–365.*

Durlach, N. I., and Colburn, H. S. (1978). Binaural Phenomena. In *Handbook of Perception: Hearing*, Vol 4, pp 365–466, edited by E. C. Carterette and M. P. Friedman. Academic Press, New York.

---

[12] References designated with an asterisk (*) appear, at least in abbreviated form, in Schubert, E. D., Ed. (1979). *Psychological Acoustics*. Dowden, Hutchinson & Ross, Stroudsburg, PA.

Durrant, J. D., Gabriel, S., and Walter, M. (1981). Psychophysical tuning functions for brief stimuli. *Am. J. Otolaryngol.* 2:108–113.

Durrant, J. D., Nozza, R. J., Hyre, R. J., and Sabo, D. L. (1989). Masking level difference at relatively high masker levels. *Audiology* 28:221–229.

Ehmer, R. H. (1959). Masking patterns of tones. *J. Acoust. Soc. Am.* 31:1115–1120.

Elliott, L. L. (1962). Backward and forward masking of probe tones of different frequencies. *J. Acoust. Soc. Am.* 34:1116–1117.*

Fausti, S. A., Rappaport, B. Z., Schechter, M. A., and Frey, R. H. (1982). An investigation of the validity of high-frequency audition. *J. Acoust. Soc. Am.* 71: 646–649.

Fechner, G. (1966). *Elements of Psychophysics*, translated by H. E. Adler and edited by D. H. Howes and E. G. Boring. Holt, Rinehart, and Winston, New York.

Festen, J. M. (1993). Contributions of comodulation masking release and temporal resolution to the speech-reception threshold masked by an interfering voice. *J. Acoust. Soc. Am.* 94:1295–1300.

Festen, J. M. and Plomp, R. (1981). Relations between auditory functions in normal hearing. *J. Acoust. Soc. Am.* 70:356–369.

Feth, L. L. (1974). Frequency discrimination of complex periodic tones. *Percept. Psychophysiol.* 15: 375–378.

Feth, L. L., O'Malley, H. and Ramsey, J., Jr. (1982). Pitch of unresolved, two-component complex tones. *J. Acoust. Soc. Am.* 72:1403–1412.

Feuerstein, J. F. (1992). Monaural versus binaural hearing: ease of listening, word recognition, and attentional effort. *Ear Hear.* 13:80–86.

Fletcher, H., and Munson, W. N. (1933). Loudness, its definition, measurement, and calculation. *J. Acoust. Soc. Am.* 5:82–108.

Gardner, M. B. (1968). Historical background of the Haas and/or precedence effect. *J. Acoust. Soc. Am.* 43:1243–1284.

Gescheider, G. A. (1985). *Psychophysics: Method, Theory, and Application*, 2nd ed. Lawrence Erlbaum Associates, Hillsdale, NJ.

Giguere, C., and Abel, S. M. (1993). Sound localization: effects of reverberation time, speaker array, stimulus frequency, and stimulus rise/decay. *J. Acoust. Soc. Am.* 94:769–776.

Gourevitch, G. (1987). Binaural hearing in land mammals. In *Directional Hearing*, pp 226–246, edited by W. A. Yost and G. Gourevitch. Springer-Verlag, New York.

Grantham, D. W., and Yost, W. A. (1982). Measures of intensity discrimination. *J. Acoust. Soc. Am.* 72: 406–410.

Green, D. M. (1970). Application of detection theory in pschophysics. *IEEE Proc.* 58:713–723.*

Green, D. M. (1971). Temporal auditory acuity. *Psychol. Rev.* 73:540–551.

Green, D. M. (1975). Pitch perception. In *The Nervous System: Human Communication and its Disorders*, Vol 3, pp 147–155, edited by E. L. Eagles. Raven Press, New York.

Greenwood, D. D. (1991). Critical bandwidth and consonance: their operational definitions in relation to cochlear nonlinearity and combination tones. *Hear. Res.* 54:209–246.

Gulick, W. L., Gescheider, G. A., and Frisina, R. D. (1989). *Physiological Acoustics, Neural Coding and Psychoacoustics.* Oxford University Press, New York.

Hafner, E. R., and Carrier, S. C. (1972). Binaural interaction in low-frequency stimuli: the inability to trade time and intensity completely. *J. Acoust. Soc. Am.* 51:1851–1862.

Hall, J. W., and Soderquist, D. R. (1975). Encoding and pitch strength of complex tones. *J. Acoust. Soc. Am.* 58:1257–1261.

Hall, J. W., Haggard, M. P., and Fernandes, M. A. (1984). Detection in noise by spectro-temporal pattern analysis. *J. Acoust. Soc. Am.* 76:50–56.

Harris, J. D. (1952). Pitch discrimination. *J. Acoust. Soc. Am.* 24:750–755.

Harris, J. D. (1963). Loudness discrimination. *J. Speech Hear. Dis.* (Monogr. Suppl. II):1–63.

Harris, J. D., Ed. (1969). *Forty Germinal Papers in Human Hearing.* Journal of Auditory Research, Groton, CT.

Harris. J. D. (1974). *Psychacoustics.* Bobbs-Merrill Co., New York.

Hawkins, J. E., Jr., and Stevens, S. S. (1950). The masking of pure tones and of speech by white noise. *J. Acoust. Soc. Am.* 22:6–13.

Hebrank, J., and Wright, D. (1974). Are two ears necessary for localization of sound sources on the median plane? *J. Acoust. Soc. Am.* 56:935–938.

Heffner, R. S., and Heffner, H. E. (1992). Visual factors in sound localization in mammals. *J. Comp. Neurol.* 317:219–232.

Hellman, R. P., and Zwislocki, J. J. (1968). Loudness determination at low sound frequencies. *J. Acoust. Soc. Am.* 43:60–64.

Hiranaka, Y., and Yamasaki, H. (1983). Envelope representations of pinna impulse responses relating to three-dimensional localizations of sound sources. *J. Acoust. Soc. Am.* 73:291–296.

Hirsh, I. J. (1952). *The Measurement of Hearing.* McGraw-Hill, New York.

Hirsh, I. J. (1975). Temporal aspects of hearing. In *The Nervous System: Human Communication and Its Disorders*, Vol 3, pp 157–162, edited by E. L. Eagles. Raven Press, New York.

Humes, L. E. (1979). Perception of the simple difference tone ($f_2 - f_1$). *J. Acoust. Soc. Am.* 66: 1064–1087.

Humes, L. E. (1980). On the nature of two-tone aural nonlinearity. *J. Acoust. Soc. Am.* 67:2073–2083.

Jeffress, L. A. (1972). Binaural signal detection: vector theory. In *Foundations of Modern Auditory*

*Theory*, Vol 2, pp 351–368, edited by J. V. Tobias. Academic Press, New York.

Jesteadt, W., and Wier, C. C. (1977). Comparison of monaural and binaural discrimination of intensity and frequency. *J. Acoust. Soc. Am.* 61:1599–1603.

Jesteadt, W., Wier, C. C., and Green, D. M. (1977). Intensity discrimination as a function of frequency and sensation level. *J. Acoust. Soc. Am.* 61: 169–177.

Jesteadt, W., Bacon, S. P., and Lehman, J. R. (1982). Forward masking as a function of frequency, masker level, and signal level. *J. Acoust. Soc. Am.* 71:950–962.

Johnson, J. H., Turner, C. W., Zwislocki, J. J., and Margolis, R. H. (1993). Just noticeable differences for intensity and their relation to loudness. *J. Acoust. Soc. Am.* 93:983-991.

Jones, F. N. (1974). History of psychophysics and judgment. In *Handbook of Perception. Vol II. Psychophysical Judgment and Measurement*, pp 1–22, edited by E. C. Carterette and M. P. Friedman. Academic Press, New York.

Killion, M. C. (1978). Revised estimate of minimum audible pressure: where is the "missing 6 dB"? *J. Acoust. Soc. Am.* 63:1501–1508.

Kohlrausch, A., and Houtsma, A. J. M. (1992). Pitch related to spectral edges of broadband signals. In *Processing of Complex Sounds by the Auditory System*, pp 375–382, edited by R. P. Carlyon, C. J. Darwin, and I. J. Russell. Clarendon Press, Oxford.

Kuhn, G. F. (1987). Physical acoustics and measurements pertaining to directional hearing. In *Directional Hearing*, pp 3–25, edited by W. A. Yost and G. Gourevitch. Springer-Verlag, New York.

Margolis, R. H., and Wiley, T. L. (1976). Monaural loudness adaptation at low sensation levels in normal and impaired ears. *J. Acoust. Soc. Am.* 59: 222–224.

Marks, L. E. (1978). Binaural summation of the loudness of pure tones. *J. Acoust. Soc. Am.* 64:107–113.

McClelland, K. D., and Brandt, J. F. (1969). Pitch of frequency-modulated sinusoids. *J. Acoust. Soc. Am.* 45:1489–1498.

McFadden, D., and Pasanen, E. G. (1975). Binaural beats at high frequencies. *Science* 190:394–396.

McFadden, D., and Pasanen, E. G. (1976). Lateralization of high frequencies based on interaural time differences. *J. Acoust. Soc. Am.* 59:634–639.

Middlebrooks, J. C., and Green, D. M. (1991). Sound localization by human listeners. *Annu. Rev. Psychol.* 42:135–159.

Mills, A. W. (1972). Auditory localization. In *Foundations of Modern Auditory Theory*, Vol 1, pp 303–348, edited by J. V. Tobias. Academic Press, New York.

Moore, B. C. J. (1978). Psychophysical tuning curves measured in simultaneous and forward masking. *J. Acoust. Soc. Am.* 63:524–532.

Moore, B. C. J. (1982). *An Introduction to the Psychology of Hearing*, 2nd Ed. Academic Press, London.

Moore, B. C. J., and Glasberg, B. R. (1982). Contralateral and ipsilateral cueing in forward masking. *J. Acoust. Soc. Am.* 71:942–945.

Moore, B. C. J., and Glasberg, B. R. (1982). Interpreting the role of suppression in psychophysical tuning curves. *J. Acoust. Soc. Am.* 72:1374–1379.

Morgan, D. E., Wilson, R. H., and Dirks, D. D. (1974). Loudness discomfort level: selected methods and stimuli. *J. Acoust. Soc. Am.* 56:577–581.

Noffsinger, P. D., and Tillman, T. W. (1970). Postexposure responsiveness in the auditory system. I. Immediate sensitization. *J. Acoust. Soc. Am.* 47: 546–551.

Nordmark, J. O. (1968). Mechanisms of frequency discrimination. *J. Acoust. Soc. Am.* 44:1533–1540.

Nordmark, J. O. (1978). Frequency and periodicity analysis. In *Handbook of Perception: Hearing*, Vol 4, pp 243–282, edited by E. C. Carterette and M. P. Friedman. Academic Press, New York.

O'Loughlin, B. J., and Moore, B. C. J. (1981). Off-frequency listening: effects on psychoacoustical tuning curves obtained in simultaneous and forward masking. *J. Acoust. Soc. Am.* 69:1119–1125.

O'Malley, H., and Feth, L. L. (1979). Relationship between psychophysical tuning curves and "suppression." *J. Acoust. Soc. Am.* 66:1075–1087.

Olsen, W. O., and Carhart, R. (1966). Integration of acoustic power at threshold by normal hearers. *J. Acoust. Soc. Am.* 40:591–599.

Patterson, R. D., and Green, D. M. (1978). Auditory masking. In *Handbook of Perception: Hearing*, Vol 4, pp 337–361, edited by E. C. Carterette and M. P. Friedman. Academic Press, New York.

Perrott, D. R., Briggs, R., and Perrott, S. (1970). Binaural fusion: its limits as defined by signal duration and signal onset. *J. Acoust. Soc. Am.* 47: 565–568.

Plenge, G. (1974). On the differences between localization and lateralization. *J. Acoust. Soc. Am.* 56: 944–951.

Plomp, R. (1971). Old and new data on tone perception. In *Contributions to Sensory Physiology*, Vol 5, pp 179–216, edited by W. D. Neff, Academic Press, New York.

Plomp, R., and Mimpen, A. M. (1968). The ear as a frequency analyzer. II. *J. Acoust. Soc. Am.* 43: 764–767.

Pollack, I. (1969). Periodicity pitch for interrupted white noise—fact or artifact. *J. Acoust. Soc. Am.* 45:237–238.

Pollack, I. (1971). Discrimination of the interval between two brief pulses. *J. Acoust. Soc. Am.* 50: 1203–1204.

Rabinowitz, W. M., Bilger, R. C., Trahiotis, C., and Nuetzel, J. (1980). Two-tone masking in normal hearing listeners. *J. Acoust. Soc. Am.* 68: 1096–1106.

Riesz, R. R. (1928). Differential sensitivity of the ear for pure tones. *Physiol. Rev.* 31:867–872.*

Robinson, D. W., and Dadson, R. S. (1956). A re-determination of the equal loudness relations for pure tones. *Br. J. Appl. Physiol.* 7:166–181.

Rudmose, W. (1982). The case of the missing 6 dB. *J. Acoust. Soc. Am.* 71:650–659.

Scharf, B. (1970). Critical bands. In *Foundations of Modern Auditory Theory*, Vol 1, pp 159–202, edited by J. V. Tobias. Academic Press, New York.

Scharf, B. (1978). Loudness. In *Handbook of Perception: Hearing*, Vol 4, pp 187–242, edited by E. C. Carterette and M. P. Friedman. Academic Press, New York.

Schneider, B., Wright, A. A., Edelheit, W., Hock, P., and Humphrey, C. (1972). Equal loudness contours derived from sensory magnitude judgments. *J. Acoust. Soc. Am.* 51:1951–1959.

Searle, C. L., Braida, L. D., Cuddy, D. R., and Davis, M. F. (1975). Binaural pinna disparity: another auditory localization cue. *J. Acoust. Soc. Am.* 57: 448–455.

Sever, J. C., Jr., and Small, A. M., Jr., (1979). Binaural critical masking bands. *J. Acoust. Soc. Am.* 66: 1343–1350.

Sivian, L. J., and White, S. D. (1933). Minimum audible pressure and minimum audible field. *J. Acoust. Soc. Am.* 4:288–321.*

Small, A. M. (1970). Periodicity pitch. In *Foundations of Modern Auditory Theory*, Vol 1, pp 3–54, edited by J. V. Tobias. Academic Press, New York.

Small, A. M., and Daniloff, R. G. (1967). Pitch of noise bands. *J. Acoust. Soc. Am.* 41:506–512.

Small, Jr., A. M., Brandt, J. F., and Cox, P. G. (1962). Loudness as a function of stimulus duration. *J. Acoust. Soc. Am.* 34:513–514.

Snyder, J. M. (1973). Threshold adaptation in normal listeners. *J. Acoust. Soc. Am.* 53:435–439.

Soderquist, D. R., and Lindsey, J. W. (1972). Physiological noise as a masker of low frequencies: the cardiac cycle. *J. Acoust. Soc. Am.* 52:1216–1220.

Stevens, S. S. (1934). The attributes of tones. *Proc. Natl. Acad. Sci. USA* 20:457–459.

Stevens. S. S. (1935). The relation of pitch to intensity. *J. Acoust. Soc. Am.* 6:150–154.

Stevens. S. S. (1959). The psychophysics of sensory function. In *Sensory Communication*, pp 1–33, edited by W. A. Rosenblight, MIT Press, Cambridge.

Stevens. S. S., and Davis, H. (1938). *Hearing: Its Psychology and Physiology*. John Wiley and Sons, New York.

Stevens, S. S., and Volkmann, J. (1940). The relation of pitch to frequency: a revised scale. *Am. J. Psychol.* 53:329–353.

Swets, J. A. (1964). Is there a sensory threshold? *Science* 134:168–177.* Also in *Signal Detection and Recognition by Human Oberservers*, pp 122–144, edited by J. A. Swets. John Wiley & Sons, New York.

Tobias, J. V. (1972). Curious binaural phenomena. In *Foundations of Modern Auditory Theory*, Vol 2, pp 465–486, edited by J. V. Tobias. Academic Press, New York.

Tobias, J. V. (1977). Low-frequency masking patterns. *J. Acoust. Soc. Am.* 61:571–575.

Trahiotis, C., and Kappauf, W. E. (1978). Regression interpretation of differences in time-intensity trading ratios obtained in studies of laterality using the method of adjustment. *J. Acoust. Soc. Am.* 64:1041–1047.

Wallach, H., Newman, E. B., and Rosenzweig, M. R. (1949). The precedence effect in sound localization. *Am. J. Psychol.* 62:315–336.

Ward, W. D. (1969). Effects of noise on hearing thresholds, In *Proceedings of the Conference on Noise as a Public Health Hazard*, pp 40–48, edited by W. D. Ward and J. E. Fricke. American Speech and Hearing Association, Washington, DC.

Ward, W. D. (1973). Adaptation and fatigue. In *Modern Developments in Audiology*, 1st Ed, pp 301–344, edited by J. J. Jerger. Academic Press, New York.

Ward, W. D., Glorig, A., and Sklar, D. L. (1959). Temporary threshold shift from octave-band noise: applications to damage-risk criteria. *J. Acoust. Soc. Am.* 31:522–528.

Wegel, R. L. (1932). Physical data and physiology of excitation of the auditory nerve. *Ann. Otol. Rhinol. Laryngol.* 41:740–779.

Wegel, R. L., and Lane, C. E. (1924). The auditory masking of one pure tone by another and its probable relation to the dynamics of the inner ear. *Physiol. Rev.* 23:266–276.*

Wever, E. G. (1929). Beats and related phenomena resulting from the simultaneous sounding of two tones. *Psychol. Rev.* 36:402–423.

Wever, E. G., and Bray, C. M. (1937). The perception of low tones and the resonance volley theory. *J. Psychol.* 3:101–114.

Wier, C. C., Jesteadt, W., and Green, D. M. (1977). Frequency discrimination as a function of frequency and sensation level. *J. Acoust. Soc. Am.* 61: 178–184.

Wightman, F. L. (1973). Pitch and stimulus fine structure. *J. Acoust. Soc. Am.* 54:397–406.

Wightman, F. L. (1973). The pattern-transformation model of pitch. *J. Acoust. Soc. Am.* 54:407–416.

Wightman, F. L., Kistler, D. J., et al. (1987). A new approach to the study of human sound localization. In *Directional Hearing*, pp 26–48, edited by W. A. Yost and G. Gourevitch. Springer-Verlag, New York.

Wilson, R. H., and Carhart, R. (1971). Forward and backward masking: interactions and additivity. *J. Acoust. Soc. Am.* 49:1254–1263.

Wright, D., Hebrank, J. H., and Wilson, B. (1974). Pinna reflections as cues for localization. *J. Acoust. Soc. Am.* 56:957–962.

Yeowart, N. S., and Evans, M. J. (1974). Thresholds of audibility for very low-frequency pure tones. *J. Acoust. Soc. Am.* 55:814–818.

Yost, W. A. (1974). Discriminations of interaural

phase differences. *J. Acoust. Soc. Am.* 55: 1299–1303.

Yost, W. A. (1981). Lateral position of sinusoids presented with interaural intensive and temporal differences. *J. Acoust. Soc. Am.* 70:397–409.

Yost, W. A. (1991). Auditory image perception and analysis: the basis for hearing. *Hear. Res.* 56:8–18.

Yost, W. A. (1994). *Fundamentals of Hearing: An Introduction*, 3rd Ed, Academic Press, San Diego.

Yost, W. A., and Hafter, E. R. (1987). Lateralization. In *Directional Hearing*, pp 49–84, edited by W. A. Yost and G. Gourevitch. Springer-Verlag, New York.

Young, L. L., and Carhart, R. (1974). Time-intensity trading functions for pure tones and a high-frequency AM signal. *J. Acoust. Soc. Am.* 56:605–609.

Zurek, P. M. (1980). The precedence effect and its possible role in the avoidance of interaural ambiguities. *J. Acoust. Soc. Am.* 67:952–964.

Zwicker, E. (1974). On a psychoacoustical equivalent of tuning curves. In *Facts and Models in Hearing,*

pp 132–141, edited by E. Zwicker and E. Terhardt. Springer-Verlag, New York.

Zwicker, E. (1976). Psychoacoustic equivalent of period histograms (in memoriam Dr. Russell Pfeiffer). *J. Acoust. Soc. Am.* 59:166–175.

Zwicker, E. (1981). Dependence of level and phase of the $(2f_1 - f_2)$-cancellation tone on frequency range, frequency difference, level of primaries, and subject. *J. Acoust. Soc. Am.* 70:1277–1288.

Zwicker, E., Flottrop, G., and Stevens, S. S. (1957). Critical bandwidth in loudness summation. *J. Acoust. Soc. Am.* 29:548–557.*

Zwislocki, J. (1965). Analysis of some auditory characteristics. In *Handbook of Mathematical Psychology*, Vol 3, pp 1–97, edited by R. Luce, R. Bush, and E. Galanter. John Wiley and Sons, New York.

Zwislocki, J. J. (1978). Masking: Experimental and theoretical aspects of simultaneous, forward, backward, and central masking. In *Handbook of Perception: Hearing*, Vol 4, pp 261–336, edited by E. C. Carterette and M. P. Friedman. Academic Press, New York.

# Appendix A

# Laws of Exponents

I. Multiplication: $a^m \times a^n = a^{m+n}$
   Examples: a) $10^5 \times 10^6 = 10^{11}$
   b) $(2 \times 10^1) \times (6 \times 10^3) =$
   $12 \times 10^4 = 1.2 \times 10^5$
   c) $(2 \times 10^{-5}) \times (3 \times 10^6)$
   $= 6 \times 10^1$

II. Division: $a^m/a^n = a^{m-n}$
   Examples: a) $10^{12}/10^8 = 10^4$
   b) $(8 \times 10^6)/(4 \times 10^2)$
   $= 2 \times 10^4$
   c) $10^6/10^{-3} = 10^9$
   d) $10^{-5}/10^2 = 10^{-7}$

Note: The addition and subtraction of exponents is algebraic. When there are coefficients (see examples Ib, Ic, and IIb), they must be multiplied or divided directly. For simplicity, the base of 10 was used in all examples. Of course, the laws of exponents only apply to the situation in which there is a common base. Thus, $a^m \times b^n = a^m b^n$, but $a^m \times b^n \neq (ab)^{m+n}$

III. Exponentiation: $(a^m)^n = a^{mn}$
   Example: $(10^2)^3 = 10^6$

There are several relationships that are consequences of the laws of exponents and that are of special interest:

1. Fractional exponents: $a^{1/n} = \sqrt[n]{a}$
   Example: $16^{1/4} = \sqrt[4]{16} = 2$
2. Negative components: $a^{-n} = 1/a^m$
   Example: $2^{-2} = 1/2^2 = 1/4 = 0.25$
3. Exponent equal to zero: $a^0 = 1$
   Example: $10^0 = 1$

# APPENDIX B

# SOME MATHEMATICS

FOR ANY TRULY comprehensive treatment of the physical principles underlying hearing, some exposure to hard-core mathematics is unavoidable. Mathematics is a symbolic language, which greatly facilitates the logical processes of deduction and inference essential to the formulation of proofs of theories. It facilitates the explanation of ideas and statement of relationships. One equation may replace a paragraph of words. Even within the context of this largely nonmathematical text, all of these virtues of mathematics have been used to full advantage. However, much of this text has skirted rigorous mathematical treatment of physical concepts and, of necessity, replaced it with an intuitive approach. This is unfortunate in many respects, because, even for some of the most fundamental notions from physics (such as velocity), the use of mathematical tools such as calculus can afford one a much more penetrating understanding of the phenomenon under consideration.

Appendix B is provided for the reader with some background and interest in mathematics who would like some exposure to the behind-the-scenes mathematics of much of what was discussed, particularly, in the earlier part of this book. Even so, time and space permit only the most cursory introduction; for more detailed and involved treatments of the physical principles underlying sound and hearing, the reader is referred to the sources listed in the bibliography immediately following this appendix.

## 1. Motion and Force

The primary index of motion is velocity. In Chapter 1, velocity ($v$) was defined as the time-rate change in displacement ($x$), or

$$\bar{v} = \frac{X - X_0}{t - t_0}$$

This relationship is expressed more generally by the differential equation:

$$v = dx/dt \qquad (B.1)$$

It follows that if acceleration ($a$) is the time-rate change in velocity, then

$$a = dv/dt = d(dx)/dt = d^2x/dt^2 \qquad (B.2)$$

In words, velocity is the first derivative of displacement, whereas acceleration is the first derivative of velocity or the second derivative of displacement.

Newton's first law can now be defined in these same terms:

$$F = ma = m\frac{dv}{dt} = m\frac{d^2x}{dt^2} \qquad (B.3)$$

where $m$ is mass and is a constant. Hooke's law, on the other hand, remains the same:

$$F = -sx \qquad (B.4)$$

However, it is worth noting that if one is interested in expressing everything in velocity terms (much like writing a loop equation in terms of current in electronics), then

$$F = -sx = \int -s\frac{dx}{dt}dt$$
$$= -s\int vdt \qquad (B.4a)$$

since $\int(dx/dt)dt = x$. Finally, the opposing force of frictional resistance (i.e., viscous damping) is given by the expression:

$$F = -rv = -r\frac{dx}{dt} \qquad (B.5)$$

(simply substituting for $v$ from Eq. B.1).

## 2. Free Vibration

The motion of the undamped simple harmonic oscillator is readily expressed in terms of the equations derived above. The inertial force of the moving mass must equal the restoring force of the distorted spring, because it is the cyclic playoff between the kinetic energy stored in the moving mass and the potential energy stored in the deformed spring that keeps the simple harmonic oscillator going once it has been started. (Remember, energy must be conserved!) Therefore,

$$m \frac{d^2x}{dt^2} = -sx$$

This equation can be rewritten in the form of

$$m \frac{d^2x}{dt^2} + sx = 0 \qquad (B.6)$$

This is the desired form, because now it is clearly recognizable as a differential equation, which can be solved for $x$ ($m$ and $s$ being constant). A solution for Eq. B.6 is

$$x = A \cos(\omega t + \phi) \qquad (B.7)$$

where A is the peak amplitude, and $\omega$ is the angular frequency ($2\pi f$). It can be shown that for Eq. B.7 to satisfy B.6, then $\omega$ must equal $\sqrt{s/m}$. Consequently, Eq. B.7 can be written as

$$x = A \cos(\sqrt{s/m}\, t + \phi) \qquad (B.7a)$$

Equation B.7a thus gives the position ($x$) of the mass ($m$), given stiffness ($s$) in the system and a starting phase of $\phi$. It also follows from Eq. B.7a and the definition of $\omega$ that

$$f = \frac{\omega}{2\pi} = \frac{1}{2\pi} \sqrt{s/m}$$

It is evident from these relationships that frequency and amplitude are independent in the case of free vibration.

## 3. Damped Vibration

Now, in the real world, friction is present. The realistic harmonic oscillator has viscous damping, so the motion of the system no longer is described adequately by Eq. B.7 or B.7a, because the amplitude of the motion will not remain constant over time. Energy is lost from the system because of the dissipative effects of frictional resistance. This situation may be approached much as in the case of the undamped oscillator (Eq. B.7), namely, by combining appropriately Eq. B.3, B.4, and B.5:

$$m \frac{d^2x}{dt^2} = -sx - r \frac{dx}{dt}$$

$$m \frac{d^2x}{dt^2} + r \frac{dx}{dt} + sx = 0 \qquad (B.8)$$

The solution to Equation B.8 is

$$x = Ae^{-\alpha t} \cos(\omega_d + \phi) \qquad (B.9)$$

where $\alpha = r/2m$ and $\omega_d = 2\pi f_d$. The term is the damped frequency of vibration. The overall amplitude decays exponentially over time. Like the undamped natural frequency of vibration, the damped frequency of vibration and the amplitude are independent. In fact, the decay function ($Ae^{-\alpha t}$) could be graphed, as illustrated by the inset drawing in Figure 1.11 in Chapter 1. The damped frequency of vibration and the natural frequency will be essentially the same as long as $\alpha^2 < \omega^2$ or, in other terms, $(r/2m)^2 < s/m$. However, because $\omega$ contains frictional as well as stiffness and mass terms, conditions can exist in which this is no longer true. Even more important is the fact that if $\alpha^2 \geq \omega^2$ the system is no longer oscillatory. In the specific case in which $\alpha^2 = \omega^2$, the system is said to be critically damped; when the mass is displaced, it simply approaches the equilibrium position without ever crossing through 0.

## 4. Forced Vibration

It is a fairly simple step to go from the damped harmonic oscillator under free vibration to forced vibration of the system. All three types of opposition are operating in the system in response to the applied force—inertia, stiffness and friction. (Recall Newton's third law, which states, in essence, that for every force there is an equal and opposing force.) These forces were already defined in Eq. B.3, B.4, and B.5, respectively, and merely need to be applied to the specific case of oscillatory motion. Because the forced response of a system will reflect some interaction of the motion imparted to it and the system's natural response, these forces may be appreciated by simply examining the underlying acceleration, velocity, and displacement components on which these forces are dependent. This can be done by substituting $f$ or $x$ in Eq. B.1 and B.2 from the general solution for $x$ given in Eq. B.7 and repeated here for convenience,

$$x = A \cos(\omega t + \phi) \propto \cos \omega t$$

Thus, from Eq. B.1

$$v = dx/dt = -\omega A \sin(\omega t + \phi)$$
$$\propto - \sin \omega t$$

From Eq. B.2,

$$a = d^2x/dt^2 = -\omega^2 A \cos(\omega t + \phi)$$
$$\propto - \cos \omega t$$

Clearly, displacement, velocity, and acceleration differ in phase by 90°, as must the respective restoring, frictional, and inertial forces. These relationships formed the basis of the intuitive treatment of reactance and impedance in Chapter 1.

Given a driving force of the form $F \cos \omega t$, all forces acting in the system must sum to equal this force. Therefore,

$$m \frac{d^2x}{dt^2} + r \frac{dx}{dt} + sx = F \cos \omega t \quad \text{(B.10)}$$

Although one could attempt to solve this equation, it is preferable at this point to consider a different (mathematical) state-

ment of the forced vibration problem and to work with an equation that is in the complex exponential form. There are several advantages to working with the exponential form. First, there is the general advantage that derivatives and integrals of exponential functions are relatively simple:

$$\frac{de^y}{dx} = e^y \frac{dy}{dx}$$

where $y = f(x)$. If $y = f(x) = x$, then

$$\frac{de^x}{dx} = e^x \frac{dx}{dx} = e^x$$

What could be simpler? Similarly,

$$\int e^x dx = e^x$$

The use of the exponential form in this particular application is made possible by virtue of the fundamental relationship between exponential and trigonometric functions, that is,

$$e^{j\theta} = \cos \theta + j \sin \theta$$

where $j = \sqrt{-1}$, the imaginary number (also frequently represented by the letter $i$). It is important to note that in the exponential form there is always a real and an imaginary part, mathematically speaking, of course. This means, for example, that if one were to graph real and imaginary numbers, their axes would be at right angles to one another. This is why the term *complex* is applied; the real and imaginary parts simply cannot be added. At first glance this might seem to complicate greatly the process of solving any problem, but it can be shown that, in practice, it is only necessary to obtain the real part of the complex solution and that, indeed, the real part is itself a complete (general) solution. Finally, the exponential form is of particular interest in this specific case because a natural byproduct of the solution to the forced vibration problem is the derivation of impedance. Again, without going into great detail, this can be shown as follows.

The equivalent complex driving force to $F \cos \omega t$ is $Fe^{j\omega t}$. Now, the displacement $x$ also will be complex and will be represented by the symbol $\mathbf{x}$, so the equation under consideration becomes:

$$m\frac{d^2\mathbf{x}}{dt^2} + r\frac{d^2\mathbf{x}}{dt} + s\mathbf{x} = Fe^{j\omega t} \quad \text{(B.10a)}$$

The solution is assumed to be of the form

$$\mathbf{x} = Ae^{j\omega t} \quad \text{(B.11)}$$

where $A$ is itself complex. By substituting for $x$ in Eq. B.10a, it can be seen that

$$(-\omega^2 m + j\omega r + s)Ae^{j\omega t} = Fe^{j\omega t}$$

Solving for $A$ and rearranging the terms in parentheses,

$$A = \frac{F}{j\omega r + (s - \omega^2 m)}$$

Substituting now for A in Eq. B.11, the complex displacement may now be given as

$$\mathbf{x} = \frac{Fe^{j\omega t}}{j\omega r + (s - \omega^2 m)}$$

$$= \frac{-jFe^{j\omega t}}{\omega[r + j(\omega m - s/\omega)]} \quad \text{(B.11a)}$$

One could proceed to solve for the real part of $\mathbf{x}$, but this stage of development will suffice here. The terms contained in the brackets in the denominator are the desired ones and will be recognized as those appearing in the general equation by which impedance was defined in Chapter 1, previously stated in the form

$$Z = R + jX$$

where $X$ is the total reactance, $\omega m - s/\omega$ and $r = R$, the resistance. This is known as the rectangular form. However, it is also possible to state impedance in the exponential (or polar) form, namely

$$Z = \mathbf{Z}e^{j\theta}$$

where $\mathbf{Z}$ is the magnitude of the impedance, $\sqrt{R^2 + X^2}$ (which was given, in essence, as the computational equation for impedance in Chapter 1), and $\theta$ is the phase of the impedance where $\theta = \arctan X/r$.

## 5. Further Considerations

The various acoustical concepts discussed in Chapter 2 could be treated in a similar manner as those more general physical concepts considered in the forgoing. However, the interested reader would be better served by reading such acoustical engineering texts as that by Kinsler and Frey or by Beranek (cited below). For a general treatment of vibratory motion, including wave phenomena, the reader's attention is also directed to the excellent treatise by French. It is worth noting an equation, without actually deriving it, which represents the basis by which nearly any form of wave phenomenon, specifically that associated with sound, can be explained. This is the wave equation. Stated in its most general form, the wave equation can be given as:

$$\frac{\partial^2 u}{\partial t^2} = c^2 \frac{\partial^2 u}{\partial x^2} \quad \text{(B.12)}$$

where $u$ is the dependent variable of interest (sound pressure), and $c$ is the wave (propagation) velocity. (Note that these are partial derivatives, because there are two independent variables: time, $t$, and displacement, $x$.) It is from this equation, for example, that Eq. 2.3 can be derived, that is, the dependence of the speed of sound in a gaseous medium on the properties of gas. It is also from this equation that the concept of wavelength finds its mathematical basis. The wave equation describes an event with parameters that vary in time and space. This is exactly the reason why a sound wave has dimensions in time (frequency or its reciprocal, period) and space (wavelength) and why, indeed, the concept of wavelength, besides frequency, is essential in describing sound.

In Chapter 3, the concept of root-mean-square (RMS) magnitude was introduced. Because RMS magnitude reflects the area under the graph of the time analysis of a particular sound or signal $[a(t)]$, it is conveniently defined in terms of an integral, as follows:

$$A_{rms} = \sqrt{\frac{1}{T} \int a^2(t) \, dt} \qquad \text{(B.13)}$$

In effect, the deviations about the zero axis, namely, the instantaneous magnitudes $(a)$, are squared and averaged over a period of time $(T)$, and then the square root of the entire term is taken. A simple proportionality between peak and RMS magnitudes of sinusoids was presented in Chapter 3. It will be worthwhile to present briefly the derivation of this relationship. This merely requires the substitution of $A_{0-p} \sin \omega t$ (the expression of the general sinusoid with a starting phase of $\phi = 0$) for $a(t)$ and computing the integral over the interval $0 - T$ (where $T = f^{-1}$, the period); that is to say,

$$A_{rms} = \sqrt{\frac{1}{T} \int_0^T (A_{0-p} \sin \omega t)^2 \, dt}$$

Squaring both sides of the equation to eliminate the radical, for the time being, and taking the constant term outside the integral:

$$A_{rms}^2 = \frac{A_{0-p}^2}{T} \int_0^T \sin^2 \omega t \, dt$$

$$= \frac{A_{0-p}^2}{T} \left( \frac{1}{2} t - \frac{1}{4} \sin 2\omega t \right) \Big|_0^T$$

Now, at $t = 0$, the value of the integral is 0, and it remains only to evaluate it at $t = T$. Having substituted for $t$ and multiplied the terms inside the brackets $A_{0-p}^2/T$ then,

$$A_{rms} = \frac{A_{0-p}^2}{2} - \frac{A_{0-p}^2}{4T} \sin 2\omega T$$

Since $\omega = 2\pi f$ and $f = 1/T$, the farthest term on the right is eliminated (that is, $\sin 2\pi f T = \sin 2\pi T/T = \sin 2\pi = 0$). Therefore,

$$A_{rms}^2 = \frac{A_{0-p}^2}{2}$$

and, taking the square root on both sides of the equation,

$$A_{rms} = \frac{1}{\sqrt{2}} A_{0-p} = 0.707 A_{0-p}$$

Finally, a brief discussion of Fourier's theorem might be beneficial without, however, going into any great detail or its derivation. For this purpose, the discussion will be focused on the simplest case, that of analyzing a complex periodic quantity, and what is known as the Fourier series (rather than the more complex Fourier transform itself). Fourier took advantage of the fundamental trigonometric relationship

$$\cos(\omega t + \phi)$$
$$= (\cos \phi \cos \omega t - \sin \phi \sin \omega t)$$

Since $\phi$ is a constant, any sinusoidal quantity can be written, consequently, as the sum of $\cos \omega t$ and $\sin \omega t$. Similarly, it should be possible to represent any complex periodic quantity, $f(t)$, as

$$\begin{aligned} f(t) = a_0 &+ a_1 \cos \omega t + b_1 \sin \omega t \\ &+ a_2 \cos 2\omega t + b_2 \sin 2\omega t \\ &\quad \cdots \\ &+ a_n \cos n\omega t + b_n \sin n\omega t \end{aligned} \qquad \text{(B.14)}$$

Thus, the different components in the series are harmonically related to the fundamental frequency $T^{-1}$, the reciprocal of the fundamental period. Rewriting Equation in a more convenient form:

$$f(t) = a_0 + \sum_{n=1}^{\infty} a_n \cos n\omega t \qquad \text{(B.14a)}$$
$$+ \sum_{n=1}^{\infty} b_n \sin n\omega t$$

The association of Fourier analysis, of which Eq. B.14a is the basis, with spectrum analysis should be evident; each frequency component of the complex waveform is represented. Its contribution to the total spectrum that is determined by the constants, $a_n$ and $b_n$, themselves must be derived using integral calculus. Thus, these constants determine the amplitude of each component. It also should be apparent that if $f(t)$ can be broken down into different frequency components, it can be built up or synthesized from them as well. This is Fourier analysis in reverse or Fourier synthesis. The Fourier transform, in fact, readily permits one to move from the frequency to the time domain, and vice versa. Herein lies perhaps the greatest importance of Fourier's theorem.

## BIBLIOGRAPHY

Beranek, L. L. (1988). *Acoustic Measurements,* 2nd ed. American Institute of Physics, New York.

Dallos, P. (1973). *The Auditory Periphery: Biophysics and Physiology.* Academic Press, New York.

Feynman, R. P. (1970). *Feynman Lectures on Physics,* Vol 1. Addison-Wesley, Reading, MA.

French, A. P. (1971). *Vibrations and Waves.* W. W. Norton, New York.

Kinsler, L. E., Frey, A. R., Coppens, A. B., and Sanders, J. V. (1982). *Fundamentals of Acoustics,* 3rd ed. John Wiley & Sons, New York.

Resnick, R., and Halliday, D. (1960). *Physics: For Students of Science and Engineering (Part I).* John Wiley & Sons, New York.

# APPENDIX C

# LAWS OF LOGARITHMS

THE LAWS OF LOGARITHMS are a natural extension of the laws of exponents. Formally, the logarithm may be defined as follows:

$$\text{If } x = a^y \text{ then } y = \log_a x$$

where $a$ is the base of the logarithm ($y$) of the number $x$ (any positive number greater than zero). It is from this fundamental definition that one can readily determine the common logarithms (base 10) of such numbers as 1, 10, 100, 1000 .... These numbers, in scientific notation, are whole powers of 10, that is, $10^0$, $10^1$, $10^2$, $10^3$, ..., $10^n$, and the logarithms of these numbers are simply equal to the exponents, 0, 1, 2, 3, ..., n (the characteristic of the log). Of course, for numbers ranging from $1.000 \ldots \times 10^n$ to $9.999 \ldots \times 10^n$ the logarithm (specifically the mantissa) must be looked up in a table of logarithms, an abbreviated version of which is provided in Table C.1. From the laws of exponents, the following laws of logarithms can be stated; these rules, then, govern how the logarithm may be used for purposes of computation.

**TABLE C.1.**
**Abbreviated Table of Common Logarithms**[a]

| No. | Mantissa | No. (cont.) | Mantissa | No. (cont.) | Mantissa |
|-----|----------|-------------|----------|-------------|----------|
| 1.0 | .00 | 4.0 | .60 | 7.0 | .85 |
| 1.1 | .04 | 4.1 | .61 | 7.1 | .85 |
| 1.2 | .08 | 4.2 | .62 | 7.2 | .86 |
| 1.3 | .11 | 4.3 | .63 | 7.3 | .86 |
| 1.4 | .15 | 4.4 | .64 | 7.4 | .87 |
| 1.5 | .18 | 4.5 | .65 | 7.5 | .88 |
| 1.6 | .20 | 4.6 | .66 | 7.6 | .88 |
| 1.7 | .23 | 4.7 | .67 | 7.7 | .89 |
| 1.8 | .26 | 4.8 | .68 | 7.8 | .89 |
| 1.9 | .28 | 4.9 | .69 | 7.9 | .90 |
| 2.0 | .30 | 5.0 | .70 | 8.0 | .90 |
| 2.1 | .32 | 5.1 | .71 | 8.1 | .91 |
| 2.2 | .34 | 5.2 | .72 | 8.2 | .91 |
| 2.3 | .36 | 5.3 | .72 | 8.3 | .92 |
| 2.4 | .38 | 5.4 | .73 | 8.4 | .92 |
| 2.5 | .40 | 5.5 | .74 | 8.5 | .93 |
| 2.6 | .41 | 5.6 | .75 | 8.6 | .93 |
| 2.7 | .43 | 5.7 | .76 | 8.7 | .94 |
| 2.8 | .45 | 5.8 | .76 | 8.8 | .94 |
| 2.9 | .46 | 5.9 | .77 | 8.9 | .95 |
| 3.0 | .48 | 6.0 | .78 | 9.0 | .95 |
| 3.1 | .49 | 6.1 | .79 | 9.1 | .96 |
| 3.2 | .51 | 6.2 | .79 | 9.2 | .96 |
| 3.3 | .52 | 6.3 | .80 | 9.3 | .97 |
| 3.4 | .53 | 6.4 | .81 | 9.4 | .97 |
| 3.5 | .54 | 6.5 | .81 | 9.5 | .98 |
| 3.6 | .56 | 6.6 | .82 | 9.6 | .98 |
| 3.7 | .57 | 6.7 | .83 | 9.7 | .99 |
| 3.8 | .58 | 6.8 | .83 | 9.8 | .99 |
| 3.9 | .59 | 6.9 | .84 | 9.9 | 1.00 (.996) |

[a] For greater accuracy, namely to avoid truncation errors due to rounding, reference should be made to four- or six-place log tables, i.e. in S. A. Selby (Ed.): *CRC Standard Mathemtical Tables.* CRC Press, Cleveland, 1974.

I. Multiplication:

$$\log_a(x \cdot y) = \log_a x + \log_a y$$

Example: Find $360,000 \times 90,000,000$.

$$\begin{aligned}
\log_{10} 360,000 &= \log_{10}(3.6 \times 10^5) \\
&= \log_{10} 3.6 + \log_{10} 10^5 \\
&= \text{(from Table C.1) } 0.56 \\
&\quad + \text{(from the exponent) } 5 \\
&= 5.56.
\end{aligned}$$

Similarly,

$$\log_{10} 90,000,000 = 7.95.$$

Adding the logs to find the product of the two numbers,

$$5.56 + 7.95 = 13.51$$

To find the final answer (in the real-number world), one simply finds the antilog of 13.51, as follows:

antilog 13.51 = antilog 13 × antilog 0.51
$$= 10^{13} \text{ (from the characteristic)} \times 3.2 \text{ (from the mantissa, working backward in Table C.1)}$$
$$= 3.2 \times 10^{13}$$

Thus,

360,000 × 90,000,000
$$= 32,000,000,000,000$$

II. Division: $\log_a(x/y) = \log_a - \log_a y$
   Example: find 1,000,000,000 ÷ 50,000
   $\log_{10} 1,000,000,000 - \log_{10} 50,000$
   $= 9 - 4.7 = 4.3$
   antilog 4.3 $= 2.0 \times 10^4 = 20,000$

III. Exponentiation: $\log_a(x^n) = n \log_a x$
   Example: find $200^{1.5}$
   $\log_{10}(200^{1.5}) = 1.5 \times \log_{10} 200$
   $= 1.5 \times 2.3 = 3.45$
   antilog 3.45 $= 2.8 \times 10^3 = 2,800$

The degree of accuracy of the answers obtained using logarithms is dependent on the log table used, i.e., four-place, six-place, etc. For instance, the answers in the first and last examples above are approximate. (Only two-place accuracy is possible with Table C.1). The answer to the division problem turns out to be exact only by virtue of the numbers chosen. Still, a reasonable approximation to the exact answer is achieved even with a simplified log table such as Table C.1, and it is evident that some otherwise unwieldy problems can be greatly simplified using the log (unless, of course, one happens to have a pocket calculator handy, which can do the job). For a more complete treatment of logarithms and exponents, the reader is referred to the *CRC Standard Mathetical Tables,* cited at the bottom of Table C.1.

# THE ADDITION OF SOUNDS IN DECIBEL LEVELS

WHEN ADDING THE SOUND levels of two or more sounds together to find the total level, the logarithmic nature of the decibel must be borne in mind; this means that one cannot simply add (arithmetically) the decibel values. The graph in Figure D.1 provides a convenient means of combining sound levels correctly as discussed in Chapter 3. To use this chart, simply follow these three steps:

1. Find the difference in decibels between the two sound levels (SPL or IL, as the case may be), $L_2 - L_1$, where $L^2$ represents the greater of the two values.

2. Project a vertical line up from the abscissa ($L_2 - L_1$ values) to intersect the curve. From that point project a horizontal line to the ordinate ($\Delta L$ values) to obtain the increase in the total sound level of $L_2$.

3. Add $\Delta L$ to $L_2$ to find the resultant decibel level:

$$L_r = L_2 + \Delta L$$

For example, suppose there are two sounds present, one with a sound pressure level of 80 dB and the other 86 dB (i.e., re 20 $\mu$Pa). The $L_1 = 80$ dB, and $L_2 = 86$ dB. The difference in levels between the two sounds is

$$L_2 - L_1 = 86 - 80 = 6 \text{ dB}$$

The value of 6 dB on the abscissa projects over to $\Delta L = 1.0$ on the ordinate, as shown by the *dotted lines*. Thus, the total sound pressure level is

$$L_r = 86 + 1 = 87 \text{ dB}$$

Now, had there been three sounds, say of 75, 80, and 86 dB SPL, this process would be carried out for two of these levels, then that total would be combined with the last sound. For instance, in this case, the total level resulting from combining 80 and 86 dB is already known—87 dB. Let this level be $L_2$, and $L_1$ will be 75 dB. Carrying through the whole process again, then,

$$L_2 - L_1 = 87 - 75 = 12 \text{ dB}$$

$$\Delta L \approx 0.3 \text{ (from Fig. D.1)}$$

$$\therefore L_r = 87 + 0.3 = 87.3 \text{ dB}$$

Consequently, by serially adding the components, the total sound level can be obtained. This arduous process, however, is only necessary when the components are of unequal levels (see Chapter 3).

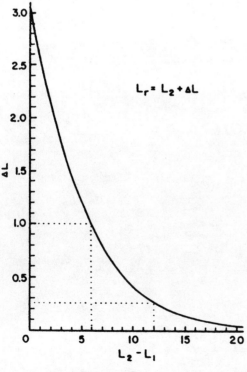

**Figure D.1**

# INDEX

Page numbers followed by *f* indicate figures; those followed by *t* indicate tables.